A-Level

Physics

Exam Board: OCR A

Physics is a big subject — it covers *everything*. Miniscule subatomic particles? Check. Mind-bendingly enormous astronomical phenomena? Check. The broader socio-historical significance of heroic archetypes in classical Greek mythology? Oh.

But even without that last one, there are still plenty of challenging topics to tackle in the OCR A Physics exams. Which is why you'll need this amazing CGP book...

It's packed with crystal-clear study notes, realistic exam questions and much more — it covers everything you need to learn for A-Level, and it's perfect for the AS exams too!

How to access your free Online Edition

This book includes a free Online Edition to read on your PC, Mac or tablet. You'll just need to go to **cgpbooks.co.uk/extras** and enter this code:

1597 9108 2366 5586

By the way, this code only works for one person. If somebody else has used this book before you, they might have already claimed the Online Edition.

A-Level revision? It has to be CGP!

Published by CGP

Editors:
Emily Garrett, Duncan Lindsay, Andy Park, Ethan Starmer-Jones, Hannah Taylor and Charlotte Whiteley

Contributors:
Tony Alldridge, Jane Cartwright, Peter Cecil, Peter Clarke, Mark Edwards, Barbara Mascetti, John Myers, Zoe Nye, Moira Steven and Andy Williams

ISBN: 978 1 78908 039 1

With thanks to Mark Edwards, Ian Francis, Glenn Rogers and Sarah Williams for the proofreading.
With thanks to Jan Greenway for the copyright research.

Clipart from Corel®
Printed by Elanders Ltd, Newcastle upon Tyne.

Based on the classic CGP style created by Richard Parsons.

Contents

If you're revising for the **AS exams**, you'll need to revise Modules 1-4.
If you're revising for the **A-level exams**, you'll need to revise the whole book.

Module 6: Section 1 — Capacitors

Module 6: Section 2 — Electric Fields

Module 6: Section 3 — Electromagnetism

Module 6: Section 4 — Nuclear and Particle Physics

Module 6: Section 5 — Medical Imaging

Do Well In Your Exams

Specification Map

This specification map tells you where each part of the OCR specification that you'll need for your exams is covered in this book.

Module 1: Development of practical skills in physics

Module 2: Foundations of physics

Module 3: Forces and motion

Module 4: Electrons, waves and photons

Specification Map

Module 5: Newtonian world and astrophysics

Module 6: Particles and medical physics

The Scientific Process

'How Science Works' is all about the scientific process — how we develop and test scientific ideas. It's what scientists do all day, every day (well, except at coffee time — never come between a scientist and their coffee).

Scientists Come Up with **Theories** — Then **Test Them...**

Science tries to explain **how** and **why** things happen — it **answers questions**. It's all about seeking and gaining **knowledge** about the world around us. Scientists do this by **asking** questions, **suggesting** answers and then **testing** their suggestions to see if they're correct — this is the **scientific process**.

1) **Ask** a question about **why** something happens or **how** something works. E.g. what is the nature of light?
2) **Suggest** an answer, or part of an answer, by forming a **theory** (a possible **explanation** of the observations) — e.g. light is a wave. (Scientists also sometimes form a **model** too — a **simplified picture** of what's physically going on.)
3) Make a **prediction** or **hypothesis** — a **specific testable statement**, based on the theory, about what will happen in a test situation. For example, if light is a wave, it will interfere and diffract when it travels through a small enough gap.
4) Carry out a **test** — to provide **evidence** that will support the prediction (or help to disprove it). E.g. Young's double-slit experiment (p.88-89).

The evidence supported Quentin's Theory of Flammable Burps.

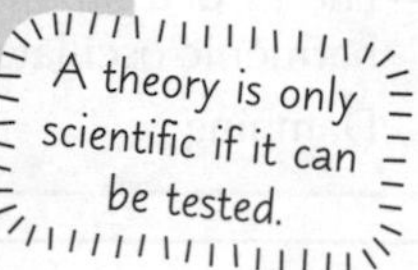

...Then They **Tell** Everyone About Their **Results...**

The results are **published** — scientists need to let others know about their work. Scientists publish their results in **scientific journals**. These are just like normal magazines, only they contain **scientific reports** (called papers) instead of the latest celebrity gossip.

1) Scientific reports are similar to the **lab write-ups** you do in school. And just as a lab write-up is **reviewed** (marked) by your teacher, reports in scientific journals undergo **peer review** before they're published.
2) The report is sent out to **peers** — other scientists that are experts in the **same area**. They examine the data and results, and if they think that the conclusion is reasonable it's **published**. This makes sure that work published in scientific journals is of a **good standard**.
3) But peer review **can't guarantee** the science is **correct** — other scientists still need to **reproduce** it.
4) Sometimes **mistakes** are made and bad work is published. Peer review **isn't perfect** but it's probably the best way for scientists to self-regulate their work and to publish **quality reports**.

...Then **Other Scientists** Will **Test** the Theory Too

Other scientists read the published theories and results, and try to **test the theory** themselves. This involves:

- Repeating the **exact same experiments**.
- Using the theory to make **new predictions** and then testing them with **new experiments**.

If the **Evidence** Supports a Theory, It's **Accepted — for Now**

1) If all the experiments in all the world provide good evidence to back it up, the theory is thought of as **scientific 'fact'** (for now).
2) But it will never become **totally indisputable** fact. Scientific **breakthroughs or advances** could provide new ways to question and test the theory, which could lead to **new evidence** that **conflicts** with the current evidence. Then the testing starts all over again...

And this, my friend, is the **tentative nature of scientific knowledge** — it's always **changing** and **evolving**.

The Scientific Process

So scientists need evidence to back up their theories. They get it by carrying out experiments, and when that's not possible they carry out studies. But why bother with science at all? We want to know as much as possible so we can use it to try and improve our lives (and because we're nosy).

Evidence Comes From **Controlled Lab Experiments...**

1) Results from **controlled experiments** in **laboratories** are **great.**
2) A lab is the easiest place to **control variables** so that they're all **kept constant** (except for the one you're investigating).

Module 1 (pages 4-9) is all about designing and carrying out experiments.

...That You can Draw **Meaningful Conclusions** From

1) You always need to make your experiments as **controlled** as possible so you can be confident that any effects you see are linked to the variable you're changing.
2) If you do find a relationship, you need to be careful what you conclude. You need to decide whether the effect you're seeing is **caused** by changing a variable (this is known as a **causal relationship**), or whether the two are just **correlated**. There's more about drawing conclusions on page 9.

"Right Geoff, you can start the experiment now... I've stopped time..."

Society **Makes Decisions** Based on **Scientific Evidence**

1) Lots of scientific work eventually leads to **important discoveries** or breakthroughs that could **benefit humankind**.
2) These results are **used by society** (that's you, me and everyone else) to **make decisions** — about the way we live, what we eat, what we drive, etc.
3) All sections of society use scientific evidence to make decisions, e.g. politicians use it to devise policies and individuals use science to make decisions about their own lives.

Other factors can **influence** decisions about science or the way science is used:

Economic factors

Society has to consider the **cost** of implementing changes based on scientific conclusions — e.g. the cost of reducing the UK's carbon emissions to limit the human contribution to **global warming**. Scientific research is often **expensive**. E.g. in areas such as astronomy, the Government has to **justify** spending money on a new telescope rather than pumping money into, say, the **NHS** or **schools**.

Social factors

Decisions affect **people's lives** — e.g. when looking for a site to build a **nuclear power station**, you need to consider how it would affect the lives of the people in the **surrounding area**.

Environmental factors

Many scientists suggest that building **wind farms** would be a **cheap** and **environmentally friendly** way to generate electricity in the future. But some people think that because **wind turbines** can **harm wildlife** such as birds and bats, other methods of generating electricity should be used.

So there you have it — how science works...

Hopefully these pages have given you a nice intro to how science works, e.g. what scientists do to provide you with 'facts'. You need to understand this, as you're expected to know how science works yourself — for the exam and for life.

Planning and Implementing

Science is all about getting good evidence to support (or disprove) your theories, so scientists need to be able to spot a badly designed experiment, interpret the results of an experiment or study, and design their own experiments too...

You Might have to **Design an Experiment** to Answer a **Question**

1) You might be asked to design a physics experiment to **investigate** something or answer a question.
2) It could be a **lab experiment** that you've seen before, or something **applied**, like deciding which building material is best for a particular job.
3) Either way, you'll be able to use the physics you know and the skills in this topic to figure out the best way to investigate the problem.

A **Variable** is Anything that has the Potential to **Change** in an Experiment

1) First, you need to identify your **independent** and **dependent variables**:

> The **independent** variable is the thing you **change**.
> The **dependent** variable is the thing you **measure**.

Example 1: If you're investigating how changing the potential difference across a component affects the current through it, the **independent variable** is the **potential difference**, and the **dependent variable** is the **current**.

2) Apart from the independent and dependent variables, **all other variables** should stay the same during your experiment. If not, you can't tell whether or not the independent variable is responsible for any changes in your dependent variable, so your results won't be **valid** (p.8). This is known as **controlling variables**. It might be worth **measuring control variables** that are likely to change during your experiment to check that they really are under control.

Example 1 (continued): In the example above, you need to use the same **circuit components**, and to keep the **temperature** of the apparatus **constant** — e.g. by letting the circuit cool down between readings.

Example 2: If you're investigating the value of **acceleration due to gravity** by dropping an object and timing its fall, **draughts** in the room could really mess up your results. Picking an object that is more **resistant** to being blown about (like a ball-bearing) will help make your results more **precise** and therefore more **valid** (p.8).

Select Appropriate **Apparatus** and **Techniques**

1) You need to think about what **units** your measurements of the independent and dependent variables are likely to be in before you begin (e.g. millimetres or metres, milliseconds or hours).
2) Think about the **range** you plan on taking measurements over too — e.g. if you're measuring the effect of increasing the force on a spring, you need to know whether you should increase the force in steps of 1 newton, 10 newtons or 100 newtons. Sometimes, you'll be able to **estimate** what effect changing your independent variable will have, or sometimes a **pilot experiment** might help.
3) Considering your measurements before you start will also help you choose the most appropriate **apparatus** and **techniques** for the experiment:

> There's a whole range of apparatus and techniques that could come up in your exam. Make sure you know how to use all the ones you've come across in class.

Example:
- If you're measuring the length of a **spring** that you're applying a force to, you might need a **ruler**. If you're measuring the diameter of a **wire**, you'd be better off with a set of **callipers**.
  If the extension will be small, the wire you use might be **too long** to suspend vertically from a clamp. You might need to use a pulley like in the Young modulus experiment on p.48.
- If you're measuring a **time interval**, you could use a **stopwatch**. If the time is **really short** (for example if you're investigating acceleration due to gravity), you might need something more sensitive, like **light gates**.

4) Whatever apparatus and techniques you use, make sure you use them **correctly**. E.g. if you're measuring a length, make sure your eye is level with the ruler when you take the measurement.
5) While you're planning, you should also think about the **risks** involved in your experiment and how to manage them — e.g. if you're investigating a material that might snap, wear safety goggles to protect your eyes.

Planning and Implementing

Figure Out how to Record your Data Before you Start

Before you get going, you'll need a **data table** to record your results in.

1) It should include space for your **independent variable** and your **dependent variable**. You should specify the **units** in the headers, not within the table itself.
2) Your table will need enough room for repeated measurements. You should aim to **repeat** each measurement at least **three times**. Taking repeat measurements can reduce the effect of random errors in your results (see p.12) and makes spotting **anomalous** results, like this one, much easier.
3) There should be space in your table for any data processing you need to do, e.g. calculating an **average** from repeated measurements, or calculating speed from measurements of distance and time.
4) Most of the time, your data will be **quantitative** (i.e. you'll be recording numerical values). Occasionally, you may have to deal with **qualitative** data (data that can be observed but not measured with a numerical value). It's still best to record this kind of data in a table, to keep your results **organised**, but the layout may be a little **different**.

P.d. / V	Current / A			
	Trial 1	Trial 2	Trial 3	Average
1.00	0.052	0.047	0.050	0.050
1.50	0.079	0.075	0.077	0.077
2.00	0.303	0.098	0.097	...
2.50	0.129	0.125	0.130	...
3.00	0.149	0.151	0.145	...
...	...	...	...	...

You Could be Asked to Evaluate An Experimental Design

If you need to evaluate an experimental design, whether it's your own or someone else's, you need to think about these sorts of things:

- Does the experiment **actually test** what it sets out to test?
- Is the method **clear** enough for someone else to follow?
- Apart from the **independent** and **dependent variables**, is everything else going to be **properly controlled**?
- Are the **apparatus** and **techniques appropriate** for what's being measured? Will they be used correctly?
- Are enough **repeated measurements** going to be taken?
- Is the experiment going to be conducted **safely**?

Greta was paying the price for not planning her experiment properly.

Warm-Up Questions

Q1 What is meant by the term independent variable? What is a dependent variable?

Q2 Why do you need to plan to control all of the other variables in an experiment?

Q3 What do you need to consider when selecting your apparatus?

Q4 Why should you take repeated measurements in an experiment?

Exam Question

Q1 A student is investigating the effect of the light level on the resistance of an LDR (light-dependent resistor). The student connects the LDR to a power supply, and measures the resistance of the LDR at various distances from a light source using a multimeter.

a) State the independent and dependent variables for this experiment. [1 mark]

b) State two variables that the student needs to control in order to ensure his results are valid. [2 marks]

The best-planned experiments of mice and men...

...often get top marks. The details of planning and carrying out an experiment will vary a lot depending on what you're investigating, but if all this stuff is wedged in your brain you shouldn't go far wrong, so make sure you've got it learned.

Analysing Results

You've planned an experiment, and you've got some results (or you've been given some in your exam). Now it's time to look into them a bit more closely...

Do any **Calculations** You Need to **First**

1) Before you calculate anything, check for any **anomalous results.** If there's something in the results that's **clearly wrong**, then don't include it in your calculations — it'll just **muck everything up**. Be careful though, you should only exclude an anomalous result if you have **good reason** to think it's wrong, e.g. it looks like a decimal point is in the **wrong place**, or you suspect that one of the control variables **changed**. And you should talk about any anomalous results when you're evaluating the experiment (pages 8-9).
2) For most experiments, you'll at least need to calculate the mean (average) of some **repeated measurements**:

$$\text{mean (average) of a measurement} = \frac{\text{sum of your repeated measurements}}{\text{number of repeats taken}}$$

In class, you could use a spreadsheet to process your data (and plot graphs), but it's important that you know how to do it by hand for the exam.

3) Calculate any quantities that you're interested in that you haven't **directly measured** (e.g. pressure, speed).

You should try to give any values you calculate to the **same number of significant figures** as the data value with the **fewest significant figures** in your calculation, **or one more** where it's sensible. If you give your result to too many significant figures, you're saying your final result is more **precise** than it actually is (see p.8).

Present Your Results on a **Graph**

Make sure you know how to plot a graph of your results:

If you need to use your graph to measure something, select axes that will let you do this easily (e.g. by measuring the gradient or the intercept, see the next page).

1) Usually, the **independent variable** goes on the *x*-**axis** and the **dependent variable** goes on the *y*-**axis**. Both axes should be **labelled** clearly, with the quantity and **units**. The **scales** used should be sensible (i.e. they should go up in sensible steps, and should spread the data out over the full graph rather than bunching it up in a corner).

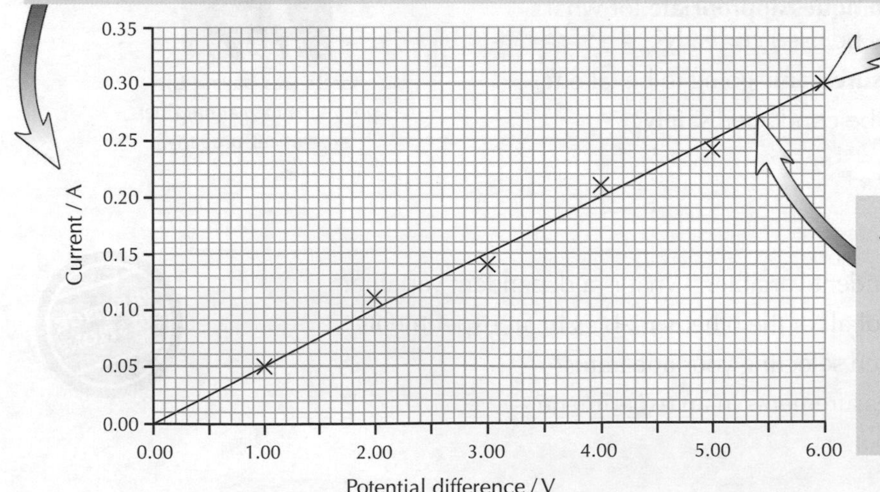

2) Plot your points using a **sharp pencil**, to make sure they're as **accurate** as possible.

3) Draw a **line of best fit** for your results. Around **half** the data points should be above the line, and half should be below it (you should ignore anomalous results). Depending on the data, the line might be **straight**, or **curved**.

Graphs can Show Different Kinds of **Correlation**

The **correlation** describes the relationship between the variables. Data can show:

Remember, correlation does not necessarily mean cause — p.3.

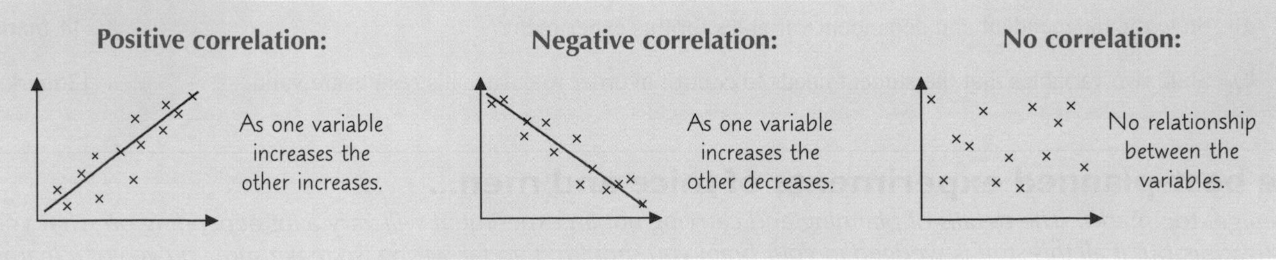

Analysing Results

You Might Need to Find a **Gradient** or **Intercept**

If the line of best fit is **straight**, then the graph is **linear**. This means a change in one always leads to a change in the other.
The **line of best fit** for a linear graph has the **equation**:

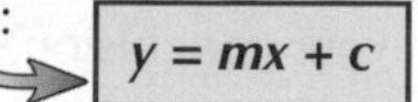

Where m is the **gradient** of the line and c is the **y-intercept**.

If the line of best fit goes through the origin (c is 0), you can say the variables are **directly proportional** to each other:

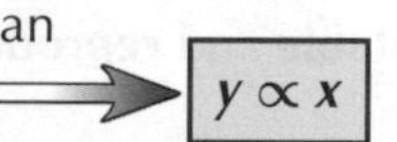

∝ just means 'is directly proportional to'.

Example: This graph shows displacement against time for a motorbike travelling west. Find the bike's velocity.

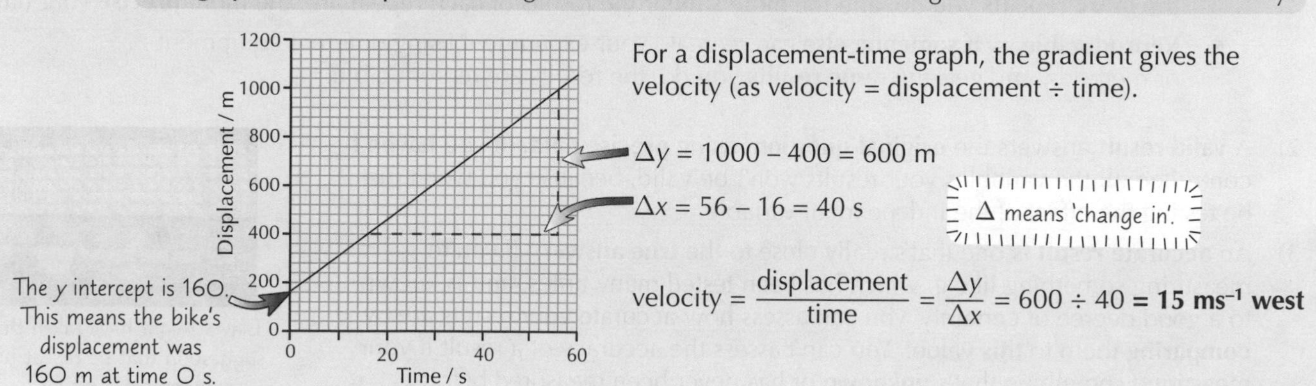

For a displacement-time graph, the gradient gives the velocity (as velocity = displacement ÷ time).

$\Delta y = 1000 - 400 = 600$ m

$\Delta x = 56 - 16 = 40$ s

Δ means 'change in'.

$$\text{velocity} = \frac{\text{displacement}}{\text{time}} = \frac{\Delta y}{\Delta x} = 600 \div 40 = \mathbf{15\ ms^{-1}\ west}$$

If a graph has a **curved** line of best fit, you can find the gradient of a given point on the line by drawing a **tangent** to the curve (see page 23). It's sometimes helpful to choose axes that turn a curved graph into a straight one:

Example:

For a given force, the graph of **pressure** applied against the **area** that the force is applied over looks like this:

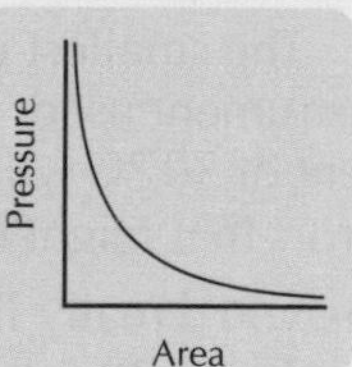

If you plot pressure against **1 ÷ area**, the graph looks like this:

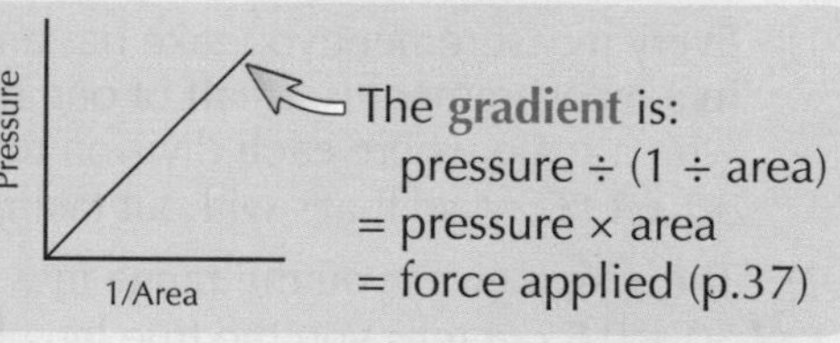

The **gradient** is:
pressure ÷ (1 ÷ area)
= pressure × area
= force applied (p.37)

Warm-Up Questions

Q1 Describe what you should do with anomalous results when processing data.
Q2 How do you calculate an average of repeated results?
Q3 Sketch a graph showing a negative correlation.

Exam Question

Q1 An engineer is investigating the performance of a prototype car with a new kind of environmentally-friendly engine. The data below shows the speed of the car, going from stationary to over 70 kilometres per hour.
(In this question, you may use the formula: acceleration = change in speed ÷ time taken to change speed.)

Time / s	0	2	4	6	8	10	12	14	16
Speed / km per hour	0	3	8	24	36	52	66	69	71

a) Draw a graph showing speed against time for this data. [4 marks]

b) State the times between which the graph is linear. [1 mark]

c) Using the graph, calculate the maximum acceleration of the car. [4 marks]

My level of boredom is proportional to the time I've spent on this page...

This stuff can get a bit fiddly, especially measuring the gradient of a curved line, but for the most part it's not too bad, and you should have seen a lot of it before. So dust off your pencil sharpener, and get to work...

Evaluating and Concluding

Once you've drawn your graphs and analysed your results, you need to think about your conclusions.

Evaluate the **Quality** of Your **Results**

Before you draw any conclusions, you should think about the quality of the results — if the quality's not great you won't be able to have much confidence in your conclusion. Good results are **precise**, **valid** and **accurate**.

1) The smaller the **range** that your data is spread over, the more **precise** it is. A **precise** result is one that is **repeatable** and **reproducible**.

Precision is sometimes called reliability.

- **Repeatable** — you can **repeat** an experiment multiple times and get the **same results**. For experiments, doing more repeats enables you to assess how precise your data are — the **more repeats** you do, and the more **similar** the results of each repeat are, the more **precise** your data.
- **Reproducible** — if **someone else** can recreate your experiment using different equipment or methods, and gets the **same results** you do, the results are reproducible.

2) A **valid result** answers the **original question**, using **precise data**. If you haven't controlled all the variables your results won't be valid, because you won't just be testing the effect of the independent variable.
3) An **accurate result** is one that's really close to the **true answer**. If you're measuring something like *g*, which has been tested many times, and is known to a good degree of certainty, you can assess how accurate your results are by **comparing** them to this value. You can't assess the accuracy of a result if your measuring something that's **unknown** or has never been measured before.

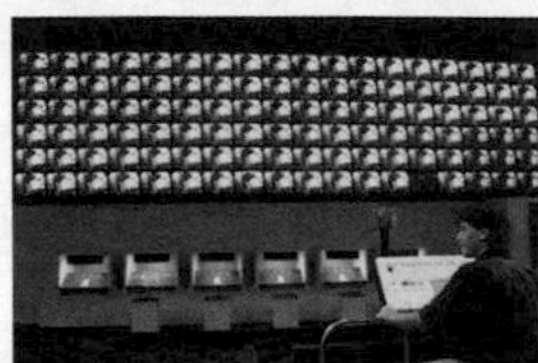
David might have taken the suggestion that he repeat his experiment a bit far...

All Results have Some **Uncertainty**

1) **Every** measurement you take has an **experimental uncertainty**. The smallest uncertainty you can have in a measurement is ± **half** of one division on the measuring instrument used. E.g. using a thermometer with a scale where each division represents 2 °C, a measurement of 30 °C will at **best** be measured to be 30 **± 1 °C**. And that's without taking into account any other errors that might be in your measurement.
2) The ± sign gives you the **range** in which the **true** length (the one you'd really like to know) probably lies. 30 ± 0.5 cm tells you the true length is very likely to lie in the range of 29.5 to 30.5 cm. The maximum difference between your value and the true value (here 0.5 cm) is sometimes called the **margin of error**.
3) The smaller the uncertainty in a result or measurement, the smaller the range of possible values the result could have and the more precise your data can be. There are two measures of uncertainty you need to know about:

Absolute uncertainty — the **total uncertainty** for a measurement.
Percentage error — the uncertainty given as a **percentage** of the measurement.

If you measure a length of something with a ruler, you actually take two measurements, one at each end of the object you're measuring. There is an uncertainty in each of these measurements. E.g. a length of 17.0 cm measured using a mm ruler will have an uncertainty of 0.05 + 0.05 = ± 0.1 cm (see page 12).

Example: The resistance of a filament lamp is given as 5.0 ± 0.4 Ω. Give the absolute uncertainty and the percentage error for this measurement.

The **absolute uncertainty** is **0.4 Ω**.
To get the percentage error, just convert this to a percentage of the lamp's resistance: (0.4 ÷ 5) × 100 = **8%**

Significant Figures give Uncertainties

If no uncertainty is given for a value, the **assumed uncertainty** is **half the increment** of the **last** significant figure that the value is **given** to. E.g. 2.0 is given to 2 **significant figures**, so you would assume an uncertainty of 0.05.

You should always assume the **largest** amount of uncertainty when doing an experiment, so make sure you keep an eye on the **significant figures** when taking measurements, doing calculations and evaluating uncertainties.

Evaluating and Concluding

Draw **Conclusions** that Your Results **Support**

1) A conclusion **explains** what the data shows. You can only draw a conclusion if your data **supports** it.
2) Your conclusion should be limited to the **circumstances you've tested** it under — if you've been investigating how the current flowing through a resistor changes with the potential difference across it, and have only used potential differences between 0 and 6 V, you can't claim to know what would happen if you used a potential difference of 100 V, or if you used a different resistor.
3) You also need to think about how much you can **believe** your conclusion, by evaluating the quality of your results (see previous page). If you can't believe your results, you can't form a **strong conclusion**.

Think About how the Experiment Could be **Improved**

Having collected the data, is there anything you think should have been done **differently**?
Were there any **limitations** to your method?

1) If the results aren't **valid**, could you change the experiment to fix this, e.g. by changing the data you're collecting?
2) If the results aren't **accurate**, what could have caused this?
   Systematic errors (p.12) can affect accuracy — are there any that you could prevent?
3) Are there any changes you could make to the **apparatus** or **procedure** that would make the results more **precise**?
   - The **less random error** there is in the measurement, the more **precise** your results. **Increasing** the number of **repeats** could help to reduce the **effect** of random errors in your results.
   - By using the most **appropriate** equipment — e.g. swapping a millimetre ruler for a micrometer to measure the diameter of a wire — you can instantly cut down the **random error** (p.12) in your experiment.
   - You can also use a **computer** to collect data — e.g. using light gates to measure a time interval rather than a **stopwatch**. This makes results more **precise** by reducing **human error**.
4) Are there any other ways you could have **reduced the errors** in the measurements?

Warm-Up Questions

Q1 What is a valid result?

Q2 What is the difference between saying the results of an experiment are precise and saying that they are accurate?

Q3 What should you think about when you are trying to improve an experimental design?

Exam Questions

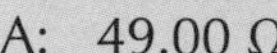

Q1 The resistance of a fixed resistor is given as 50.00 Ω.
According to the manufacturer, there is a 0.02% uncertainty in this value.
What is the minimum possible resistance of the resistor in Ω, to 2 decimal places?

A: 49.00 Ω B: 49.99 Ω C: 49.90 Ω D: 49.09 Ω [1 mark]

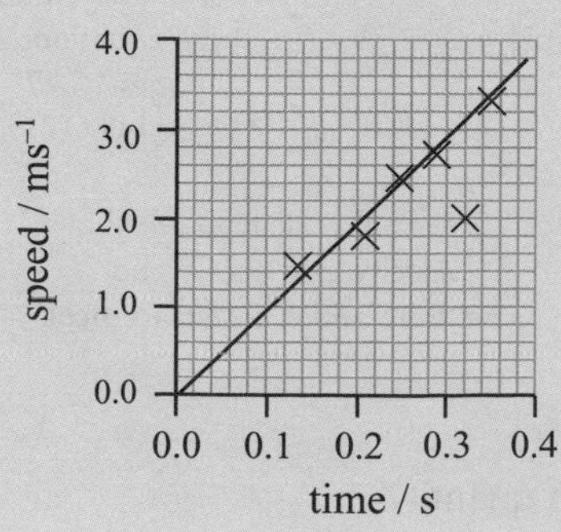

Q2 A student is investigating how the speed of a falling object is affected by how long it has been falling for. He drops an object from heights between 10 cm and 60 cm and measures its speed at the end of its fall, and the time the fall takes, using light gates. He plots a graph of the final speed of the object against the time it took to fall, as shown on the left.

a) Identify the anomalous result. [1 mark]

b) The student concludes that the speed of any falling object is always proportional to the time it has been falling for.
Explain whether or not the results support this conclusion. [2 marks]

In conclusion, Physics causes headaches...

Valid, precise, and accurate... you'd think they all mean the same thing, but they really don't.
Make sure you know the difference, and are careful about which one you use, or you'll be throwing marks away.

Quantities and Units

Learning Physics is a lot like building a house — both involve drinking a lot of tea. Also, both have important foundations — if you skip this stuff everything else is likely to go a bit wrong. So, here goes brick-laying 101...

A **Physical Quantity** has both a **Numerical Value** and a **Unit**

1) Every time you measure something or calculate a quantity you need to give the **units.**
2) The **Système International** (S.I.) includes a set of **base units** for physical quantities from which lots of other units are derived. Here are the S.I. base units that you need to know:

Quantity	S.I. base unit
mass	kilogram, kg
length	metre, m
time	second, s
current	ampere, A
temperature	kelvin, K
amount of a substance	mole, mol

Kilograms are a bit odd — they're the only S.I. unit with a scaling prefix (see the next page).

You might also see temperatures given in °C.

3) Many more units can be derived from these base units — e.g. newtons, N, for force are defined by $kg\,ms^{-2}$. The newton is an **S.I. derived unit**.
4) The S.I. derived units you'll need will be covered throughout the book and you need to remember them.
5) You also need to have a rough idea of the size of each S.I. base unit and S.I. derived unit in this book, so that you can **estimate quantities** using them.

Remembering how S.I. derived units are defined will help you make sure the other quantities in your equations are in the right units.

You Can **Check** Your Units **Mathematically**

The units in any equation must always be the **same on both sides** — this is called **homogeneity of units**. You can use this rule to work out some of the simpler S.I. derived units, like speed:

They always checked the homogeneity of their outfits before leaving the house.

Example: Show that the S.I. derived unit for speed is ms^{-1}.

You know that speed = distance ÷ time

Distance is a length, so its S.I. base unit is the metre, m.

The base unit of time is the second, s.

To find the unit for speed, just put the units for distance and time into the equation for speed: $\mathbf{m \div s = ms^{-1}}$

You can also use this rule to help you to **check your working** if you have to combine or rearrange equations:

Example: For an object moving with uniform acceleration, $v = u + at$ and $s = \frac{1}{2}(u + v)t$. Combine these equations to get an equation for s in terms of u, v and a. Check the homogeneity of your answer.

There's more about these equations on pages 16-17.

v = final velocity, u = initial velocity, a = acceleration, t = time and s = displacement

Rearrange $v = u + at$ to get: $t = \frac{v-u}{a}$

The substitute this into $s = \frac{1}{2}(u + v)t \Rightarrow s = \frac{1}{2}(u + v)\left(\frac{v-u}{a}\right)$

Then simplify the equation: $\mathbf{s = \frac{1}{2a}(v^2 - u^2)}$

To check the units are the same on both sides, substitute the units for each quantity into the equation, then cancel down (you can ignore any numbers, e.g. the 2):

s is a length in metres, v and u are velocities in ms^{-1} and a is acceleration in ms^{-2}.

$$m = \frac{1}{ms^{-2}}((ms^{-1})^2 - (ms^{-1})^2) = \frac{1}{\cancel{m}\cancel{s^{-2}}}(m^{\cancel{2}}\cancel{s^{-2}} - m^{\cancel{2}}\cancel{s^{-2}})$$

There are only metres left on both sides of the equation, so the equation is homogeneous.

Quantities and Units

Prefixes Let You **Scale Units**

Physical quantities come in a **huge range** of sizes. Prefixes are scaling factors that let you write numbers across this range without having to put everything in standard form.
These are the prefixes you need to know:

prefix	**pico (p)**	**nano (n)**	**micro (μ)**	**milli (m)**	**centi (c)**	**deci (d)**	**kilo (k)**	**mega (M)**	**giga (G)**	**tera (T)**
multiple of unit	1×10^{-12}	1×10^{-9}	1×10^{-6}	0.001 (1×10^{-3})	0.01 (1×10^{-2})	0.1 (1×10^{-1})	1000 (1×10^{3})	1×10^{6}	1×10^{9}	1×10^{12}

If you're a bit uncertain about moving between these scaling factors, then convert quantities into the standard unit before you do anything else with them:

Example 1: Convert 1869 picometres into nanometres.

First, convert the value to metres: $1869 \text{ pm} = 1869 \times 10^{-12} \text{ m}$

Then divide by 1×10^{-9} to convert to nanometres: $1869 \times 10^{-12} \div 1 \times 10^{-9} =$ **1.869 nm**

Or, you can convert between prefixes directly:

Example 2: Convert 0.247 megawatts into kilowatts.

$1 \text{ MW} = 1 \times 10^6 \text{ W}$ and $1 \text{ kW} = 1 \times 10^3 \text{ W}$

So the scaling factor to move between MW and kW is:

$(1 \times 10^6) \div (1 \times 10^3) = 1 \times 10^3$.

So $0.247 \text{ MW} = 0.247 \times 1 \times 10^3 =$ **247 kW**

It's really easy to get muddled up when you're converting between prefixes. The rule is, if you're moving to the right in the table above, your number should get smaller, and if you're moving to the left the number should get larger. If your answer doesn't match the rule, you've made a mistake.

Be careful with using these prefixes in the middle of calculations — they'll change the units of your final answer, and could get you in a mess. It's generally safest to do your calculations with everything in its S.I. or S.I. derived units, then convert the answer to include a sensible prefix when you're done.

Warm-Up Questions

Q1 What is the S.I. unit of mass?

Q2 What is meant by an S.I. base unit and an S.I. derived unit?

Q3 What does the term homogeneity of units mean?

Q4 What is: a) 20 000 W in kilowatts, b) 2×10^{-6} W in milliwatts c) 1.23×10^7 W in gigawatts?

Exam Question

Q1 The density, ρ, of a material gives its mass per unit volume. It is given by $\rho = m / V$, where m = mass and V = volume.

a) Express the units of density in terms of S.I. base units. [1 mark]

b) Calculate the density of a cube of mass 9.8 g, and side length 11 mm.
Give your answer in the units stated in part a). [2 marks]

What's the S.I. base unit for boring...

Not the most exciting pair of pages these, I'll admit, but it's important that you have the basics down, or else you're leaving yourself open to simple little mistakes that'll cost you marks. So make sure you've memorised all the S.I. units in the table, then try and write down all the prefixes and their scaling factors. If you don't get them all first time, keep trying until you can. Remember, you need to know the units for every other quantity you meet in this book, too.

Measurements and Uncertainties

There are errors and uncertainties in every measurement. You need to know how to deal with them...

Uncertainty is Caused by Random and Systematic Errors

Every measurement you take has an experimental uncertainty (p.8) caused by two types of error:

1) **Systematic errors** (including **zero errors**) are the same every time you repeat the experiment (they shift all the values by the same amount). They may be caused by the **equipment** you're using or how it's **set-up**, e.g. not lining up a ruler correctly when measuring the extension of a spring. Systematic errors are really **hard to spot**, and they affect the **accuracy** of your results. It's always worth **checking your apparatus** at the start of an experiment, e.g. measure a few known masses to check that a mass meter is **calibrated** properly.

2) **Random errors** vary — they're what make the results a bit different each time you repeat an experiment. If you measured the length of a wire 20 times, the chances are you'd get a slightly different value each time, e.g. due to your head being in a slightly different position when reading the scale. It could be that you just can't keep controlled variables (p.4) exactly the same throughout the experiment.
Using **more sensitive apparatus** can reduce random errors, so your results can be more **precise** (p.8) and **repeating measurements** can reduce the effect of random errors.

Sometimes You Need to Combine Uncertainties

You have to combine the uncertainties of different measured values to find the uncertainty of a calculated result:

Adding or Subtracting Data — ADD the Absolute Uncertainties

Example: A wire is stretched from 0.3 ± 0.1 cm to 0.5 ± 0.1 cm. Calculate the extension of the wire.

1) First subtract the lengths without the uncertainty values: 0.5 – 0.3 = 0.2 cm
2) Then find the total uncertainty by adding the individual absolute uncertainties: 0.1 + 0.1 = 0.2 cm
So, the extension of the wire is **0.2 ± 0.2 cm.**

Multiplying or Dividing Data — ADD the Percentage Uncertainties

Example: A force of 15 N ± 3% is applied to a stationary object which has a mass of 6.0 ± 0.3 kg. Calculate the acceleration of the object and state the percentage uncertainty in this value.

1) First calculate the acceleration without uncertainty: $a = F \div m = 15 \div 6.0 = 2.5 \text{ ms}^{-2}$
2) Next, calculate the percentage uncertainty in the mass: % uncertainty in $m = \frac{0.3}{6.0} \times 100 = 5\%$
3) Add the percentage uncertainties in the force and mass values to find the total uncertainty in the acceleration: Total uncertainty = 3% + 5% = 8%
So, the acceleration = **2.5 ms^{-2} ± 8%**

Raising to a Power — MULTIPLY the Percentage Uncertainty by the Power

Example: The radius of a circle is r = 40 cm ± 2.5%. What will the percentage uncertainty be in the area of this circle (πr^2)?

The radius will be raised to the power of **2** to calculate the area.
So, the percentage uncertainty will be 2.5% × 2 = **5%**

Percentage uncertainty (or percentage error) is on page 8.

Percentage Difference Shows How Close Your Answer is to the True Value

If you know the **true value** of what you're investigating you can measure the **accuracy** of your result using **percentage difference**. This is the difference between your value and the true value, **expressed as a percentage** of the true value. Don't get it confused with percentage uncertainty (p.8).

Measurements and Uncertainties

Error Bars Show the **Uncertainty** of **Individual Points**

1) Most of the time, you work out the **uncertainty** in your **final** result using the uncertainty in **each measurement** you make.
2) When you're plotting a **graph**, you can show the uncertainty in **each measurement** by using **error bars** to show the **range** the point is likely to lie in. E.g. the error bars on the graph on the right show the error in each measurement of the extension of an object when a force is applied.
3) You can have error bars for both the dependent and the independent variable.

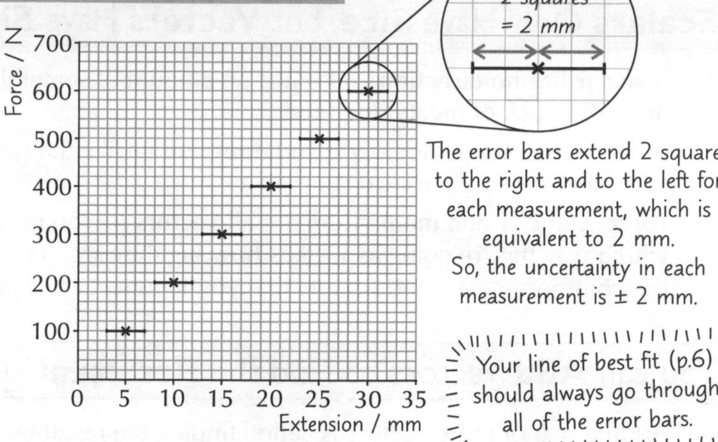

Your line of best fit (p.6) should always go through all of the error bars.

You Can **Calculate** the **Uncertainty** of **Final Results** from a **Line of Best Fit**

Normally when you draw a graph you'll want to find the **gradient** or **intercept** (p.7). For example, you can calculate *k*, the **force constant** of the object being stretched, from the **gradient** of the graph on the right — here it's about 20 000 Nm^{-1}. You can find the **uncertainty** in that value by using **worst lines**:

1) Draw lines of best fit which have the **maximum** and **minimum** possible slopes for the data and which should go through all of the **error bars** (see the pink and blue lines on the right). These are the **worst lines** for your data.
2) Calculate the **worst gradient** — the gradient of the slope that is **furthest** from the gradient of the line of best fit. The blue line's gradient is about 21 000 Nm^{-1} and the pink line's gradient is about 19 000 Nm^{-1}, so you can use either here.
3) The **uncertainty** in the gradient is given by the **difference** between the **best gradient** (of the line of best fit) and the **worst gradient** — here it's 1000 Nm^{-1}. So this is the uncertainty in the value of the force constant. For this object, the force constant is 20 000 ± 1000 Nm^{-1} (or 20 000 Nm^{-1} ± 5%).
4) Similarly, the uncertainty in the ***y*-intercept** is just the **difference** between the **best** and **worst** intercepts (although there's no uncertainty here since the best and worst lines both go through the origin).

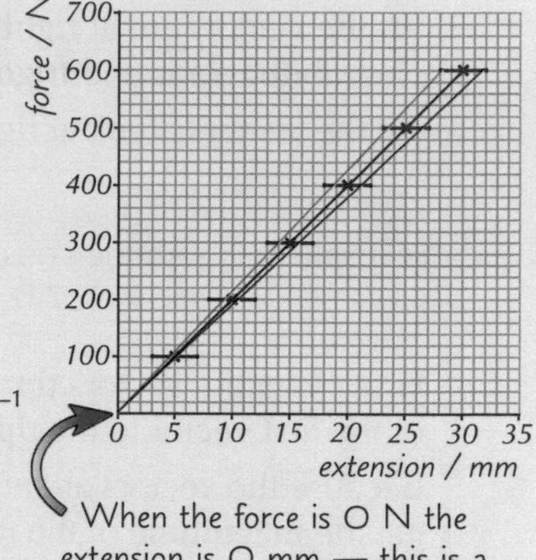

When the force is 0 N the extension is 0 mm — this is a measurement with no uncertainty.

Warm-Up Questions

Q1 Give two examples of possible sources of random error and one example of a possible source of systematic error in an experiment. Which kind of error is least likely to affect the precision of the results?

Q2 What is meant by percentage difference?

Q3 What are worst lines? How could you use them to find the uncertainty in the intercept of a graph?

PRACTICE QUESTIONS

Exam Question

Q1 A student is investigating the acceleration of a remote controlled car. The car has an initial velocity of 0.52 ± 0.02 ms^{-1} and accelerates to 0.94 ± 0.02 ms^{-1} over an interval of 2.5 ± 0.5 s.

a) Calculate the percentage uncertainty in the car's initial speed. [1 mark]

b) Calculate the percentage uncertainty in the car's final speed. [1 mark]

c) Calculate the car's average acceleration over this interval. Include the absolute uncertainty of the result in your answer. (acceleration = change in velocity ÷ time taken). [4 marks]

My percentage uncertainty about these pages is 99.99%...

Uncertainties are a bit of a pain, but they're really important. Learn the rules for combining uncertainties, and make sure you don't get percentage uncertainty and percentage difference confused. Random and systematic errors are an exam favourite too, so make sure you know the difference, and how to minimise both in your experiments.

Scalars and Vectors

And now time to draw some lovely triangles. Please, don't all thank me at once...

Scalars Only Have **Size**, but **Vectors** Have **Size** and **Direction**

1) A **scalar** has **no direction** — it's **just an amount** of something, like the **mass** of a **sack of meaty dog food**.
2) A **vector** has magnitude (**size**) and **direction** — like the **speed and direction** of next door's **cat** running away.
3) **Force, velocity and momentum** are all **vectors** — you need to know **which way** they're going as well as **how big** they are. Here are some of the common scalars and vectors that you'll come across in your exams:

Scalars	Vectors
mass, time, temperature, length, speed, energy	displacement, force, velocity, acceleration, momentum

You can **Add** Vectors to Find the **Resultant**

1) Adding two or more vectors is called finding the **resultant** of them. Whatever the quantity is — displacement, force, momentum, the procedure is the same.
2) You should always start by drawing a **diagram**. Draw the vectors **'tip to tail'**. If you're doing a **vector subtraction**, draw the vector you're subtracting with the same magnitude but pointing in the **opposite direction**.
3) If the vectors are at **right angles** to each other, then you can use **Pythagoras** and **trigonometry** to find the resultant vector.
4) If the vectors aren't at right angles, you may need to draw a **scale diagram**.

Trig's really useful in physics, so make sure you're completely okay with it. Remember SOH CAH TOA.

Example 1: Jemima goes for a walk. She walks 3.0 m north and 4.0 m east. She has walked 7.0 m but she isn't 7.0 m from her starting point. Find the magnitude and direction of her displacement.

Jemima's 'displacement' gives her position relative to her starting point, see p.16.

First, draw the vectors **tip-to-tail**. Then draw a line from the **tail** of the first vector to the **tip** of the last vector to give the **resultant**:

4.0 m
3.0 m
resultant vector, R

Because the vectors are at right angles, you get the **magnitude** of the resultant using Pythagoras:

$R^2 = 3.0^2 + 4.0^2 = 25.0$ So $R = \mathbf{5.0\ m}$

Now find the **bearing** of Jemima's new position from her original position. You use the triangle again, but this time you need to use trigonometry. You know the opposite and the adjacent sides, so you can use:

$\tan\theta = 4.0 / 3.0$ So $\theta =$ **053° (to 2 s.f.)**

4.0 m
3.0 m
θ
resultant vector = 5.0 m

Jemima

A bearing is just an angle measured clockwise from the north line, represented by three digits, e.g. 10° = 010°.

Example 2: A van is accelerating north, with a resultant force of 510 N. A wind begins to blow on a bearing of 150°. It exerts a force of 200 N on the van. What is the new resultant force acting on the van?

The vectors **aren't** at right angles, so you need to do a scale drawing. Pick a sensible scale. Here, 1 cm = 100 N seems good.

Using a really sharp pencil, draw the initial resultant force on the van. As the van is going north, this should be a 5.1 cm long line going straight up.

The force of the wind acts on a bearing of 150°, so add this to your diagram. Using the same scale, this vector has a length of 2.0 cm.

Then you can draw on the new resultant force and measure its length. Measure the angle carefully to get the bearing.

The resultant force has a magnitude of 350 N (to 2 s.f.), acting on a bearing of 017° (to 2 s.f.).

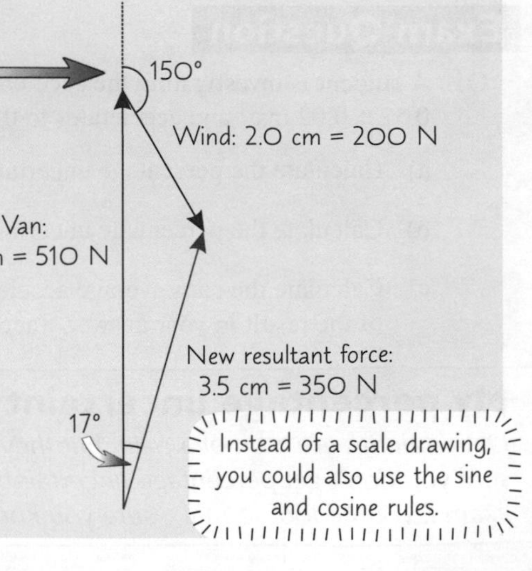

Instead of a scale drawing, you could also use the sine and cosine rules.

Scalars and Vectors

It's Useful to Split a **Vector** into **Horizontal** and **Vertical Components**

This is the opposite of finding the resultant — you start from the resultant vector and split it into two **components** at right angles to each other. You're basically **working backwards** from Example 1 on the last page.

Resolving a vector v into horizontal and vertical components:

You get the **horizontal** component v_h like this:

$$\cos\theta = v_h / v$$

$$v_h = v\cos\theta$$

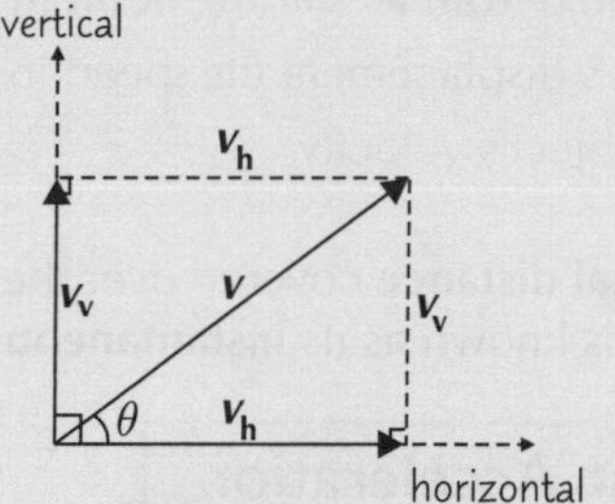

...and the **vertical** component v_v like this:

$$\sin\theta = v_v / v$$

$$v_v = v\sin\theta$$

Where θ is the angle from the horizontal.

Example: Charley's amazing floating home is travelling at a speed of 5 ms^{-1} at an angle of 60° up from the horizontal. Find the vertical and horizontal components.

The **horizontal** component v_h is:

$v_h = v\cos\theta = 5\cos 60° = \mathbf{2.5\ ms^{-1}}$

The **vertical** component v_v is:

$v_v = v\sin\theta = 5\sin 60° = \mathbf{4.3\ ms^{-1}}$ **(to 2 s.f.)**

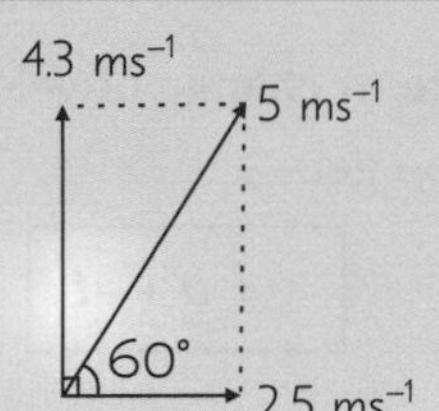

Charley's mobile home was the envy of all his friends.

Resolving is dead useful because the two components of a vector **don't affect each other**. This means you can deal with the two directions **completely separately**.

It also gives you another way to find the resultant vector of two vectors that aren't at **right angles** to each other. **Resolve the vectors** into their horizontal and vertical components, and add up the vertical and horizontal components separately. Then you just need to **combine** the two to get the resultant vector. It can be a lot less fiddly than drawing accurate scale diagrams.

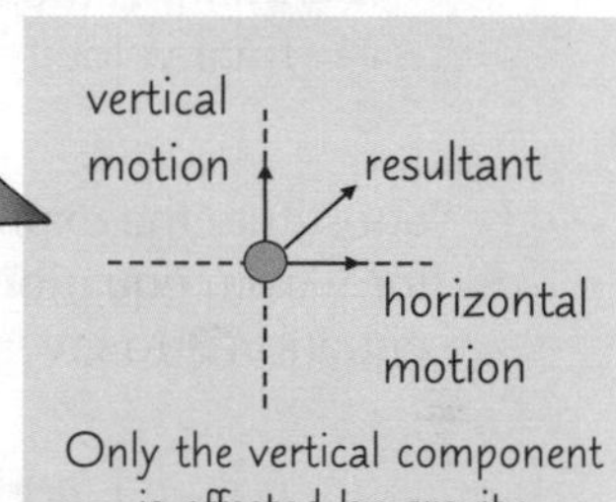

Only the vertical component is affected by gravity.

Warm-Up Questions

Q1 What is the difference between a vector and a scalar? Give three vector quantities and three scalar quantities.

Q2 Describe how to find a resultant vector using a scale diagram.

PRACTICE QUESTIONS

Exam Questions

Q1 The wind applies a horizontal force of 20 N on a falling rock of weight 75 N.
Calculate the magnitude and direction of the resultant force. [2 marks]

Q2 A glider is travelling at a velocity of 20.0 ms^{-1} at an angle of 15.0° below the horizontal.
Calculate the horizontal and vertical components of the glider's velocity. [2 marks]

Q3 A remote controlled boat is placed in a river. The boat produces a driving speed of 1.54 ms^{-1} at an angle of 60° to the current (travelling with the current). The river is flowing at 0.20 ms^{-1}.
By resolving the vectors into their horizontal and vertical components, show that the resultant velocity of the boat is 1.6 ms^{-1} at an angle of 54° to the current. [4 marks]

I think I'm a scalar quantity, my Mum says I'm completely direction-less...

Lots of different ways to solve vector problems on these pages, it must be your lucky day. Personally, I avoid doing scale drawings unless I absolutely have to (too fiddly for my liking), but if they work for you that's great. And you may get told to draw one in your exams, so you need to be prepared in case they come up.

Motion with Constant Acceleration

All the equations on this page are for motion with constant acceleration. It makes life a whole lot easier, trust me.

Learn the Definitions of Speed, Displacement, Velocity and Acceleration

Displacement, velocity and acceleration are all **vector** quantities (page 14), so the **direction** matters.

Speed — How fast something is moving, regardless of direction.
Displacement (s) — How far an object's travelled from its starting point in a given direction.
Velocity (v) — The rate of change of an object's displacement (its speed in a given direction).
Acceleration (a) — The rate of change of an object's velocity.

During a journey, the **average speed** is just the **total distance** covered over the **total time** elapsed. The speed of an object at any given point in time is known as its **instantaneous** speed.

Uniform Acceleration is Constant Acceleration

Acceleration could mean a change in speed or direction or both.

Uniform means **constant** here. It's nothing to do with what you wear.
There are **four main equations** that you use to solve problems involving **uniform acceleration**. You need to be able to **use them**, but you don't have to know how they're **derived** — we've just put it in to help you learn them.

1) **Acceleration is the rate of change of velocity.**
From this definition you get:

$$a = \frac{(v - u)}{t} \quad \text{so} \quad \boldsymbol{v = u + at}$$

where:
u = initial velocity
v = final velocity
a = acceleration
t = time taken

2) **s = average velocity × time**
If acceleration is constant, the average velocity is just the average of the initial and final velocities, so:

$$s = \frac{(u + v)}{2} \times t$$

s = displacement

3) Substitute the expression for v from equation 1 into equation 2 to give:

$$s = \frac{(u + u + at) \times t}{2} = \frac{2ut + at^2}{2}$$

$$\boldsymbol{s = ut + \tfrac{1}{2}at^2}$$

4) You can **derive** the fourth equation from equations **1** and **2**:
Use equation **1** in the form: $a = \frac{v - u}{t}$
Multiply both sides by s, where: $s = \frac{(u + v)}{2} \times t$

This gives us: $as = \frac{(v - u)}{t} \times \frac{(u + v)t}{2}$

The t's on the right cancel, so:
$2as = (v - u)(v + u)$
$2as = v^2 - uv + uv - u^2$

so: $\boldsymbol{v^2 = u^2 + 2as}$

Example: A tile falls from a roof 25 m high. Calculate its speed when it hits the ground and how long it takes to fall. Take $g = 9.81\ \text{ms}^{-2}$.

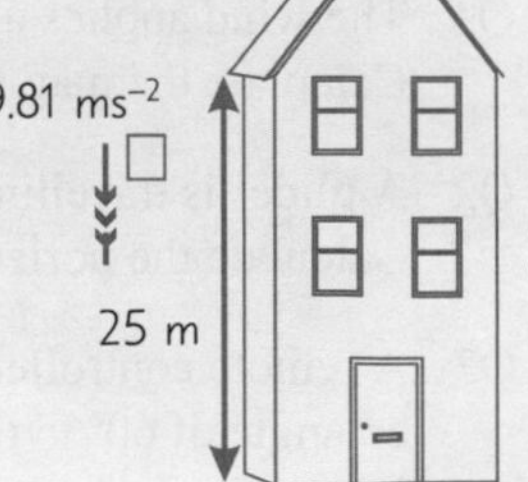

Usually you take upwards as the positive direction. In this question it's probably easier to take downwards as positive, so you get $g = +9.81\ \text{ms}^{-2}$ instead of $g = -9.81\ \text{ms}^{-2}$.

First of all, write out what you know:
$s = 25$ m
$u = 0\ \text{ms}^{-1}$ since the tile's stationary to start with
$a = 9.81\ \text{ms}^{-2}$ due to gravity
$v = ?$ $t = ?$

Then, choose an equation with only **one unknown quantity**.
So start with $v^2 = u^2 + 2as$
$v^2 = 0 + 2 \times 9.81 \times 25$
$v^2 = 490.5$
v = **22.1 ms^{-1} (to 3 s.f.)**

Now, find t using:
$s = ut + \frac{1}{2}at^2$
$25 = 0 + \frac{1}{2} \times 9.81 \times t^2$
$t^2 = \frac{25}{4.905}$

Final answers:
t = **2.26 s (to 3 s.f.)**
v = **22.1 ms^{-1} (to 3 s.f.)**

Motion with Constant Acceleration

Example: A car accelerates steadily from rest at a rate of 4.2 ms^{-2} for 6 seconds.
a) Calculate the final speed.
b) Calculate the distance travelled in 6 seconds.

Remember — always start by writing down what you know.

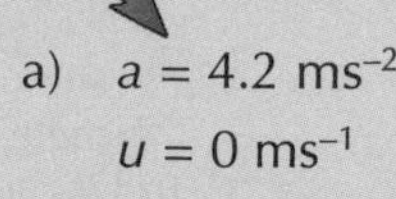

a) $a = 4.2$ ms^{-2}
$u = 0$ ms^{-1}
$t = 6$ s
$v = ?$

choose the right equation... $v = u + at$

$v = 0 + 4.2 \times 6$

Final answer: $v = 25.2 =$ **25 ms^{-1} (to 2 s.f.)**

b) $s = ?$
$t = 6$ s
$u = 0$ ms^{-1}
$a = 4.2$ ms^{-2}
$v = 25.2$ ms^{-1}

you can use: $s = \frac{(u + v)}{2} \times t$ **or:** $s = ut + \frac{1}{2}at^2$

$s = \frac{(0 + 25.2) \times 6}{2}$ $\qquad$ $s = 0 + \frac{1}{2} \times 4.2 \times (6)^2$

Final answer: $s =$ **76 m (to 2 s.f.)** $\qquad$ $s =$ **76 m (to 2 s.f.)**

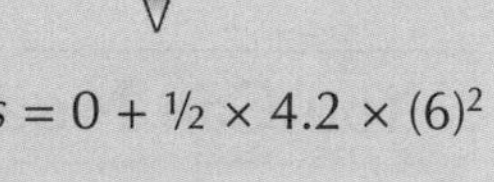

Warm-Up Questions

Q1 Write down definitions for speed, displacement, average velocity, instantaneous velocity and acceleration.

Q2 Write out the four constant acceleration equations.

Exam Questions

PRACTICE QUESTIONS

Q1 A skydiver jumps from an aeroplane when it is flying horizontally.
She accelerates due to gravity for 5 s.
a) Calculate her maximum vertical velocity. (Assume no air resistance.) [2 marks]
b) Calculate how far she falls in this time. [2 marks]

Q2 A motorcyclist slows down uniformly as he approaches a red light.
He takes 3.2 seconds to come to a halt and travels 40 m in this time.
a) Calculate how fast he was travelling initially. [2 marks]
b) Calculate his acceleration. (N.B. a negative value shows a deceleration.) [2 marks]

Q3 A stream provides a constant acceleration of 6 ms^{-2}. A toy boat is pushed directly against the current and then released from a point 1.2 m upstream from a small waterfall. Just before it reaches the waterfall, it is travelling at a speed of 5 ms^{-1}.
a) Calculate the initial velocity of the boat. [2 marks]
b) Calculate the maximum distance upstream from the waterfall the boat reaches. [2 marks]

Q4 A cyclist is travelling at a constant speed of 3 ms^{-1} as he starts to roll down a hill. He rolls down the hill with a constant acceleration. During the third second, he travels a distance of 6 m.
a) Calculate the cyclist's acceleration. [2 marks]
b) Calculate how far he travels during the 4th second. [1 mark]

Constant acceleration — it'll end in tears...

If a question talks about "uniform" or "constant" acceleration, it's a dead giveaway they want you to use one of these equations. The tricky bit is working out which one to use — start every question by writing out what you know and what you need to know. That makes it much easier to see which equation you need. To be sure. Arrr.

Free Fall

So, how do you work this parachute thing agaiAAAAAaaaaaarrrrrrggghhhhhhhhhhhhh...

Free Fall is when there's Only **Gravity** and Nothing Else

Free fall is defined as "the motion of an object undergoing an acceleration of 'g'".
You need to remember:

1) Acceleration is a **vector quantity** — and 'g' acts **vertically downwards**.
2) Unless you're given a different value, take the magnitude of g as **9.81 ms^{-2}**, though it varies slightly at different points on the Earth's surface.
3) The **only force** acting on an object in free fall is its **weight**.
4) Objects can have an initial velocity in any direction and still undergo **free fall** as long as the **force** providing the initial velocity is **no longer acting**.

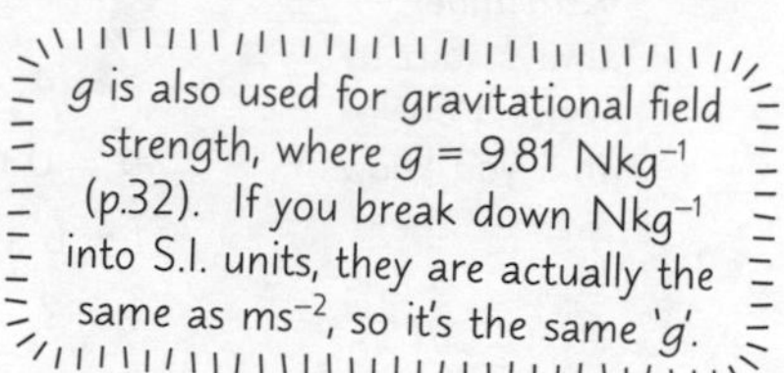
g is also used for gravitational field strength, where g = 9.81 Nkg^{-1} (p.32). If you break down Nkg^{-1} into S.I. units, they are actually the same as ms^{-2}, so it's the same 'g'.

You Can **Measure g** by using an Object in **Free Fall**

You don't have to do it this way — but if you don't know a method of measuring g already, learn this one.
You need to be able to:

1) **Sketch** a diagram of the **apparatus**.
2) **Describe** the **method**.
3) **List** the **measurements** you make.
4) **Explain** how 'g' is **calculated**.
5) Be aware of sources of **error**.

Another gravity experiment.

Experiment to Measure the Acceleration Due to Gravity

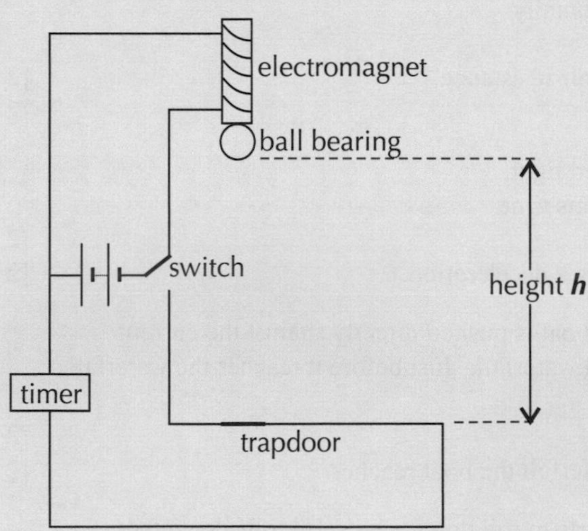

In this experiment you have to assume that the effect of air resistance on the ball bearing is negligible and that the magnetism of the electromagnet decays instantly.

The Method:

1) Measure the height ***h*** from the **bottom** of the ball bearing to the **trapdoor**.
2) Flick the switch to **simultaneously** start the timer and disconnect the electromagnet, releasing the ball bearing.
3) The ball bearing falls, knocking the trapdoor down and breaking the circuit — which stops the timer.

Use the time t measured by the timer, and the height h that the ball bearing has fallen, to calculate a value for g, using $h = \frac{1}{2}gt^2$ (see next page for more on acceleration formulas).

By using a computer, errors in the timing are reduced — human error can be introduced when using a stopwatch.

The most **significant** source of error in this experiment will be in the measurement of ***h***.
Using a ruler, you'll have an uncertainty of about 1 mm.
This dwarfs any error from switch delay or air resistance.

You could reduce the error in your measurement of h by using a set square to make sure your eye is level with the ruler.

Free Fall

You can Just Replace *a* with *g* in the Equations of Motion

You need to be able to work out **speeds**, **distances** and **times** for objects in **free fall**. Since g is a **constant acceleration** you can use the **constant acceleration equations**. But g acts downwards, so you need to be careful about directions. To make it clear, there's a sign convention: **upwards is positive**, **downwards is negative**.

Sign Conventions — Learn Them:

g is always downwards so it's usually negative — t is always positive

u and v can be either positive or negative — s can be either positive or negative

Case 1: No initial velocity (it just falls)

Initial velocity $u = 0$

Acceleration $a = g = -9.81\ \text{ms}^{-2}$

So the constant acceleration equations become: ⟹

$$v = gt \qquad v^2 = 2gs$$
$$s = \frac{1}{2}gt^2 \qquad s = \frac{vt}{2}$$

Case 2: An initial velocity upwards (it's thrown up into the air)

The constant acceleration equations are just as normal, but with $a = g = -9.81\ \text{ms}^{-2}$

Case 3: An initial velocity downwards (it's thrown down)

Example: Alex throws a stone down a cliff. She gives it a downwards velocity of $2\ \text{ms}^{-1}$. It takes 3 s to reach the water below. How high is the cliff?

1) You know $u = -2\ \text{ms}^{-1}$, $a = g = -9.81\ \text{ms}^{-2}$ and $t = 3$ s. You need to find s.

2) Use $s = ut + \frac{1}{2}gt^2 = (-2 \times 3) + (\frac{1}{2} \times -9.81 \times 3^2) = -50.145$ m.

The cliff is 50 m high (to 2 s.f.)

s will be negative because the stone ends up further down than it started.

Warm-Up Questions

Q1 What is the value of the acceleration of a free-falling object?

Q2 What is the initial velocity of an object which is dropped?

Q3 Describe how you would find a value for g by using a trapdoor and electromagnet set-up.

PRACTICE QUESTIONS

Exam Questions

Q1 A student has designed a device to estimate the value of 'g'. It consists of two narrow strips of card joined by a piece of transparent plastic. The student measures the widths of the strips of card then drops the device through a light gate connected to a computer. As the device falls, the strips of card break the light beam.

a) Give three pieces of data that the student will need from the computer to estimate g. [3 marks]

b) Explain how these measurements can be used to estimate 'g'. [3 marks]

c) Give one reason why the student's value of 'g' will not be entirely accurate. [1 mark]

Q2 Charlene is bouncing on a trampoline. She reaches her highest point a height of 5 m above the trampoline. Assume air resistance is negligible.

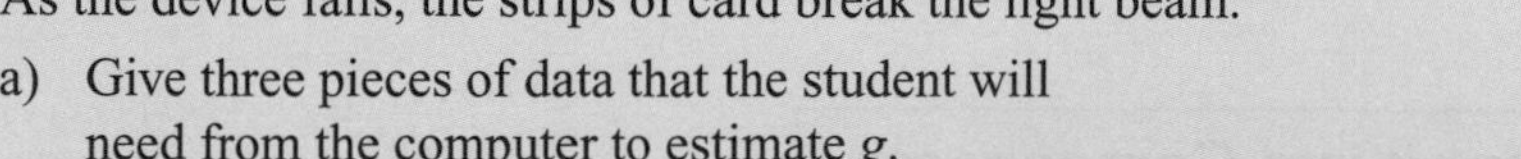

a) Calculate the speed with which she leaves the trampoline surface. [2 marks]

b) Calculate how long it takes Charlene to reach her highest point. [2 marks]

c) Calculate her velocity as she lands back on the trampoline. [1 mark]

It's not the falling that hurts — it's the being pelted with rotten vegetables... okay, okay...

The hardest bit with free fall questions is getting your signs right. Draw yourself a little diagram before you start doing any calculations, and label it with what you know and what you want to know. That can help you get the signs straight in your head. It also helps the person marking your paper if it's clear what your sign convention is. Always good.

Projectile Motion

Any object given an initial velocity and then left to move freely under gravity is a projectile, which handily you can predict the motion of by resolving its velocity. If you're doing Maths, you might have to cover this again there. Double the fun.

You have to think of **Horizontal** and **Vertical** Motion **Separately**

In projectiles, the **horizontal** and **vertical** components of the object's motion are **completely independent**. Projectiles follow a **curved path** because the horizontal velocity remains **constant**, while the vertical velocity is affected by the **acceleration due to gravity**, *g*.

Example: Sharon fires a scale model of a TV talent show presenter horizontally with a velocity of 100 ms^{-1} from 1.5 m above the ground. How long does it take to hit the ground, and how far does it travel horizontally? Assume the model acts as a particle, the ground is horizontal and there is no air resistance.

Think about vertical motion first:

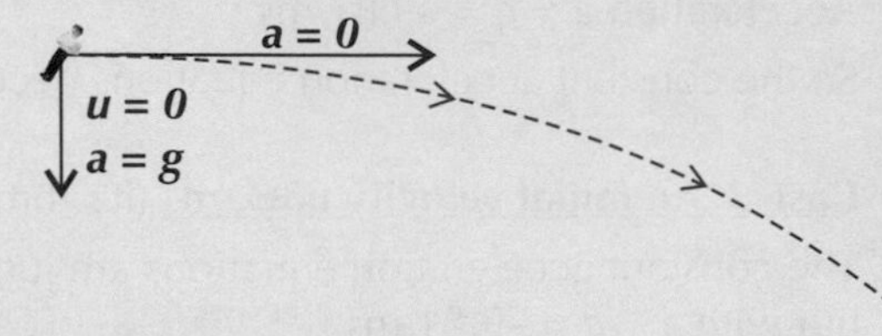

1) It's **constant acceleration** under gravity...
2) You know $u = 0$ (no vertical velocity at first), $s = -1.5$ m and $a = g = -9.81$ ms^{-2}. You need to find t.
3) Use $s = \frac{1}{2}gt^2 \Rightarrow t = \sqrt{\frac{2s}{g}} = \sqrt{\frac{2 \times -1.5}{-9.81}} = 0.553...$ s

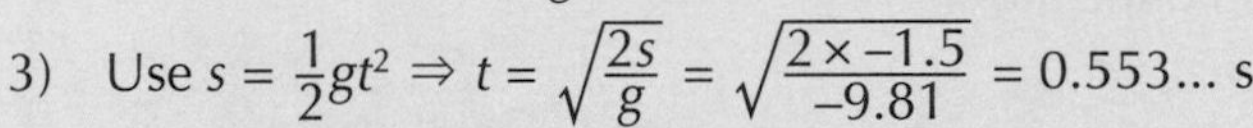

4) So the model hits the ground after **0.55 (to 2 s.f.)** seconds.

Then do the horizontal motion:

1) The horizontal motion isn't affected by gravity or any other force, so it moves at a **constant speed.**
2) That means you can just use good old **speed = distance / time.**
3) Now $v_h = 100$ ms^{-1}, $t = 0.553...$ s and $a = 0$. You need to find s_h.
4) $s_h = v_h t = 100 \times 0.553... =$ **55 m (to 2 s.f.)**

Where v_h is the horizontal velocity, and s_h is the horizontal distance travelled (rather than the height fallen).

It's **Slightly Trickier** if it **Starts Off** at an **Angle**

1) Forces can be in **any direction**, so they're not always at right angles to each other. This is sometimes a bit **awkward** for **calculations.**
2) If something's projected at an **angle** (like, say, a javelin) you start off with both **horizontal** and **vertical velocity**:

Method:
1) **Resolve** the initial velocity into horizontal and vertical components (see below).
2) Use the vertical component to work out **how long** it's in the air and/or **how high** it goes.
3) Use the horizontal component to work out **how far** it goes while it's in the air.

Resolving a **Velocity** means **Splitting** it into **Components**

You'll also find examples of resolving on p.15, p.30 and p.52.

Example: A box is pushed at a velocity of 10 ms^{-1} at an angle of 0.52 radians above the horizontal. Find the vertical and horizontal components of the velocity.

10 ms^{-1}, v_V, 0.52 rad, v_H

Use these formulas when resolving velocities:

$\frac{v_H}{v} = \cos\theta$ *or* $v_H = v\cos\theta$ And $\frac{v_V}{v} = \sin\theta$ *or* $v_V = v\sin\theta$

Remember that θ is the angle from the **horizontal**.

$v_H = 10 \times \cos(0.52) = 8.67... =$ **8.7 ms^{-1} (to 2 s.f.)**

$v_V = 10 \times \sin(0.52) = 4.96... =$ **5.0 ms^{-1} (to 2 s.f.)**

To convert from degrees to radians (rad), multiply by $\pi/180°$. To convert from radians to degrees, multiply by $180°/\pi$.

Projectile Motion

Time for a **Resolving Example**

Example: An athlete throws a javelin from a height of 1.8 m with a velocity of 21 ms^{-1} at an upward angle of 45° to the ground. How far is the javelin thrown? Assume the javelin acts as a particle, the ground is horizontal and there is no air resistance.

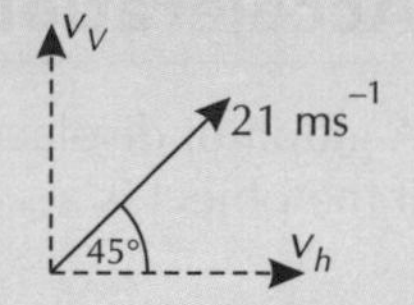

1) Draw a quick sketch of the information given in the question.

2) Start by resolving the velocity into horizontal and vertical components:
$u_h = \cos 45° \times 21 = 14.84...\ \text{ms}^{-1}$
$u_v = \sin 45° \times 21 = 14.84...\ \text{ms}^{-1}$

3) Then find how long it's in the air for — start by finding v_v. The javelin starts from a height of 1.8 m and finishes at ground level, so its final vertical distance $s_v = -1.8$ m:

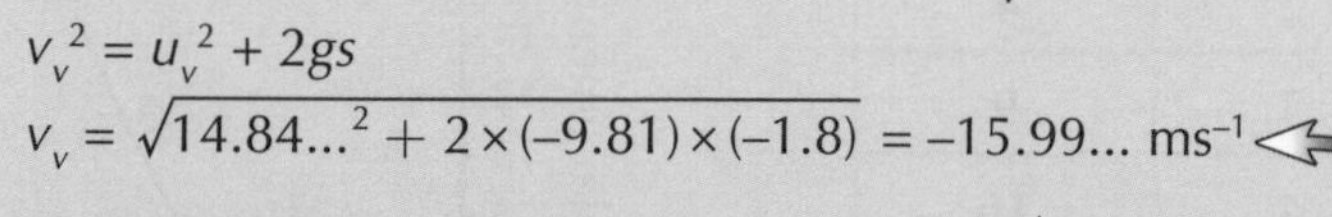

$v_v^2 = u_v^2 + 2gs$
$v_v = \sqrt{14.84...^2 + 2 \times (-9.81) \times (-1.8)} = -15.99...\ \text{ms}^{-1}$

You need the negative square root, as this is a velocity towards the ground.

Now you can use this v_v value and $s = \left(\frac{u+v}{2}\right)t$ to find the time it stays in the air:

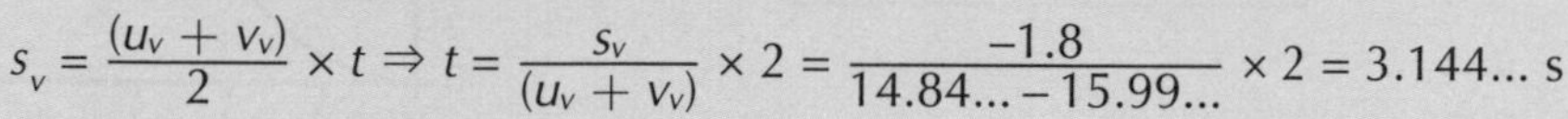

$s_v = \frac{(u_v + v_v)}{2} \times t \Rightarrow t = \frac{s_v}{(u_v + v_v)} \times 2 = \frac{-1.8}{14.84... - 15.99...} \times 2 = 3.144...\ \text{s}$

4) Finally, as $a_h = 0$, you can use **speed = distance / time** to work out how far it travels horizontally in this time. The horizontal velocity is just u_h, so:
$s_h = u_h t = 14.84... \times 3.144... =$ **46.7 m (to 3 s.f.)**

Warm-Up Questions

PRACTICE QUESTIONS

Q1 What is the initial vertical velocity for an object projected horizontally with a velocity of 5 ms^{-1}?

Q2 How does the horizontal velocity of a projectile change with time?

Q3 What is the horizontal component of the velocity of a stone, hurled at 30 ms^{-1} at 35° to the horizontal.

Exam Questions

Q1 Jason stands on a vertical cliff edge throwing stones into the sea below.
He throws a stone horizontally with a velocity of 20 ms^{-1}, 560 m above sea level.

a) Calculate how long it takes for the stone to hit the water from leaving Jason's hand. Use $g = 9.81$ ms^{-2} and ignore air resistance. [2 marks]

b) Calculate the distance of the stone from the base of the cliff when it hits the water. [2 marks]

Q2 Robin fires an arrow into the air with a vertical velocity of 30 ms^{-1}, and a horizontal velocity of 20 ms^{-1}, from 1 m above horizontal ground. Choose the correct option which shows the maximum height from the ground (to 2 significant figures) reached by his arrow. Use $g = 9.81$ ms^{-2} and ignore air resistance. [1 mark]

A	45 m	C	47 m
B	46 m	D	48 m

All this physics makes me want to create projectile motions...

...by throwing my revision books out of the window. The maths on this page can be tricky, but take it step by step and all will be fine. On the plus side, the next page is full of lovely graphs. Who doesn't love a good graph?

Displacement-Time Graphs

Drawing graphs by hand — oh joy. You'd think examiners had never heard of the graphical calculator. Ah well, until they manage to drag themselves out of the Dark Ages, you'll just have to grit your teeth and get on with it.

Acceleration Means a **Curved Displacement-Time Graph**

A graph of displacement against time for an **accelerating object** always produces a **curve**.
If the object is accelerating at a **uniform rate**, then the **rate of change** of the **gradient** will be constant.

Example: Plot a displacement-time graph for a lion who accelerates constantly from rest at 2 ms^{-2} for 5 seconds.

You want to find **s**, and you know that:
$a = 2$ ms^{-2}
$u = 0$ ms^{-1}

Use $s = ut + \frac{1}{2}at^2$
If you substitute in u and a, this simplifies to:
$s = 0 \times t + \frac{1}{2} \times 2t^2$
$s = t^2$

Do a **table of values**:

t / s	s / m
0	**0**
1	**1**
2	**4**
3	**9**
4	**16**
5	**25**

...then plot the **graph**:

Different Accelerations Have **Different Gradients**

In the example above, if the lion has a **different acceleration** it'll change the **gradient** of the curve like this:

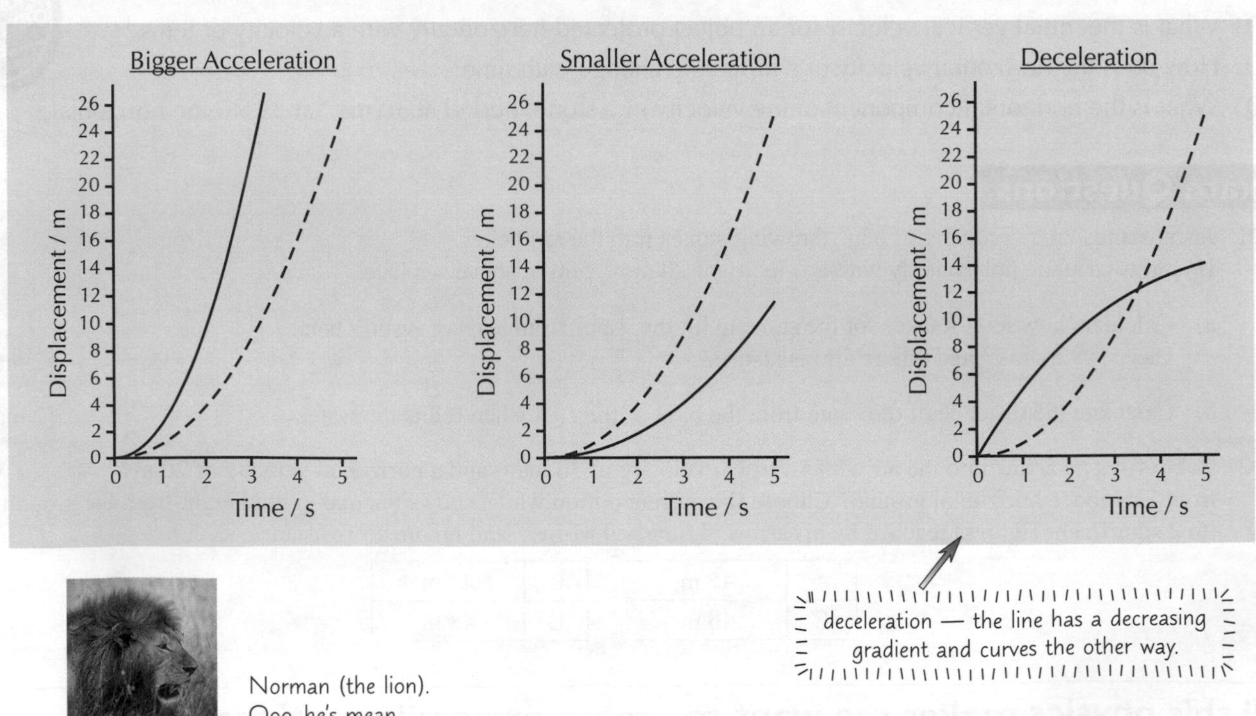

deceleration — the line has a decreasing gradient and curves the other way.

Norman (the lion). Ooo, he's mean...

Displacement-Time Graphs

The **Gradient** of a **Displacement-Time Graph** Tells You the Velocity

When the velocity is constant, the graph's a **straight line**.
Velocity is defined as...

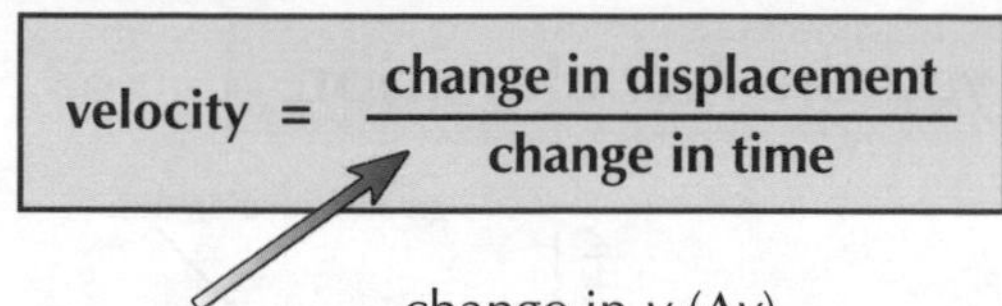

On the graph, this is $\frac{\text{change in } y\ (\Delta y)}{\text{change in } x\ (\Delta x)}$, i.e. the gradient.

So to get the velocity from a displacement-time graph, just find the gradient.

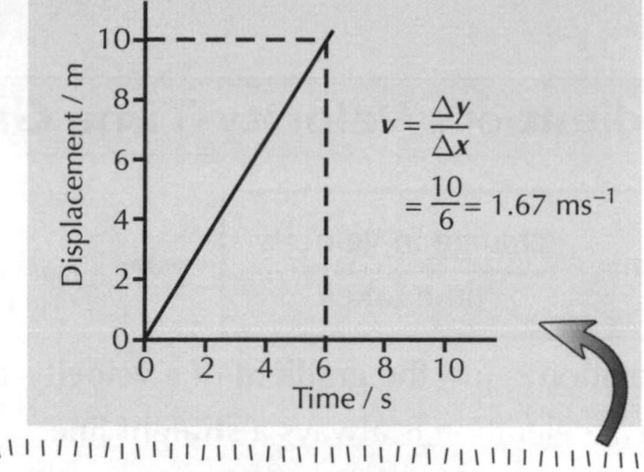

Acceleration is $\frac{\text{change in velocity } (\Delta v)}{\text{change in time } (\Delta t)}$, so it is the rate of change of this gradient. If the gradient is constant (straight line) then there is no acceleration, and if it's changing (curved line) then there's acceleration or deceleration.

It's the Same with **Curved Graphs**

If the gradient **isn't constant** (i.e. if it's a curved line), it means the object is **accelerating**.

To find the **instantaneous velocity** at a certain point you need to draw a **tangent** to the curve at that point and find its gradient.

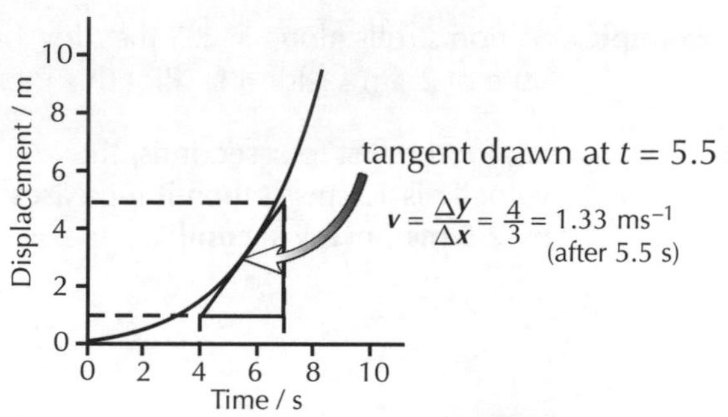

To find the **average velocity** over a period of time, just divide the final (change in) displacement by the final (change in) time — it doesn't matter if the graph is curved or not.

Warm-Up Questions

PRACTICE QUESTIONS

Q1 What is given by the slope of a displacement-time graph?

Q2 Sketch a displacement-time graph to show: a) constant velocity, b) acceleration, c) deceleration

Exam Questions

Q1 Describe the motion of the cyclist as shown by the graph below. [4 marks]

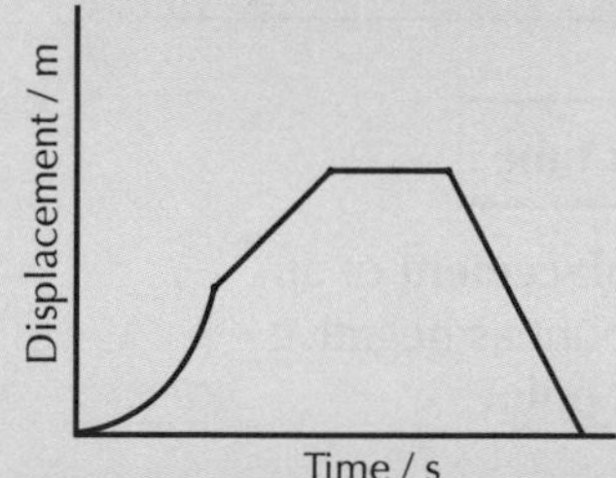

Q2 A baby crawls 5 m in 8 seconds at a constant velocity. She then rests for 5 seconds before crawling a further 3 m in 5 seconds. Finally, she makes her way back to her starting point in 10 seconds, travelling at a constant speed all the way.

a) Draw a displacement-time graph to show the baby's journey. [4 marks]

b) Calculate her velocity at all the different stages of her journey. [2 marks]

Be ahead of the curve, get to grips with this stuff now...

Whether it's a straight line or a curve, the steeper it is, the greater the velocity. There's nothing difficult about these graphs — the problem is that it's easy to confuse them with velocity-time graphs (next page). If in doubt, think about the gradient — is it velocity or acceleration, is it changing (curve), is it constant (straight line), is it 0 (horizontal line)...

Velocity-Time Graphs

Speed-time graphs and velocity-time graphs are pretty similar. The big difference is that velocity-time graphs can have a negative part to show something travelling in the opposite direction:

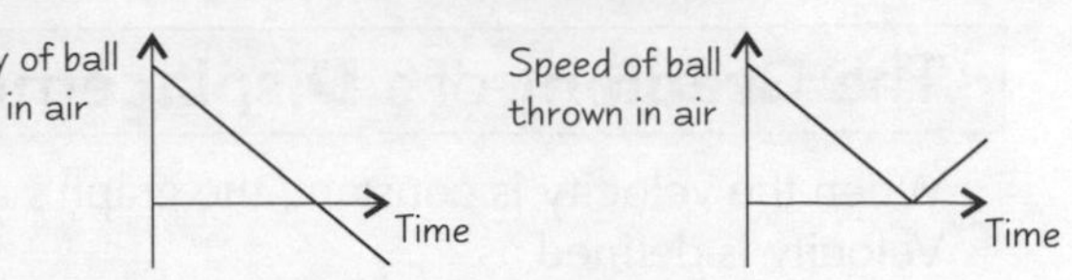

The **Gradient** of a **Velocity-Time Graph** tells you the **Acceleration**

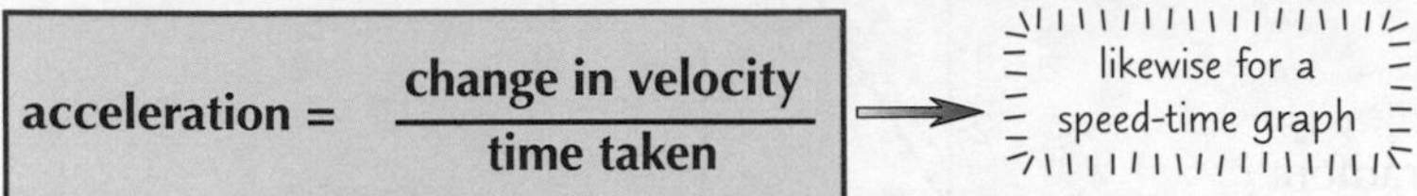

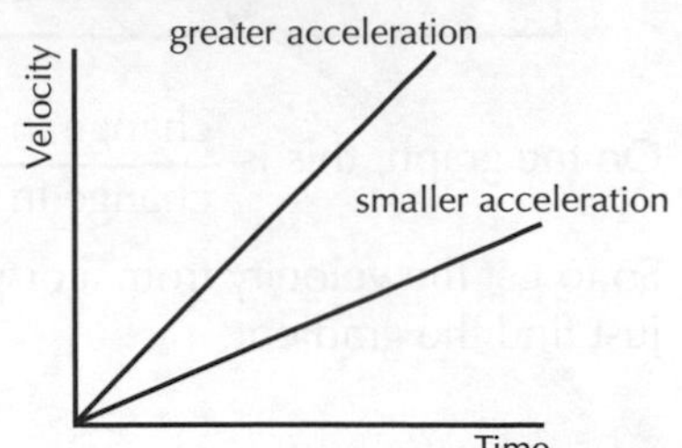

So the acceleration is just the **gradient** of a **velocity-time graph**.

1) **Uniform** acceleration is always a **straight line**.
2) The **steeper** the **gradient**, the **greater** the **acceleration**.

When the **acceleration** is **constant**, you get a **straight-line** *v-t* graph. The equation for a straight line is $\boldsymbol{y = mx + c}$. You can rearrange the acceleration equation into the same form, getting $\boldsymbol{v = u + at}$. So on a linear *v-t* graph, **acceleration**, *a*, is the **gradient** (*m*) and the **initial speed**, *u*, is the ***y*-intercept** (*c*).

Example: A lion strolls along at 1.5 ms^{-1} for 4 s and then accelerates uniformly at a rate of 2.5 ms^{-2} for 4 s. Plot this information on a velocity-time graph.

So, for the first four seconds, the velocity is 1.5 ms^{-1}, then it increases by **2.5 ms^{-1} every second**:

t (s)	v (ms^{-1})
0 – 4	**1.5**
5	**4.0**
6	**6.5**
7	**9.0**
8	**11.5**

Norman (the lion)...

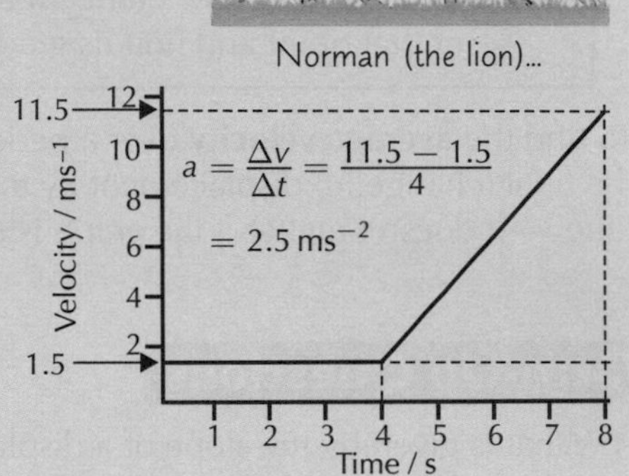

You can see that the **gradient of the line** is **constant** between 4 s and 8 s and has a value of 2.5 ms^{-2}, representing the **acceleration of the lion.**

Displacement = **Area** under **Velocity-Time Graph**

You know that: **distance travelled = average speed × time**

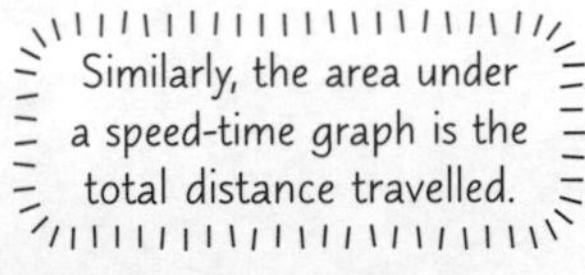

The **area** under a velocity-time graph tells you the **displacement** of an object. Areas under any **negative** parts of the graph count as negative areas, as they show the object moving **back** to its **start point**.

Example: A racing car on a straight track accelerates uniformly from rest to 40 ms^{-1} in 10 s. It maintains this speed for a further 20 s before coming to rest by decelerating at a constant rate over the next 15 s. Draw a velocity-time graph for this journey and use it to calculate the total displacement of the racing car.

Split the **graph** up into **sections**: A, B and C

Calculate the **area** of each and **add** the three results together.

A: Area = ½ base × height = ½ × 10 × 40 = 200 m

B: Area = $b \times h$ = 20 × 40 = 800 m

C: Area = ½ $b \times h$ = ½ × 15 × 40 = 300 m

Total displacement = 1300 m

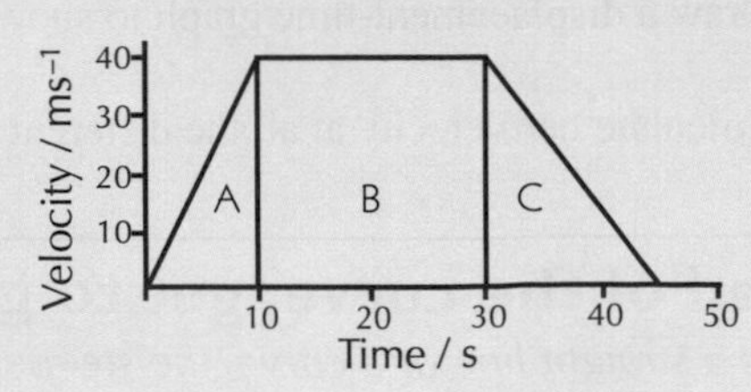

Velocity-Time Graphs

Non-Uniform Acceleration is a Curve on a V-T Graph

1) If the acceleration is changing, the gradient of the velocity-time graph will also be changing — so you **won't** get a **straight line**.
2) **Increasing acceleration** is shown by an **increasing gradient** — like in curve ①.
3) **Decreasing acceleration** is shown by a **decreasing gradient** — like in curve ②.

Simple enough...

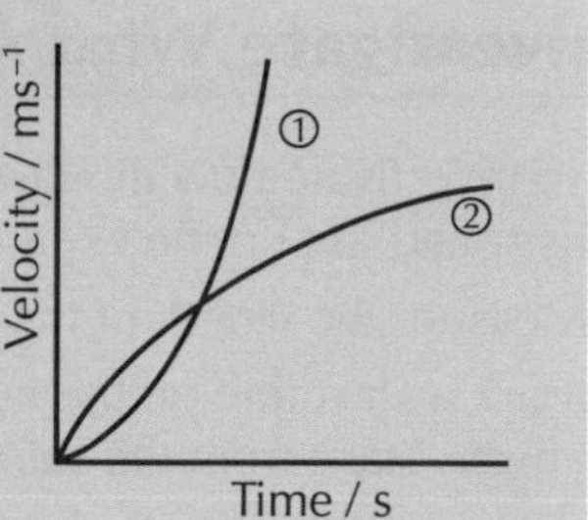

To Find Displacement from a Curved V-T Graph You Estimate the Area

As our velocity-time graph is no longer a simple straight line, we have to use methods to **estimate** the area under the curve. If the graph is on **squared paper**, an easy way to do this is just **count** the squares under the curve. Another way is to split the curve up into **trapeziums**, calculate the **area** of each one and then **add** them all up.

Example: A car decreases its acceleration as it approaches 15 ms^{-1}. Estimate its displacement between 0 and 3 seconds from the velocity-time graph.

Split the area under the curve up into trapeziums and a triangle.

0-1 s — estimate the area with a triangle.
The height of the triangle is 4.
The base of the triangle is 1.
$A = \frac{1}{2}(1 \times 4) = 2\,\text{m}$

1-2 s — estimate the area using a trapezium.
$\text{Area} = \frac{1}{2}(a + b)h$
a is the length of the first side, $a = 4$
b is the length of the second side, $b = 7$
h is the width of each strip, so $h = 1$
$A = \frac{1}{2}(4 + 7) \times 1 = 5.5\,\text{m}$

2-3 s — trapezium, $a = 7$, $b = 9$, $h = 1$
$A = \frac{1}{2}(7 + 9) \times 1 = 8\,\text{m}$

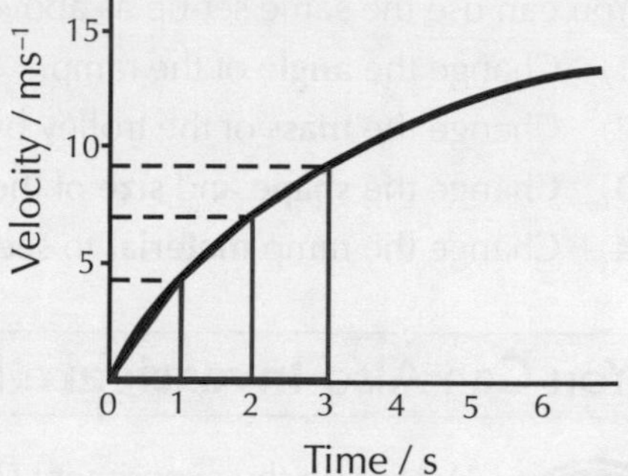

Now add the areas together — Total area = 2 + 5.5 + 8 = 15.5 m

The estimated overall displacement of the car is 15.5 m = **16 m (to 2 s.f.)**

Warm-Up Questions

PRACTICE QUESTIONS

Q1 How do you calculate acceleration from a velocity-time graph?

Q2 How do you calculate the distance travelled from a speed-time graph?

Q3 Sketch velocity-time graphs for constant velocity and constant acceleration.

Q4 Three trapeziums are drawn side by side under a curve on a *v-t* graph to estimate the area. They have equal widths of 2 s, and side lengths of 1, 3, 7 and 9 ms^{-1}. Show that the displacement for this period is about 30 m.

Exam Question

Q1 A skier accelerates uniformly from rest at 2 ms^{-2} down a straight slope.

a) Sketch a velocity-time graph for the first 5 s of his journey. [2 marks]

b) Use a constant acceleration equation to calculate his displacement at t = 1, 2, 3, 4 and 5 s, and plot this information onto a displacement-time graph. [4 marks]

c) Suggest another method of calculating the skier's distance travelled after each second and use this to check your answers to part b). [2 marks]

Still awake — I'll give you five more minutes...

There's a lovely sunset outside my window. It's one of those ones that makes the whole landscape go pinky-yellowish. And that's about as much interest as I can muster on this topic. Normal service will be resumed on page 26, I hope.

Motion Experiments and Stopping Distances

It's all getting a bit hi-tech now — using light gates and video cameras to look at how an object's velocity changes as it rolls down a ramp or crashes into something. Who doesn't love a good motion experiment...

You Can **Investigate** What **Affects** the **Motion** of a Trolley on a Slope

1) To investigate how the **distance** a trolley has rolled affects its speed, set up the experiment shown in the diagram.
2) Measure the **length** of the trolley.
3) Mark a **start line** on the ramp to make sure the trolley always starts from the **same position**.
4) Measure the **angle** of the ramp, θ, and the **distance** from the chosen **start line** to the **light gate**, d.
5) Place the trolley on the **ramp** and **line it up** with the start line. Let go of it so its **initial velocity**, u, is **0**.

trolley
light gate
data logger
d
start line
ramp
θ
angle of ramp

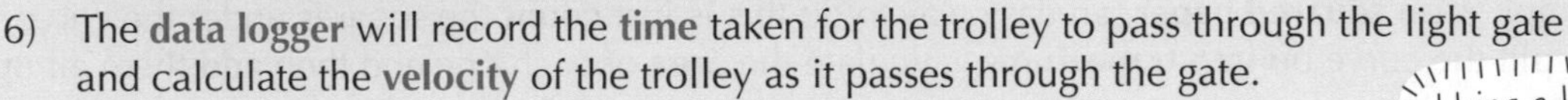

6) The **data logger** will record the **time** taken for the trolley to pass through the light gate and calculate the **velocity** of the trolley as it passes through the gate.
7) Change the **starting position** of the trolley, so d is varied.
8) **Repeat** this experiment for each distance 3 times and average the recorded velocities to reduce the **error** in your final result.

Using a light gate gives a much lower uncertainty in the measurement than using a stopwatch and calculating the velocity manually.

You can use the same set-up as above to investigate other factors. Keep d the same and:

1) Change the **angle** of the ramp.
2) Change the **mass** of the trolley by adding weights to it.
3) Change the **shape** and **size** of the trolley.
4) Change the ramp **material** to see how **friction** affects motion.

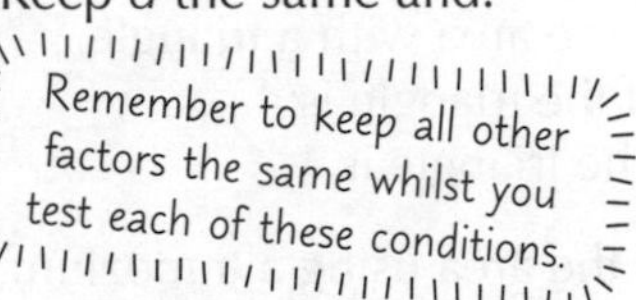

After trolleys the next step is goats.

You Can Also **Investigate** How **Collisions** Affect the **Motion** of a Trolley

1) Set up the experiment shown, with a **video camera** to record the experiment side-on (perpendicular to the trolley's direction of travel).

2) Measure the **length** of the trolley.
3) Turn on the video camera and start **recording**.

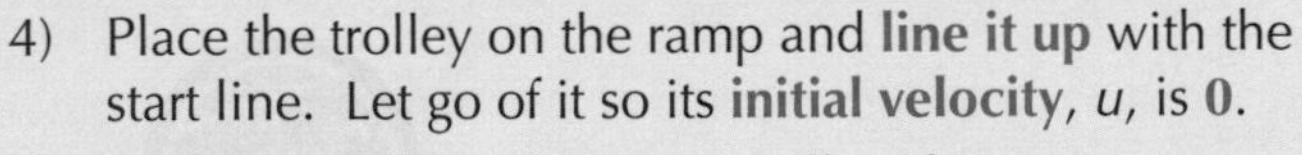

4) Place the trolley on the ramp and **line it up** with the start line. Let go of it so its **initial velocity**, u, is **0**.
5) Once the trolley has hit the wall and is at **rest**, stop recording.

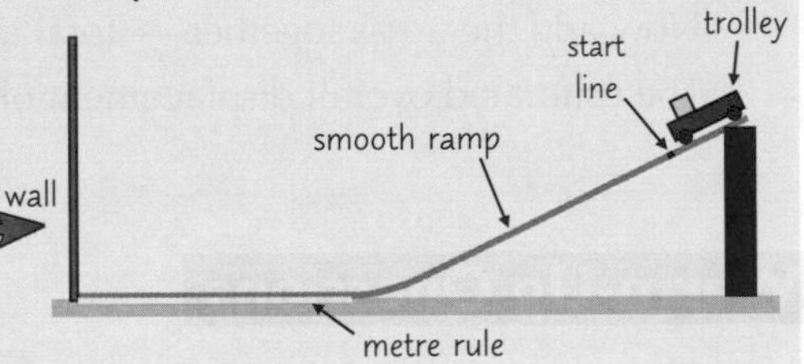

You can also investigate what affects the final velocities of **two** trolleys colliding.

1) Set up the experiment shown in the diagram below, with a **video camera** positioned side-on to the motion of the trolleys.
2) Measure the **lengths** of both trolleys.
3) Turn on the video camera and **start recording**.
4) **Push** one trolley so it hits the second trolley.
5) When both trolleys have come to a stop, stop recording.

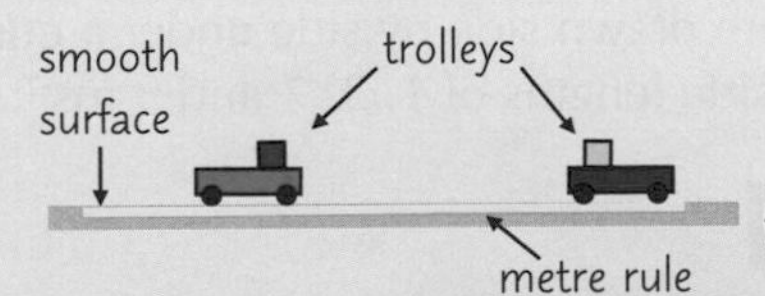

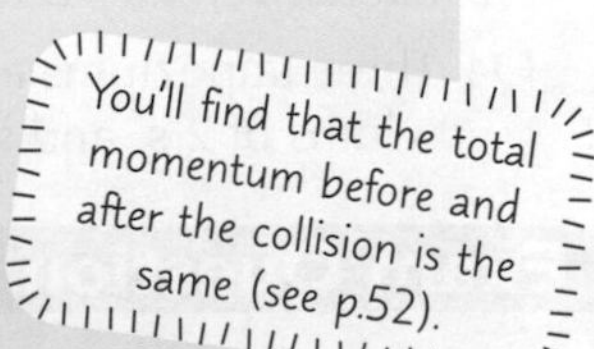

1) You can use both of these experiment set-ups to investigate how the **mass** and **velocity** of a trolley (or trolleys) just **before** a collision **affect** the **velocity** (or velocities) after the **collision**.
2) Using **video analysis** software, you can view your videos **frame by frame**. Pick a **point of reference** on the metre stick and count how many **frames** it takes a trolley to pass that point.
3) By knowing how many **frames per second** the video is shot at (the frame rate of the video), you can calculate the **time taken** (t) for the whole trolley to pass that point. You should have recorded the **length** (l) of the trolley, and so you can calculate its **velocity**.

$$\text{Time taken for the trolley to pass the point} = \text{Number of frames for a trolley to pass the point} \times \frac{1\text{ second}}{\text{Frame rate of camera}}$$

$$\text{velocity} = \frac{l}{t}$$

Motion Experiments and Stopping Distances

From crashing trolleys into each other to trying to avoid crashing a car. There are lots of different factors that affect how quickly a car can stop — the biggest one being its initial velocity.

Many Factors Affect How Quickly a Vehicle Stops

The braking distance and thinking distance together make the **total distance you need to stop** after you see a problem:

Thinking distance + Braking distance = Stopping distance

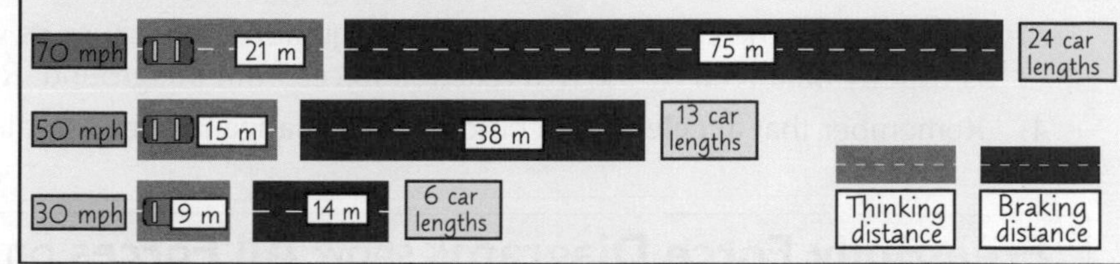

1) The **reaction time** is the time your body takes to **react** and **hit** the brakes after seeing a hazard.
2) The **thinking distance** is the distance the vehicle travels during the driver's **reaction time**.
3) The **braking distance** is the distance the vehicle travels after the **brakes are applied** until it comes to a complete **stop**.

There are many factors which can affect both the **thinking** and **braking** distances:

Thinking distance = speed × reaction time

Reaction time is increased by:

1) **Tiredness.**
2) **Alcohol** or other **drug** use.
3) **Illness.**
4) **Distractions** such as noisy children and loud music.

Braking distance depends on the **braking force**, **friction** between the tyres and the road, the **mass** and the **speed.**

1) **Braking force** is reduced by **reduced friction** between the brakes and the wheels (**worn** or **badly adjusted brakes**).
2) **Friction** between the tyres and the road is reduced by **wet** or **icy** roads, **leaves or dirt** on the road, **worn-out tyre treads**, etc.
3) **Mass** is affected by the size of the car and what you put in it.

Warm-Up Questions

PRACTICE QUESTIONS

Q1 Describe an experiment to determine how the masses and velocities of two objects affect their final velocities after a collision.

Q2 Name a factor which affects thinking distance.

Q3 Name a factor which affects braking distance.

Q4 What is the formula for calculating stopping distance?

Exam Questions

Q1 Sarah sees a cow step into the road 30 m ahead of her. Sarah's reaction time is 0.5 s. She is travelling at 20 ms^{-1}. Her maximum braking force is 10 000 N and her car (with her in it) has a mass of 850 kg.

a) How far does she travel before applying her brakes? [2 marks]

b) Calculate Sarah's braking distance. Assume she applies the maximum braking force until she stops. [3 marks]

c) Does Sarah hit the cow? Justify your answer with a suitable calculation. [1 mark]

Q2 Joey is using a light gate and a ramp to investigate how the motion of a toy car can be changed.

a) Explain how using a ramp with a rougher surface would change Joey's results. [2 marks]

b) State another variable you could investigate using the experiment set-up. Explain what effect changing this variable would have on the motion of the car. [2 marks]

...Huh?... Slow reaction time... Don't know what you mean...

Being safe in a car is mainly common sense — don't drive if you're ill, drunk or just tired, and don't drive a car with dodgy brakes. But you still have to do exam questions, so don't go on till you're sure you know this all by heart.

Forces and Acceleration

You did most of this at GCSE, but that doesn't mean you can just skip over it now. Don't miss out on easy marks...

A Force is Needed to Start, Stop, Accelerate or Decelerate

1) A **net** (or **resultant**) **force** is needed for an object to **accelerate** (start or stop moving, or change velocity). There is a net force when the forces acting on an object are **not balanced**.
2) If the **forces** acting on a body are **balanced**, it is in **equilibrium** (i.e. not accelerating).
3) For example, the cat in the diagram is in equilibrium because its weight is **exactly balanced** by the two reaction forces from the ground (R).
4) Remember that **acceleration** could mean a **change** in **speed** or **direction**, or **both**.

This is known as Newton's First Law — see p.54.

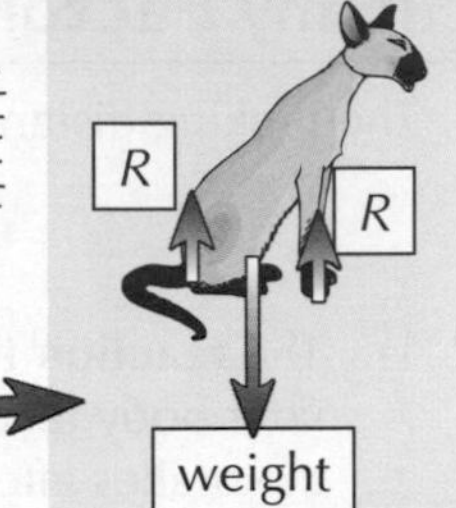

Free-Body Force Diagrams show All Forces on a Single Body

1) The best way to work out if there is a **net force** is to draw a **free-body force diagram**.
2) **Free-body force** diagrams show a **single body** on its own.
3) The diagram should include all the **forces** that **act on** the body, but **not** the **forces it exerts** on the rest of the world.
4) Remember **forces** are **vector quantities** (p.14) so the **size** and **direction** of the forces should be shown.

Drawing free-body force diagrams isn't too hard — you just need practice. Here are a few **examples**:

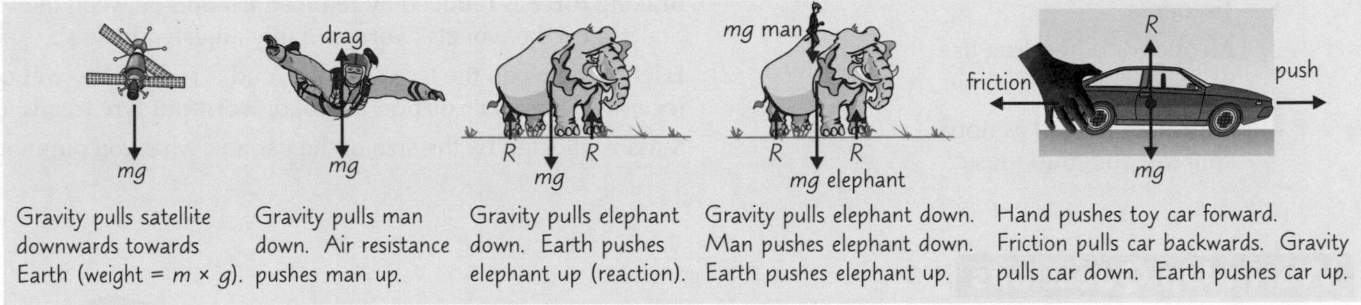

Gravity pulls satellite downwards towards Earth (weight = $m \times g$).

Gravity pulls man down. Air resistance pushes man up.

Gravity pulls elephant down. Earth pushes elephant up (reaction).

Gravity pulls elephant down. Man pushes elephant down. Earth pushes elephant up.

Hand pushes toy car forward. Friction pulls car backwards. Gravity pulls car down. Earth pushes car up.

You Need to Think About All the Forces and What Causes Them

When working out **force** problems, you have to make sure you've caught **every** force that could be acting on the body. Here's a few examples of **common forces** acting on objects:

1) **Weight** — every object has weight on Earth due to gravity, acting directly downwards (see p.32).
2) **Normal contact force** (or reaction force) — if an object exerts a force on a surface, the surface exerts an equal but opposite force on the object. The force acts normal (perpendicular) to the surface.
3) **Tension** — if a string is pulled tight, tension is the force pulling equally on the objects at either end of the string.
4) **Friction** — if an object is moving, it usually has a friction force acting on it in the opposite direction to motion.

Example — Tension:

Each side pulls on the rope with force 410 N. Tension in the rope balances this force.

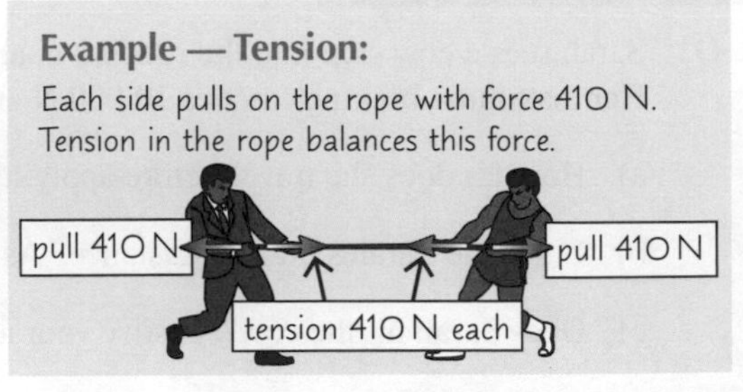

Examples — Normal Contact Force:

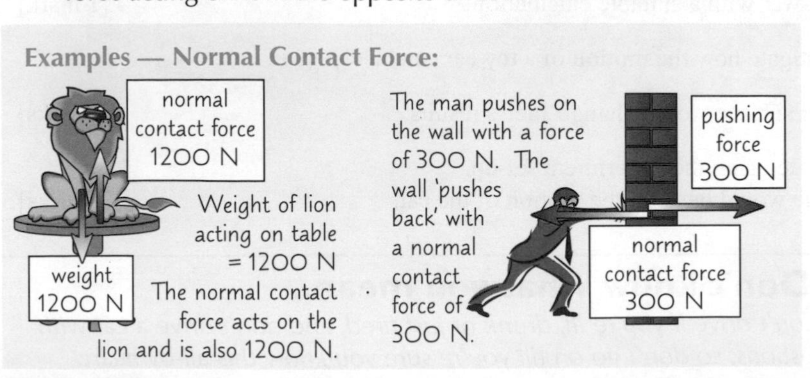

Weight of lion acting on table = 1200 N. The normal contact force acts on the lion and is also 1200 N.

The man pushes on the wall with a force of 300 N. The wall 'pushes back' with a normal contact force of 300 N.

Example — Friction:

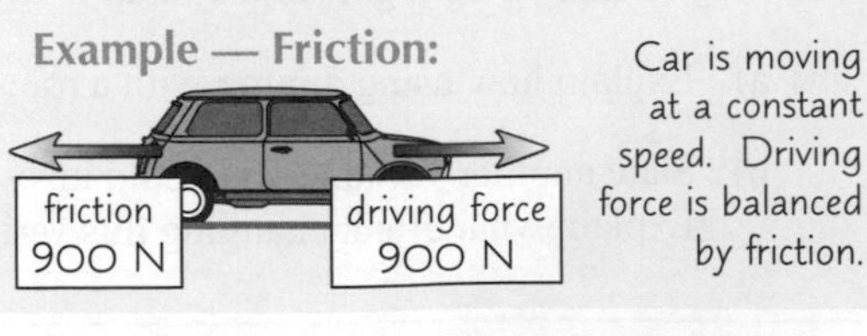

Car is moving at a constant speed. Driving force is balanced by friction.

Note: These aren't all free-body force diagrams — the forces don't all act on one object.

Forces and Acceleration

Acceleration is Proportional to Force

...which can be written as the well-known equation:

net force (N) = mass (kg) × acceleration (ms^{-2}) or **$F = ma$**

From this equation, 1 N = 1 kg ms^{-2}. This is the definition of a newton. $F = ma$ is a special case of Newton's Second Law — see page 54.

Learn this — you won't be given it in your exam.
And learn what it means too:

1) It says that the **more force** you have acting on a certain mass, the **more acceleration** you get.
2) It says that for a given force the **more mass** you have, the **less acceleration** you get.

REMEMBER:
1) The **resultant force** is the **vector sum** of all the forces.
2) The force is **always** measured in **newtons**.
3) The **mass** is always measured in **kilograms**.
4) The **acceleration** is always in the **same direction** as the **resultant force** and is measured in **ms^{-2}**.

Galileo said that All Objects Fall at the Same Rate*

*(if you ignore air resistance)

You can see **why** with a bit of ball dropping and a dash of $F = ma$...

Example: Imagine dropping two balls at the same time — ball **1** being heavy, and ball **2** being light. Then use $F = ma$ to find their acceleration.

mass = m_1 resultant force = F_1 acceleration = a_1

$$F_1 = m_1a_1$$

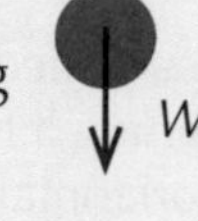

Ignoring air resistance, the only force acting on the ball is weight, given by $W_1 = m_1g$ (where g = gravitational field strength = 9.81 Nkg^{-1} — see p.32).

So: $F_1 = m_1a_1 = W_1 = m_1g$

So: $m_1a_1 = m_1g$, then m_1 cancels out to give: $a_1 = g$

mass = m_2 resultant force = F_2 acceleration = a_2

$$F_2 = m_2a_2$$

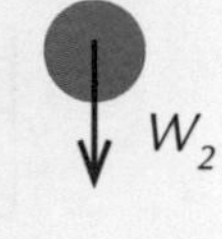

Ignoring air resistance, the only force acting on the ball is weight, given by $W_2 = m_2g$ (where g = gravitational field strength = 9.81 Nkg^{-1}).

So: $F_2 = m_2a_2 = W_2 = m_2g$

So: $m_2a_2 = m_2g$, then m_2 cancels out to give: $a_2 = g$

... in other words, the **acceleration** is **independent of the mass**. It makes **no difference** whether the ball is **heavy or light**. And I've kindly **hammered home the point** by showing you two almost identical examples.

Warm-Up Questions

Q1 Sketch a free-body force diagram for an ice hockey puck moving across the ice (assuming no friction).

Q2 Give an example of: a) a tension force, b) a normal contact force.

Q3 Write down the equation that links mass, force and acceleration, and explain what it means for a given mass.

Q4 Ball A has a mass of 5 kg and ball B has a mass of 3 kg. Both balls are dropped from the same height at the same time — which one hits the ground first? Why?

Exam Questions

Q1 Draw labelled free-body force diagrams to show the forces acting on a parachutist:

a) accelerating downwards. [1 mark]

b) falling at a constant speed. [1 mark]

Q2 A boat is being driven with a constant force of 500 N in the direction of motion. It experience a drag force of 300 N from the water and air resistance of 100 N. The total mass of the boat and its passengers is 250 kg.

a) Calculate the magnitude of the net force acting on the boat at this point in time. [1 mark]

b) Calculate the magnitude of the acceleration of the boat at this point in time. [1 mark]

<body> Force diagram, one careful owner, free to good home... </body>

So there you have it — if you drop a cannonball and a football, they'll both fall at the same rate. Who'd have thought they were so similar. This is all pretty straightforward — make sure you know it, don't slip up on the simple stuff.

Forces and Equilibrium

Remember the vector stuff from pages 14-15...? Good, you're going to need it...

Resolving a Force means Splitting it into Components

1) **Forces** are **vector quantities** and so when you draw the forces on an object, the **arrow labels** should show the **size** and **direction** of the forces.
2) Forces can be in **any direction**, so they're not always at right angles to each other. This is sometimes a bit **awkward** for **calculations**.
3) To make an 'awkward' force easier to deal with, you can think of it as **two separate forces**, acting at **right angles** to **each other**.

The force F has exactly the same effect as the horizontal and vertical forces, F_H and F_V.
Replacing F with F_H and F_V is called **resolving the force F**.

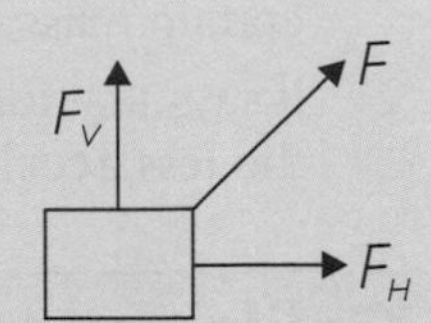

4) To find the size of a component force in a particular direction, you need to use **trigonometry**.
Forces are vectors, so you treat them in the same way as velocities — put them end to end.

So this... 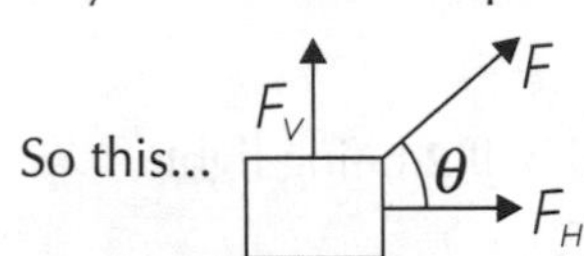

...could be drawn like this: 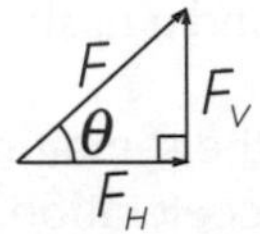

Using trig. you get:

$$\frac{F_H}{F} = \cos\theta \quad \text{or} \quad F_H = F\cos\theta$$

And:

$$\frac{F_V}{F} = \sin\theta \quad \text{or} \quad F_V = F\sin\theta$$

Remember 'SOH CAH TOA' for right-angle triangles.

Example:

A tree trunk is pulled along the ground by an elephant exerting a force of 1200 N at an angle of 25° to the horizontal. Calculate the components of this force in the horizontal and vertical directions.

Horizontal force =
1200 × cos 25° = **1090 N (to 3 s.f.)**

Vertical force =
1200 × sin 25° = **507 N (to 3 s.f.)**

Three Forces Acting on a Point in Equilibrium form a Triangle

1) When **three** coplanar (all in the same plane) forces all act on an object in **equilibrium**, you know there is **no net force** on the object — the sum of the forces is zero.

$$F_1 + F_2 + F_3 = 0$$

2) You can draw the forces as a triangle, forming a **closed loop** like these:

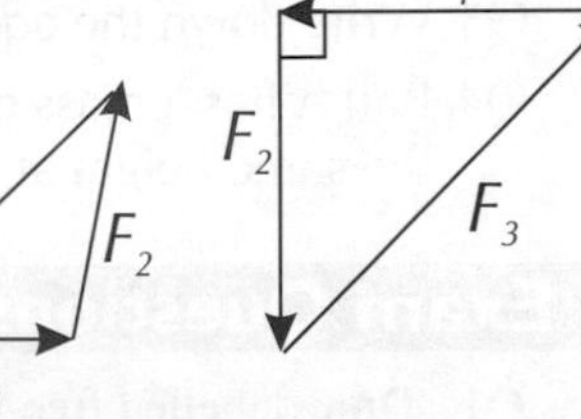

3) Be careful when you draw the triangles not to go into autopilot and draw F_3 as the sum of F_1 and F_2 — it has to be in the **opposite** direction to balance the other two forces.
4) You can then use the triangles to while away Saturday nights in with your friends working out the magnitude or direction of a missing force, either by using Pythagoras, or by measuring on a scale diagram (p.14).

The sum of all the angles in a triangle is 180° — you might need to use this to answer exam questions.

Example:

Tim hangs a picture of his brother up using a piece of string. The picture weighs 0.3 N and is in equilibrium, as shown. Find the magnitude of F.

Draw a vector triangle.

Then you need to use **Pythagoras** to find the magnitude of F.

$$F = \sqrt{0.3^2 + 0.4^2} = \sqrt{0.25^2} = \mathbf{0.5\,N}$$

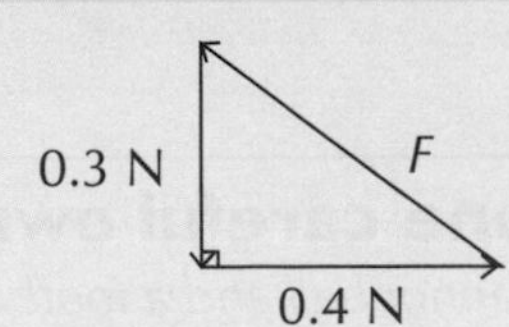

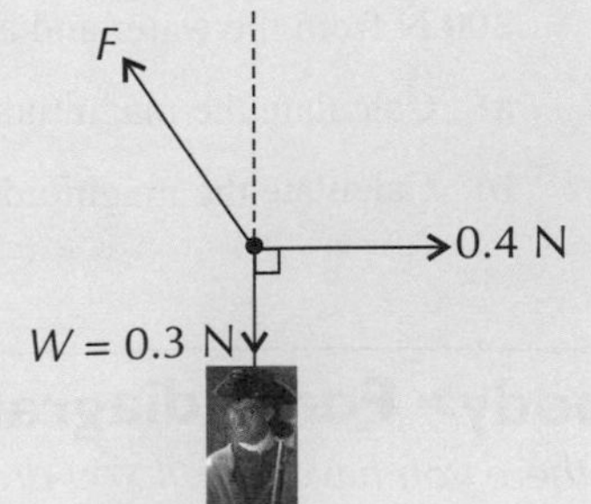

Forces and Equilibrium

You **Add Components Back Together** to get the **Resultant Force**

1) If **two forces** act on an object, you find the **resultant** (net) **force** by adding the **vectors** together and creating a **closed triangle**, with the resultant force represented by the **third side**.
2) Forces are vectors (as you know), so you use **vector addition** — draw the forces as vector arrows put 'tip-to-tail'.
3) Then it's yet more trigonometry to find the **angle** and the **length** of the third side.

Example: Two dung beetles roll a dung ball along the ground at constant velocity. Beetle A applies a force of 0.5 N northwards, beetle B exerts a force of 0.2 N eastwards. Find the resultant force on the dung ball.

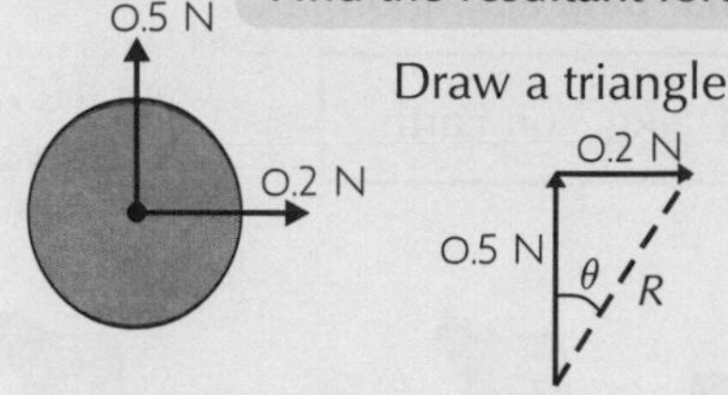

Draw a triangle:

0.2 N, 0.5 N, θ, R

By Pythagoras, $R^2 = 0.5^2 + 0.2^2$, so $R = \sqrt{0.29} = 0.54$ N (to 2 s.f.)

$\tan\theta = \frac{0.2}{0.5}$ so $\theta = \tan^{-1}0.4 = 22°$ (to 2 s.f.)

So the resultant force is **0.54 N** at an angle of **22°** from north.

Choose sensible **Axes** for **Resolving**

Use directions that **make sense** for the situation you're dealing with. If you've got an object on a slope, choose your directions **along the slope** and **at right angles to it**. You can turn the paper to an angle if that helps.

Always choose sensible axes

Examiners like to call a slope an "inclined plane".

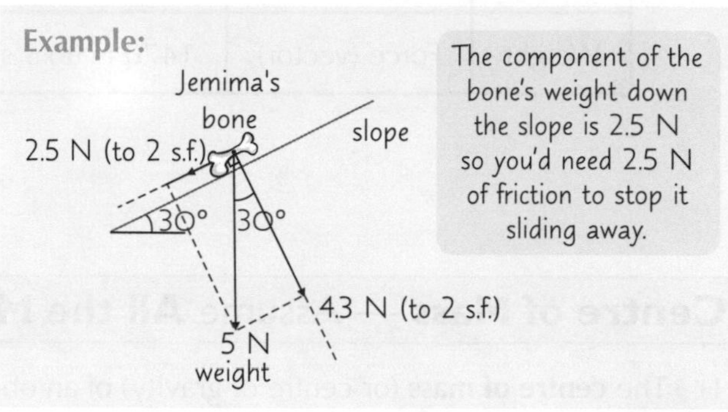

The component of the bone's weight down the slope is 2.5 N so you'd need 2.5 N of friction to stop it sliding away.

Warm-Up Questions

Q1 What are the horizontal and vertical components of the force F?

Q2 How could you use a scale drawing to show that three coplanar forces are producing no net force?

Q3 Three forces act on an object in equilibrium. What is the sum of the forces?

Exam Questions

Q1 A picture is suspended from a hook as shown in the diagram.
Calculate the tension force, T, in the string.

[2 marks]

Q2 Two elephants pull a tree trunk as shown in the diagram.
Calculate the resultant force on the tree trunk.

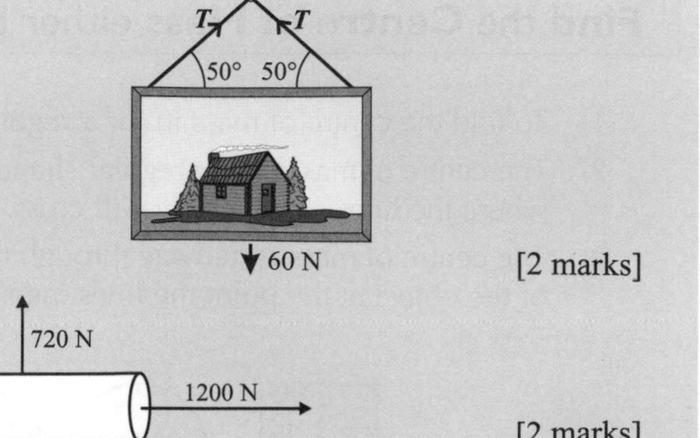

[2 marks]

I'm in e-quill-ibrium — if I lose my pen, I always order a new one right away...

Remember those $F\cos\theta$ and $F\sin\theta$ bits. Write them on bits of paper and stick them to your wall. Scrawl them on your pillow. Tattoo them on your brain. Whatever it takes — you just have to learn them.

Mass, Weight and Centre of Mass

I'm sure you know all this 'mass', 'weight' and 'centre of mass' stuff from GCSE. But let's just make sure...

The Mass of a Body makes it Resist Changes in Motion

1) The **mass** of an object is the **amount of 'stuff'** (or **matter**) in it. It's measured in **kg**.
2) The greater an object's mass, the greater its **resistance** to a **change in velocity** (called its **inertia**).
3) The **mass** of an object **doesn't change** if the strength of the **gravitational field** changes.
4) Weight is a **force**. It's measured in **newtons** (N), like all forces.
5) Weight is the **force experienced by a mass** due to a **gravitational field**.
6) The weight of an object **does vary** according to the size of the **gravitational field** acting on it.

weight = mass × gravitational field strength ($W = mg$) where $g = 9.81$ Nkg^{-1} on Earth.

Learn this equation — you won't be given it in the exam.

This table shows Gerald (the lion*)'s mass and weight on the Earth and the Moon.

Name	Quantity	Earth (g = 9.81 Nkg^{-1})	Moon (g = 1.6 Nkg^{-1})
Mass	Mass (scalar)	150 kg	150 kg
Weight	Force (vector)	1470 N (to 3 s.f.)	240 N (to 2 s.f.)

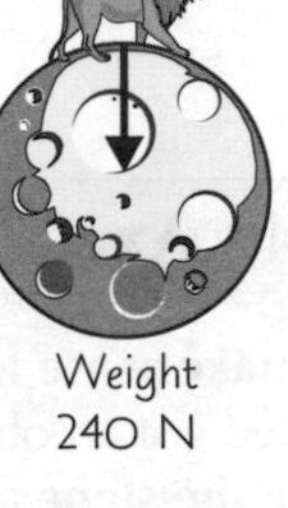

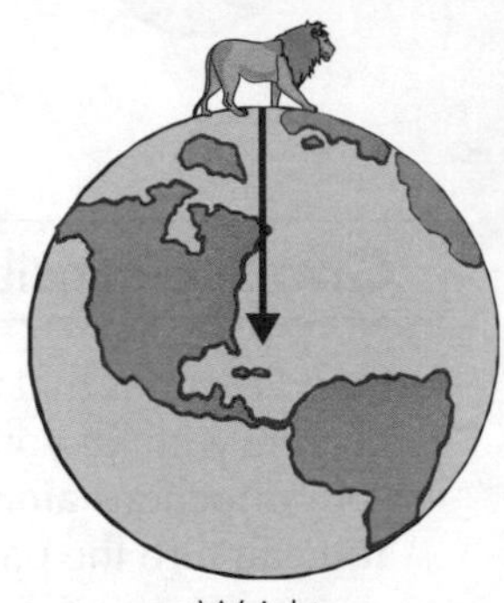

Centre of Mass — Assume All the Mass is in One Place

1) The **centre of mass** (or centre of gravity) of an object is the **single point** that you can consider its **whole weight** to **act through** (whatever its orientation).
2) The object will always **balance** around this **point**, although in some cases the **centre of mass** will **fall outside** the object.

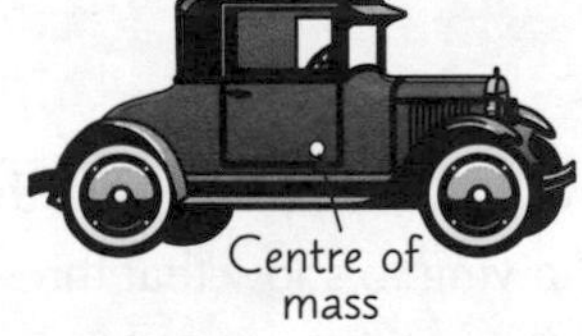

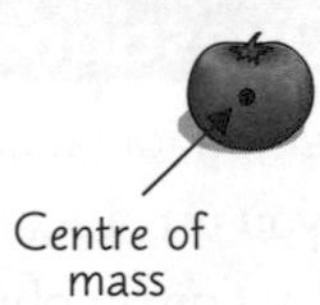

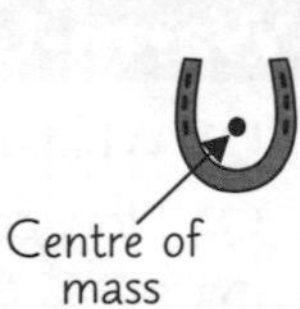

Find the Centre of Mass either by Symmetry...

1) To find the centre of mass in for a **regular** object you can just use **symmetry**.
2) The centre of mass of any regular shape is at its **centre** — where the lines of symmetry will cross.
3) The centre of mass is **halfway** through the **thickness** of the object at the point the lines meet.

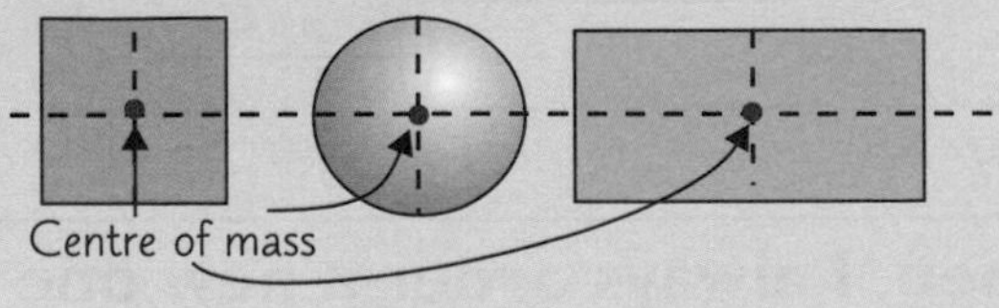

The symmetry in this picture shows the centre of cuteness.

*Yes, I know — I just like lions, OK...

Mass, Weight and Centre of Mass

... Or By Experiment

PRACTICAL SKILLS

Experiment to find the Centre of Mass of an Irregular Object

1) **Hang** the object freely from a point (e.g. one corner).
2) Draw a **vertical line** downwards from the point of suspension — use a plumb bob to get your line exactly vertical.
3) Hang the object from a different point.
4) Draw another vertical line down.
5) The centre of mass is where the two lines **cross**.

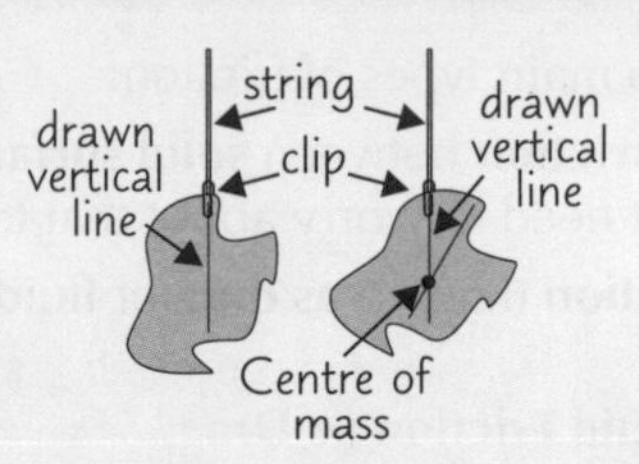

A plumb bob is just a weight on a string — when suspended, the string will be exactly vertical.

How High the Centre of Mass is tells you How Stable the Object is

1) An object will be nice and **stable** if it has a **low centre** of **mass** and a **wide base area**. This idea is used a lot in design, e.g. racing cars.

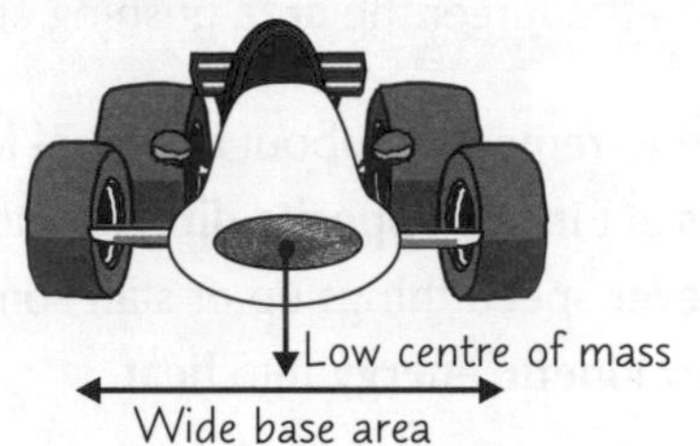

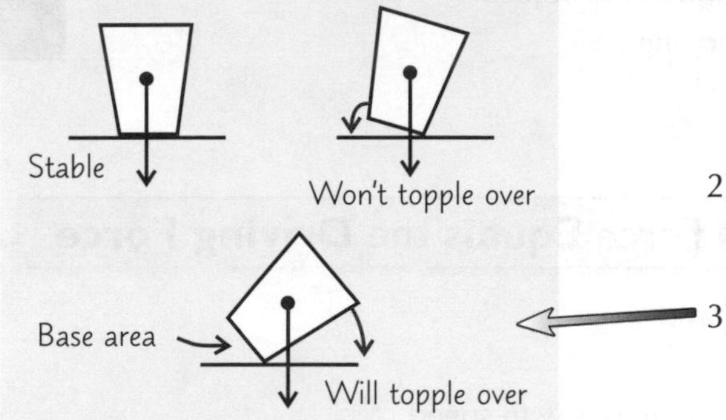

2) The **higher** the **centre of mass**, and the **smaller** the **base area**, the **less stable** the object will be. Think of unicyclists...
3) An object will topple over if a **vertical line** drawn **downwards** from its **centre of mass** falls **outside** its **base area**. This is because of the moments about the pivot — see p.38.

Warm-Up Questions

Q1 A lioness has a mass of 200 kg. What would be her mass and weight on Earth and on the Moon (where $g = 1.6$ Nkg^{-1})?

Q2 Define centre of mass.

Exam Questions

Q1 Joanne weighs X N on Earth. Which of the following statements are correct?

A She will weigh the same on the Moon as on Earth.

B Her mass is equal to $\frac{X}{g}$ kg.

C Her mass depends on the gravitational field strength.

D Her acceleration due to gravity will be the same on Earth as the Moon. [1 mark]

Q2 a) Describe an experiment to find the centre of mass of an object of uniform density with a constant thickness and irregular cross-section. [3 marks]

b) Identify one major source of uncertainty and suggest a way to reduce its effect on the precision of the result. [2 marks]

The centre of mass of this book should be round about page 112...

This is a really useful area of physics. To would-be nuclear physicists it might seem a little dull, but if you want to be an engineer — something a bit more useful (no offence Einstein) — then things like centre of mass and weight are dead important things to understand. You know, for designing things like cars and submarines... yep, pretty useful I'd say.

Drag and Terminal Velocity

If you jump out of a plane at 2000 metres, you want to know that you're not going to be accelerating all the way.

Friction is a Force that Opposes Motion

There are two main types of friction:

1) **Contact friction** between **solid surfaces** (which is what we usually mean when we just use the word 'friction'). You don't need to worry about that too much for now.
2) **Fluid friction** (known as **drag** or fluid resistance or air resistance).

Fluid Friction or Drag:

1) 'Fluid' is a word that means either a **liquid or a gas** — something that can **flow**.
2) The force depends on the thickness (or **viscosity**) of the fluid.
3) It **increases** as the **speed increases** (for simple situations it's directly proportional, but you don't need to worry about the mathematical relationship).
4) It also depends on the **shape** and **size** of the object moving through it — the larger the **area** pushing against the fluid, the greater the resistance force.

Things you need to remember about frictional forces:

1) They **always** act in the **opposite direction** to the **motion** of the object.
2) They can **never** speed things up or start something moving.
3) They convert **kinetic energy** into **heat**.

Terminal Velocity — when the Friction Force Equals the Driving Force

You will reach a **terminal velocity** at some point, if you have:

1) a **driving force** that stays the **same** all the time
2) a **frictional** or **drag force** (or collection of forces) that increases with speed

There are **three main stages** to reaching terminal velocity:

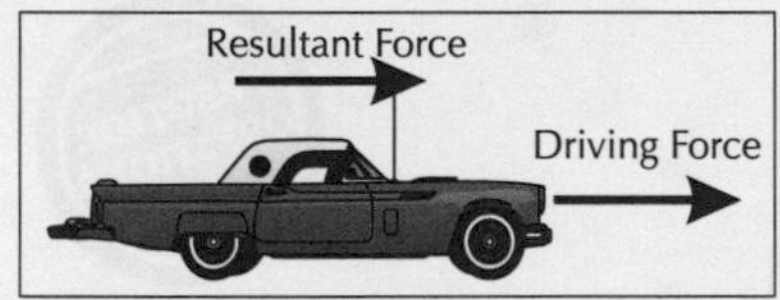

The car **accelerates** from **rest** using a constant driving force.

As the **velocity increases**, the **resistance forces increase** (because of things like turbulence — you don't need the details). This **reduces the resultant force** on the car and hence **reduces its acceleration.**

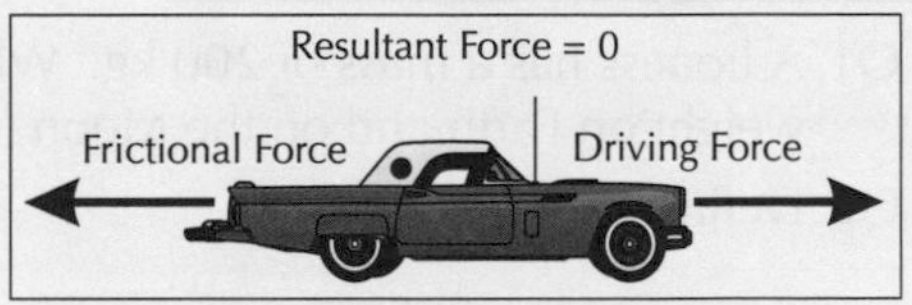

Eventually the car reaches a velocity at which the **resistance forces are equal to the driving force**. There is now **no resultant force** and **no acceleration**, so the car carries on at **constant velocity**.

Sketching a Graph for Terminal Velocity

You need to be able to **recognise** and **sketch** the graphs for **velocity against time** and **acceleration against time** for the **terminal velocity** situation.

Nothing for it but practice — shut the book and sketch them from memory. Keep doing it till you get them right every time.

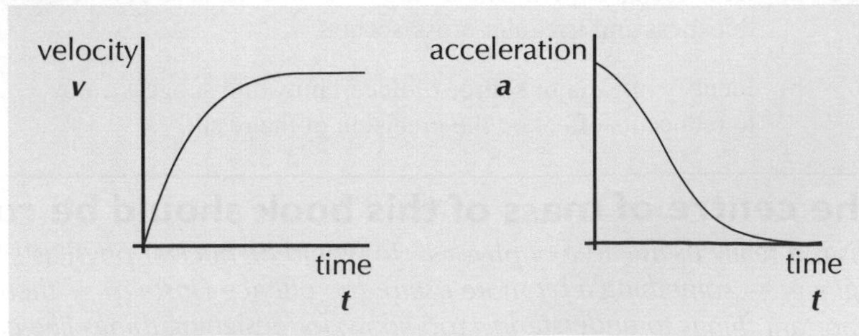

Drag and Terminal Velocity

Things **Falling** through **Air** or **Water** Reach a **Terminal Velocity** too

When something's falling through air, the weight of the object is a **constant** force accelerating the object downwards. Air resistance is a frictional force opposing this motion, which **increases** with **speed**.

So before a parachutist opens the parachute, exactly the same thing happens as with the car example:

1) A skydiver leaves a plane and will **accelerate** until the **air resistance** equals his **weight**.

2) He will then be travelling at a **terminal velocity**.

But... the terminal velocity of a person in free fall is too great to land without dying a horrible death. The **parachute increases** the **air resistance massively**, which slows him down to a lower terminal velocity:

3) Before reaching the ground he will **open his parachute**, which immediately **increases the air resistance** so it is now **bigger** than his **weight**.

4) This **slows him down** until his speed has dropped enough for the **air resistance** to be **equal to his weight** again. This new terminal velocity is small enough to survive landing.

The *v-t* graph is a bit different, because you have a new terminal velocity being reached after the parachute is opened:

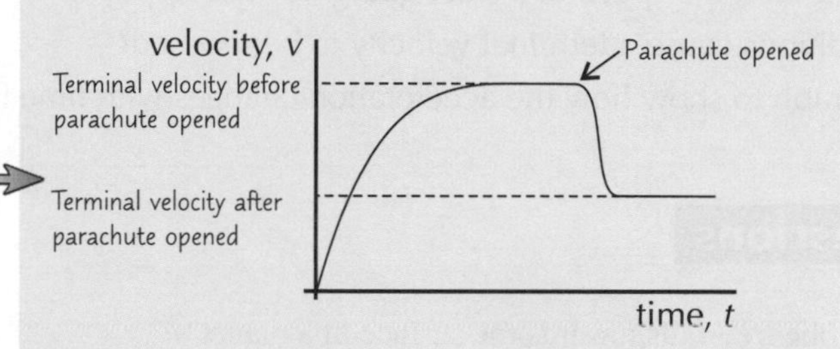

Measure the **Terminal Velocity** of a **Ball Bearing**

PRACTICAL SKILLS

You can calculate the terminal velocity of a **ball bearing** (a little steel ball) in a **viscous** (thick) liquid by setting up an experiment like this:

You don't have to use elastic bands — you could also use insulation tape or another marker for your intervals.

1) Put **elastic bands** around the tube of viscous liquid at **fixed distances** using a **ruler**.
2) **Drop** a ball bearing into the tube, and use a **stopwatch** to record the time at which it reaches **each band**. Record your results in a **table** (see below).
3) **Repeat** this a few times to reduce the effect of **random errors** on your results. You can use a **strong magnet** to remove the ball bearing from the tube.
4) **Calculate** the times taken by the ball bearing to travel between consecutive elastic bands and calculate an **average** for each reading. Use the **average times** and the **distance between bands** to calculate the **average velocity** between **each pair** of elastic bands.
5) You should find that the average velocity **increases** at first, then **stays constant** — this is the ball bearing's **terminal velocity** in the viscous liquid used.

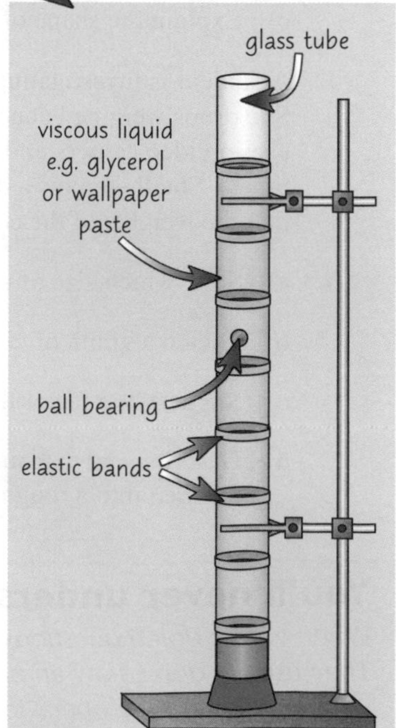

Elastic band	Time / s	Time from last band / s	Average time / s	Average velocity / ms^{-1}
2	1			
	2			
	3			
3	1			
	2			
	3			

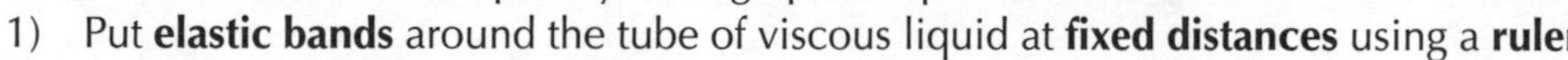

If your stopwatch has a lap timer, you might be able to measure these times directly.

Drag and Terminal Velocity

You can Work Out what **Affects** Terminal Velocity

Prof. Fraise dedicated his life to investigating terminal velocity in fluids.

1) Use your average velocity data to plot a graph of **velocity** against **time**. Draw a smooth curve and use it to estimate the terminal velocity.
2) You might be asked to draw **force diagrams** as the ball bearing falls. Remember that the forces are balanced when the ball reaches terminal velocity.
3) You can change parts of your experiment to see what effect they have on terminal velocity and the time taken to reach terminal velocity. For example you could:
   - Change the **liquid** — the terminal velocity will be **lower** in more viscous (thicker) liquids because the drag is **greater**. Try mixing water into wallpaper paste and see by how much the terminal velocity increases when the drag is lower.
   - Change the **size** of the ball. What happens if the ball is larger? Or smaller?
   - Change the **shape** of the thing you are dropping. The drag force will be greater on **less streamlined** shapes.
   - Change the **mass** of the thing you are dropping, while keeping the **size** the **same** (this might be a bit tricky). You should find that **heavier objects** reach a **faster** terminal velocity because a **greater drag force** is needed to balance the extra weight. (Remember, objects with different masses only fall at the same rate if drag is ignored — p.29.)

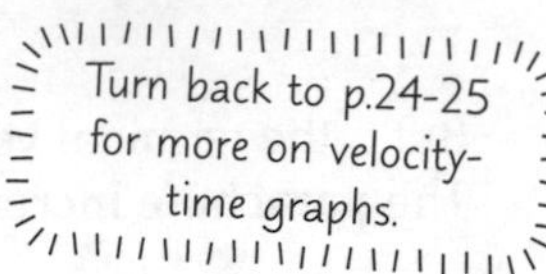
Turn back to p.24-25 for more on velocity-time graphs.

Warm-Up Questions

Q1 What forces limit the speed of a skier going down a slope?

Q2 What conditions cause a terminal velocity to be reached?

Q3 Sketch a graph to show how the acceleration changes with time for an object falling through air.

Exam Questions

Q1 A space probe free-falls towards the surface of a planet.
The graph on the right shows the velocity data recorded by the probe as it falls.

velocity, v / time, t

a) The planet does not have an atmosphere. Explain how you can tell this from the graph. [2 marks]

b) On the graph, sketch the line you would expect to see if the planet did have an atmosphere. [2 marks]

c) Explain the shape of the graph you have drawn. [3 marks]

Q2 A student is investigating how the terminal velocity of paper cones varies with cone size.
She drops weighted cones of base diameter 5 cm, 10 cm and 15 cm point-down from a height of 2 m and uses a video camera and video analysis software to obtain data on the displacement of the cone at certain times. She then plots a displacement-time graph to calculate the terminal velocity. You may assume that the weights of the cones are negligible compared to that of the weights used to stabilise them.

a) State which size of cone you expect to have the lowest terminal velocity. Explain your answer. [2 marks]

b) Sketch a graph of velocity against time for the three cones. Put all three curves on the same axes. [3 marks]

c) Suggest one factor the student must keep the same in her experiment and explain why. [1 mark]

d) Describe and explain how the velocity-time graph would change if the largest cone was crushed into a rough ball shape. [3 marks]

You'll never understand this without going parachuting...*

When you're doing questions about terminal velocity, remember the frictional forces reduce acceleration, not speed. They usually don't slow an object down, apart from in the parachute example, where the skydiver is travelling faster when the parachute opens than the terminal velocity for the parachute-skydiver combination.

* No. 37 in a series of the 100 least convincing excuses for an interesting holiday.

Density, Pressure and Upthrust

Yikes, three whole things on one page. Grab a coffee, take a deep breath and put on your snazziest learning hat...

Density is Mass per Unit Volume

Density is a measure of the '**compactness**' (for want of a better word) of a substance. It relates the **mass** of a substance to how much **space** it takes up.

The symbol for density is a Greek letter rho (ρ) — it looks like a p but it isn't.

$$\text{density} = \frac{\text{mass}}{\text{volume}} \qquad \rho = \frac{m}{V}$$

The units of density are g cm^{-3} or kg m^{-3}
1 g cm^{-3} = 1000 kg m^{-3}

1) The density of an object depends on what it's made of. Density **doesn't vary** with **size or shape**.
2) The **average density** of an object determines whether it **floats** or **sinks**.
3) A solid object will **float** on a fluid if it has a **lower density** than the **fluid**.
   E.g. The density of iron is 7.9 g cm^{-3} — this is **greater** than the density of water (1 g cm^{-3}) so it will **sink** in water.

Pressure is Force per Unit Area

1) Pressure is the **amount of force** applied per **unit area**. It is measured in **pascals (Pa)**, which are equivalent to newtons per square metre (Nm^{-2}).

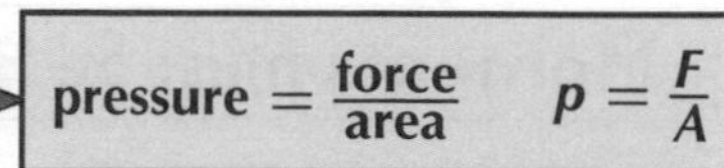

$$\text{pressure} = \frac{\text{force}}{\text{area}} \qquad p = \frac{F}{A}$$

2) The extra pressure acting on an object due to a fluid depends on the **depth** of the object in the fluid (h), the **density** of the fluid (ρ) and the **acceleration** due to gravity (g).

$$p = h\rho g$$

Bodies in Fluids Experience Upthrust

1) Upthrust is an **upward force** that fluids exert on objects that are **completely** or **partially submerged** in the fluid. It's caused because the top and bottom of a submerged object are at different depths. Since $p = h\rho g$, there is a difference in pressure which causes an overall upwards force known as upthrust.
2) **Archimedes' principle** says that when a body is completely or partially immersed in a fluid, it experiences an **upthrust** equal to the **weight** of the fluid it has **displaced**.

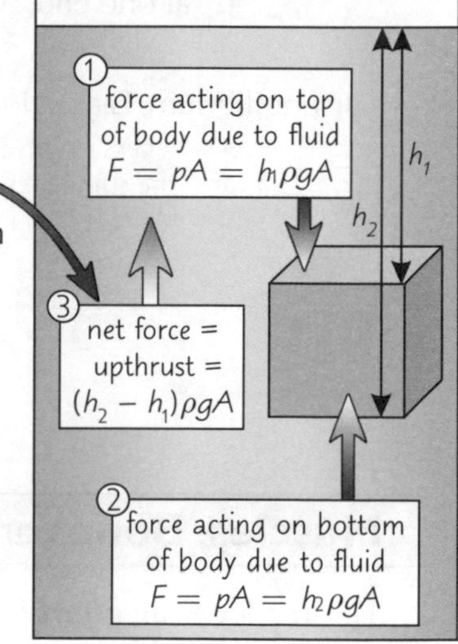

upthrust = weight of fluid displaced

This is just because $(h_2 - h_1)\rho gA = V\rho g = mg = W$

Example: **Submarines** make use of upthrust to dive underwater and return to the surface. To sink, large tanks are filled with water to **increase** the weight of the submarine so that it **exceeds** the upthrust. To rise to the surface, the tanks are filled with compressed air to **reduce** the weight so that it's **less** than the upthrust.

Warm-Up Questions

Q1 State the equation that gives the pressure on an object due to the density of the fluid it is submerged in.

Q2 State Archimedes' principle.

PRACTICE QUESTIONS

Exam Questions

Q1 a) A cylinder of aluminium with radius 4 cm and height 6 cm, has a mass of 820 g. Calculate its density. [2 marks]

b) Use the information from part a) to calculate the mass of a cube of aluminium of side 5 cm. [1 mark]

Q2 Calculate the pressure when a force of 17.0 N is applied over a square table top with side length 1.72 m. [2 marks]

Q3 Calculate the pressure due to seawater acting on a point that is 2.4 m below the surface of a sea. Water in the sea has a density of 1024 kg m^{-3}. [1 mark]

Q4 Find the upthrust acting on a ball of radius 5.20 cm submerged in water of density 1050 kg m^{-3}. [3 marks]

Don't be dense — you must learn the thrust of this page (no pressure...)

You might have met density and pressure before. Perhaps you even invite them around for tea sometimes. Upthrust combines them and adds in a whole extra layer of fun. Yes, fun. I'll start to believe it if I say it often enough...

Moments and Torques

*This is not a time for jokes. There is not a moment to lose. The time for torquing is over. Oh ho ho ho *bang*. (Ow.)*

A **Moment** is the **Turning Effect** of a **Force**

The **moment**, or **torque**, of a **force** depends on the **size** of the force and **how far** the force is applied from the **turning point**:

> **moment of a force** (in Nm) = **force** (in N) × **perpendicular distance from the pivot to the line of action of the force** (in m)

The line of action of a force is a line along which it acts.

In symbols, that's: $$M = F \times d$$

Moments must be **Balanced** or the **Object** will **Turn**

The **principle of moments** states that for a body to be in **equilibrium**, the **sum of the clockwise moments** about any point **equals** the **sum of the anticlockwise moments** about the same point.

Example: Two children sit on a seesaw as shown in the diagram. An adult balances the seesaw at one end. Calculate the size and direction of the force that the adult needs to apply.

In equilibrium, Σ anticlockwise moments = Σ clockwise moments

Σ means "the sum of"

$$400 \times 1.5 = 300 \times 1 + 1.5F$$
$$600 = 300 + 1.5F$$

Final Answer: F = **200 N downwards**

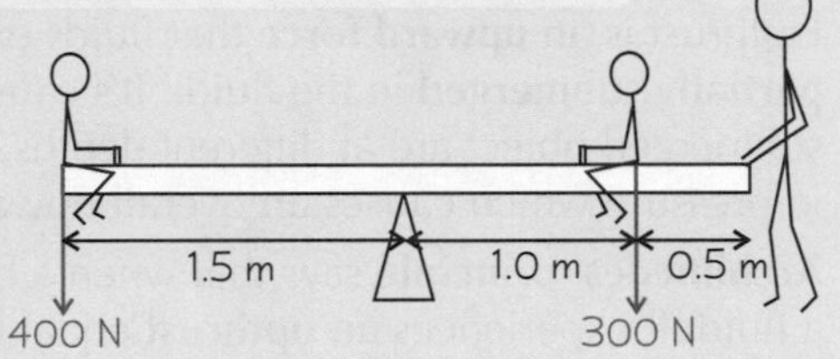

Muscles, Bones and **Joints** Act as **Levers**

1) In a lever, an **effort force** acts against a **load force** by means of a **rigid object** rotating around a **pivot**.
2) You can use the **principle of moments** to answer lever questions:

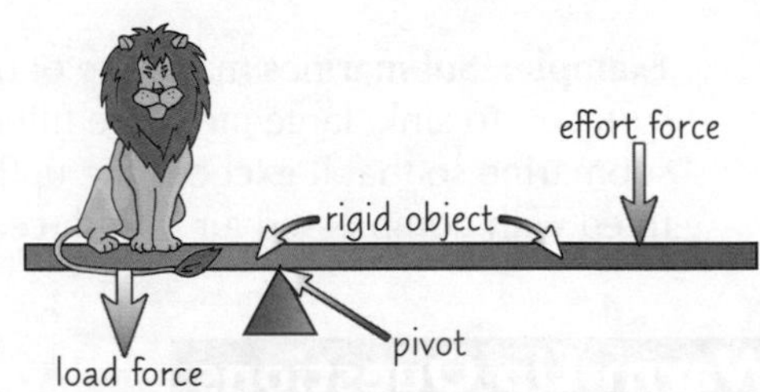

Example: A bag of gold weighing 100 N is being held still by biceps in a forearm weighing 20 N. Calculate the force E exerted by the biceps.

Take moments about **A**.
In equilibrium:

Σ anticlockwise moments = Σ clockwise moments

$$(100 \times 0.4) + (20 \times 0.2) = 0.04E$$
$$40 + 4 = 0.04E$$

Final answer: E = **1100 N upwards**

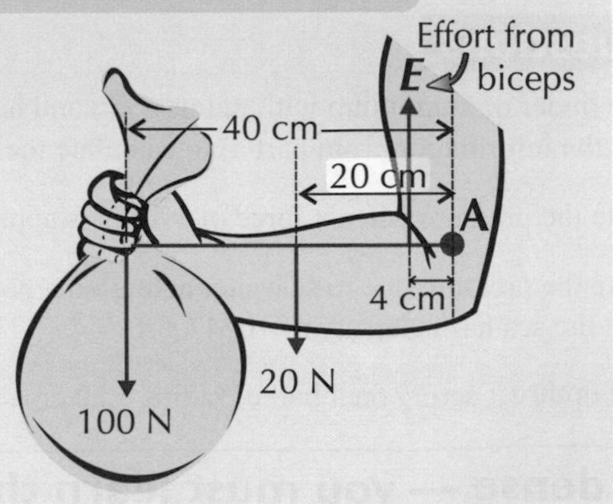

This is a bit of a simplified example — there are actually lots of muscles involved, but the biceps does the majority of the work so it's a good illustration of what's going on.

Moments and Torques

A Couple is a Pair of Forces

1) A couple is a **pair** of **forces** of **equal size** which act **parallel** to each other, but in **opposite directions**.
2) A couple doesn't cause any resultant linear force, but **does** produce a **turning force** (usually called a **torque** rather than a moment).

The **size** of this **torque** depends on the **size** of the **forces** and the **distance** between them.

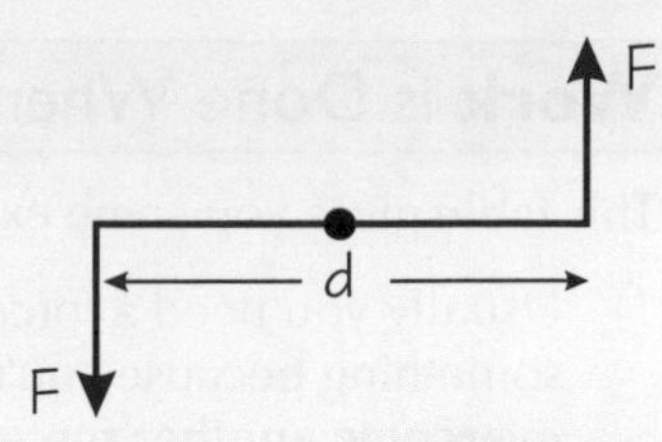

Torque of a couple (in Nm) = size of one of the forces (in N) × perpendicular distance between the forces (in m)

In symbols, that's: $\boldsymbol{T = F \times d}$

Example:

A cyclist turns a sharp right corner by applying equal but opposite forces of 20 N to the ends of the handlebars. The length of the handlebars is 0.6 m. Calculate the torque applied to the handlebars.

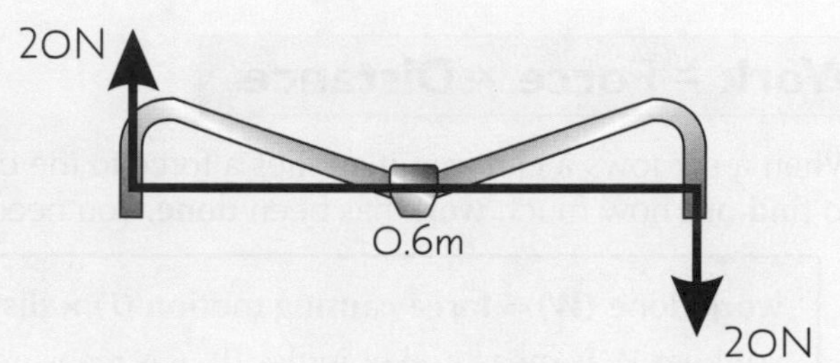

Torque = $F \times d = 20 \times 0.6 =$ **12 Nm**

Warm-Up Questions

Q1 A force of 54 N acts at a perpendicular distance of 84 cm from a pivot. Calculate the moment of the force.

Q2 A girl of mass 40 kg sits 1.5 m from the middle of a seesaw.
Show that her brother, mass 50 kg, must sit 1.2 m from the middle if the seesaw is to balance.

Q3 What is meant by the word 'couple'?

Q4 A racing car driver uses both hands to apply equal and opposite forces of 65 N to the edge of a steering wheel with radius 20 cm. Calculate the torque of the forces.

Exam Questions

Q1 A driver is changing his flat tyre. The torque required to undo the nut is 60 Nm. He uses a 0.4 m long double-ended wheel wrench as shown. Calculate the force that he must apply at each end of the wrench.

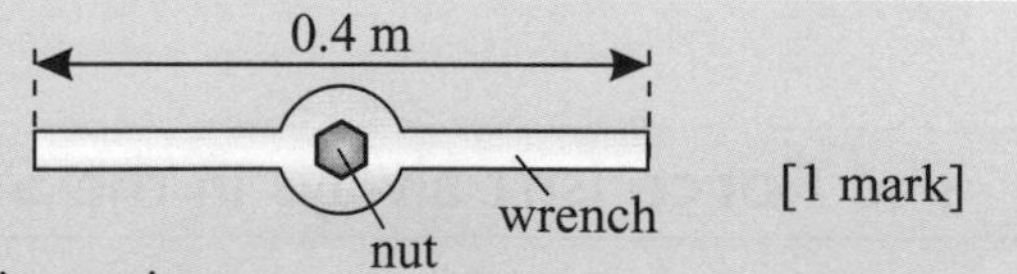

[1 mark]

Q2 A diver of mass 60 kg stands on the end of a diving board 2 m from the pivot point. Calculate the upward force exerted on the retaining spring 30 cm from the pivot.

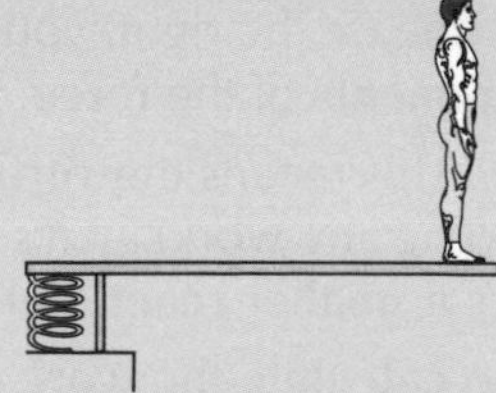

[2 marks]

It's all about balancing — just ask a tightrope walker...

Moments are great. They explain why using wheelbarrows is loads easier (no pun intended) than plain old lifting. And why wrenches are better at unscrewing than fingers. They help us understand why things topple over too — see p.33.

Work and Power

As everyone knows, work in Physics isn't like normal work. It's harder. Work also has a specific meaning that's to do with movement and forces. You'll have seen this at GCSE — it just comes up in more detail here.

Work is Done Whenever **Energy** is **Transferred**

This table gives you some examples of **work being done** and the **energy changes** that happen.

1) Usually you need a force to move something because you're having to **overcome another force**.
2) The thing being moved has **kinetic energy** while it's **moving**.
3) The kinetic energy is transferred to **another form of energy** when the movement stops.

ACTIVITY	WORK DONE AGAINST	FINAL ENERGY FORM
Lifting up a box.	gravity	gravitational potential energy
Pushing a chair across a level floor.	friction	heat
Pushing two magnetic north poles together.	magnetic force	magnetic energy
Stretching a spring.	stiffness of spring	elastic potential energy

The word **'work'** in Physics means the **amount of energy transferred** from one form to another when a force causes a movement of some sort. It's measured in **joules** (J).

Work = Force × Distance

When a car tows a caravan, it applies a force to the caravan to move it to where it's wanted. To **find out** how much **work** has been **done**, you need to use the **equation**:

work done (W) = force causing motion (F) × distance moved (x), or $W = Fx$
...where W is measured in joules (J), F is measured in newtons (N) and x is measured in metres (m).

Points to remember:

1) **Work** is the **energy** that's been **changed** from one form to another — it's not necessarily the **total** energy. E.g. moving a book from a low shelf to a higher one will increase its gravitational potential energy, but it had some potential energy to start with. Here, the **work done** would be the **increase** in potential energy, **not the total** potential energy.
2) Remember the distance needs to be measured in metres — if you have **distance in centimetres or kilometres**, you need to **convert** it to metres first.
3) The force F will be a **fixed** value in any calculations, either because it's **constant** or because it's the **average** force.
4) The equation assumes that the **direction of the force** is the **same** as the **direction of movement**.
5) The equation gives you the **definition** of the joule (symbol J): 'One joule is the work done when a force of 1 newton moves an object through a distance of 1 metre'.

The **Force** isn't always in the **Same Direction** as the **Movement**

Sometimes the **direction of movement** is **different** from the **direction of the** force.

Example:

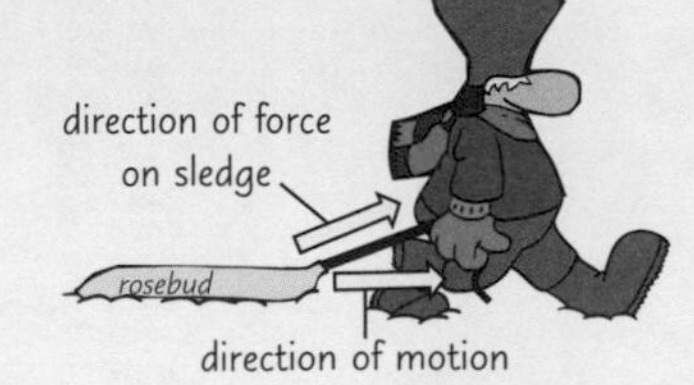

1) To **calculate the work done** in a situation like the one on the right, you need to consider the **horizontal** and **vertical components** of the **force**.
2) The only **movement** is in the **horizontal** direction. This means the **vertical force** is not causing any motion (and hence not doing any work) — it's just **balancing** out some of the **weight**, meaning there's a **smaller reaction force**.
3) The horizontal force is causing the motion — so to **calculate** the **work done**, this is the **only force** you need to consider. Which means we get: $W = Fx\cos\theta$

Where θ is the **angle** between the **direction of the force** and the **direction of motion**. See page 30 for more on resolving forces.

F θ $F\cos\theta$ Direction of motion

Work and Power

Power = Work Done per Second

Power means many things in everyday speech, but in physics (of course!) it has a special meaning. Power is the **rate of doing work** — in other words it is the **amount of energy transformed** from one form to another **per second**. You **calculate power** from this equation:

> Power (P) = work done (W) / time (t), or $P = \frac{W}{t}$ ...where P is measured in watts (W), W is measured in joules (J) and t is measured in seconds (s).

The **watt** (symbol W) is defined as a **rate of energy transfer** equal to **1 joule per second** (Js^{-1}).
Yep, that's another **equation and definition** for you to **learn**.

> W stands for watts (the unit of power) — don't get it confused with W, work done.

Power is also Force × Velocity ($P = Fv$)

Sometimes, it's **easier** to use **this version** of the power equation. This is how you get it:

1) You **know** $P = W/t$.
2) You also **know** $W = Fx$, which gives $P = Fx/t$.
3) But $v = x/t$, which you can substitute into the above equation to give $P = Fv$.
4) It's easier to use this if you're given the **speed** in the question.
   Learn this equation as a **shortcut** to link **power** and **speed**.

Example: A car is travelling at a speed of $10\ ms^{-1}$ and is kept going against the frictional force by a driving force of 500 N in the direction of motion. Find the power supplied by the engine to keep the car moving.

Use the shortcut $P = Fv$, which gives:
$P = 500 \times 10 = $ **5000 W**

If the force and motion are in different directions, you can replace F with $F \cos\theta$ to get: $P = Fv\cos\theta$

You **aren't** expected to **remember** this equation, but it's made up of bits that you **are supposed to know**, so be ready for the possibility of calculating **power** in a situation where the **direction of the force and direction of motion are different.**

Warm-Up Questions

Q1 Write down the equation used to calculate work if the force and motion are in the same direction.
Q2 Write down the equation for work if the force is at an angle to the direction of motion.
Q3 Write down the equations relating i) power and work and ii) power and speed.

Exam Questions

Q1 A traditional narrowboat is drawn by a horse walking along the towpath. The horse pulls the boat at a constant speed between two locks which are 1500 m apart. The tension in the rope is 100 N at 40° to the direction of motion.

40°
direction of motion
direction of force on boat

a) How much work is done on the boat? [2 marks]

b) The boat moves at $0.8\ ms^{-1}$. Calculate the power supplied to the boat. [2 marks]

Q2 A motor is used to lift a 20 kg load a height of 3 m. ($g = 9.81\ ms^{-2}$)

a) Calculate the work done in lifting the load. [2 marks]

b) The speed of the load during the lift is $0.25\ ms^{-1}$. Calculate the power delivered by the motor. [2 marks]

Work — there's just no getting away from it...

Loads of equations to learn. Well, that's what you came here for, after all. Can't beat a good bit of equation-learning, as I've heard you say quietly to yourself when you think no one's listening. Aha, can't fool me. Ahahahahahahahahaha.

Conservation of Energy and Efficiency

Energy *can never be* ***lost****. I repeat —* ***energy*** *can* ***never*** *be lost.*

Kinetic Energy — the Energy an Object has Because it is Moving

Kinetic energy is energy an object has due to its **movement**. You can calculate it using the equation $E_k = \frac{1}{2}mv^2$, where v is the velocity it's travelling at and m is its mass. You need to know how to **derive** this equation...

- The change in kinetic energy of an object equals **work done** (Fx, see p.40), so $E_k = Fx$.
- You know $F = ma$ (see p.29), $a = \frac{v - u}{t}$, and $x = \text{average } v \times t = \frac{(u + v)}{2}t$ (see p.16).
- Substituting these into the E_k equation gives $E_k = max = m \times \frac{(v - u)}{t} \times \frac{(u + v)}{2} \times t$.
- **Cancelling** the 't's and **expanding** the brackets gives you a slightly more familiar looking $E_k = \frac{1}{2}mv^2 - \frac{1}{2}mu^2$.
- The kinetic energy of an object is the kinetic energy compared to when the object is at rest, i.e. when $u = 0$ and the object has **no kinetic energy**.
- Substituting $u = 0$ into the equation above gives you: $E_k = \frac{1}{2}mv^2$

An Object's Gravitational Potential Energy Depends on its Position in a Field

1) **Gravitational potential energy** (E_p) is the energy an object has due to its **position** in a gravitational field. The **greater** the **height** of the object, the **greater** its gravitational potential energy.
2) You normally want to find the change in an object's E_p, which you can work out using the equation $E_p = mgh$, where m is the mass of the object, h is the change in height and g is the gravitational field strength.
3) Sadly you need to know the derivation for this equation too... (at least it's a bit shorter).

- The gravitational energy gained is equal to the work done in moving the object a distance h upwards, so $E_p = W = F \times h$.
- The force that work is done against is the force of **gravity**, which is equal to mg. So $E_p = mgh$.

Learn the Principle of Conservation of Energy

The **principle of conservation of energy** says that:

> Energy **cannot be created** or **destroyed**. Energy **can be transferred** from one form to another but the total amount of energy in a closed system **will not change**.

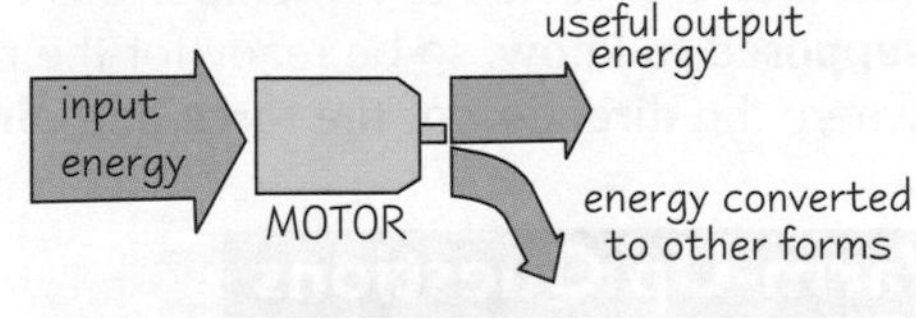

Total energy in = Total energy out

The key point to remember when answering questions is that the **total energy** will always be the same. E.g. after a **ball** is thrown **upwards**, its **kinetic energy** is converted into **gravitational potential energy**. When it **comes down** again, that **gravitational potential** energy is all **converted back** into **kinetic** energy (assuming no air resistance). The **total** amount of energy stays the **same**, but how much of it is kinetic or gravitational potential energy changes.

Example: A pendulum has a mass of 700 g and a length of 50 cm. It is pulled out to an angle of 30° from the vertical.

a) Find the gravitational potential energy stored in the pendulum bob.

Start by drawing a diagram.

You can work out the increase in height, h, of the end of the pendulum using trig.

$E_p = mg\Delta h = 0.7 \times 9.81 \times (0.5 - 0.5 \cos 30°) = 0.460... = \mathbf{0.46\ J}$ **(to 2 s.f.)**

b) The pendulum is released. Find the maximum speed of the pendulum bob as it passes the vertical position. Assume there is no air resistance.

When travelling at its maximum speed, $mgh = \frac{1}{2}mv^2$.

So $\frac{1}{2}mv^2 = 0.460...$, so $v = \sqrt{\frac{2 \times 0.460...}{0.7}} = \mathbf{1.1\ ms^{-1}}$ **(to 2 s.f.)**

Or, you could cancel the 'm's and rearrange to give: $v = \sqrt{2gh}$
$= \sqrt{2 \times 9.81 \times (0.5 - 0.5 \cos 30°)}$
$= \mathbf{1.1\ ms^{-1}}$ **(to 2 s.f.)**

Conservation of Energy and Efficiency

All Energy Transfers Involve Losses

You saw on the last page that **energy can never be created or destroyed**. But whenever **energy** is **converted** from one form to another, some is always **'lost'**. It's still there (i.e. it's **not destroyed**) — it's just not in a form you can **use**. Most often, **energy** is lost as **heat** — e.g. **computers** and **TVs** are always **warm** when they've been on for a while. In fact, **no device** (except possibly a heater) is ever **100% efficient** (see below) because some energy is **always** lost as **heat**. (You want heaters to give out heat, but in other devices the heat loss isn't useful.) Energy can be **lost** in other forms too (e.g. **sound**) — the important thing is the lost energy **isn't** in a **useful** form and you **can't** get it back. Often the heat that is lost is caused by **friction**. Luckily you can usually assume that **friction** is **zero** in exams.

Efficiency is the Ratio of Useful Energy Output to Total Energy Input

Efficiency is one of those words we use all the time, but it has a **specific meaning** in Physics.
It's a measure of how well a **device** converts the **energy** you put **in** into the energy you **want** it to give **out**.
So, a device that **wastes** loads of **energy** as heat and sound has a really **low efficiency**.

$$\text{Efficiency} = \frac{\text{useful output energy}}{\text{total input energy}} \times 100\ \%$$

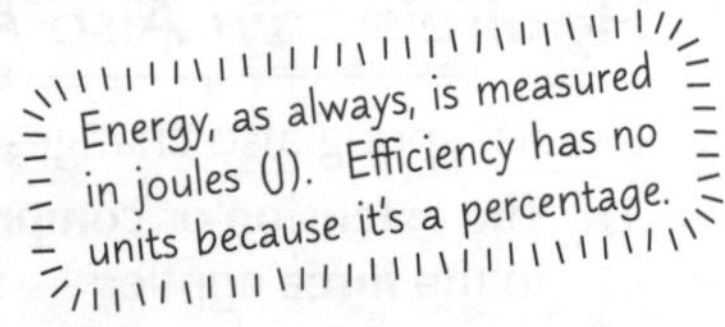

Some questions will be kind and **give you** the **useful output energy** — others will tell you how much is **wasted.** You just have to **subtract** the **wasted energy** from the **total input energy** to find the **useful output energy**, so it's not too tricky if you keep your wits about you.

Warm-Up Questions

Q1 State the principle of conservation of energy.

Q2 What are the equations for calculating kinetic energy and gravitational potential energy?

Q3 Show that, if there's no air resistance and the mass of the string is negligible, the speed of a pendulum is independent of the mass of the bob.

Q4 Why can a device never be 100% efficient?

Q5 What is the equation for efficiency?

Exam Questions

acceleration of free fall, $g = 9.81\ ms^{-2}$

Q1 A skateboarder is skating on a half-pipe. He lets the board run down one side of the ramp and up the other. The height of the ramp is 2.0 m.

a) Calculate his speed at the lowest point of the ramp. Assume friction is negligible. [3 marks]

b) State how high he will rise up the other side of the half-pipe. [1 mark]

c) Real ramps are not frictionless. Describe what the skater must do to reach the top on the other side. [1 mark]

Q2 A 20 g rubber ball is released from a height of 8 m. Assume that the effect of air resistance is negligible.

a) Calculate the kinetic energy of the ball just before it hits the ground. [2 marks]

b) The ball strikes the ground and rebounds to a height of 6.5 m.
Calculate the amount of energy that is converted to heat and sound in the impact with the ground. [2 marks]

Q3 Calculate the efficiency of a device that wastes 65 J for every 140 J of input energy. [1 mark]

Energy is never lost — it just sometimes prefers the scenic route...

Remember to check your answers — I can't count the number of times I've forgotten to square the velocities or to multiply by the ½... I reckon it's definitely worth the extra minute to check. You never know what you might find.

Hooke's Law

Hooke's law applies to all materials, but only up to a point. For some materials that point is so tiny you wouldn't notice...

Hooke's Law Says that Extension is Proportional to Force

If a **metal wire** is supported at the top and then a weight attached to the bottom, it **stretches**. The weight pulls down with force ***F***, producing an equal and opposite force at the support.

The material will only deform (stretch, bend, twist etc.) if there's a pair of opposite forces acting on it.

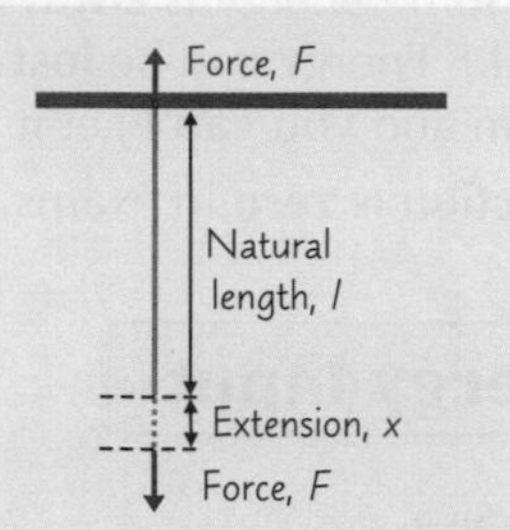

1) **Robert Hooke** discovered in the 17th century that the extension of a stretched wire, ***x***, is proportional to the load or force, ***F***. This relationship is now called **Hooke's law**.
2) Hooke's law can be written:

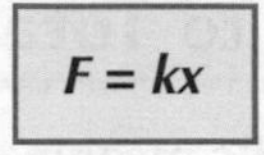

$F = kx$

Where ***k*** is a constant that depends on the object being stretched. ***k*** is called the **force constant** (or **stiffness** of the object) and has units Nm^{-1}.

Hooke's Law Also Applies to Springs

A metal spring also changes length when you apply a **pair of opposite forces**.

1) The **extension** or **compression** of a spring is **proportional** to the **force** applied — so Hooke's law applies.
2) For springs, ***k*** in the formula ***F = kx*** can also be called the **spring stiffness** or **spring constant**.

Hooke's law works just as well for **compressive** forces as **tensile** forces. For a spring, ***k*** has the **same value** whether the forces are tensile or compressive (that's not true for all materials).

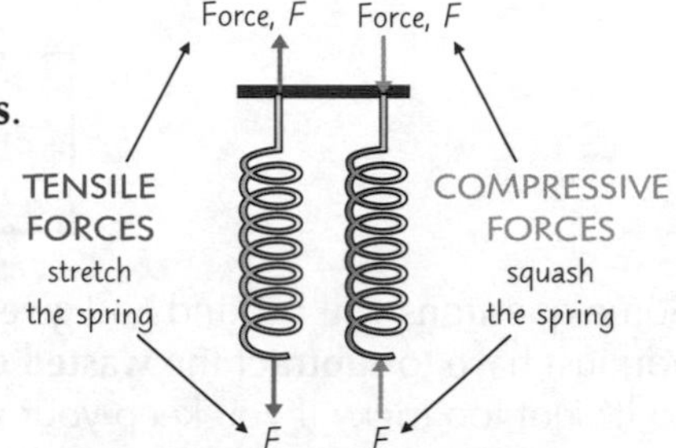

Extension and compression are sometimes called tensile deformation and compressive deformation.

3) **Hooke's Law** doesn't just apply to metal **springs** and **wires** — most **other materials** obey it up to a point.

Hooke's Law Stops Working when the Load is Great Enough

There's a **limit** to the force you can apply for Hooke's law to stay true.

1) The graph shows force against extension for a **typical metal wire** or **spring**.
2) The first part of the graph (up to point P) shows Hooke's law being obeyed — there's a **straight-line relationship** between **force** and **extension**.
3) When the force becomes great enough, the graph starts to **curve**. **Metals** generally obey Hooke's law up to the **limit of proportionality**, **P**.
4) The point marked **E** on the graph is called the **elastic limit**. If you exceed the elastic limit, the material will be **permanently stretched**. When all the force is removed, the material will be **longer** than at the start.
5) Be careful — there are some materials, like **rubber**, that only obey Hooke's law for **really small** extensions.

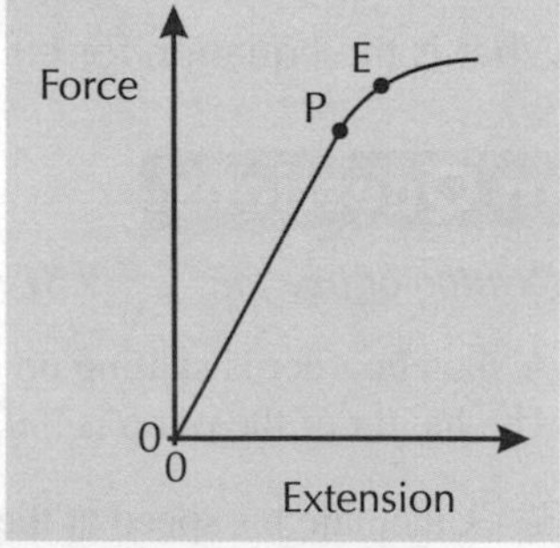

You can Combine k in Parallel or in Series

If a force is applied to more than one spring (or wire), you can **combine** the force constants of the **individual objects** to find the overall force constant of the **system**. You can then treat the system as **one spring** with force constant k. How you combine the force constants depends on how the springs are **arranged**:

In **series**:

$$\frac{1}{k} = \frac{1}{k_1} + \frac{1}{k_2}$$

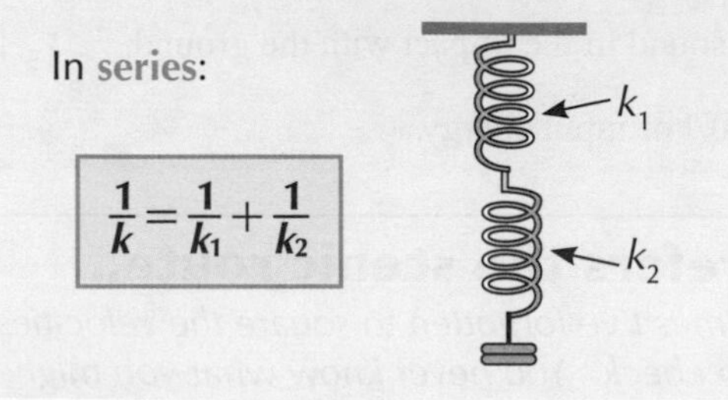

In **parallel**:

$$k = k_1 + k_2$$

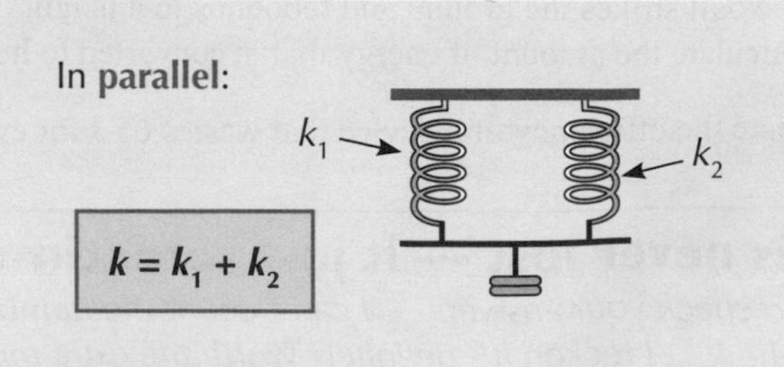

Hooke's Law

A Stretch can be **Elastic** or **Plastic**

A material will show elastic deformation **up to** its **elastic limit**, and plastic deformation **beyond** it.
If a **deformation** is **elastic**, the material returns to its **original shape** once the forces are removed.

1) When the material is put under **tension**, the **atoms** of the material are **pulled apart** from one another.
2) Atoms can **move** slightly relative to their **equilibrium positions**, without changing position in the material.
3) Once the **load** is **removed**, the atoms **return** to their **equilibrium** distance apart.

If a deformation is **plastic**, the material is **permanently stretched**.

1) Some atoms in the material move position relative to one another.
2) When the load is removed, the **atoms don't return** to their original positions.

PRACTICAL SKILLS

Investigating Extension

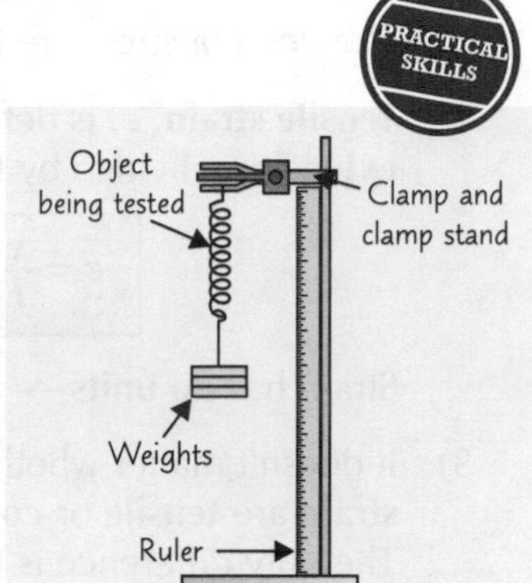

1) Set up the experiment shown in the diagram. Support the object being tested at the top (e.g. with a clamp) and measure its original length with a ruler.
2) Add weights one at a time to the bottom of the object.
3) After each weight is added, measure the new length of the object, then **calculate the extension**:

   extension = new length – original length

4) Plot a graph of **force** (weight) against **extension** for your results. Where the line of best fit is **straight**, then the object obeys Hooke's law and the gradient = $\boldsymbol{k}$ (as $F = kx$). If you've loaded the object beyond its limit of proportionality, the graph will start to curve.
5) Make sure you carry out the experiment **safely**. You should be **standing up** so you can get out of the way quickly if the weights fall, and wearing **safety goggles** to protect your eyes in case the object snaps.

Warm-Up Questions

PRACTICE QUESTIONS

Q1 State Hooke's law and explain what is meant by the elastic limit of a material.
Q2 Define tensile forces and compressive forces.
Q3 From studying the force-extension graph for a material as it is loaded and unloaded, how can you tell:
a) if Hooke's law is being obeyed, b) if the elastic limit has been reached?
Q4 What is meant by plastic deformation of a material?
Q5 Describe how you could investigate the effect of force on extension for a length of wire.

Exam Questions

Q1 A metal guitar string stretches 4.0 mm when a 10 N force is applied.

a) If the string obeys Hooke's law, calculate how far the string will stretch when a 15 N force is applied. [1 mark]

b) Calculate the force constant for this string in Nm^{-1}. [1 mark]

c) The string is then stretched beyond its elastic limit. Describe the effect this will have on the string. [1 mark]

Q2 A rubber band is 6.0 cm long. When it is loaded with 2.5 N, its length becomes 10.4 cm.
Further loading increases the length to 16.2 cm when the force is 5.0 N.

Does the rubber band obey Hooke's law when the force on it is 5.0 N? Explain your answer. [2 marks]

Sod's Law — if you don't learn it, it'll be in the exam...

Three things you didn't know about Robert Hooke — he was the first person to use the word 'cell' (as in biology, not prisons), he helped Christopher Wren with his designs for St. Paul's Cathedral and no-one's sure what he looked like. I'd like to think that if I did all that stuff, then someone would at least remember what I looked like — poor old Hooke.

Stress, Strain and Elastic Potential Energy

How much a material stretches for a particular applied force depends on its dimensions.
If you want to compare one material to another, you need to use stress and strain instead.
A stress-strain graph is the same for any sample of a particular material — the size of the sample doesn't matter.

A Stress Causes a Strain

A material subjected to a pair of **opposite forces** might **deform**, i.e. **change shape**.
If the forces **stretch** the material, they're **tensile**. If the forces **squash** the material, they're **compressive**.

1) **Tensile stress**, σ, is defined as the **force applied**, F, divided by the **cross-sectional area**, A:

$$\sigma = \frac{F}{A}$$

The **units** of stress are $\mathbf{Nm^{-2}}$ or pascals, **Pa**.

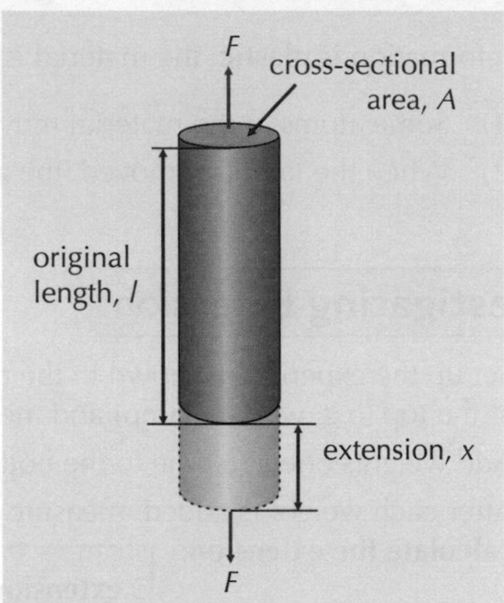

2) **Tensile strain**, ε, is defined as the **change in length**, i.e. the **extension**, divided by the **original length** of the material:

$$\varepsilon = \frac{x}{l}$$

Strain has **no units** — it's just a **number**.

3) It doesn't matter whether the forces producing the **stress** and **strain** are **tensile** or **compressive** — the **same equations** apply. The only difference is that you tend to think of **tensile** forces as **positive**, and **compressive** forces as **negative**.

The Ultimate Tensile Strength is the Maximum Stress a Material can Take

As a greater and greater tensile **force** is applied to a material, the **stress** on it **increases**.

1) The effect of the **stress** is to start to **pull** the **atoms apart** from one another.
2) Eventually the stress becomes **so great** that atoms **separate completely**, and the **material breaks**. This is shown by point **B** on the graph. The stress at which this occurs is called the **breaking stress**.
3) The point marked **UTS** on the graph is called the **ultimate tensile strength**. This is the **maximum stress** that the material can withstand before breaking.
4) **Engineers** have to consider the **UTS** and **breaking stress** of materials when designing a **structure**.

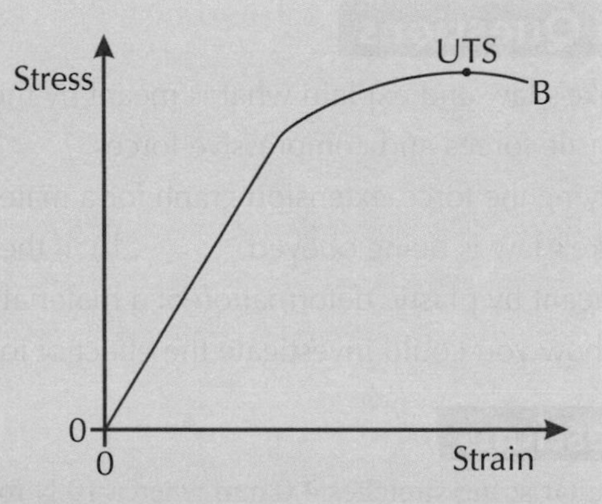

Elastic Potential Energy is the Energy Stored in a Stretched Material

When a material is **stretched** or **compressed**, **work** is done in **deforming** the material.

1) On a **graph** of **force against extension**, the **work done** is given by the **area under the graph**.
2) **Before** the **elastic limit**, **all** the **work done** in stretching or compressing the material is **stored** as **potential energy** in the material.
3) This stored energy is called **elastic potential energy**. There's more about how to calculate elastic potential energy on the next page.

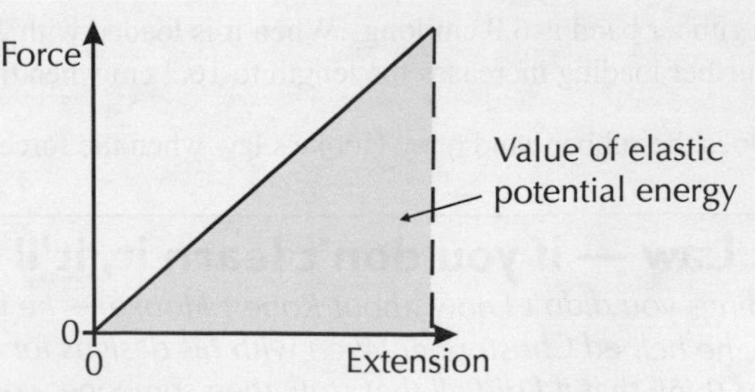

Stress, Strain and Elastic Potential Energy

You can Calculate the **Energy Stored** in a **Stretched Wire**

Provided a material obeys Hooke's law, the **potential energy** stored inside it can be **calculated** quite easily.

1) The work done on the wire in stretching it is equal to the energy stored.
2) **Work done** equals **force × displacement**.
3) However, the **force** on the material **isn't constant**. It rises from zero up to force F. To calculate the **work done**, use the average force between zero and F, i.e. $\frac{1}{2}F$.

work done = $\frac{1}{2}Fx$

This is the triangular area under the force-extension graph — see previous page.

4) Then the **elastic potential energy**, E, is:

$E = \frac{1}{2}Fx$

5) Because Hooke's law is being obeyed, $F = kx$, which means F can be replaced in the equation to give:

$E = \frac{1}{2}kx^2$

6) If the material is stretched beyond the **elastic limit**, some work is done separating atoms. This will **not** be **stored** as elastic potential energy and so isn't released when the force is removed.

Warm-Up Questions

PRACTICE QUESTIONS

Q1 Write a definition for tensile stress.

Q2 Explain what is meant by the tensile strain on a material.

Q3 What is meant by the ultimate tensile strength of a material?

Q4 How can the work done be found from the force against extension graph of a material under load?

Q5 The work done is usually calculated as force multiplied by displacement. Explain why the work done in stretching a wire is $\frac{1}{2}Fx$.

Exam Questions

Q1 A steel wire is 2.00 m long. When a 300 N force is applied to the wire, it stretches 4.0 mm. The wire has a circular cross-section with a diameter of 1.0 mm.

a) Calculate the tensile strain of the wire. [1 mark]

b) Calculate the tensile stress on the wire. [2 marks]

Q2 A copper wire (which obeys Hooke's law) is stretched by 3.0 mm when a force of 50 N is applied.

a) Calculate the force constant for this wire in Nm^{-1}. [1 mark]

b) Calculate the value of the elastic potential energy in the stretched wire. [1 mark]

Q3 A pinball machine contains a spring which is used to fire a small, 12.0 g metal ball to start the game. The spring has a spring constant of 40.8 Nm^{-1}. It is compressed by 5.00 cm and then released to fire the ball.

Calculate the maximum possible speed of the ball. [3 marks]

UTS a laugh a minute, this stuff...

Bet you thought I was going to make a joke about this being stressful then, didn't you? There's a pile of equations to learn on these pages, as well a couple of graphs to drill into your brain, and they all might come up in the exam, so you need to learn the lot I'm afraid. Plus, it'll come in handy if you ever want to, I dunno, build a skyscraper or something.

The Young Modulus

Busy chap, Thomas Young. He did this work on tensile stress as something of a sideline. Light was his main thing. He proved that light behaved like a wave, explained how we see in colour and worked out what causes astigmatism.

The **Young Modulus** is Stress ÷ Strain

When you apply a **load** to stretch a material, it experiences a **tensile stress**, σ, and a **tensile strain**, ε.

1) Up to a point called the **limit of proportionality** (see p.44), the stress and strain of a material are proportional to each other.
2) So below this limit, for a particular material, stress divided by strain is a constant. This constant is called the **Young modulus**, ***E***.

Young modulus = $\dfrac{\textbf{tensile stress}}{\textbf{tensile strain}}$

$$E = \frac{\sigma}{\varepsilon} = \frac{F \div A}{x \div l} = \frac{Fl}{xA}$$

Where F = force in N, A = cross-sectional area in m², l = unstretched length in m and x = extension in m.

3) The **units** of the Young modulus are the same as stress (**Nm⁻²** or pascals), since strain has no units.
4) The Young modulus is a measure of the **stiffness** of a **material**. It is used by **engineers** to make sure their materials can withstand sufficient forces.

To **Find** the Young Modulus, You Need a **Very Long Wire**

PRACTICAL SKILLS

This is the experiment you're most likely to do in class:

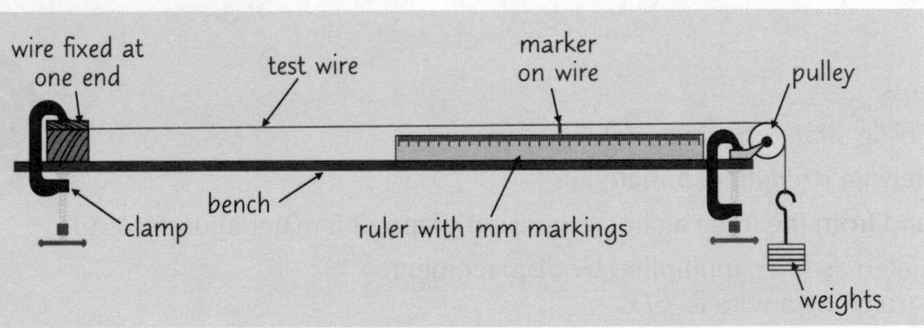

"Okay, found one. Now what?"

If you're doing this experiment, make sure you're standing up so you can get out of the way quickly if the weights fall. And wear safety goggles — if the wire snaps, it could get very messy...

1) The test wire should be thin, and as long as possible. The **longer and thinner** the wire, the more it **extends** for the same force. This reduces the **uncertainty** (p.8) in your measurements.
2) First you need to find the **cross-sectional area** of the wire. Use a **micrometer** to measure the **diameter** of the wire in several places and take an **average** of your measurements. By assuming that the cross-section is **circular**, you can use the formula for the area of a circle: ⟹ **area of a circle =** πr^2
3) **Clamp** the wire to the bench (as shown in the diagram above) so you can hang **weights** off one end of it. Start with the **smallest weight** necessary to **straighten** the wire. (**Don't** include this weight in your final calculations.)
4) Measure the **distance** between the **fixed end of the wire** and the **marker** — this is your unstretched length.
5) Then if you increase the weight, the **wire stretches** and the **marker moves**.
6) **Increase** the **weight** in steps (e.g. 1 N intervals), recording the marker reading each time — the **extension** is the **difference** between this reading and the **unstretched length**. Use a **mass meter** or a set of **digital scales** to accurately find the weight you add at each step.
7) You can use your results from this experiment to calculate the **stress** and **strain** on the wire and plot a stress-strain graph (see next page).

To reduce random errors you should use a thin marker on the wire, and always look from directly above the marker and ruler when measuring the extension.

As you unload the wire, re-measure the extension for each weight to make sure you haven't gone past the wire's elastic limit.

(The other standard way of measuring the Young modulus in the lab is using **Searle's apparatus**. This is a bit more accurate, but it's harder to do and the equipment's more complicated.)

The Young Modulus

Plot a Stress-Strain Graph of Your Results to Find *E*

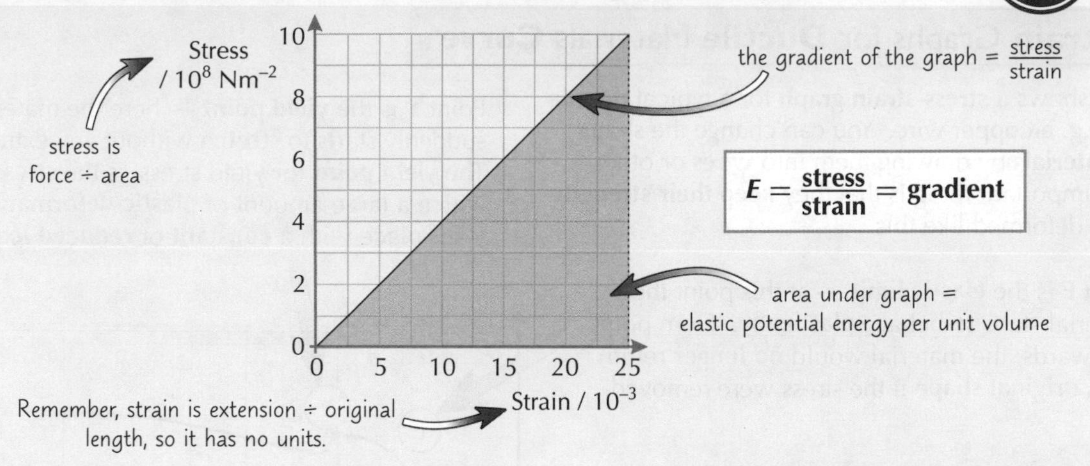

1) The **gradient** of the graph gives the Young modulus, ***E***.
2) The **area under the graph** gives the **elastic potential energy** (or energy stored) **per unit volume** (i.e. the energy stored per 1 m^3 of wire).
3) The stress-strain graph is a **straight line** provided that Hooke's law is obeyed, so you can also calculate the energy per unit volume as:

Energy per unit volume = ½ $\sigma\varepsilon$

Example: The stress-strain graph above is for a thin metal wire. Find the Young modulus of the wire from the graph.

***E* = stress ÷ strain = gradient**

The gradient of the graph = $\frac{\Delta\text{stress}}{\Delta\text{strain}} = \frac{10\times10^8}{25\times10^{-3}}$

$= \mathbf{4\times10^{10}\ Nm^{-2}}$

Warm-Up Questions

Q1 Define the Young modulus for a material. What are the units for the Young modulus?

Q2 Describe an experiment to find the Young modulus of a test wire. Explain why a thin test wire is used.

Q3 What is given by the area contained under a stress-strain graph?

Exam Questions

Q1 A steel wire is stretched elastically. For a load of 80 N, the wire extends by 3.6 mm. The original length of the wire is 2.50 m and its average diameter is 0.6 mm.

a) Calculate the cross-sectional area of the wire in m^2. [1 mark]

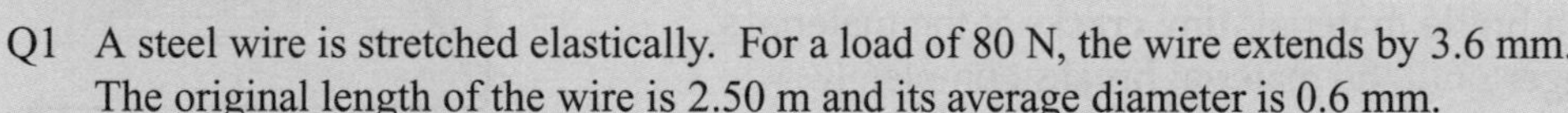

b) Find the tensile stress applied to the wire. [1 mark]

c) Calculate the tensile strain of the wire. [1 mark]

d) Calculate the value of the Young modulus for steel. [2 marks]

Q2 The Young modulus for copper is 1.3×10^{11} Nm^{-2}.

a) The stress on a copper wire is 2.6×10^8 Nm^{-2}. Calculate the strain of the wire. [2 marks]

b) The load applied to the copper wire is 100 N. Calculate the average cross-sectional area of the wire. [1 mark]

c) Calculate the elastic potential energy per unit volume for this loaded wire. [1 mark]

Learn that experiment — it's important...

Getting back to the good Dr Young... As if ground-breaking work in light, the physics of vision and materials science wasn't enough, he was also a well-respected physician, a linguist and an Egyptologist. He was one of the first to try to decipher the Rosetta stone (he didn't get it right, but nobody's perfect). Makes you feel kind of inferior, doesn't it?

Interpreting Stress-Strain Graphs

Remember the stress-strain graph from page 49? Well, it turns out that because materials have different properties, their stress-strain graphs look different too — you need to know the graphs for ductile, brittle and polymeric materials.

Stress-Strain Graphs for **Ductile** Materials **Curve**

The diagram shows a **stress-strain graph** for a typical **ductile** material — e.g. a copper wire. You can change the **shape** of **ductile materials** by drawing them into **wires** or other shapes. The important thing is that they **keep their strength** when they're deformed like this.

Point **Y** is the **yield point** — here the material suddenly starts to **stretch** without any extra load. The **yield point** (or yield stress) is the **stress** at which a large amount of **plastic deformation** takes place with a **constant** or **reduced load.**

Point **E** is the **elastic limit** — at this point the material starts to behave **plastically**. From point E onwards, the material would **no longer** return to its **original shape** if the stress were removed.

Point **P** is the **limit of proportionality** — after this, the graph is no longer a straight line but starts to **bend**. At this point, the material **stops** obeying **Hooke's law**, but would still **return** to its **original shape** if the stress were removed.

Before point **P**, the graph is a **straight line** through the **origin**. This shows that the material is obeying **Hooke's law** (page 44).

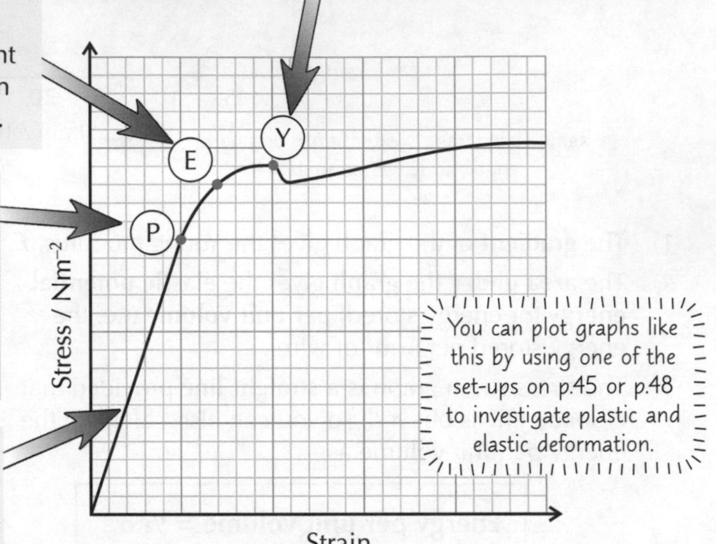

Stress-Strain Graphs for **Brittle** Materials **Don't Curve**

The graph on the right is typical of a **brittle** material.

1) The graph starts the same as the one above — with a **straight line through the origin**. So brittle materials also obey **Hooke's law**.
2) However, when the **stress** reaches a certain point, the material **snaps** — it doesn't deform plastically.
3) When **stress** is applied to a brittle material, **tiny cracks** at the material's surface get **bigger** and **bigger** until the material **breaks** completely.
4) This is called **brittle fracture**.

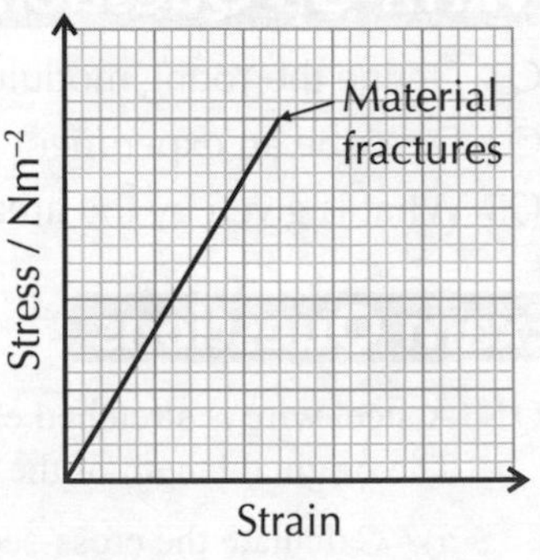

Stronger Materials can Withstand **More Stress** Before they **Break**

The graph below shows the stress-strain curves for materials of different strengths and stiffnesses.

1) Different materials have different **breaking stresses** (p.46).
2) The **stronger** the material, the **higher** the **breaking stress**.
3) **Stiff** materials are difficult to stretch or compress. They have a **large** Young's modulus.
4) For a given stress, a stiff material will have a **lower strain** (i.e. a smaller extension) than a less stiff material.
5) A stiff material **isn't** necessarily strong (and vice versa). Some stiff materials **break** under a low stress, and some strong materials **aren't** very stiff.

When a line on a stress-strain graph just stops, you can assume the material has reached its breaking stress and fractured (unless the question says otherwise).

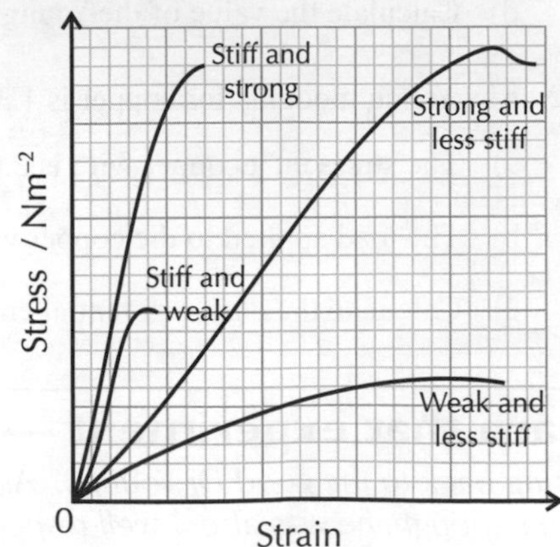

Interpreting Stress-Strain Graphs

Rubber and Polythene Are Polymeric Materials

1) The **molecules** that make up **polymeric** (or polymer) **materials** are arranged in **long chains**.
2) They have a **range** of properties, so different polymers have different **stress-strain graphs**.

Example: This is the stress-strain graph for **polythene**.

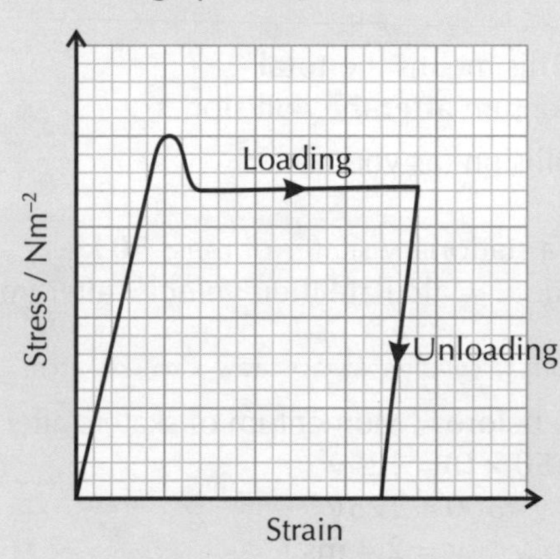

1) Polythene behaves **plastically** — applying a stress to it stretches it into a new shape.
2) Polythene is a **ductile** material.

Example: This is the stress-strain graph for **rubber**.

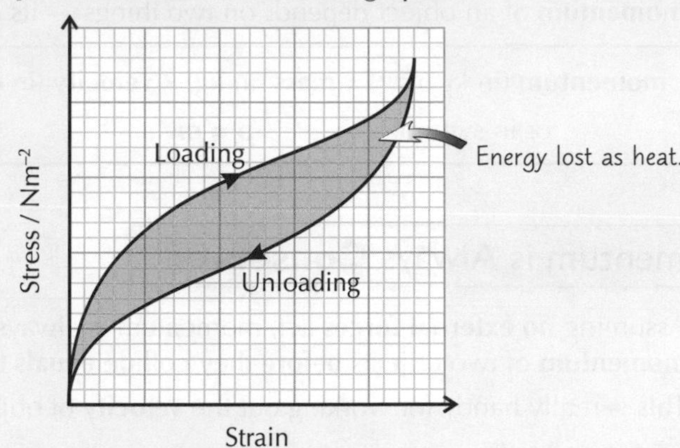

1) **Rubber** returns to its original length when the load is removed — it behaves **elastically**.
2) The loading and unloading curves for rubber are **different**. The energy released when the rubber is unloaded is **less** than the work done to stretch the rubber. This is because some of the elastic potential energy stored in the stretched rubber is **converted to heat**.
3) The amount of energy converted to heat per unit volume is given by the **area between the loading and unloading curves**.

If you repeatedly stretch and release a rubber band, it gets hotter. Give it a go.

Warm-Up Questions

Q1 Define the terms ductile and brittle. Sketch typical stress-strain graphs for ductile and brittle materials.
Q2 What is the difference between the limit of proportionality and the elastic limit?
Q3 What are polymeric materials?

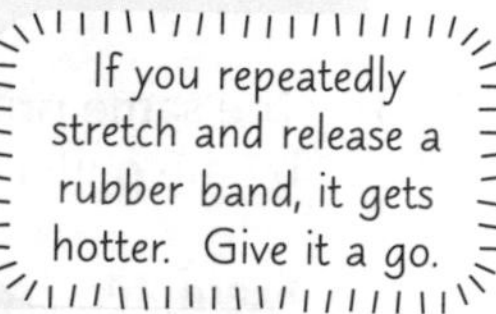

Exam Questions

Q1 Hardened steel is a hard, brittle form of steel made by heating it up slowly and then quenching it in cold water.

a) Sketch a stress-strain graph for hardened steel. [1 mark]

b) Describe how the behaviour of hardened steel under increasing load will differ from that of ductile copper. [2 marks]

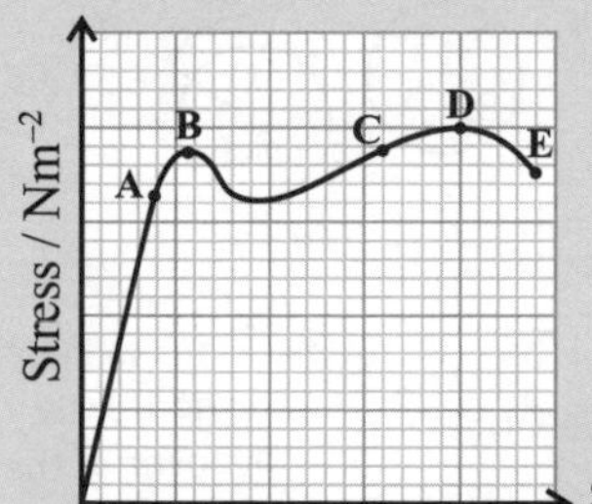

Q2 The graph on the left shows a stress-strain curve for mild steel.

a) State which letter, A-E, corresponds to the steel's limit of proportionality. [1 mark]

b) State which letter, A-E, corresponds to the steel's yield point. [1 mark]

My sister must be brittle — she's always snapping...

In case you were wondering, I haven't just drawn the graphs on these two pages for fun (though I did enjoy myself) — they're there for you to learn. I find the best way to remember each one is to understand why it has the shape it does — if that sounds too much like hard work, then at least make sure you can describe the shape of all four of them.

Momentum and Impulse

Linear momentum is just momentum in a straight line (not a circle or anything complicated like that).

Understanding **Momentum** helps you do **Calculations** on **Collisions**

The **momentum** of an object depends on two things — its **mass** and **velocity**:

> **momentum** (in kg ms^{-1}) = **mass** (in kg) × **velocity** (in ms^{-1})
> or in symbols: $p = mv$

Momentum is a vector quantity (see p.14), so just like velocity, it has size and direction.

Momentum is Always **Conserved**

1) Assuming **no external forces** act, momentum is always **conserved**. This means the **total momentum** of two objects **before** they collide **equals** the total momentum **after** the collision.
2) This is really handy for working out the **velocity** of objects after a collision (as you do...):

Example: A skater of mass 75 kg and velocity 4 ms^{-1} collides with a stationary skater of mass 50 kg. The skaters join together and move off in the same direction. Calculate their velocity after impact.

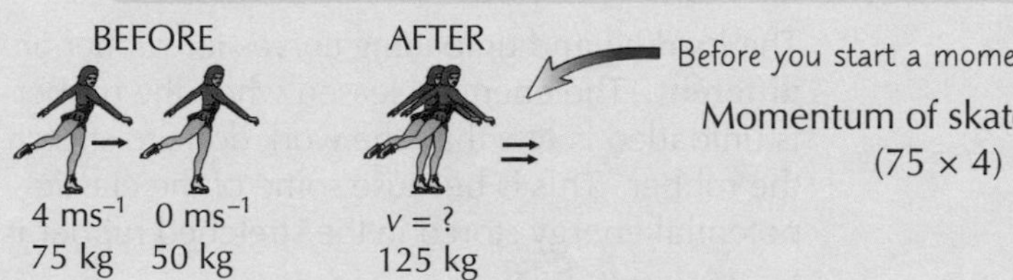

Before you start a momentum calculation, always draw a quick sketch.

Momentum of skaters before = Momentum of skaters after

$(75 \times 4) + (50 \times 0) = 125v$

$300 = 125v$

So... $v = \mathbf{2.4\ ms^{-1}}$

3) The same principle can be applied in **explosions**. E.g. if you fire an **air rifle**, the **forward momentum** gained by the pellet **equals** the **backward momentum** of the rifle, and you feel the rifle recoiling into your shoulder.

Example: A bullet of mass 0.005 kg is shot from a rifle at a speed of 200 ms^{-1}. The rifle has a mass of 4 kg. Calculate the velocity at which the rifle recoils.

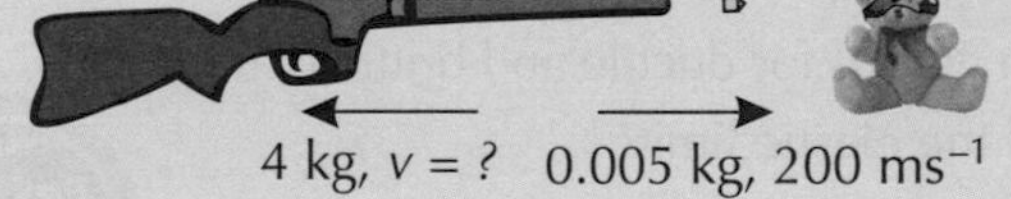

Momentum before explosion = Momentum after explosion

$0 = (0.005 \times 200) + (4 \times v)$

$0 = 1 + 4v$ so $v = \mathbf{-0.25\ ms^{-1}}$

4) In reality, collisions and explosions usually happen in more than one dimension. In **two-dimensional collisions**, momentum is conserved in **both dimensions**. You can solve two-dimensional collision problems by **resolving vectors** (see page 15).

Example: Ball A collides with stationary ball B, as shown in diagram 1. After the collision, the two balls move off as shown in diagram 2. Ball A has a mass of 40 g. Calculate the mass, *m*, of ball B.

DIAGRAM 1: Ball A, 36.9°, 10 ms^{-1}, Ball B

DIAGRAM 2: Ball A, 36.9°, 5 ms^{-1}; Ball B, 66.0°, 6.57 ms^{-1}

NOT TO SCALE

You can work this using conservation of momentum in just the horizontal direction (or just the vertical). Start by picking the positive direction — let's say right is positive.

horizontal momentum before the collision = horizontal momentum after the collision

$$(0.04 \times 10 \sin 36.9°) + (m \times 0) = -(0.04 \times 5 \sin 36.9°) + (m \times 6.57 \sin 66.0°)$$

$$\text{so, } m = \frac{0.04 \times (10 \sin 36.9° + 5 \sin 36.9°)}{6.57 \sin 66.0°} = 0.0600...\text{ kg} = \mathbf{60\ g\ (to\ 2\ s.f.)}$$

The horizontal component of the velocity of ball A is negative after the collision — it's to the left.

You could check your answer by doing the same calculation for the vertical direction.

Momentum and Impulse

Collisions can be Elastic or Inelastic

A **perfectly elastic** collision is one where **momentum** is **conserved** and **kinetic energy** is **conserved** — i.e. no energy is dissipated as heat, sound, etc. If a collision is **inelastic** it means that some of the kinetic energy is converted into other forms during the collision. But **momentum is always conserved.**

Example: A toy lorry (mass 2.0 kg) travelling at 3.0 ms^{-1} crashes into a smaller toy car (mass 800 g to 2 s.f.), travelling in the same direction at 2.0 ms^{-1}. The velocity of the lorry after the collision is 2.6 ms^{-1} in the same direction. Calculate the new velocity of the car and the total kinetic energy (KE) before and after the collision.

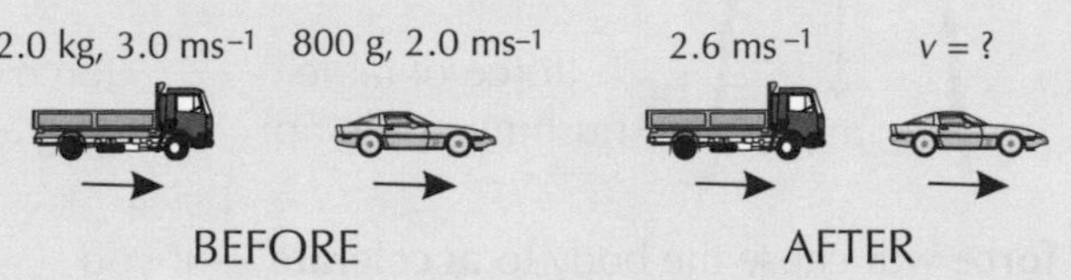

Momentum before collision = Momentum after collision

$(2.0 \times 3.0) + (0.80 \times 2.0) = (2.0 \times 2.6) + (0.80v)$

$7.6 = 5.2 + 0.80v$

$2.4 = 0.80v$ so $v =$ **3.0 ms^{-1}**

KE before = KE of lorry + KE of car

$= \frac{1}{2}mv^2$ (lorry) $+ \frac{1}{2}mv^2$ (car)

$= \frac{1}{2}(2.0 \times 3.0^2) + \frac{1}{2}(0.80 \times 2.0^2)$

$= 9 + 1.6 =$ **11 J (to 2 s.f.)**

KE after $= \frac{1}{2}(2.0 \times 2.6^2) + \frac{1}{2}(0.80 \times 3.0^2)$

$= 6.76 + 3.6 =$ **10 J (to 2 s.f.)**

The difference in the two values is the amount of kinetic energy dissipated as heat or sound, or in damaging the vehicles — so this is an inelastic collision.

You can use the rule of the conservation of momentum, (and the conservation of kinetic energy in elastic collisions) to predict the behaviour of real-world objects, for example balls in sports games.

Impulse = Change in Momentum

1) Newton's second law says **force = rate of change of momentum** (see page 54), or $F = \Delta p \div \Delta t$
2) **Rearranging** Newton's 2nd law gives:
   Impulse is defined as **average force × time**, $F\Delta t$.
   The units of impulse are **newton seconds**, Ns.

   $$F\Delta t = \Delta p$$
   so **impulse = change of momentum**
3) The area under a force-time graph is $F \times \Delta t$ = impulse.

See p.25 for how to estimate the area under non-linear graphs.

Warm-Up Questions

Q1 Give two examples of conservation of momentum in practice.

Q2 How is calculating the momentum before and after a collision different when objects collide in two dimensions rather than one?

Q3 Describe how to find the impulse of a collision from a force-time graph.

Exam Question

Q1 A snooker ball of mass 0.145 kg moving at 1.94 ms^{-1} collides with a stationary snooker ball of mass 0.148 kg. The first ball rebounds along its initial path at 0.005 ms^{-1}, and the second ball moves off in the opposite direction.

a) Calculate the velocity of the second ball immediately after the collision. [2 marks]

b) State whether or not the collision is perfectly elastic. Explain your answer. [3 marks]

c) The first ball then hits the cushion at the edge of the table and comes to a stop. The collision takes 0.15 seconds. Calculate the average force experienced by the ball in this collision. [2 marks]

Momentum will never be an endangered species — it's always conserved...

Remember, impulse is only talking about the change of momentum of one of the objects, whilst conservation of momentum applies to the whole system. So the impulse of an object can change although momentum is conserved.

Newton's Laws of Motion

You did most of this at GCSE, but that doesn't mean you can just skip over it now. You'll be kicking yourself if you forget this stuff in the exam — it's easy marks...

Newton's **1st Law** says that a **Force** is Needed to Change Velocity

1) On page 28, you saw that a net force is needed for an object to **accelerate**.
2) **Newton's 1st law of motion** states that the **velocity** of an object will **not change** unless a **net force** acts on it.
3) In plain English this means a body will remain at rest or continue to move in a **straight line** at a **constant speed**, unless acted on by a **net force**.

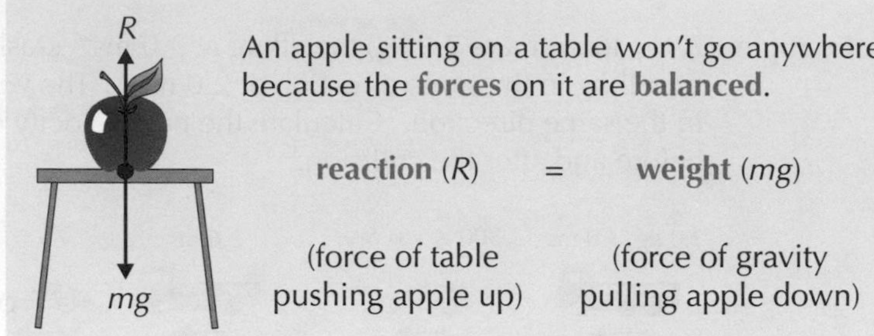

4) If the forces **aren't balanced**, the **overall net force** will cause the body to **accelerate** — if you gave the apple above a shove, there'd be a net force acting on it and it would roll off the table. Acceleration can mean a change in **direction**, or **speed**, or both. (See Newton's 2nd law, below.)

Newton's 2nd Law says that Force is the **Rate of Change in Momentum**

Newton's 2nd Law states that:

> "The **rate of change of momentum** of an object is **directly proportional** to the **net force** which acts on the object." or $F = \frac{\Delta p}{\Delta t}$

Remember, $p = mv$, (see page 52).

If mass is constant, this can be written as:

> **net force = mass × acceleration** or $F = ma$

See page 29 for more on this equation.

Example: Sarah is playing hockey. The ball is coming towards her at a speed of 4.6 ms^{-1}. She hits it so that it travels back in the same direction at a speed of 10.2 ms^{-1}. Her stick is in contact with the ball for 0.84 seconds. The ball has a mass of 161 g. Calculate the average force exerted on the ball during this time.

Use $F = \frac{\Delta p}{\Delta t}$: $\Delta p = 0.161 \times 10.2 - 0.161 \times (-4.6)$
$= 0.161 \times (10.2 + 4.6)$
$= 2.3828 \text{ kg ms}^{-1}$

The ball reverses direction, so you need to give one of the velocities a negative value. Choose whichever makes the maths easier.

$\Delta t = 0.84$ s

$F = 2.3828 \div 0.84 = 2.8366... =$ **2.84 N (to 3 s.f.)**

F = ma is a **Special Case** of **Newton's 2nd Law**

Newton's 2nd law says that if the **mass** of an object is **constant**, then the **bigger** the **force** acting on it, the **greater** its **acceleration** — i.e. ***F = ma***. But, if the **mass** of the object is **changing** — e.g. if it is accelerating at close to the **speed of light** — then you **can't** use ***F = ma***.
(You don't need to know why this happens.)

Don't worry though — **Newton's 2nd law still applies**, it's just that the 'rate of **change of momentum**' bit refers to a **change in mass** and velocity.

Daisy always knew she was special.

Newton's Laws of Motion

Newton's 3rd Law says each Force has an Equal, Opposite Reaction Force

There are a few different ways of stating Newton's 3rd law, but the clearest way is:

If an object A EXERTS a FORCE on object B, then object B exerts AN EQUAL BUT OPPOSITE FORCE on object A.

You'll also hear the law as "every action has an equal and opposite reaction". But this confuses people who wrongly think the forces are both applied to the same object. (If that were the case, you'd get a resultant force of zero and nothing would ever move anywhere...)

The two forces actually represent the **same interaction**, just seen from two **different perspectives**:

1) If you **push against a wall**, the wall will **push back** against you, **just as hard**. As soon as you stop pushing, so does the wall. Amazing...
2) If you **pull a cart**, whatever force **you exert** on the rope, the rope exerts the **exact opposite** pull on you.
3) When you go **swimming**, you push **back** against the water with your arms and legs, and the water pushes you **forwards** with an equal-sized force.

This looks like Newton's 3rd law...

But it's NOT.

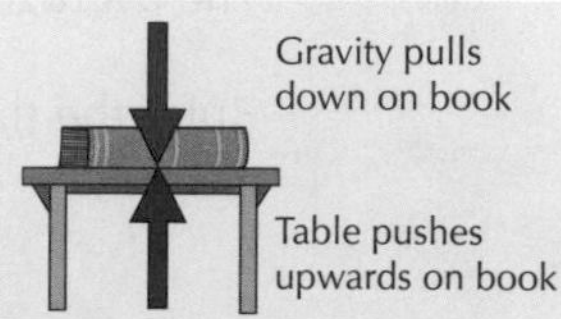

...because both forces are acting on the book, and they're not of the same type. These are two separate interactions. The forces are equal and opposite, resulting in zero acceleration, so this is an example of Newton's 1st law.

Newton's 3rd law applies in **all situations** and to all **types of force**. But the pairs of forces are always the **same type**, e.g. both gravitational or both electrical.

Newton's 3rd law is a consequence of the **conservation of momentum** (page 52). A **net force** acting on an object means a change in **acceleration** (***F*** = ***ma***) — which means a **change in momentum**. Momentum is always **conserved**, so whenever one object exerts a force on another (and changes its momentum) the second object must exert an equal-sized force back onto the first object so that the overall change in momentum is zero.

Warm-Up Questions

Q1 State Newton's 1st, 2nd and 3rd laws of motion, and explain what they mean.

Q2 Sketch a force diagram of a book resting on a table to illustrate Newton's 3rd law.

Exam Questions

Q1 A parachutist with a mass of 78 kg jumps out of a plane. As she falls, the net force acting on her changes.

a) Use Newton's 2nd law to explain why she initially accelerates. [2 marks]

b) Calculate the initial vertical force on the parachutist. ($g = 9.81\ \text{ms}^{-2}$) [1 mark]

c) After a time, the parachutist reaches terminal velocity and stops accelerating. Use Newton's 1st law to explain why the net force on the parachutist is zero at this point. [1 mark]

Q2 A car with mass 1244 kg increases its velocity from 5.5 ms^{-1} to 26.3 ms^{-1} over a period of 15 seconds. The car is producing a driving force of 2143 N, and experiences frictional forces of 213 N. The car contains two passengers. Calculate their combined mass (assume the car contains nothing else). [3 marks]

Newton's three incredibly important laws of motion...

These laws may not seem all that exciting but they're pretty powerful if you stop to think about it. These three laws are acting pretty much every time you see something moving or staying still. Which is, I'll hazard a guess, all the time. So, if you can't escape from Newton's laws, make sure you know 'em.

Car Safety

Newton's laws aren't all about apples on tables — they're also particularly important for designing cars...

If a Car **Crashes**, the Forces are Very **Large**

1) Newton's second law of motion (p.54) says: $F = \frac{\Delta p}{\Delta t}$
2) When a car **crashes**, there is a big **change in speed** — possibly from 70 mph (about 110 km h^{-1}) to zero. This means there is a big change in **momentum**.
3) If the car comes to a stop **quickly** (Δt is small), then the **force acting** on the car, anyone inside it and whatever it has collided with is very **large**.
4) If Δt can be **increased**, this force can be made **much smaller** for a given change of momentum.
5) So, the **force** of an impact can be **reduced** by **increasing the time** the impact takes place over.

Example: A toy car with a mass of 1 kg, travelling at 5 ms^{-1}, hits a wall and stops in a time of 0.5 seconds.

The average force on the car is: $F = \frac{\Delta p}{\Delta t} = \frac{(1\times 5)-(1\times 0)}{0.5} = 10\text{ N}$

But if the time of impact is doubled to **1 second**, the force on the car is halved.

Most Car Safety Features are Designed to **Slow You Down Gradually**

Modern cars have lots of built-in **safety features.** A lot of them reduce the forces acting on passengers in a crash by **increasing the time** over which the **change in momentum** takes place.

Crumple Zones:

Crumple zones are areas at the front and rear of a car that are designed to **crumple on impact**. They have two effects:

1) They absorb some of the car's **kinetic energy** when they deform, which would otherwise be **transferred to the passengers** and whatever the car had collided with (e.g. other cars).
2) They **increase time** taken for the car to slow down, (Δt in the equation above) which **reduces the forces** acting on passengers and whatever the car has hit.

Air Bags:

Air bags are 'cushions' in the dashboard and elsewhere that **inflate** very quickly on collision.
They protect the passengers by:

1) Making passengers **slow down more gradually** (increasing Δt).
2) Stopping passengers from hitting the dashboard, steering wheel, etc. during a crash.

Seat Belts:

Seat belts are designed to **stretch** slightly. They protect wearers in a crash by:

1) Holding the wearer **in place** in the car, stopping them from being thrown from their seats.
2) **Absorbing** some of the wearer's **kinetic energy** by stretching (p.46).
3) **Increasing the time** that the wearer comes to a stop over, Δt (again, by stretching).

Example: Giles's car bumps into the back of a stationary bus. The car was travelling at 2 ms^{-1} and comes to a stop in 0.2 s. Giles was wearing his seatbelt and takes 0.8 s to stop. Giles's mass is 75 kg.

a) Calculate the average force acting on Giles during the accident.

b) Calculate the average force that would have acted on Giles if he had stopped as quickly as the car.

a) $F = \frac{\Delta p}{\Delta t}$ So, for Giles: $F = \frac{75\times 2 - 75\times 0}{0.8} = 187.5 =$ **190 N (to 2 s.f.)**

b) Again, $F = \frac{\Delta p}{\Delta t}$ but $\Delta t = 0.2$ s. So: $F = \frac{75\times 2 - 75\times 0}{0.2} =$ **750 N (to 2 s.f.)**

Car Safety

Crash Tests are Used to Analyse the Forces in a Crash

1) Early cars didn't have many safety features in the event of a crash. But as cars became **faster** and the **number** of cars on the roads increased, car manufacturers started to think about how to make cars **safer**.
2) This led to the development of the **three-point seat belt**, **crumple zones** and **air bags** back in the 1950's.
3) At the same time, engineers were developing better ways of **understanding** the **forces** acting on passengers in a collision. They developed increasingly sophisticated **crash test dummies** that could **measure** all the forces that different passengers experience in different **kinds** of collisions.
4) **Crash tests** also allowed car manufacturers to test the **effectiveness** of certain **safety features**, so they could see how much they reduced the likelihood of injury.
5) Wearing a seat belt is now **mandatory** (everyone has to do it), and features such as crumple zones and air bags have become **standard features** of modern cars (along with many more sophisticated safety features).
6) Understanding the forces involved in road collisions has **saved many lives** — it's estimated that the three-point seat belt alone has saved **over a million lives worldwide** in the last 50 years.

Car Safety Features Have Some Risks

1) Seat belts can cause **bruising** during a crash.
2) They can also be dangerous for **small children** — if the top part of the belt lies across the child's **neck** this can cause injury in a crash and if the child is **too small** for a seat belt it may not **secure them properly**. In the UK, children must use **booster seats** or **cushions** to reduce these risks.

June didn't care how many safety features the car had — if Fido was driving, she wasn't getting in.

3) **Air bags** are designed for use with seat belts and can be **dangerous** if you're not wearing one. Air bags inflate very **rapidly**, with a lot of **force**. If a passenger seat belt isn't **secured properly** then the passenger can keep moving forwards quickly as the car slows down and hit the air bag as it is inflating with a **force** big enough to cause **injury**.
4) Air bags are also dangerous when using **rear-facing child seats** — the air bag inflates **behind** the child and can throw the child seat towards the car seat with some force. It is now **illegal** to use a rear-facing child seat in the UK in a seat fitted with an air bag.

Most of these risks are caused by not using a car's **safety features properly**.
If you use a seat belt and air bags as you are meant to, you are **far safer** in a car than you would be without them.

Warm-Up Questions

Q1 Give three safety features of a car that are designed to protect passengers in the event of a crash.

Q2 Give one feature of a car's design that might protect passengers in another vehicle in the event of a collision.

Exam Question

Q1* Explain the ways that air bags protect passengers in the event of a crash, and describe some of the risks associated with their use and how these risks can be reduced. [6 marks]

*The quality of your extended response will be assessed in this question.

Here endeth the lesson...

Some real, applied physics here to get your head round, but it's important stuff. Understanding forces has had a huge effect on how cars are designed, and in doing so has saved a lot of people's lives. Not bad for a few equations, hey?

Extra Exam Practice

Phew — that's Module 3 all sewn up. Time to put it all into practice with a few mixed questions.

- Have a look at this example of how to answer a tricky exam question.
- Then check how much you've understood from Module 3 by having a go at the questions on the next page.

You might need to go back to Module 2 and use what you've learnt about scalars and vectors on p.14-15 when answering these questions.

1 A golf ball is struck off a tee at an angle of 42° to the horizontal. The ball has an initial velocity of 60.0 ms^{-1}, as shown in **Figure 1**.

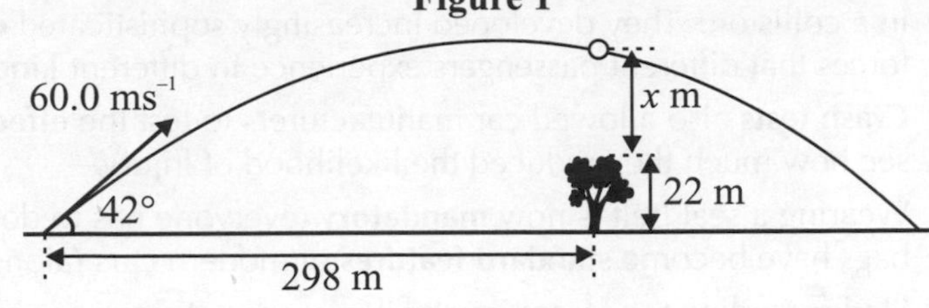

(a) The golf ball flies directly over a tree. The tree is 22 m tall, and is a distance of 298 m from the tee. Calculate the vertical distance, x, between the ball and the tree when the ball is above the tree. Assume that no air resistance acts on the ball. (g = 9.81 ms^{-2})

(3 marks)

(b) Sketch a graph to show how the horizontal velocity of the golf ball would change with time if air resistance were considered. Explain the shape of the graph you have drawn. You can assume the golf ball is falling vertically by the time it hits the ground.

(4 marks)

1(a)

Resolve the initial velocity into the horizontal component (u_h) and the vertical component (u_v): $u_h = 60\cos 42°$ ms^{-1}, $u_v = 60\sin 42°$ ms^{-1}

There is no air resistance, so the ball does not accelerate horizontally.

velocity = $\frac{\text{displacement}}{\text{time}}$, so the time taken for the ball to reach the tree is:

horizontal displacement ÷ horizontal velocity = 298 ÷ 60cos 42° = 6.6833... s

The vertical motion of the ball is accelerating at a constant rate due to gravity:

Taking **upwards as positive**:

$\boldsymbol{s = ?,\ u = 60\sin 42°\ \text{ms}^{-1},\ a = -9.81\ \text{ms}^{-2},\ t = 6.6833...\ \text{s}}$

$s = ut + \frac{1}{2}at^2 = (60\sin 42° \times 6.6833...) + \left(\frac{1}{2} \times (-9.81) \times 6.6833...^2\right) = 49.2306...$ m

This is the vertical displacement of the ball at the point it passes over the tree. As the ball was at ground level when it was hit, this gives how high the ball is above the ground, so x = 49.2306... – 22 = 27.2306... m = 27 m (to 2 s.f.).

You'd get 3 marks for the correct answer. If you got the answer wrong, you'd get 1 mark for calculating the time taken for the ball to reach the tree and 1 mark for calculating the vertical displacement of the ball at the tree.

You should bear in mind that s, u, v and a can have negative or positive values, so you'll have to think about which direction you're taking as being positive at the start of the calculation.

Writing out all of the variables you know, as well as the variable you want to calculate, will often make it easier to choose a suitable equation for uniform acceleration.

1(b)

Air resistance provides a horizontal resultant force against the direction of motion. Newton's second law ($F = ma$) shows that this resultant force will cause the ball to decelerate, **so v_h decreases with time**. The ball's velocity is vertical by the time it hits the ground, **so v_h will decrease to zero.** The air resistance acting horizontally on the ball will decrease as v_h decreases. This means the horizontal deceleration of the ball will decrease with time. Deceleration is represented by the gradient of a v-t graph, **so the gradient of the graph decreases with time.**

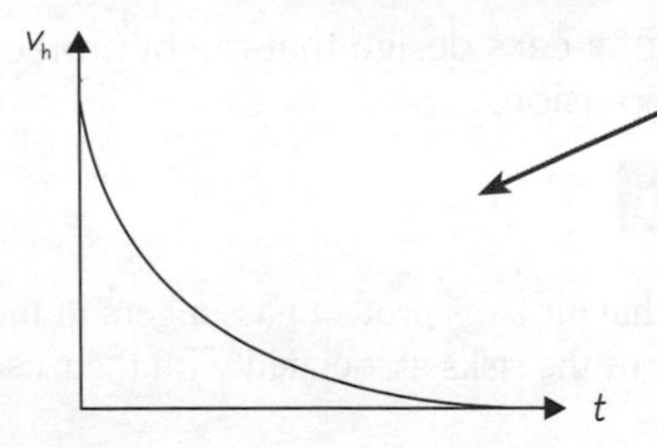

If you're asked to sketch a graph, you don't need to be accurate, but you do need to get the rough shape of the graph right.

Make sure you explain all the key features of the graph.

Extra Exam Practice

2 A child has a toy gun that fires 1.2 g foam pellets. The toy works by compressing a spring. When the spring is released, the energy stored in the spring is transferred to the kinetic energy of the pellet with an efficiency of 92%. The child holds the gun still, before shooting a pellet out of the first floor window of his house and onto the lawn below, as shown in **Figure 2**. You may assume that the pellet does not experience any air resistance.

Figure 2

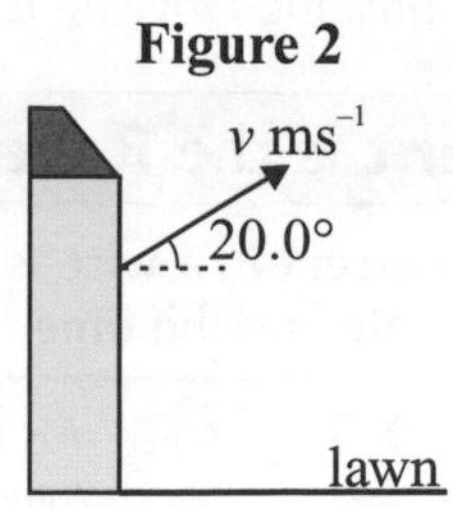

(a) The spring in the toy has a force constant of 275 Nm^{-1}. It is compressed by 4.0 cm before it is released. Show that the speed, v, of a pellet immediately after it has been pushed out of the gun is 18 ms^{-1}. You may assume that the spring obeys Hooke's law as it is compressed.

(4 marks)

(b) The pellet applies a force of 4.1 N to the gun, causing the gun to recoil. Calculate the time over which this force is applied to the gun.

(2 marks)

(c) The pellet hits the lawn 1.7 s after leaving the gun. Calculate the speed and the angle from the horizontal at which the pellet hits the lawn. ($g = 9.81$ ms^{-2})

(3 marks)

3 A wooden mobile for a baby's crib is shown in **Figure 3**. The mobile is made up of four cylindrical rods that are attached to four sides of a central cube. Identical spheres, moons and stars are attached to each of the four rods using wire. The mobile is suspended by a piece of string that is attached to the centre of the top surface of the cube. The rods are all horizontal when the mobile is hung up by the piece of string. The components of the mobile are all made from wood with a uniform density of 0.55×10^3 $kg\,m^{-3}$. **Table 1** shows the weight of some of the mobile's components.

Table 1

Component	Weight / N
Central cube	1.165
Rod A, rod D	0.120
Rod B, rod C	0.150
Moon	0.025
Wire	Negligible

Figure 3

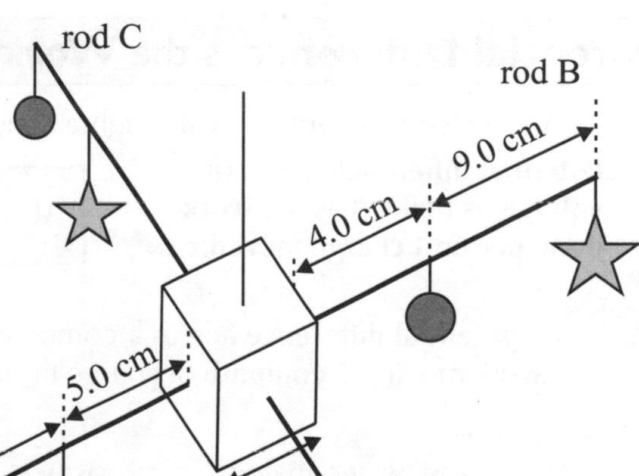

(a) Each sphere has a circumference of 9.2 cm. Show that the weight of a sphere is 0.071 N.

(3 marks)

(b) Calculate the weight of one of the wooden stars.

(4 marks)

(c) The piece of string that the mobile is suspended by has a diameter of 2.0 mm. The Young modulus of the string is 2.2 GPa. Calculate how much the string extends by when the mobile is hung up, as a percentage of the string's original length. You may assume that the string is cylindrical.

(4 marks)

Charge, Current and Potential Difference

Electricity's brilliant, I love it. It's what gets me out of bed in the morning. (Not literally of course, that'd be quite painful.)

Current is the Rate of Flow of Charge

1) The **current** in a **wire** is like **water** flowing in a **pipe**. The **amount** of water that flows depends on the **flow rate** and the **time**. It's the same with electricity — **current is the rate of flow of charge.**

$$I = \frac{\Delta Q}{\Delta t}$$

Where I is the current in amperes, ΔQ is the charge in coulombs, and Δt is the time taken in seconds.

Remember that conventional current flows from + to −, the opposite way from electron flow.

2) The **coulomb** is the **unit of charge**.

One **coulomb** (C) is defined as the **amount of charge** that passes in **1 second** when the **current** is **1 ampere.**

3) You can measure the current flowing through part of a circuit using an **ammeter**. This is the circuit symbol for an ammeter:

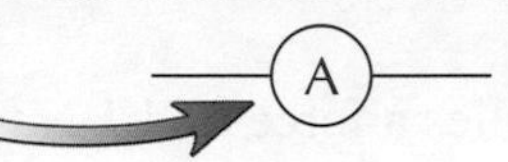

Attach an ammeter in series with the component you're investigating.

The Charge on an Electron is the Smallest Unit of Charge

1) In electrical circuits, charge is usually carried by **electrons** (or sometimes by ions — see the next page). Electrons all carry the **same charge**, **−e**, where **e** is the **elementary charge**: $e = 1.60 \times 10^{-19}$ C
2) Protons carry an **opposite charge** of the **same magnitude**, **+e** (see p.166).
3) The elementary charge is the **smallest unit** that charge comes in — the net charge on any particle or object will **always** be a **multiple of e**. We say that charge is **quantised**.

Potential Difference is the Work Done per Unit Charge

1) To make electric charge flow through a conductor, you need to do **work** on it.
2) **Potential difference** (p.d.), or **voltage**, is defined as the **work done per unit charge moved**:

$$W = VQ \quad \text{or} \quad V = \frac{W}{Q}$$

W is the work done in joules (see p.66). It's the energy transferred in moving the charge.

The **potential difference** across a component is **1 volt** (V) when you do **1 joule** of work moving **1 coulomb** of charge through the component. This **defines** the volt.

$$1\text{ V} = 1\text{ J C}^{-1}$$

Back to the 'water analogy' again. The p.d. is like the pressure that's forcing water along the pipe.

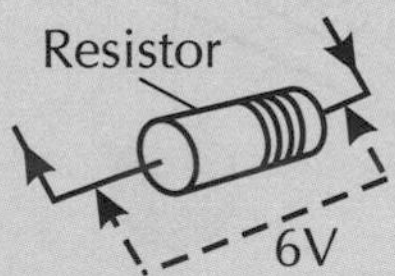

Here you do 6 J of work moving each coulomb of charge through the resistor, so the p.d. across it is 6 V. The energy gets converted to heat.

3) You can measure the potential difference across a component using a **voltmeter**. This is the circuit symbol for a voltmeter:

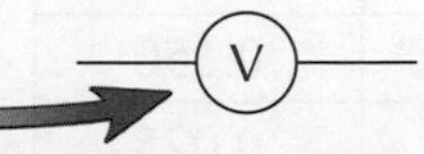

4) Remember, the potential difference across components in parallel is **the same**, so the **voltmeter** should be connected in **parallel** with the component you're investigating.

The maximum value that a voltmeter or ammeter can measure is called the full scale deflection.

Work Done on a Charge Equals the Kinetic Energy it Gains

1) When a **charged particle** is accelerated by a **potential difference**, the energy transferred to it is equal to the work done on the particle, $W = VQ$ (see above). For an electron (with charge of size e), this can be written as $W = Ve$.
2) The energy transferred is equal to the **kinetic energy** gained by the electron.
3) **Kinetic energy = ½mv^2** (see page 42), so:

$$eV = \frac{1}{2}mv^2$$

where m is the electron's mass and v is its velocity

This gives you the velocity of a single electron accelerated through a potential difference — don't get it confused with mean drift velocity (coming up on the next page).

Charge, Current and Potential Difference

The Mean Drift Velocity is the Average Velocity of the Charge Carriers

When **current** flows through a wire, you might imagine the **electrons** all moving uniformly in the **same direction**. In fact, they move **randomly** in **all directions**, but tend to **drift** one way. The **mean drift velocity** is just the **average velocity** and it's **much, much less** than the electrons' **actual speed**. (Their actual speed is about 10^6 ms^{-1}.)

The Current Depends on the Mean Drift Velocity:

If you're using different charge carriers, just replace e with the charge on each carrier, and let n be the number density of charge carriers.

The **current** is given by the continuity equation: $I = Anev$

where: I = electrical current (A)
n = number density of electrons (m^{-3}) (number per unit volume)
v = mean drift velocity (ms^{-1})
A = cross-sectional area (m^2)
e = size of charge on one electron (C)

So...
- If you double the **number of electrons**, the **current doubles**.
- If you double the **area** the **current doubles**, like this:
- If the electrons move **twice as fast**, the **current doubles** as twice as many electrons move past a point in the same amount of time.

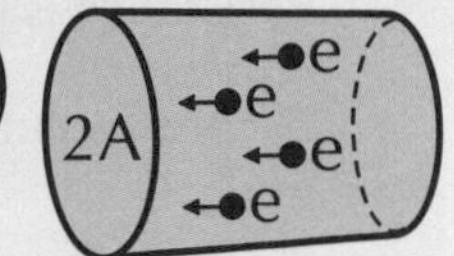

Different Materials have Different Numbers of Charge Carriers

1) In a **metal**, the **charge carriers** are **free electrons** — they're the ones from the **outer shell** of each atom. Thinking about the formula $I = Anev$, there are **loads** of charge carriers per unit volume, making n **big**. The **drift velocity** is **small**, even for a **high current**.
2) **Semiconductors** have **fewer charge carriers**, so the **drift velocity** needs to be **higher** to give the **same current**.
3) A **perfect insulator** wouldn't have **any charge carriers**, so $n = 0$ in the formula and you'd get **no current**. **Real** insulators have a **very small** n.

Charge Carriers in Liquids and Gases are Ions

1) **Ionic crystals** like sodium chloride are **insulators**. Once **molten**, though, the liquid **conducts**. Positive and negative **ions** are the **charge carriers**. The **same thing** happens in an **ionic solution** like copper sulfate solution.
2) A substance containing ions that conducts electricity like this is called an **electrolyte**.
3) **Gases** are **insulators**, but if you apply a **high enough voltage** electrons get **ripped out** of **atoms**, giving you **ions** along a path. You get a **spark**.

Warm-Up Questions

Q1 Describe in words and symbols how current and charge are related.
Q2 Explain what is meant by the sentence "charge is quantised".
Q3 Define potential difference.
Q4 Write an equation for the velocity of an electron accelerated by a p.d. of V, in terms of its charge and mass.
Q5 What happens to the current in a wire if the mean drift velocity of the electrons is halved?
Q6 Describe how metals, semiconductors and insulators differ in terms of n.

Exam Questions

Q1 A battery delivers 4500 C of electric charge to a circuit in 10 minutes. Calculate the average current. [1 mark]

Q2 A kettle runs off the mains supply (230 V) and has an overall efficiency of 88%. Calculate how much electric charge will pass through the kettle if it transfers 308 J of energy to the water it contains. [2 marks]

Q3 Copper has 1.0×10^{29} free electrons per m^3. Calculate the mean drift velocity of the electrons in a copper wire of cross-sectional area 5.0×10^{-6} m^2 when it is carrying a current of 13 A. [2 marks]

I can't even be bothered to make the current joke...

Talking of currant jokes, I saw this bottle of wine the other day called 'raisin d'être' — 'raison d'être' meaning 'reason for living', but spelled slightly differently to make 'raisin', meaning 'grape'. Ho ho. Chuckled all the way home.

Resistance and Resistivity

Resistance and resistivity. Not quite the same word, not quite the same thing. Make sure you know which is which...

Everything has Resistance

1) If you put a **potential difference** (p.d.) across an **electrical component**, a **current** will flow.
2) **How much** current you get for a particular **p.d.** depends on the **resistance** of the component.
3) You can think of a component's **resistance** as a **measure** of how **difficult** it is to get a **current** to **flow** through it.

Mathematically, **resistance** is:
This equation really **defines** what is meant by resistance.

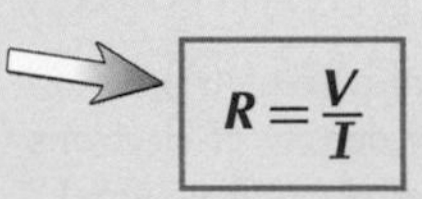

$$R = \frac{V}{I}$$

This is the **circuit symbol** for a resistor:

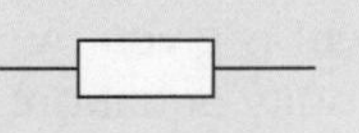

Learn this equation — you won't be given it in the exam.

4) **Resistance** is measured in **ohms** (Ω).

A component has a resistance of **1 Ω** if a **potential difference** of **1 V** makes a **current** of **1 A** flow through it.

Three Things Determine Resistance

If you think about a nice, **simple electrical component**, like a **length of wire**, its **resistance** depends on:

1) **Length** (L). The **longer** the wire the **more difficult** it is to make a **current flow**.
2) **Area** (A). The **wider** the wire the **easier** it will be for the electrons to pass along it.
3) **Resistivity** (ρ). This **depends** on the **material** the wire's made from, as the **structure** of the material may make it easy or difficult for charge to flow. In general, resistivity depends on **environmental factors** as well, like **temperature**.

ρ is the Greek letter rho, the symbol for resistivity.

The **resistivity** of a material is defined as the **resistance** of a **1 m length** with a **1 m² cross-sectional area**, so $\rho = \frac{RA}{L}$. Resistivity is measured in **ohm metres** (Ωm).

In your exams, you'll be given this equation in the **form**:

$$R = \frac{\rho L}{A}$$

where A = cross-sectional area in m², and L = length in m

Rho, rho, rho your boat...

Typical values for the **resistivity** of **conductors** are **really small**.
For example, the resistivity of **copper** (at 25 °C) is just 1.72×10^{-8} Ωm.
However, if you **calculate** a **resistance** for a **conductor** and end up with something **really small** (e.g. 1×10^{-7} Ω), go back and **check** that you've **converted** your **area** into **m²**.

For an Ohmic Conductor, *R* is a Constant

A chap called **Ohm** did most of the early work on resistance. He developed a rule to **predict** how the **current** would **change** as the applied **potential difference increased**, for **certain types** of conductor.
The rule is now called **Ohm's law** and the conductors that **obey** it (mostly metals) are called **ohmic conductors**.

Provided the **temperature** is **constant**, the **current** through an ohmic conductor is **directly proportional** to the **potential difference** across it (that's $V = IR$).

1) As you can see from the graph, **doubling** the **p.d. doubles** the **current**.
2) What this means is that the **resistance** is **constant**.
3) Often **external factors**, such as **temperature** will have a **significant effect** on resistance, so you need to remember that Ohm's law is **only** true for **ohmic conductors** at **constant temperature**.

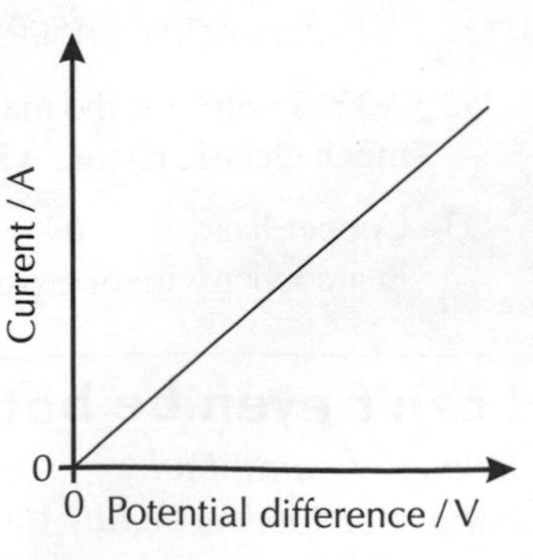

Resistance and Resistivity

To Find the Resistivity of a Wire You Need to Find its Resistance

Before you start, you need to know the **cross-sectional area** of your test wire. Assume that the wire is **cylindrical**, and so the cross-section is **circular**.

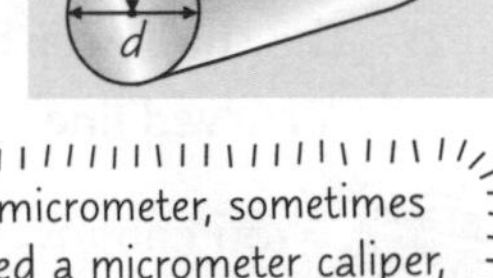

Then you can find its **cross-sectional area** using: **area of a circle = πr^2**

Use a **micrometer** to measure the **diameter** of the test wire in at least **three** different points along the wire. Take an **average** value of the diameter and divide by **2** to get the **radius** (make sure this is in m). Plug it into the equation for cross-sectional area and... **ta da**. Now you can get your teeth into the electricity bit...

A micrometer, sometimes called a micrometer caliper, is used to precisely measure very small distances.

1) The **test wire** should be **clamped** to a ruler and connected to the rest of the circuit at the point where the ruler reads zero.
2) Attach the **flying lead** to the test wire — the lead is just a wire with a crocodile clip at the end to allow connection to any point along the test wire.
3) Record the **length** of the test wire **connected** in the circuit, the **voltmeter reading** and the **ammeter reading**.
4) Use your readings to calculate the **resistance** of the length of wire, using: $R = \frac{V}{I}$
5) Repeat for several **different** lengths within a sensible range, e.g. at 0.10 m intervals from 0.10 m to 1.00 m.
6) Plot your results on a graph of **resistance** against **length**, and draw a **line of best fit** (see page 6).

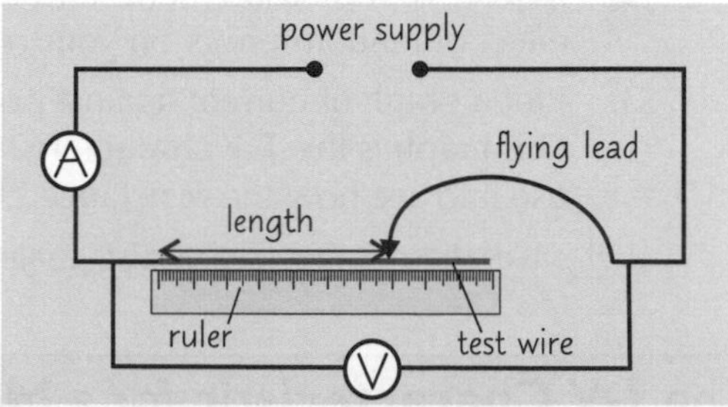

You could also use a digital multimeter, which can measure voltage, current and resistance.

The **gradient** of the line of best fit is equal to $\frac{R}{L} = \frac{\rho}{A}$. So **multiply** the **gradient** of the line of best fit by the **cross-sectional area** of the wire to find the resistivity of the wire material.

7) The **resistivity** of a material depends on its **temperature**, so you can only find the resistivity of a material **at a certain temperature**. Current flowing in the test wire can cause its temperature to increase, so failing to keep the wire at a **constant temperature** could invalidate your results (see p.4). Try to keep the temperature of the test wire constant by e.g. only having small currents flow through the wire.

Warm-Up Questions

Q1 Draw the circuit symbol for a resistor.
Q2 What are the three factors that determine the resistance of a length of wire?
Q3 What is special about an ohmic conductor?
Q4 Describe an experiment to find the resistivity of a metal.

Exam Questions

Q1 Aluminium has a resistivity of 2.8×10^{-8} Ω m at 20 °C.
Calculate the resistance of a pure aluminium wire of length 4 m and diameter 1 mm, at 20 °C. [3 marks]

Q2 The table on the right shows some measurements taken by a student during an experiment investigating an unknown electrical component.

Potential Difference (V)	3.00	7.00	11.00
Current (mA)	4.00	9.33	14.67

a) Calculate the resistance of the component when a p.d. of 7.00 V is applied. [1 mark]

b) State whether the component is an ohmic conductor. Explain your answer. [3 marks]

I find the resistivity to my chat-up lines is very high...

Examiners love to ask questions about this experiment, so make sure you learn it well. Make sure you can think of some ways to reduce random errors too — e.g. by repeating measurements and by using more sensitive equipment.

I-V Characteristics

Woohoo — real physics. This stuff's actually kind of interesting.

Make sure you learn all the circuit symbols that come up in this section, and know how to design and use circuits using them.

I-V Graphs Show How Resistance Varies

1) The term '***I-V* characteristic**' refers to a **graph** which shows how the **current** (*I*) flowing through a **component changes** as the **potential difference** (*V*) across it is increased.
2) The **shallower** the **gradient** of a characteristic ***I-V*** graph, the **greater** the **resistance** of the component.
3) A **curved line** shows that the resistance of the component **changes** with the potential difference across it.

You can investigate the *I-V* characteristic of a component using a **test circuit** like this one:

1) Use the **variable resistor** to alter the **potential difference** across the component and the **current** flowing through it, and record *V* and *I*.
2) **Repeat** your measurements and take **averages** to reduce the effect of random errors on your results.
3) **Plot a graph** of current against potential difference from your results. This graph is the ***I-V* characteristic** of the component and you can use it to see how the **resistance** changes.

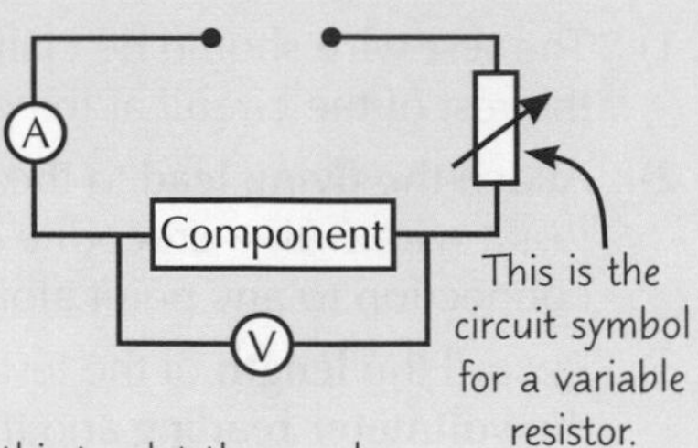

If you have access to a computer, you could enter your data into a spreadsheet and use this to plot the graph.

The *I-V* Characteristic for a Metallic Conductor is a Straight Line

1) At **constant temperature**, the **current** through a **metallic conductor**, e.g. a **wire** or a **resistor**, is **directly proportional** to the **potential difference**.
2) The fact that the characteristic graph is a **straight line through the origin** tells you that the **resistance doesn't change** — it's equal to 1 / gradient.
3) **Metallic conductors** are **ohmic** — they have **constant resistance provided** their temperature doesn't change (see below).

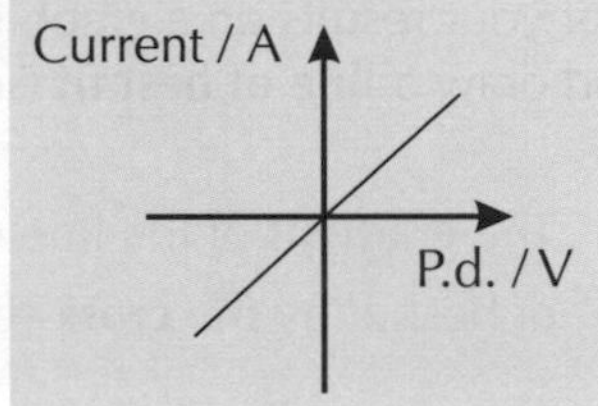

The *I-V* Characteristic for a Filament Lamp is Curved

Filament lamp circuit symbol:

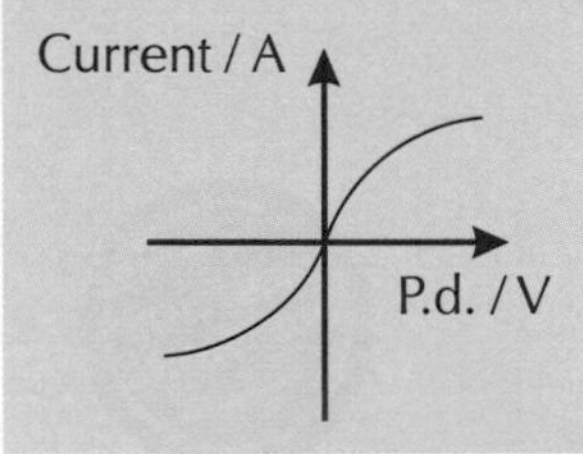

1) The characteristic graph for a **filament lamp** is a **curve**, which starts **steep** but gets **shallower** as the **potential difference rises**.
2) The **filament** in a lamp is just a **coiled up** length of **metal wire**, so you might think it should have the **same characteristic graph** as a **metallic conductor**.
3) However, **current** flowing through the lamp **increases** its **temperature**, so its **resistance increases** (see below).

The Resistivity of a Metal Increases with Temperature

1) **Charge** is carried through **metals** by **free electrons** in a **lattice** of **positive ions**.
2) Heating up a metal makes it **harder** for electrons to **move about**. The **ions vibrate more** when heated, so the electrons **collide** with them more often, **losing energy** to other forms.

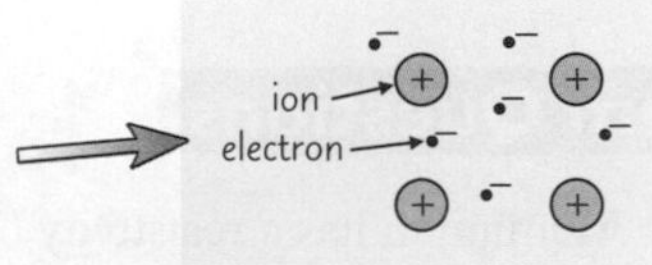

The **resistivity** of a **metal increases** as the **temperature increases**.

This means the resistance of a metal wire increases with temperature.

Semiconductors are Used in Sensors

Semiconductors have a **higher resistivity** than **metals** because there are fewer **charge carriers** available. However, if **energy** is supplied to some types of semiconductor (e.g. by increasing temperature), **more charge carriers** are **released**, so their resistivity **decreases**. This means that they make **excellent sensors** for detecting **changes** in their **environment**. You need to know about **three** semiconductor components — **thermistors**, **LDRs** and **diodes**.

I-V Characteristics

The **Resistance** of a **Thermistor** Depends on **Temperature**

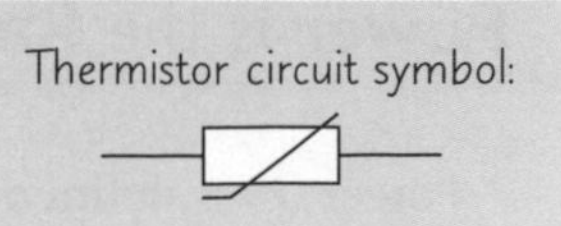

A **thermistor** is a **resistor** with a **resistance** that depends on its **temperature**. You only need to know about **NTC** thermistors — NTC stands for 'Negative Temperature Coefficient'. This means that the **resistance decreases** as the **temperature goes up**. The characteristic *I-V* graph for an NTC thermistor curves upwards.

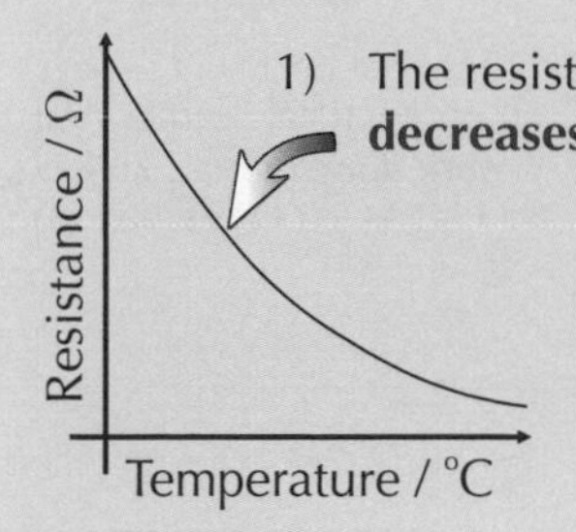

1) The resistance of an NTC thermistor **decreases** with **temperature**.

2) Increasing the **current** through the thermistor increases its **temperature**. The **increasing gradient** of this characteristic graph tells you that the **resistance is decreasing** as the thermistor heats up.

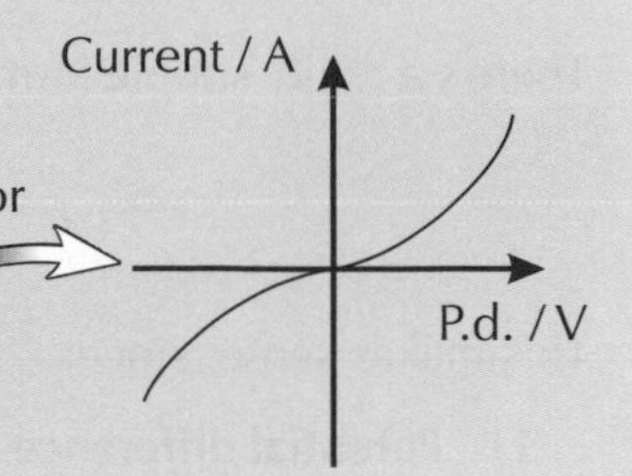

Warming the thermistor gives more **electrons** enough **energy** to **escape** from their atoms. This means that there are **more charge carriers** available, so the resistance is lower.

The **Resistance** of an **LDR** Depends on **Light Intensity**

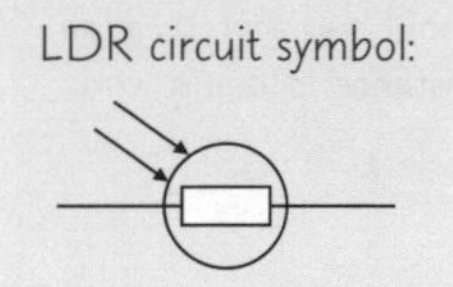

LDR stands for **Light-Dependent Resistor**. The **greater** the intensity of **light** shining on an LDR, the **lower** its **resistance**.

The explanation for this is similar to that for the thermistor. In this case, **light** provides the **energy** that releases more electrons. More charge carriers means a lower resistance.

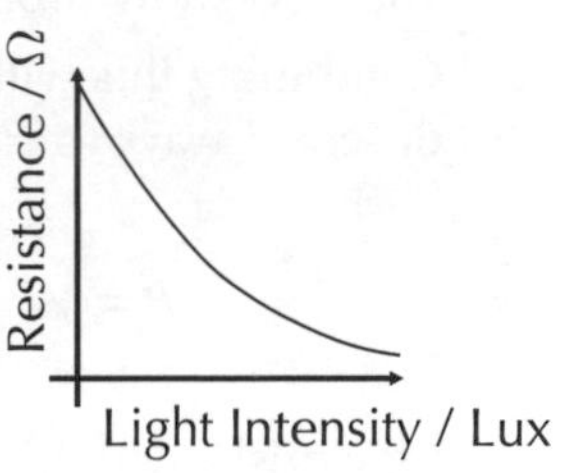

Diodes Only Let **Current Flow** in **One Direction**

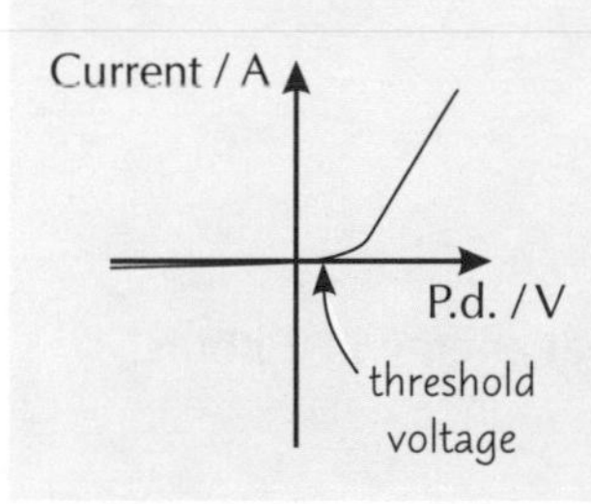

Diodes (including light emitting diodes (LEDs)) are designed to let **current flow** in **one direction** only. You don't need to be able to explain how they work, just what they do.

1) **Forward bias** is the **direction** in which the **current** is **allowed to flow** — it's the direction the triangle points in the circuit symbols on the right.
2) **Most** diodes require a **threshold voltage** of about **0.6 V** in the **forward direction** before they will conduct.
3) In **reverse bias**, the **resistance** of the diode is **very high** and the current that flows is **very tiny**.

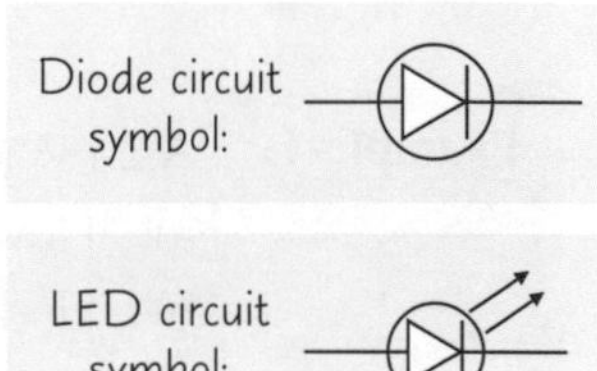

Warm-Up Questions

Q1 If an *I-V* graph is curved, what does this tell you about the resistance?

Q2 Sketch the test circuit used to investigate the *I-V* characteristic of a component, and explain how it is used.

Q3 Draw an *I-V* characteristic graph for a resistor.

Q4 What is an LDR?

Q5 Draw an *I-V* characteristic graph for a diode. Label the areas of forward bias and reverse bias.

Exam Question

Q1 a) Sketch a characteristic *I-V* graph for a filament lamp. [1 mark]

b) Compare your sketch to the *I-V* graph of a thermistor. Explain any differences. [4 marks]

You light up my world like an LED — with One-Directional current...

Make sure you learn all these graphs and can explain them all. It's all about energy — for metals, more energy means more heat and a higher resistance. For semiconductors, more energy means more charge carriers and lower resistance.

Electrical Energy and Power

Power and energy are pretty familiar concepts — and here they are again. Same principles, just different equations.

Power is the **Rate** of **Transfer** of **Energy**

Power (P) is **defined** as the **rate** of **doing work**. It's measured in **watts** (W), where **1 watt** is equivalent to **1 joule of work done per second**.

in symbols: $P = \frac{W}{t}$

In an electrical circuit, W is the work done moving a charge.

There's a really simple formula for **power** in **electrical circuits**:

$$P = VI$$

This makes sense, since:

1) **Potential difference** (V) is defined as the **work done** per **coulomb**.
2) **Current** (I) is defined as the **number** of **coulombs** transferred per **second**.
3) So **p.d.** × **current** is **work done per second**, i.e. **power**.

Arnold had a pretty high resistance to doing work.

You also know (from the definition of **resistance**) that $V = IR$ (see p.62). **Combining** this with the equation above gives you loads of **different ways** to **calculate power**.

$$P = VI \qquad P = \frac{V^2}{R} \qquad P = I^2R$$

Obviously, which equation you should use depends on what **quantities** you're given in the **question**.

Phew... that's quite a few equations to get acquainted with.
And as if they're not exciting enough, here are some examples to get your teeth into...

Example 1: A 24 W car head lamp is connected to a 12 V car battery.
a) How much electrical energy will the lamp convert into light and heat energy in 2 hours?
b) Find the total resistance of the lamp.

a) Number of seconds in 2 hours = 2 × 60 × 60 = 7200 s
$P = W \div t$, so $W = P \times t$ = 24 × 7200 = 172 800 J = **170 kJ (to 2 s.f.)**

b) $P = \frac{V^2}{R}$ so $R = \frac{V^2}{P} = \frac{12^2}{24} = \frac{144}{24} = \mathbf{6.0\ \Omega}$

Example 2: A robotic mutant Santa from the future converts 750 J of electrical energy into heat every second.
a) What is the operating power of the robotic mutant Santa?
b) All of the robotic mutant Santa's components are connected in series, with a total resistance of 30 Ω. What current flows through his wire veins?

a) Power = $W \div t$ = 750 ÷ 1 = **750 W**

b) $P = I^2R$ so $I = \sqrt{\frac{P}{R}} = \sqrt{\frac{750}{30}} = \sqrt{25} = \mathbf{5.0\ A}$

Electrical Energy and Power

Energy is Easy to Calculate if you Know the Power

Sometimes it's the **total energy** transferred that you're interested in. In this case you simply need to **multiply** the **power** by the **time**. So:

$$W = VIt \quad \left(\text{or } W = \frac{V^2}{R}t \text{ or } W = I^2Rt\right)$$

Make sure that the time is in seconds before you use this equation.

Example: The circuit diagram on the right is part of an electric kettle. A current of 4 A flows through the kettle's heating element once it is connected to the mains (230 V).
The kettle takes 4.5 minutes to boil the water it contains. How much energy does the kettle's heating element transfer to the water in the time it takes to boil?

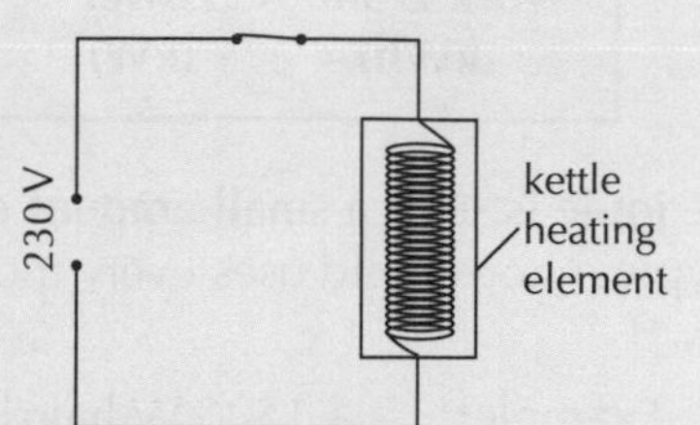

Time the kettle takes to boil in seconds = 4.5 × 60 = 270 seconds.

Use the equation $W = VIt$ = 230 × 4 × 270 = 248 400 J = **250 kJ (to 2 s.f.)**

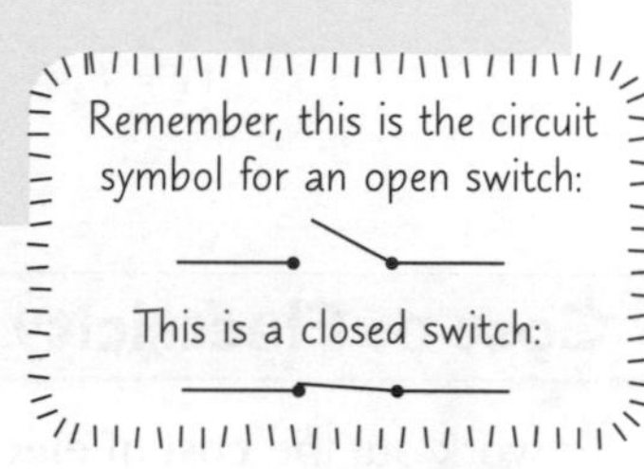

Warm-Up Questions

Q1 Power is measured in watts. What is 1 watt equivalent to?
Q2 What equation links power, voltage and resistance?
Q3 Write down the equation linking power, current and resistance.

Exam Questions

Q1 The circuit diagram for a mains-powered hairdryer is shown below.

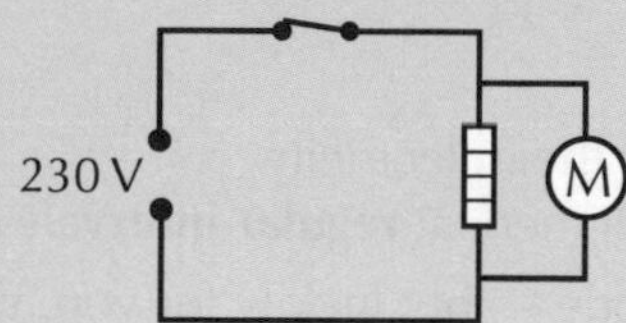

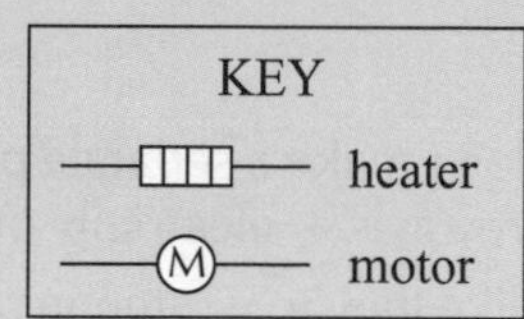

a) The heater has a power of 920 W in normal operation. Calculate the current in the heater. [1 mark]

b) The motor's resistance is 190 Ω. Calculate the current through the motor when the hairdryer is used. [1 mark]

c) Show that the total power of the hairdryer in normal operation is just under 1.2 kW. [2 marks]

Q2 A 12 V car battery supplies a current of 48 A for 2.0 seconds to the car's starter motor.
The total resistance of the connecting wires is 0.01 Ω.

a) Calculate the energy transferred by the battery in this time. [1 mark]

b) Calculate the energy wasted as heat in the wires. [1 mark]

Ultimate cosmic powers...

Another load of equations on these pages to add to your collection, oh joy. I used to find it helped to stick big lists of equations all over my walls in the run up to exams — the least cool wallpaper imaginable. Make sure you learn the circuit symbol for a heater in exam question 1 — you won't get a key in the exam (I gave you one because I'm nice).

Domestic Energy and Energy Saving

If you went into an electricity shop and asked for a 100 joule packet of electricity you'd be laughed out of town. Why? Because electricity companies use kilowatt-hours, not joules — phew, you kids don't know anything these days.

Electricity Companies Don't Use **Joules** and **Watts**

Electricity companies charge their customers for '**units**' of electricity. Another name for a unit is a **kilowatt-hour (kWh)**. If you know the **power** of an **appliance** and the **length of time** it's used for you can calculate the **work** it does in kWh.

Remember, power is the work done per second: $P = W/t$ (see page 66).

Work Done (kWh) = Power (kW) × Time (h)

1 kWh = 3.6 million joules

1 kW = 1000 W
1 hour = 3600 seconds

The **joule** is such a **small amount** of energy compared with the amount a typical household uses every month that it's **impractical**.

Example: A 1500 W hairdryer is on for 10 minutes. How much energy does it use in J and kWh?

$W = Pt = 1500 \times 10 \times 60 =$ **900 000 J (to 2 s.f.)** $W = Pt = 1.5 \times 10/60 =$ **0.25 kWh (to 2 s.f.)**

Cost of Electricity is the **Price per Unit** Times the **Number of Units** Used

To work out the **cost of electricity** you need to know **how much you've used** (in **units**) and the **price of each unit**. Then it's a simple matter of **multiplying** these two numbers together:

Cost = No. of units × Price per unit

Example: How much does it cost to use an 800 W microwave oven for 6 minutes? Electricity costs 16.1p per unit.

$W = Pt = 0.8 \times 6/60 = 0.08$ kWh

Cost = units × price per unit = 0.08 × 16.1
= 1.288 = **1.3p (to 2 s.f.)**

Watch out for the units — you need power in kW (not watts), time in hours (not minutes or seconds) and money in either pence or pounds.

Of course, most people don't make a separate payment for their electricity each time they use a microwave — electricity providers bill them at **regular intervals** instead.

Electricity bills can look like they're written in a strange code — but luckily for you, the examples you'll see are easy to understand. Real ones aren't really that bad either — you just need to know **where to look** to find the **important information**. Take a look at the lovely **example** below:

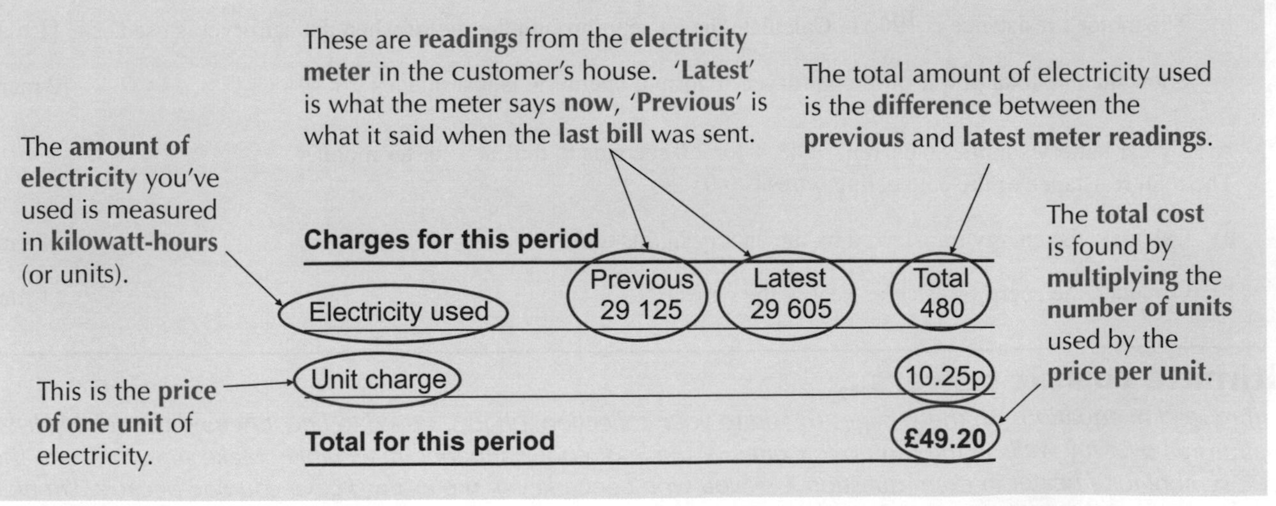

Domestic Energy and Energy Saving

It's **Important** to **Save Energy**

Electricity doesn't just cost a packet — producing it has **environmental impacts** too:

- Burning **fossil fuels** (**coal**, **oil** and **gas**) releases **carbon dioxide** into the atmosphere, which adds to the **greenhouse effect** and contributes to **global warming**. Sulfur dioxide released by burning oil and coal can also cause **acid rain**.
- **Nuclear** power stations produce **radioactive waste**, which can be **dangerous** to the environment and human health if it isn't **disposed of safely**.
- Even **renewable** energy sources like **biofuels** have an impact because lots of **land** is needed to produce them.

Using **energy saving devices** can not only save you **money**, but helps to **reduce these impacts**.

1) **Energy saving** (fluorescent) **light bulbs** are more expensive than **traditional filament bulbs**, but are about four times more **efficient**. They also last for about **ten years** (as opposed to a year for filament bulbs) so reduce the environmental impact of sending used bulbs to **landfill**, and of making **replacement bulbs**.
2) **LED light bulbs** are even **more efficient** than energy saving bulbs, and last even longer, but they **cost more**.
3) **Domestic appliances** (e.g. washing machines and ovens) sold in the UK all have an **energy rating**. This helps customers choose the appliance that's **most efficient to run**, which can reduce their **environmental impact**.

Remember, efficiency is given by:

$$\text{efficiency} = \frac{\text{useful output energy}}{\text{total input energy}} \times 100$$

Warm-Up Questions

Q1 Why aren't joules used on electricity bills? What is used instead?

Q2 What equation would you use to find the cost of using an electrical appliance for a given amount of time?

Q3 Why is it important to think about energy efficiency when you buy domestic appliances?

Q4 Compare filament, energy saving and LED bulbs in terms of their environmental impact.

PRACTICE QUESTIONS

Exam Questions

Q1 A vacuum cleaner has a power of 1550 W.

a) Calculate the energy transferred when the vacuum cleaner is operated for 15 minutes. Give your answer in:

i) joules, [1 mark]

ii) kilowatt-hours. [1 mark]

b) Calculate the cost of using the vacuum cleaner for 15 minutes.
Electricity costs 15.9 pence per unit. [1 mark]

Q2 A television is connected to a 230 V power supply. Electricity costs 16.2 pence per unit.
When the television is in standby mode, it draws a current of 6.5 mA.
Calculate the cost of leaving the television on standby for 10 hours. [3 marks]

Q3 A customer is buying a washing machine. Model A has an average power of 470 W on a typical cycle, and model B has an average power of 410 W. Model A takes 135 minutes to wash a load of laundry, and model B takes 125 minutes.

a) Calculate how many kilowatt-hours each model uses in a typical cycle. [2 marks]

b) The customer does two loads of laundry a week on a typical cycle. Electricity costs 16.2p per unit.
Calculate how much each model of washing machine would cost him a year to run. [4 marks]

It's suddenly all got very serious, hasn't it...

Paying bills and being a responsible consumer? Bring back the circuit diagrams, I say. It's important that you learn this stuff though, as it'll not only save you money and make you a better person, but crucially it might also help you pass your exams. So turn on your energy saving lamp and give these pages another read.

E.m.f. and Internal Resistance

There's resistance everywhere — inside batteries, in all the wires (although it's very small) and in the circuit components themselves. Who said current had it easy?

Batteries have an **Internal Resistance**

Because the resistance of wires is so small, on these two pages I'm assuming they have zero resistance.

Resistance comes from **electrons colliding** with **atoms** and **losing energy**.

In a **battery**, **chemical energy** is used to make **electrons move**. As they move, they collide with atoms inside the battery — so batteries **must** have resistance. This is called **internal resistance**.

Internal resistance is what makes **batteries** and **cells warm up** when they're used.

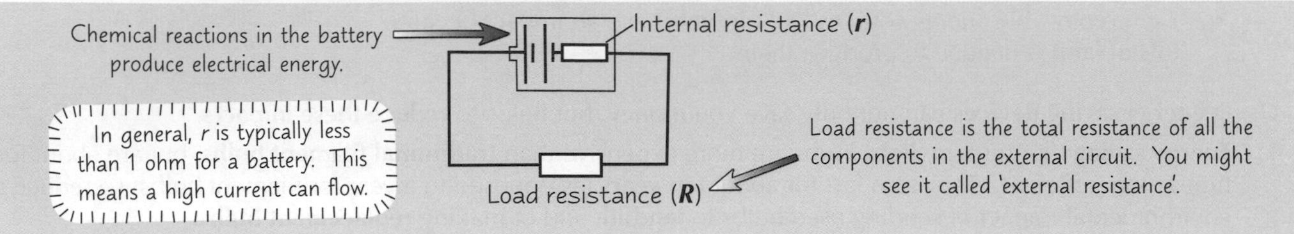

1) The total amount of **work** the battery does on each **coulomb** of charge is called its **electromotive force** or **e.m.f.** (ε). Be careful — e.m.f. **isn't** actually a force. It's measured in **volts**.

$$W = \varepsilon Q \quad \text{or} \quad \varepsilon = \frac{W}{Q}$$

W is the work done on the charge (i.e. the energy transferred to the charge) in joules.

2) The **potential difference** across the **load resistance** (***R***) is the **work done** when **one coulomb** of charge flows through the **load resistance**. This potential difference is called the **terminal p.d.** (***V***).
3) If there was **no internal resistance**, the **terminal p.d.** would be the **same** as the **e.m.f.** However, in **real** power supplies, there's **always some energy lost** overcoming the internal resistance.
4) The **energy wasted per coulomb** overcoming the internal resistance is called the **lost volts** (***v***).

Conservation of energy tells us:

energy per coulomb supplied by the source = **energy per coulomb used in load resistance** + **energy per coulomb wasted in internal resistance**

There are Loads of **Calculations** with **E.m.f.** and **Internal Resistance**

Examiners can ask you to do **calculations** with **e.m.f.** and **internal resistance** in loads of **different** ways. You've got to be ready for whatever they throw at you.

$$\varepsilon = V + v \qquad \varepsilon = I(R + r)$$
$$V = \varepsilon - v \qquad \varepsilon = V + Ir$$

Learn all of these equations for the exam. Only these two will be on your formula sheet.

These are all basically the **same equation**, just written differently. If you're given enough information you can calculate the e.m.f. (ε), terminal p.d. (***V***), lost volts (***v***), current (***I***), load resistance (***R***) or internal resistance (***r***). Which equation you should use depends on what information you've got, and what you need to calculate.

You Can Work Out the **E.m.f.** of **Multiple** Cells in **Series** or **Parallel**

For cells **in series**, you can calculate the **total e.m.f.** of the cells by **adding** their individual e.m.f.s.

$$\varepsilon_{total} = \varepsilon_1 + \varepsilon_2 + \varepsilon_3 + ...$$

This makes sense if you think about it, because each charge goes through each of the cells and so gains e.m.f. from each one.

See p.72 for all the rules for parallel and series circuits.

For identical cells **in parallel**, the **total e.m.f.** of the combination of cells is the **same size** as the e.m.f. of each of the individual cells.

$$\varepsilon_{total} = \varepsilon_1 = \varepsilon_2 = \varepsilon_3 = ...$$

This is because the current will split equally between identical cells. The charge only gains e.m.f. from the cells it travels through — so the overall e.m.f. in the circuit doesn't increase.

E.m.f. and Internal Resistance

Time for an Example E.m.f. Calculation Question...

Example Three identical cells each with an e.m.f. of 2.0 V and an internal resistance of 0.20 Ω are connected in parallel in the circuit shown to the right. A current of 0.90 A is flowing through the circuit. Calculate the total p.d. across the cells.

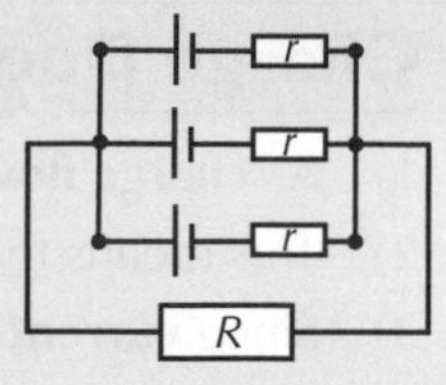

First calculate the lost volts, v, for 1 cell using $v = Ir$.

Since the current flowing through the circuit is split equally between each of the three cells, the current through one cell is $I/3$. So for 1 cell: $v = I/3 \times r = 0.90/3 \times 0.20 = 0.30 \times 0.20 = 0.06$ V

Then find the terminal p.d. across 1 cell using the equation: $V = \varepsilon - v = 2 - 0.06 = 1.94$

So the total p.d. across the cells combined = 1.94 = **1.9 V (to 2 s.f.)**

Investigate Internal Resistance and E.m.f. With This Circuit

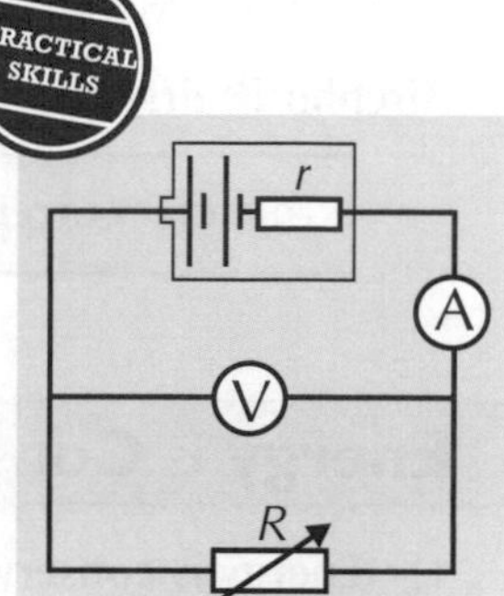

1) **Vary** the **current** in the circuit by changing the value of the **load resistance** (***R***) using the variable resistor. **Measure** the **p.d.** (*V*) for several different values of **current** (***I***).
2) Record your data for V and I in a table, and **plot the results** in a graph of V against I.

To find the **e.m.f.** and **internal resistance** of the cell, start with the equation: $\boldsymbol{\varepsilon = V + Ir}$

1) Rearrange to give $\boldsymbol{V = -rI + \varepsilon}$
2) Since $\boldsymbol{\varepsilon}$ and $\boldsymbol{r}$ are constants, that's just the equation of a **straight line**:

Equation of a straight line
$y = mx + c$
gradient, y-intercept

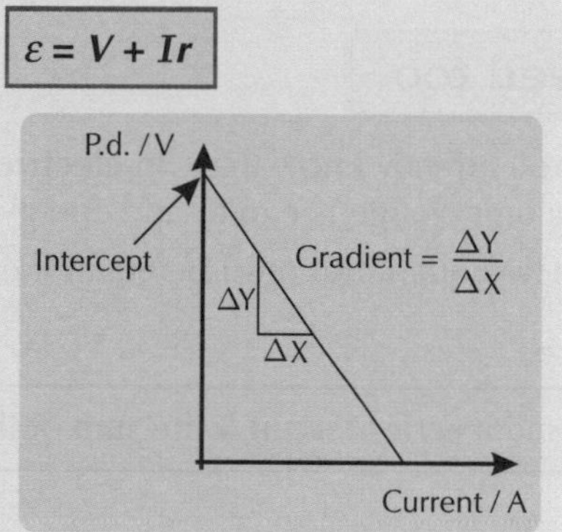

3) So the intercept on the vertical axis is ε.
4) And the gradient is $\boldsymbol{-r}$.

Geoff didn't quite calculate the gradient correctly.

An **easier** way to **measure** the **e.m.f.** of a **power source** to just connect a **voltmeter** across its **terminals**. Voltmeters have a very **high resistance**, but a **small current** will still flow through them, so there must be some **lost volts**, which means you measure a value **very slightly less** than the **e.m.f.** (Although in practice the difference isn't usually significant.)

Warm-Up Questions

Q1 What causes internal resistance? Write down the equation linking work, e.m.f. and charge.

Q2 What is the difference between e.m.f. and terminal p.d.?

Q3 What is meant by 'lost volts'?

Q4 Give an example of a source of e.m.f and describe an experiment to find the value of its e.m.f.

Exam Questions

Q1 A battery with an internal resistance of 0.8 Ω and an e.m.f. of 24 V powers a dentist's drill with resistance 4.0 Ω.

a) Calculate the current in the circuit when the drill is connected to the power supply. [1 mark]

b) Calculate the voltage across the drill while it is being used. [1 mark]

Q2 A bulb of resistance R is powered by two cells connected in series, each with internal resistance r and e.m.f. ε. Which expression represents the current flowing through each cell? [1 mark]

A $\frac{\varepsilon}{R+r}$ **B** $\frac{\varepsilon}{2(R+2r)}$ **C** $\frac{2\varepsilon}{R+2r}$ **D** $\frac{\varepsilon}{R+2r}$

Why'd the physicist swallow a multimeter? To find his internal resistance...

Thank you, thank you, I'm here all week. A jam-packed pair of pages here, but it's all stuff you need to know. Make sure you know the difference between terminal p.d. and e.m.f., and that you've got a handle on all those equations.

Conservation of Charge & Energy in Circuits

There are some things in Physics that are so fundamental that you just have to accept them. Like the fact that there's loads of Maths in it. And that energy is conserved. And that Physicists get more homework than everyone else.

Charge Doesn't 'Leak Away' Anywhere — it's Conserved

1) As **charge flows** through a circuit, it **doesn't** get **used up** or **lost**.
2) This means that whatever charge flows **into** a junction will flow **out** again.
3) Since **current** is **rate of flow of charge**, it follows that whatever current flows **into** a junction is the same as the current flowing **out** of it.

Example: 6 coulombs of charge flow into a junction in 1 second, and split in the ratio 1:2.

$Q_1 = 6\text{ C} \Rightarrow I_1 = 6\text{ A}$ → at junction, current branches in two → $Q_2 = 2\text{ C} \Rightarrow I_2 = 2\text{ A}$ and $Q_3 = 4\text{ C} \Rightarrow I_3 = 4\text{ A}$

$I_1 = I_2 + I_3$

Kirchhoff's first law says:

> The total **current entering a junction** = the total **current leaving it.**

Betsy believed in conservation of charge.

Energy is Conserved too

1) **Energy is conserved**. You already know that. In **electrical circuits**, **energy** is **transferred round** the circuit. Energy **transferred to** a unit charge is **e.m.f.**, and energy **transferred from** a unit charge is **potential difference**.
2) In a **closed loop**, these two quantities must be **equal** if energy is conserved (which it is).

Kirchhoff's second law says:

> The **total e.m.f.** around a **series circuit** = the **sum** of the **p.d.**s across each component.

(or $\varepsilon = \Sigma IR$ in symbols)

You Can Apply Kirchhoff's Laws to Different Combinations of Resistors

A **typical exam question** will give you a **circuit** with bits of information missing, leaving you to fill in the gaps. Not the most fun... but on the plus side you get to ignore any internal resistance stuff (unless the question tells you otherwise)... hurrah. You need to remember the **following rules**:

Series Circuits:

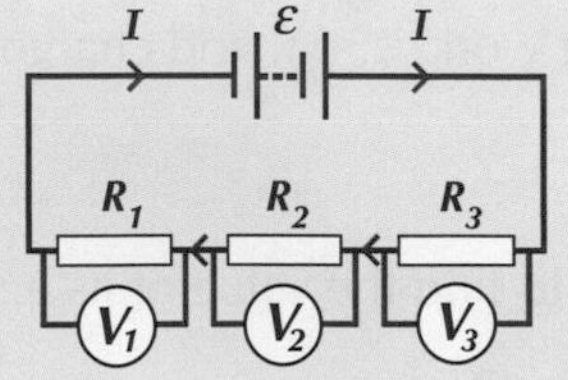

1) **same current** at **all points** of the circuit (since there are no junctions)
2) **e.m.f. split** between **components** (by Kirchhoff's 2nd law), so: $\varepsilon = V_1 + V_2 + V_3$
3) $V = IR$, so if I is constant: $IR_{total} = IR_1 + IR_2 + IR_3$
4) cancelling the Is gives:

$$R_{total} = R_1 + R_2 + R_3$$

Parallel Circuits:

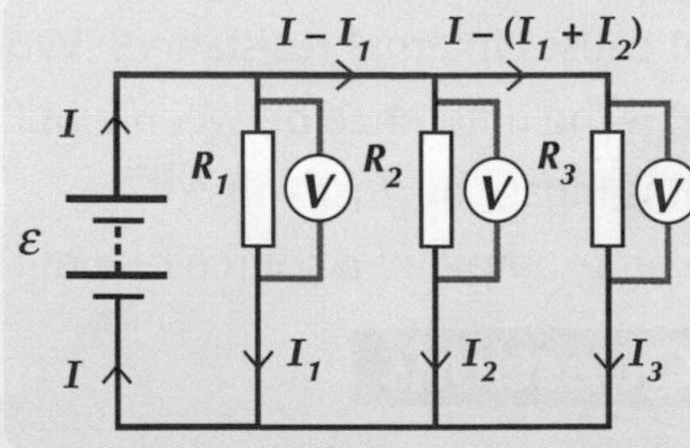

1) **current** is **split** at each **junction**, so: $I = I_1 + I_2 + I_3$
2) **same p.d.** across **all components** (remember that within a loop the e.m.f. equals the sum of individual p.d.s)
3) so, $V/R_{total} = V/R_1 + V/R_2 + V/R_3$
4) cancelling the Vs gives:

$$\frac{1}{R_{total}} = \frac{1}{R_1} + \frac{1}{R_2} + \frac{1}{R_3}$$

...and there's an example on the next page to make sure you know what to do with all that...

Conservation of Charge & Energy in Circuits

Worked Exam Question

Example:

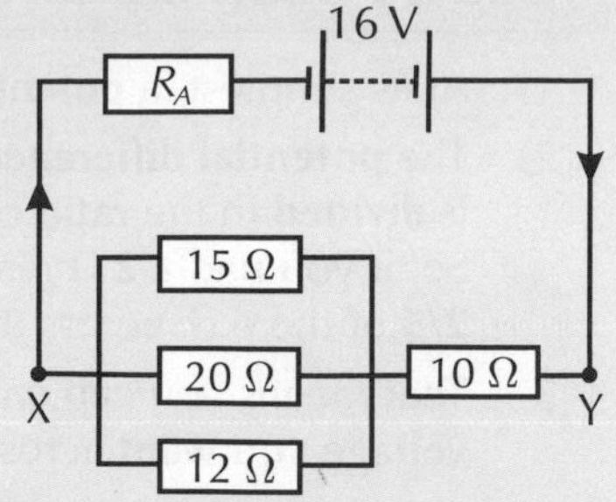

A battery with an e.m.f. of 16 V and negligible internal resistance is connected in a circuit as shown on the right.

a) Show that the group of resistors between X and Y could be replaced by a single resistor of resistance 15 Ω.

You can find the combined resistance of the 15 Ω, 20 Ω and 12 Ω resistors using:
$1/R = 1/R_1 + 1/R_2 + 1/R_3 = 1/15 + 1/20 + 1/12 = 1/5 \Rightarrow R = 5\ \Omega$
So overall resistance between X and Y can be found by: $R = R_1 + R_2 = 5 + 10 =$ **15 Ω**

b) If $R_A = 20\ \Omega$:
i) calculate the potential difference across R_A,

Careful — there are a few steps here. You need the p.d. across R_A, but you don't know the current through it. So start there: total resistance in circuit = 20 + 15 = 35 Ω,
so current through R_A can be found using $I = V_{total}/R_{total} = 16/35$ A
then you can use $V = IR_A$ to find the p.d. across R_A: $V = 16/35 \times 20 =$ **9.1 V (to 2 s.f.)**

ii) calculate the current in the 15 Ω resistor.

You know the current flowing into the group of three resistors and out of it, but not through the individual branches. But you know that their combined resistance is 5 Ω from part a), so you can work out the p.d. across the group:
$V = IR = 16/35 \times 5 = 16/7$ V
The p.d. across the whole group is the same as the p.d. across each individual resistor, so you can use this to find the current through the 15 Ω resistor:
$I = V/R = (16/7) / 15 =$ **0.15 A (to 2 s.f.)**

Warm-Up Questions

Q1 State Kirchhoff's first and second laws.

Q2 Find the current through and potential difference across each of two 5 Ω resistors when they are placed in a circuit containing a 5 V battery, and are wired: a) in series, b) in parallel.

Exam Question

Q1 For the circuit on the right:

a) Calculate the total effective resistance of the three resistors in this combination. [2 marks]

b) Calculate the main current, I_3. [1 mark]

c) Calculate the potential difference across the 4 Ω resistor. [1 mark]

d) Calculate the potential difference across the parallel pair of resistors. [1 mark]

e) Calculate the currents I_1 and I_2. [2 marks]

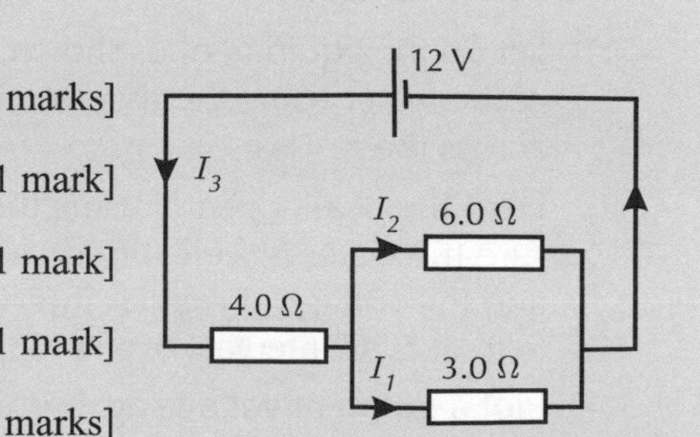

Conservation of energy is really important — time for a nap I think...

V = IR is the formula you'll use most often in these questions. Make sure you know whether you're using it on the overall circuit, or just one specific component. It's amazingly easy to get muddled up — you've been warned.

The Potential Divider

It's probably best not to bring up this topic when you're having dinner with your in-laws — it's potentially quite divisive.

Use a **Potential Divider** to Get a **Fraction** of an **Input Voltage**

1) At its simplest, a **potential divider** is a circuit with a **voltage source** and a couple of **resistors** in series.
2) The **potential difference** of the voltage source (e.g. a power supply) is **divided** in the **ratio** of the **resistances**. As an equation: $\frac{V_1}{V_2} = \frac{R_1}{R_2}$
   So, if you had a **2 Ω** resistor and a **3 Ω** resistor, you'd get **2/5** of the p.d. across the **2 Ω** resistor and **3/5** across the **3 Ω**.
3) That means you can **choose** the **resistances** to get the **voltage** you **want** across one of them.

This rearranges to give $V_1/R_1 = V_2/R_2$. As $I = V/R$ this just means the current is the same through both resistors, which you know from page 72.

In the circuit shown, R_2 has $\frac{R_2}{R_1 + R_2}$ of the total resistance.

So:

$$V_{out} = \frac{R_2}{R_1 + R_2} V_{in}$$

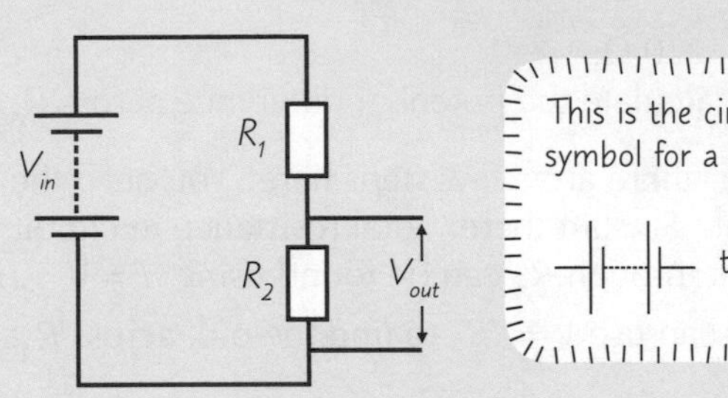

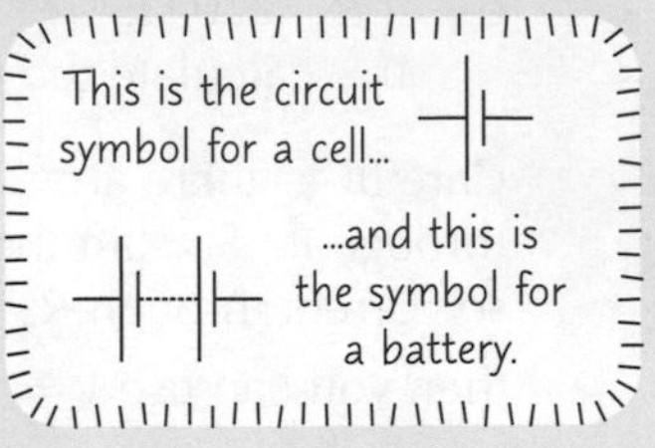

E.g. if V_{in} = 9 V and you want V_{out} to be 6 V,

then you need: $\frac{R_2}{R_1 + R_2} = \frac{6}{9}$ which gives $R_2 = 2R_1$.

So you could have, say, R_1 **= 100 Ω,** R_2 **= 200 Ω**

4) This circuit can be used for **calibrating voltmeters**, which have a **very high resistance**.
5) If you put something with a **relatively low resistance** across R_2 though, you start to run into **problems**. You've **effectively** got **two resistors** in **parallel**, which will **always** have a **total** resistance **less** than R_2. That means that V_{out} will be **less** than you've calculated, and will depend on what's connected across R_2. Hrrumph.

Add an **LDR** or **Thermistor** for a **Light** or **Temperature Sensor**

1) You can make a potential divider using a **light-dependent resistor** (LDR) or a **thermistor** (see page 65).
2) An **LDR** has a very **high resistance** in the **dark**, but a **lower resistance** in the **light**.
3) An **NTC thermistor** has a **high resistance** at **low temperatures**, but a much **lower resistance** at **high temperatures** (it varies in the opposite way to a normal resistor, only much more so).
4) This means V_{out} **varies** with light or heat, so you can make a potential divider that works as a light or heat **sensor**.

Here's a potential divider using an **NTC thermistor**.

Think about safety before you start. Keep the rest of the circuit as far away from the bunsen burner and the water bath as possible and make sure you waterproof the thermistor, e.g. by wrapping it in polythene.

You can investigate this circuit using the equipment shown on the right:

1) Set up the equipment as shown, then measure the **temperature** of the water using the **thermometer**, and record the **voltage** across the resistor.
2) **Heat** the beaker **gently** using the Bunsen burner (make sure the water is well-stirred), and record the temperature and the voltage at **regular intervals** over a **suitable range** (e.g. at 5 °C intervals over a range of 0-100 °C).
3) Plot a **graph** of voltage against temperature from your results.

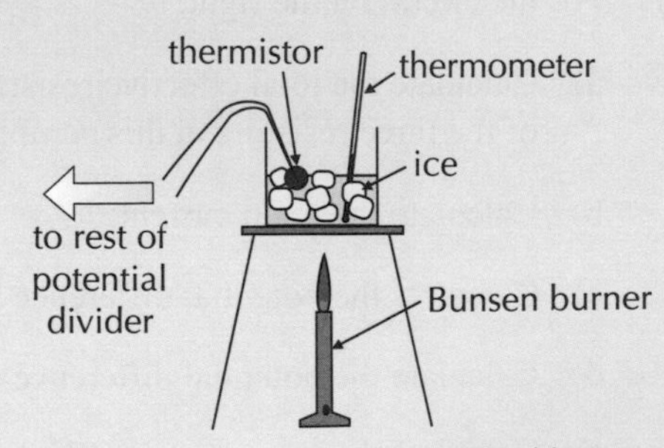

This kind of circuit could form the basis of a digital thermometer (the graph of voltage against temperature would be the thermometer's **calibration curve**), or could form part of the circuit for a thermostat in a central heating system.

Pick your fixed resistor carefully — if its resistance is too high, V_{out} won't vary enough with temperature, and if it's too low V_{out} might vary over a bigger range than your voltmeter can handle.

The Potential Divider

A **Potentiometer** Uses a **Variable Resistor** to Give a **Variable Voltage**

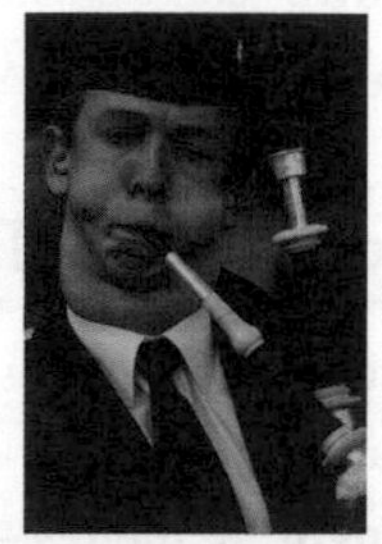

1) A **potentiometer** has a **variable resistor** replacing R_1 and R_2 of the potential divider, but it uses the **same idea** (it's even sometimes **called** a potential divider just to confuse things).
2) You move a **slider** or turn a knob to **adjust** the **relative sizes** of R_1 and R_2. That way you can vary V_{out} from 0 V up to the input voltage, V_{in}.
3) This is dead handy when you want to be able to **change** a **voltage continuously**, like in the **volume control** of a stereo.

Here, V_{in} is replaced by the input signal (e.g. from a CD player) and V_{out} is the output to the amplifier and loudspeaker.

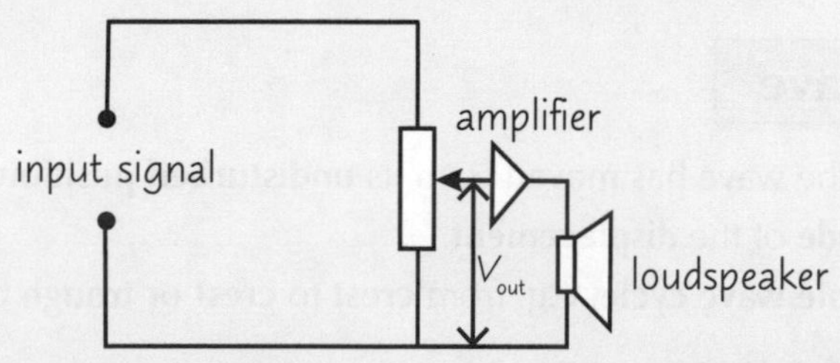

I've often wished bagpipes had a volume control. Or just an off switch.

Warm-Up Questions

PRACTICE QUESTIONS

Q1 Write down the equation linking output p.d., input p.d., and component resistance for a potential divider circuit.

Q2 Draw the circuit diagram for a potential divider that works as a light sensor, where the output p.d. increases when the light level increases.
How could you change the circuit so that the output p.d. decreases when the light level increases?

Q3 What is a potentiometer?

Exam Questions

Q1 Two resistors, A and B, are connected in series as shown in the circuit diagram.
Resistor A has a resistance of 35 Ω and resistor B has a resistance of 45 Ω.

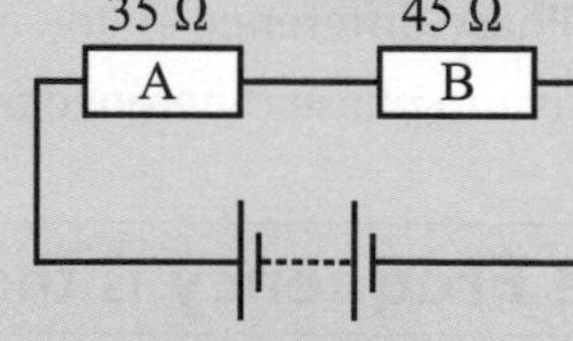

a) Given that the potential difference across resistor B is 6.75 V, calculate the potential difference across resistor A. [1 mark]

b) Calculate the input p.d. supplied by the battery. [1 mark]

c) Resistor A is removed, and replaced with a 75 Ω resistor. Calculate the new potential difference across resistor B. [1 mark]

Q2 Look at the circuit on the right.

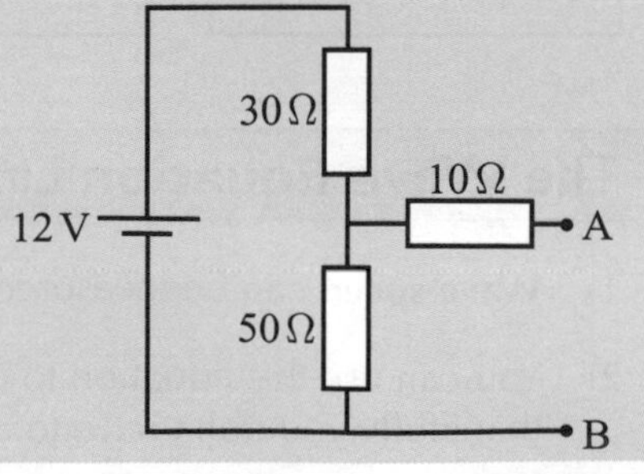

a) Calculate the p.d. between A and B as shown by a high resistance voltmeter placed between the two points. [1 mark]

b) A 40 Ω resistor is now placed between points A and B. Calculate the p.d. across AB and the current flowing through the 40 Ω resistor. [4 marks]

OI...YOU... [bang bang bang]... turn that potentiometer down...

Potentiometers come up a lot in experiments to do with electricity, so like them or not, you'd better get used to them. I can't stand the things myself, but then lab and me don't mix — it's all far too technical I'm afraid.

Wave Basics

Aaaah... waggling ropes about. It's all good clean fun as my mate Richard used to say...

A **Wave** Transfers **Energy** Away From Its **Source**

A **progressive** (moving) wave carries **energy** from one place to another **without transferring any material**. The transfer of energy is in the **same direction** as the wave is **travelling**. Here are some ways you can tell waves carry energy:

1) Electromagnetic waves cause things to **heat up**.
2) **X-rays** and **gamma rays** knock electrons out of their orbits, causing **ionisation**.
3) Loud **sounds** cause large oscillations in air particles which can make things **vibrate**.
4) **Wave power** can be used to **generate electricity**.

Since waves carry energy away, the **source** of the wave **loses energy**.

You Need to Know These **Bits** of a **Wave**

1) **Displacement**, ***x***, metres — how far a **point** on the wave has **moved** from its **undisturbed position**.
2) **Amplitude**, ***A***, metres — the **maximum magnitude** of the **displacement**.
3) **Wavelength**, **λ**, metres — the **length** of **one whole wave cycle**, e.g. from **crest** to **crest** or **trough** to **trough**.

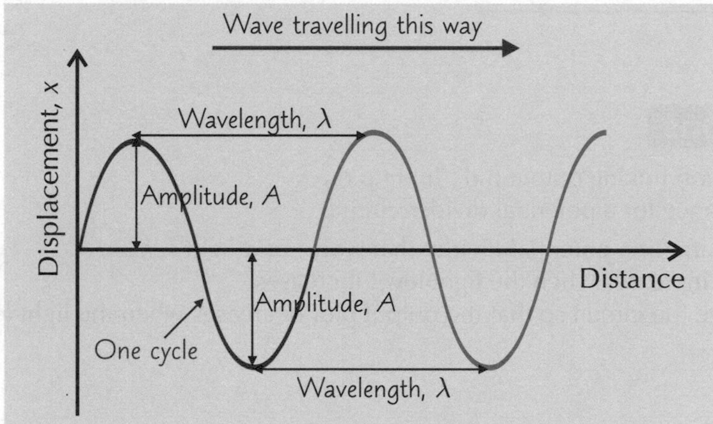

4) **Period**, ***T***, seconds — the **time taken** for a **whole cycle** (vibration) to complete.
5) **Frequency**, ***f***, hertz — the **number** of **cycles** (vibrations) **per second** passing a given **point**.
6) **Phase** — a measurement of the **position** of a certain **point** along the wave cycle.
7) **Phase difference** — the amount one wave lags behind another.

Phase and phase difference are measured in angles (in degrees or radians). See p.86.

The **Frequency** is the **Inverse** of the **Period**

$$\textbf{Frequency} = \frac{\textbf{1}}{\textbf{Period}} \qquad f = \frac{1}{T}$$

It's that simple.
Get the **units** straight: **1 Hz = 1 s^{-1}**.

The **Wave Equation** Links **Wave Speed, Frequency** and **Wavelength**

1) **Wave speed** can be measured just like the speed of anything else:

$$\textbf{Wave speed } (v) = \frac{\textbf{Distance } (d)}{\textbf{Time } (t)}$$

2) You can use this equation to derive the **wave equation** (but thankfully you don't have to do that, you just need to be able to use it).

$$\textbf{Speed of wave } (v) = \textbf{frequency } (f) \times \textbf{wavelength } (\lambda) \qquad v = f\lambda$$

Remember, you're not measuring how fast a physical point (like one molecule of rope) moves. You're measuring how fast a point on the the **wave pattern** moves.

Wave Basics

Oscilloscopes Display Waves

PRACTICAL SKILLS

1) A cathode ray **oscilloscope** (CRO) measures **voltage**. It **displays** waves from a **signal generator** as a function of **voltage** over **time**.
2) The displayed wave is called a **trace**.
3) The screen is split into squares called **divisions**.
4) The vertical axis is in **volts**. The **volts per division** shown on this axis is controlled by the **gain dial**.
5) The horizontal axis is in **seconds** — also called the **timebase**. The **seconds per division** shown on this axis is controlled by the **timebase** dial.
6) You can alter the gain and timebase to make it **easy to read** off measurements.

Screen split into divisions

Gain dial in volts/div

Timebase dial in ms/div

You Get Different **Traces** Depending on the **Source**

1) If you plug an **AC** (**alternating**) **supply** into an oscilloscope, you get a trace that goes up and down in a regular pattern — some of the time it's positive and some of the time it's negative.
2) A **microphone** converts **sound waves** into **electrical signals** which can be seen on an **oscilloscope**.

You Can Find Wave **Frequency** Using an **Oscilloscope**

Example: Find the frequency shown by the oscilloscope trace on the right. The timebase is set to 4.0 ms / div.

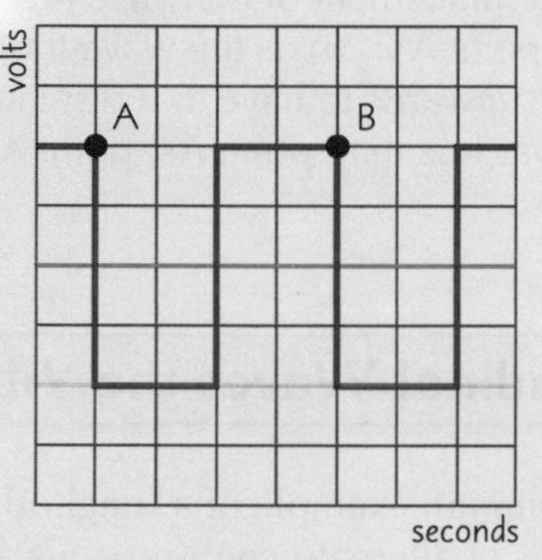

First calculate the period of the wave.
Point A to B is one cycle — which is **4** squares wide.

This means for one cycle it takes 4 × 4.0 ms = 16 ms.
So, the period T = **16 ms**.
Now, use $f = \frac{1}{T}$ to find the frequency:

$$f = \frac{1}{16 \times 10^{-3}} = \mathbf{62.5\,Hz = 63\,Hz\ (to\ 2\ s.f.)}$$

Warm-Up Questions

Q1 Does a wave carry matter **or** energy from one place to another?

Q2 Give the units of frequency, displacement and amplitude.

Q3 Write down the wave equation.

Q4 What settings could you alter to make an oscilloscope wave trace easier to measure?

Exam Question

Q1 An oscilloscope has the gain set to 2.0 volts/div and a timebase set to 3.0 ms/div. It is displaying the trace of a wave that has a wave speed of 280 ms^{-1}.

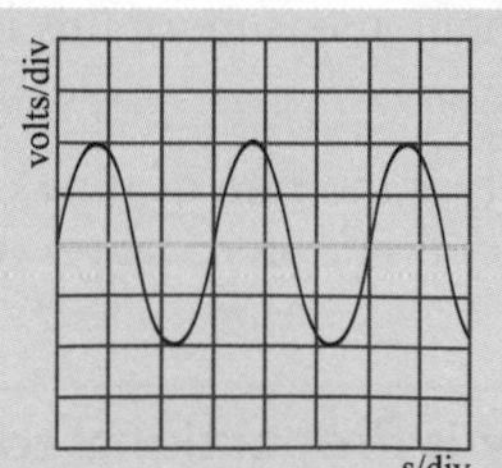

a) State the maximum voltage of the trace. [1 mark]

b) Calculate the frequency of the wave. [3 marks]

c) Calculate the wavelength of the wave. [2 marks]

Hope you haven't phased out...

You should have met some of this stuff at GCSE, but it's all really important stuff. Make sure you know what all the waves terms (amplitude, frequency etc.) mean — otherwise the rest of the section is going sound like a confusing wavey mess...

Types of Wave

Get a long spring and have a go at making different waves. Or sit there beeping pretending to be a microwave.

In **Transverse Waves**, **Vibration** is at Right Angles to the **Direction** of Travel

1) All **electromagnetic waves** are **transverse**. Other examples of transverse waves are ripples on water or waves on strings.
2) There are **two** main ways of **drawing** transverse waves:

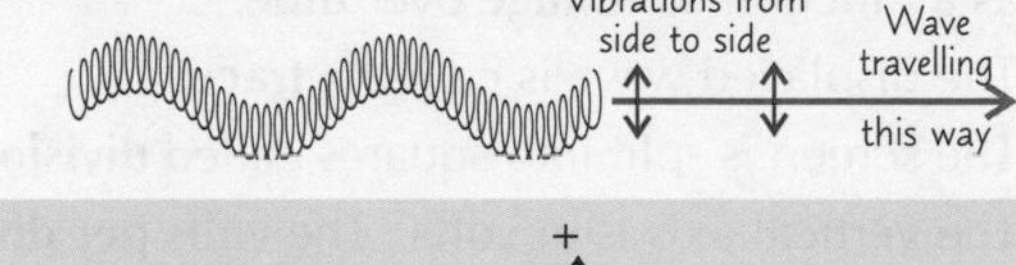

They can be shown as **graphs of displacement** against **distance along the path of the wave.**

Or, they can be shown as graphs of **displacement against time** for a point as the wave passes.

3) Both sorts of graph often give the **same shape**, so make sure you check out the label on the ***x*-axis.** Displacements **upwards** from the centre line are given a **+ sign**. Displacements downwards are given a **– sign**.
4) You can work out what **direction** a point on a wave is moving in when given a snapshot of the wave.

Example: Look at the snapshot of the wave on the right. Which direction is point A on the wave moving in?

1) Look at which **direction** the wave is **travelling** in — here the wave is moving from **left** to **right**.
2) The displacement of the wave **just to the left** of point A is **greater** than point A's. So as the wave travels along, point A will need to move **upwards** to have that displacement. (If the displacement to the left was less than point A's, point A would need to move down.)

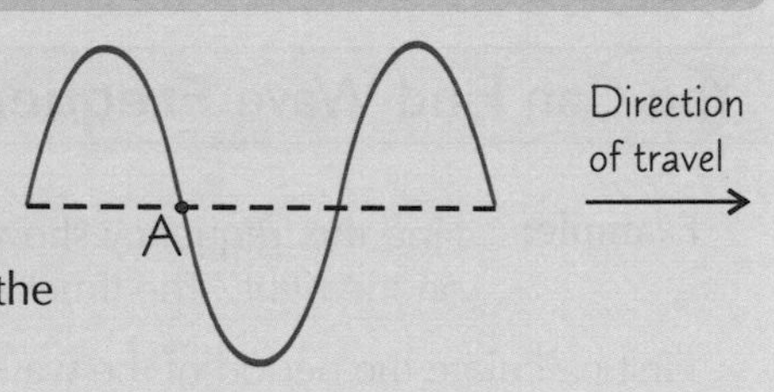

In **Longitudinal Waves** the **Vibrations** are **Along** the Direction of Travel

The most **common** example of a **longitudinal wave** is **sound**. A sound wave consists of alternate **compressions** and **rarefactions** of the **medium** it's travelling through. (That's why sound can't go through a vacuum.) Some types of **earthquake shock waves** are also longitudinal.

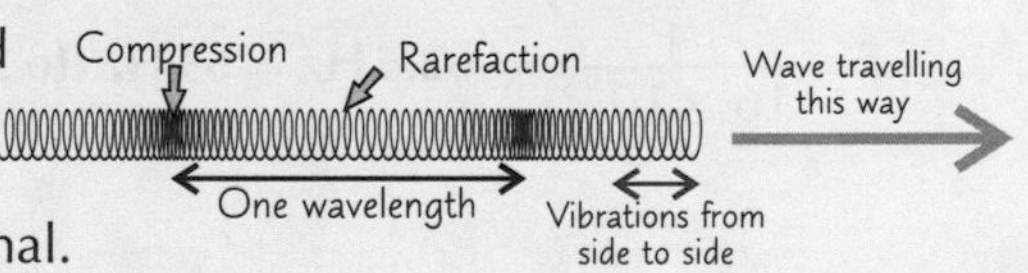

It's hard to **represent** longitudinal waves **graphically**. You'll usually see them plotted as **displacement** against **time**. These can be **confusing** though, because they look like a **transverse wave**.

Intensity is a Measure of How Much **Energy** a Wave is **Carrying**

1) When you talk about "**brightness**" for light or "**loudness**" for sound, what you really mean is **how much light** or **sound** energy hits your eyes or your ears **per second**.
2) The scientific measure of this is **intensity**.

Intensity is the **rate of flow** of **energy** per **unit area** at **right angles** to the **direction of travel** of the wave. It's measured in **Wm^{-2}**.

$$\textbf{Intensity} = \frac{\textbf{Power}}{\textbf{Area}} \qquad I = \frac{P}{A}$$

Intensity is Proportional to **Amplitude Squared**

1) This comes from the fact that **intensity** is **proportional** to **energy**, and the energy of a wave depends on the square of the **amplitude**.
2) From this you can tell that for a **vibrating source** it takes four times as much energy to double the size of the vibrations.

$$\textbf{Intensity} \propto \textbf{(Amplitude)}^2$$

Types of Wave

All **Electromagnetic (EM) Waves** Have Some **Properties** In Common

1) All EM waves travel in a **vacuum** at a **speed** of **3.00×10^8 ms^{-1}** (to 3 s.f.), and at **slower** speeds in other media.
2) They are **transverse** waves consisting of **vibrating electric** and **magnetic fields**. The **electric** and **magnetic** fields are at **right angles** to each other and to the **direction of travel**.
3) Like all waves, EM waves can be **refracted** (p.84), **reflected** and **diffracted** (p.82-83) and can undergo **interference** (p.86). They also obey $v = f\lambda$ (v = velocity, f = frequency, λ = wavelength).
4) Like all progressive waves, progressive EM waves **carry energy**.
5) EM waves are transverse so, like all transverse waves, they can be **polarised** (see page 80).

Some **Properties Vary** Across the **EM Spectrum**

EM waves with different wavelengths behave differently in some respects. The spectrum is split into seven categories: **radio waves**, **microwaves**, **infrared**, **visible light**, **ultraviolet**, **X-rays** and **gamma rays**.

1) The longer the wavelength, the more **obvious** the wave characteristics — long radio waves diffract round hills.
2) **Energy** is directly proportional to **frequency**. **Gamma rays** have the **highest energy**; **radio waves** the **lowest**.
3) In general, the **higher** the **energy**, the more **dangerous** the wave — some can even cause **ionisation**.

Type	Approximate Wavelength /m	Penetration	Uses
Radio waves	10^{-1} — 10^6	Pass through matter.	Radio transmissions.
Microwaves	10^{-3} — 10^{-1}	Mostly pass through matter, but cause some heating.	Radar. Microwave cooking. TV transmissions.
Infrared (IR)	7×10^{-7} — 10^{-3}	Mostly absorbed by matter, causing it to heat up.	Heat detectors. Night vision cameras. Remote controls. Optical fibres.
Visible light	4×10^{-7} — 7×10^{-7}	Absorbed by matter, causing some heating.	Human sight. Optical fibres.
Ultraviolet (UV)	10^{-8} — 4×10^{-7}	Absorbed by matter. Slight ionisation.	Sunbeds. Security marks that show up under UV.
X-rays	10^{-13} — 10^{-8}	Mostly pass through matter, but cause ionisation as they pass.	To see damage to bones and teeth. Airport security scanners. To kill cancer cells.
Gamma rays	10^{-16} — 10^{-10}	Mostly pass through matter, but cause ionisation as they pass.	Irradiation of food. Sterilisation of medical instruments. To kill cancer cells.

Warm-Up Questions

PRACTICE QUESTIONS

Q1 Draw a displacement-time graph for a point on a wave as the wave passes.
Q2 Describe the difference between the vibrations in a transverse wave and a longitudinal wave.
Q3 State the two types of field that make up an EM wave and describe the direction of their vibrations.
Q4 Name four properties that all electromagnetic waves have.
Q5 Name the main types of EM wave that make up the electromagnetic spectrum.
Q6 Which types of electromagnetic radiation have the highest and lowest energies?
Q7 What are the approximate wavelengths for: a) radio waves b) microwaves?

Exam Question

Q1 a) A 10.0 W light beam is shone onto a screen with an area of 0.002 m^2. Calculate the intensity of the light beam on the screen. [1 mark]

b) The intensity of the light on the screen is increased until it is exactly triple the original beam intensity. Which of the following describes the amplitude of the light waves in the beam compared to their original amplitude?

A It is 3 times larger. B It has halved. C It is 9 times larger. D It is $\sqrt{3}$ larger. [1 mark]

I've got UV hair...

No really I have, you just can't see it. Aaanyway... moving swiftly on. Loads of facts to learn on this page — and that's just what you have to do I'm afraid, sit and learn it then make sure you really know it. Not much fun, but there you go.

Polarisation of Waves

Light waves shake about all over the place. Polarisation is just getting rid of the directions that you don't want.

A **Polarised Wave** Only **Oscillates** in One Direction

1) If you **shake a rope** to make a **wave** you can move your hand **up and down** or **side to side** or in a **mixture** of directions — it still makes a **transverse wave.**
2) But if you try to pass **waves in a rope** through a **vertical fence**, the wave will only get through if the **vibrations** are **vertical**. The fence filters out vibration in other directions. This is called **polarising** the wave.

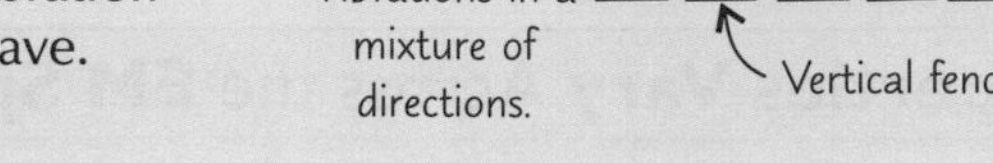

3) The **plane** in which a wave **vibrates** is called the **plane of polarisation** — e.g. the rope wave was polarised in the **vertical** plane by the fence.

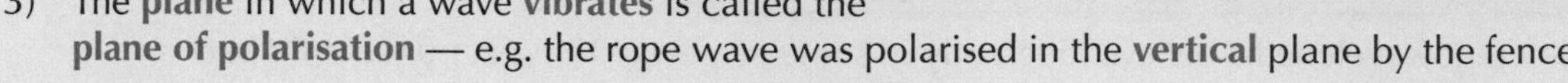

4) Polarising a wave so that it only oscillates in one direction is called **plane polarisation.**
5) Ordinary **light waves** are a mixture of **different directions** of **vibration.** (The things vibrating are electric and magnetic fields).

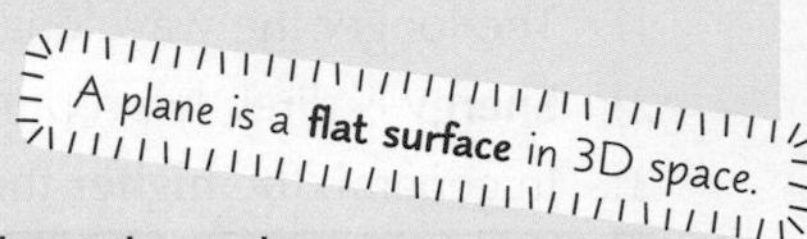

6) A **polarising filter** only transmits vibrations in one direction.

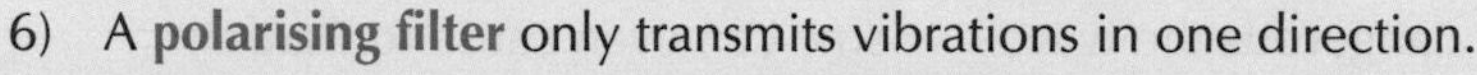

7) If you have two polarising filters at **right angles** to each other, then **no** light will get through.

8) Polarisation **can only happen** for **transverse** waves. The fact that you can polarise light is one **proof** that it's a transverse wave.

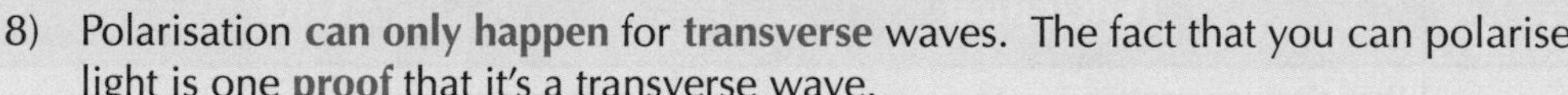

Investigating **Polarisation** of **Light** Using Two **Polarising Filters**

PRACTICAL SKILLS

You can observe polarisation by shining unpolarised white light through two polarising filters.

1) Align the transmission axes of two **polarising filters** so they are both **vertical.** Shine unpolarised light on the first filter. Keep the position of the **first filter fixed** and **rotate** the second one.
2) Light that passes through the first filter will always be **vertically polarised.**
3) When the transmission axes of the two filters are **aligned**, **all** of the light that passes through the first filter also passes through the second.
4) As you rotate the second filter, the amount of light that passes through the second filter **varies.**

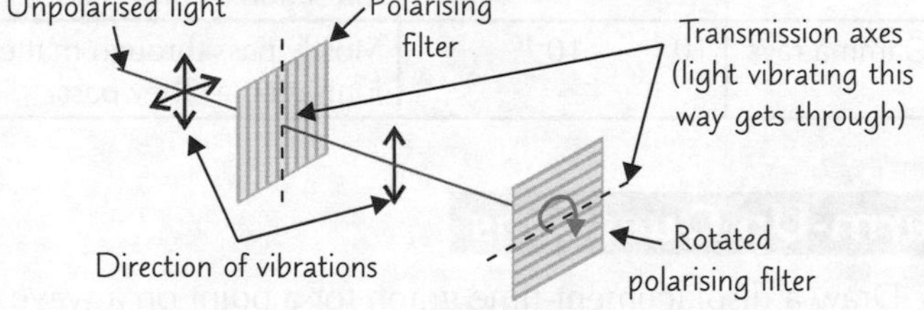

Just like vectors, you can think of the transmission axis of the rotating filter as having a **vertical** and **horizontal component**. The **larger** the **vertical component**, the **more** vertically polarised light will pass through the filter.

5) As the second filter is rotated, **less** light will get through it as the **vertical** component of the second filter's transmission axis **decreases.** This means the **intensity** of the light getting through the second filter will gradually **decrease.**
6) When the two transmission axes are at **45°** to each other, the intensity will be **half** that getting through the first filter. When they're at **right angles** to each other **no** light will pass through — **intensity** is **0.**
7) As you continue turning, the intensity should then begin to **increase** once again.
8) When the two axes **realign** (after a 180° rotation), **all** the light will be able to pass through the second filter again.

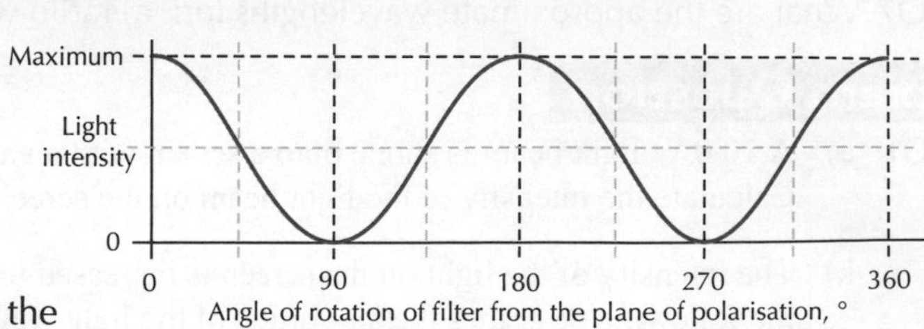

You come across polarising filters more often than you'd think. For example, **3D films** use polarised light to create depth — the filters in each lens are at right angles to each other so each eye gets a slightly different picture. **Polaroid sunglasses** also use polarising filters — light reflected off some surfaces is partially polarised so the sunglasses block this out to help prevent glare.

Polarisation of Waves

You Can Also **Polarise Microwaves**

Polarising filters don't work on **microwaves** — their **wavelength** is too long. Instead, **metal grilles** (squares full of metal wires which are all aligned) are used to polarise them.

You can investigate the polarisation of microwaves using a **microwave transmitter** and a **microwave receiver** linked to a **voltmeter**.

PRACTICAL SKILLS

1) Place a metal **grille** between the microwave **transmitter** and **receiver** as shown on the right. (Handily, microwave transmitters transmit **vertically polarised** microwaves, so you only need one metal grille.)
2) The intensity of microwaves passing through the grille is at a **maximum** when the direction of the vibration of the microwaves and the wires on the grille are at **right angles** to each other.
3) As you rotate the grille, the **intensity** of polarised microwaves able to pass through the grille **decreases**, so the reading on the voltmeter **decreases**.
4) When the wires of the metal grille are **aligned** with the direction of the polarised waves, **no signal** will be shown on the voltmeter.

Metal grille at right angle to direction of microwaves

Microwave transmitter transmitting vertically polarised waves

Microwave receiver (receives vertically polarised waves)

Voltmeter

Polarised microwaves (direction of vibrations)

Microwaves with slightly reduced amplitudes

Make sure all of your electrical equipment is safely connected before you turn it on — microwave transmitters operate at very high voltages.

The **intensity** drops to **zero** when the wires are **aligned** with the direction of the microwaves, because the grille is **absorbing their energy**.

1) The vibrating electric field of the microwave **excites** electrons in the metal grille.
2) The energy of the incoming microwaves is **absorbed** and **re-emitted** in **all directions**.
3) Only a few of those re-emitted waves are vibrating in the **direction** of the microwave receiver.
4) The microwave **receiver** only receives microwaves in **one plane**, so even if the **re-emitted** wave travels towards to receiver, it might not be picked up.
5) When the wires and vibrations of the waves are **aligned, more** electrons are excited than when the grille and vibration of the waves are at right angles to each other — causing the drop in **intensity** that you see.

Warm-Up Questions

PRACTICE QUESTIONS

Q1 What is plane polarisation?

Q2 Why can't you polarise sound waves?

Q3 Describe an experiment that shows visible light can be polarised.

Q4 Explain why the intensity of vertically polarised microwaves passing through a metal grille will drop to zero when the grille is aligned with the direction of polarisation.

Exam Question

Q1 Two polarising filters are placed on top of each other and held in front of a source of white unpolarised light.

a) No light can be seen through the filters. State the angle between the transmission axes of the two filters. [1 mark]

b) The filters are rotated so that the angle between their transmission axes is 45°. Describe the difference in the intensity of the light once it has passed through both filters compared to the light once it has only passed through the first filter. [1 mark]

c) Give one use of polarising filters. [1 mark]

Forget polarisation, I need a mental filter...

...to stop me talking rubbish all the time. Polarisation isn't too bad once you get your head around it. It's just a case of filtering out different directions of wave vibrations. Make sure you really know it though as you'll have to be able to explain how both the experiments for polarising light and microwaves work. Doesn't that sound like a barrel of laughs.

Diffraction and Reflection

All waves share some properties — they spread out (diffract), reflect off stuff and refract (more on that on p.84-85).

Waves Go **Round Corners** and **Spread out** of **Gaps**

The way that **waves spread out** as they come through a **narrow gap** or go round obstacles is called **diffraction**. **All** waves diffract, but it's not always easy to observe. The amount of diffraction depends on the **size of the gap** in comparison to the **wavelength** of the wave.

You Can Use a **Ripple Tank** to Investigate **Diffraction**

1) **Ripple tanks** are shallow tanks of water that you can generate a wave in.
2) This is done by an **oscillating paddle**, which continually dips into the water and creates regular waves with straight, parallel wave fronts.
3) Objects are then placed into the ripple tank to create a **barrier** with a **gap** in the middle of it.
4) This gap can be varied to see the effects this has on how the waves spread through the tank.

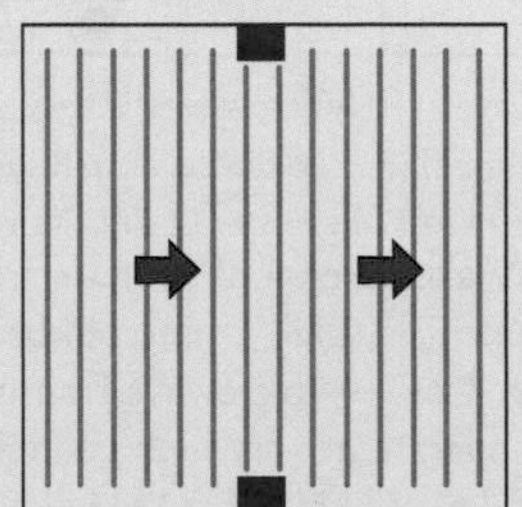

When the gap is **a lot bigger** than the **wavelength**, diffraction is **unnoticeable**.

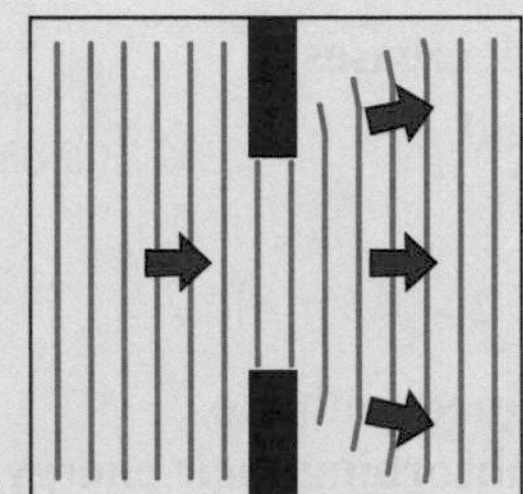

You get **noticeable diffraction** through a gap **several** wavelengths wide.

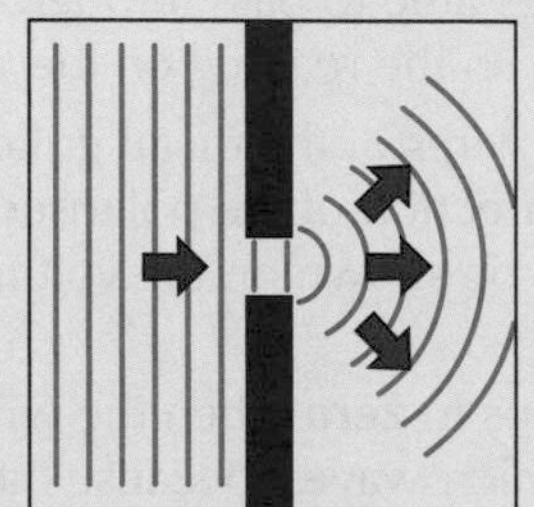

You get the **most** diffraction when the gap is **the same** size as the **wavelength**.

As the gap decreases, the diffraction becomes more noticeable until the gap becomes too small and the water waves cannot pass through it anymore. The waves are then **reflected** back on themselves.

When **sound** passes through a **doorway**, the **size of gap** and the **wavelength** are usually roughly **equal**, so **a lot** of **diffraction** occurs. That's why you have no trouble **hearing** someone through an **open door** to the next room, even if the other person is out of your **line of sight**. The reason that you can't **see** him or her is that when **light** passes through the doorway, it is passing through a **gap** around a **hundred million times bigger** than its wavelength — the amount of diffraction is **tiny**.

Demonstrate **Diffraction** in **Light** Using **Laser Light**

1) Diffraction in **light** can be demonstrated by shining a **laser light** through a very **narrow slit** onto a screen (see the next page). You can alter the amount of diffraction by changing the width of the slit.
2) You can do a similar experiment using a **white light** source instead of the laser (which is monochromatic) and a set of **colour filters**. The size of the slit can be kept constant while the **wavelength** is varied by putting different **colour filters** over the slit.

Warning. Use of coloured filters may result in excessive fun.

You Get a **Similar** Effect Around an Obstacle

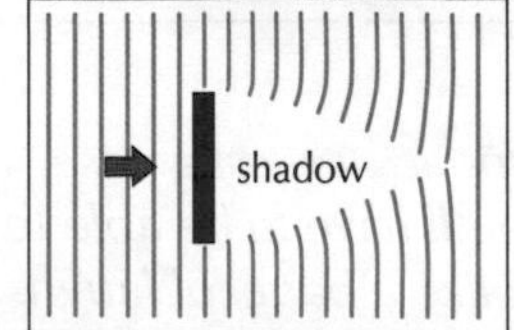

When a wave meets an **obstacle**, you get diffraction around the edges. Behind the obstacle is a '**shadow**', where the wave is blocked. The **wider** the obstacle compared with the wavelength of the wave, the less diffraction you get, and so the **longer** the shadow.

Diffraction and Reflection

With **Light Waves** you get a Pattern of **Light** and **Dark Fringes**

1) If the **wavelength** of a **light wave** is roughly similar to the size of the **aperture**, you get a **diffraction pattern** of light and dark fringes.
2) The pattern has a **bright central fringe** with alternating **dark and bright fringes** on either side of it.
3) The **narrower** the slit, the **wider** the diffraction pattern.

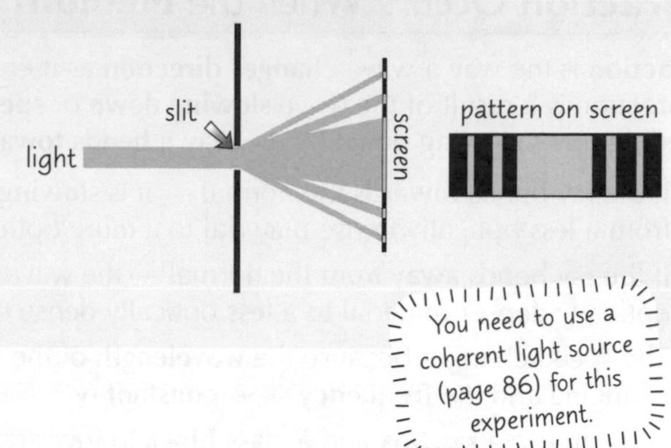

You need to use a coherent light source (page 86) for this experiment.

Waves Can Be **Reflected**

Reflection means the wave is **bounced back** when it **hits a boundary**.
The **angle of incidence** always **equals** the **angle of reflection.**

PRACTICAL SKILLS

You can show the reflection of water waves in a **ripple tank**.

1) Set up the ripple tank so the oscillating paddle is creating **regular** waves with straight, **parallel** wave fronts. Place a **barrier** in the tank at an **angle** to the wave fronts.
2) The **angle** the incoming waves make with the **normal** to the barrier is called the **angle of incidence**, ***i***.
3) You should see the waves **reflecting** off the barrier and travelling in a different direction to the way they arrived.
4) The angle between the **direction** of the **reflected waves** and the **normal** to the barrier is called the **angle of reflection**, ***r***.
5) You can **change** the **angle** of **incidence** to see that the angle of **reflection** changes by the same amount. They are always **equal** to each other.

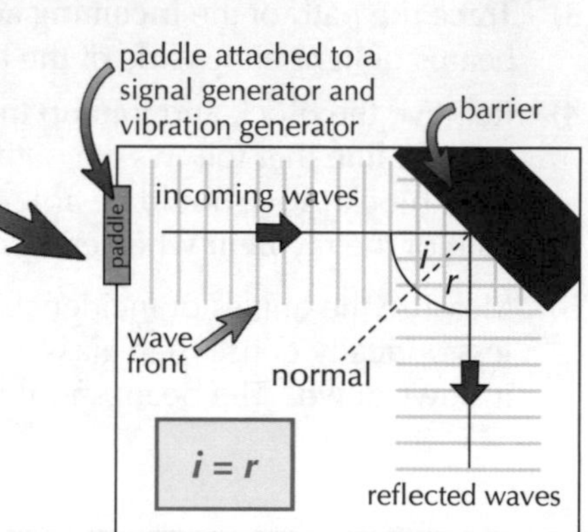

Warm-Up Questions

PRACTICE QUESTIONS

Q1 What is diffraction?

Q2 For a long time some scientists argued that light couldn't be a wave because it did not seem to diffract. Suggest why they might have got this impression.

Q3 Sketch what happens when plane waves meet an obstacle about as wide as one wavelength.

Q4 In a ripple tank experiment, incident waves arrive at a barrier's surface at an angle of 30° to the normal. What is the angle between the incident waves and the reflected waves?

Exam Questions

Q1 A mountain lies directly between you and a radio transmitter. Explain, with the use of a diagram, why you can pick up long-wave radio broadcasts from the transmitter but not short-wave radio broadcasts. [3 marks]

Q2 Describe how you would use a ripple tank to investigate how the wavelength of a wave and the size of the gap a wave travels through relates to the amount of diffraction which occurs. Comment on when maximum diffraction will be seen. [3 marks]

Even hiding behind a mountain, you can't get away from long-wave radio...

Unfortunately "Bay FM" don't transmit using long wave radio. So as I'm giving the singing-in-the-car performance of my life, I go over a hill and the signal cuts out. Where's diffraction when I need it then hmm? How will I ever become famous? Diffraction crops up again in stuff like quantum physics so make sure you really understand it.

Refraction and Refractive Index

The stuff on the next two pages explains why your legs look short in a swimming pool.

Refraction Occurs When the Medium a Wave is Travelling in Changes

Refraction is the way a wave **changes direction** as it enters a **different medium**. The change in direction is a result of the wave **slowing down** or **speeding up**. You can tell if the wave is speeding up or slowing down by the way it **bends towards** or **away** from the normal.

Knowing there are biscuits also causes a change in speed.

1) If the ray bends **towards** the normal — it is **slowing** down. The ray is going from a **less** optically dense material to a **more** optically dense material.
2) If the ray bends **away** from the normal — the wave is **speeding up**. It is going from an optically **denser** material to a **less** optically dense material.
3) The speed changes because the **wavelength** of the wave is changing and the **frequency** stays **constant** ($v = f\lambda$).
4) You can use a **ray box** and a **glass block** to investigate refraction:

1) Place a glass block on a piece of paper and draw around it.
2) Use the ray box to shine a beam of light into the glass block. Turn off any other lights so you can see the path of the light beam through the block clearly.
3) **Trace** the path of the **incoming** and **outgoing** beams of light either side of the block.
4) Remove the block and join up the two paths you've drawn with a **straight line** that follows the path the light beam took through the glass block. You should be able to see from your drawing how the path of the ray **bent** when entering and leaving the block.

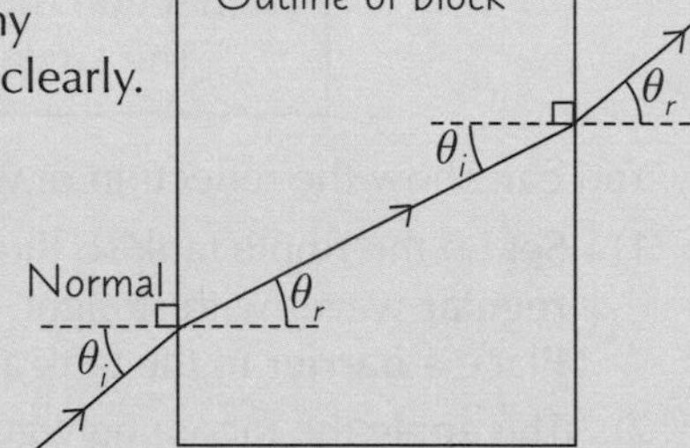

5) Measure the angles of incidence (θ_i) and refraction (θ_r) where the light enters and exits the block. Air is **less** optically dense than glass, so as the light **enters** the glass block it **bends towards** the normal ($\theta_i > \theta_r$) as it **slows down**. The beam should **bend away** from the normal as it **exits** the block ($\theta_r > \theta_i$) and **speeds up**.

The Refractive Index of a Material Measures How Much It Slows Down Light

Light goes fastest in a **vacuum**. It **slows down** in other materials, because it **interacts** with the particles in them. The more **optically dense** a material is, the more light **slows down** when it enters it.

The **absolute refractive index** of a material, n, is the **ratio** between the **speed of light** in a **vacuum**, c, and the speed of light in that **material**, v.

$$n = \frac{c}{v}$$

$c = 3.00 \times 10^8$ ms^{-1}.

The speed of light in air is only a tiny bit smaller than c. So you can assume the refractive index of air is 1.

Snell's Law uses Angles to Calculate the Refractive Index

When a light ray passes across a boundary between two materials: $n \sin\theta = \text{constant}$

Where n is the refractive index of the material light travels in, and θ is the angle the light ray makes with the normal of the boundary.

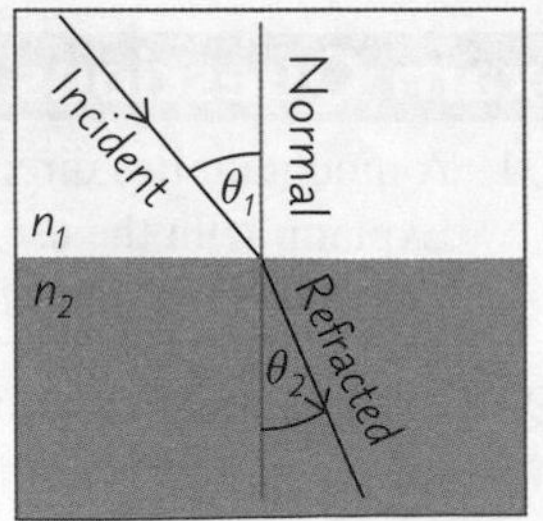

This means that for a light ray at a boundary between two materials, **$n \sin\theta$** must be the same on either side. This can be written nicely as **Snell's Law**:

$$n_1 \sin\theta_1 = n_2 \sin\theta_2$$

where n_1 is the refractive index of the first material, θ_1 is the angle of incidence, n_2 is the refractive index of the second material and θ_2 is the angle of refraction.

You can use a device called a **refractometer** to accurately measure the refractive index of a material. The machine shines a beam of light at the sample. You then view the refracted beam through a **microscope** and measure its angle of refraction.

You'll only get given the '$n \sin\theta$ = constant' equation in the exam, so make sure you remember what that equation actually tells you — that $n_1 \sin\theta_1 = n_2 \sin\theta_2$ at any boundary.

Refraction and Refractive Index

When the Angle of **Refraction** is a **Right Angle**, the Angle of **Incidence** is **Critical**

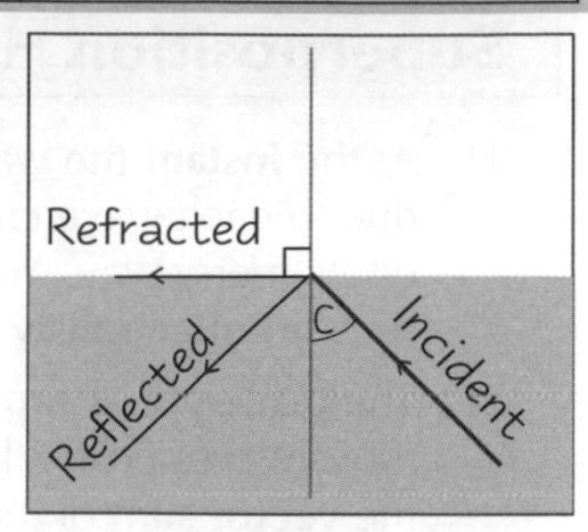

When light **goes from** an optically dense material into an optically **less dense** material (e.g. glass to air), interesting things can start to happen.

Shine a ray of light at a **glass to air** boundary, then gradually **increase** the angle of incidence. As you increase the angle of incidence, the angle of **refraction** gets closer and closer to **90°**. Eventually the angle of incidence, θ_i reaches a **critical angle C** for which the angle of refraction, θ_r **= 90°**. The light is refracted **along the boundary**.

At angles of incidence **greater than** C, refraction is **impossible**. That means **all** the light is reflected back into the material. This effect is called **total internal reflection.**

For light hitting a **material-to-air boundary** (assuming the material is more optically **dense**) at the critical angle, **Snell's law** simplifies to become:

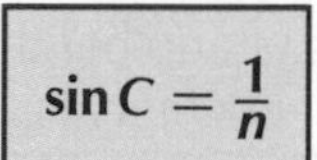

$$\sin C = \frac{1}{n}$$

This happens because n_{air} = 1 and sin(90°) = 1. n is the refractive index of the material.

You can Investigate **Critical Angles** and **Total Internal Reflection** with **Glass Blocks**

PRACTICAL SKILLS

1) Shine a light ray into the **curved face** of a semi-circular glass block so that it always enters at **right angles** to the edge — this means the ray won't **refract** as it enters the block, just when it leaves from the straight edge.
2) Vary the angle of **incidence**, θ_i, until the light beam refracts so much that it exits the block along the **straight edge**. This angle of incidence is the **critical angle**, C, for glass-air boundary.
3) If you increase the angle of incidence so it's **greater** than C, you'll find the ray is reflected from the straight edge of the block.

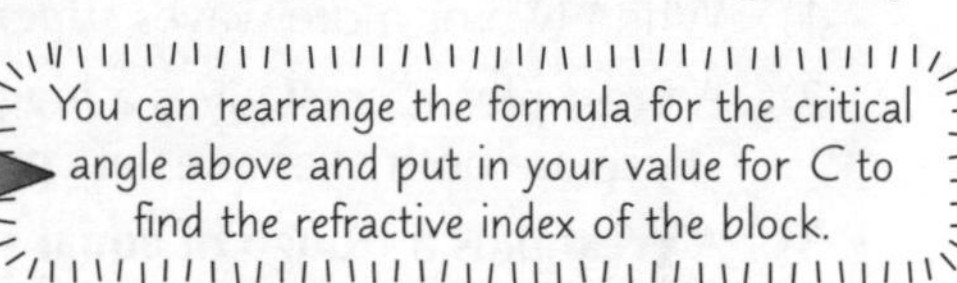

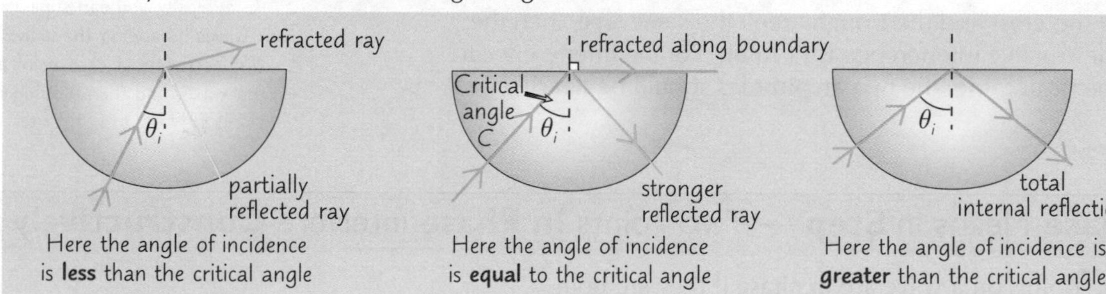

Warm-Up Questions

PRACTICE QUESTIONS

Q1 What happens to the wavelength of light at an air-water boundary?

Q2 Why does light go fastest in a vacuum and slow down in other media?

Q3 Describe an experiment you could do to determine the critical angle of a boundary between a material and air.

Exam Questions

Q1 a) Light travels in diamond at 1.24×10^8 ms^{-1}. What is the refractive index of diamond? [1 mark]

b) Calculate the angle of refraction if light strikes a facet of a diamond ring at an angle of 50° to the normal of the air/diamond boundary. [2 marks]

Q2 An adjustable underwater spotlight is placed on the floor of an aquarium tank. When the light points upwards at a steep angle a beam comes through the surface of the water into the air, and the tank is dimly lit. When the spotlight is placed at a shallower angle, no light comes up through the water surface, and the tank is brightly lit.

a) Explain what is happening. [2 marks]

b) It is found that the beam into the air disappears when the spotlight is pointed at any angle of less than 41.25° to the floor. Calculate the refractive index of water. [2 marks]

Critical angles are never happy...

Total internal reflection doesn't sound like the most riveting subject, but it's super useful. Optical fibres wouldn't work without it, and we use them for all sorts of things — broadband connections, telephone cables, making things sparkley...

Superposition and Coherence

When two waves get together, it can be either really impressive or really disappointing.

Superposition Happens When **Two** or **More** Waves **Pass Through** Each Other

1) At the **instant** the waves **cross**, the **displacements** due to each wave **combine**. Then **each wave** goes on its merry way. You can **see** this if **two pulses** are sent **simultaneously** from each end of a rope.
2) The **principle of superposition** says that when two or more **waves cross**, the **resultant** displacement equals the **vector sum** of the **individual** displacements.

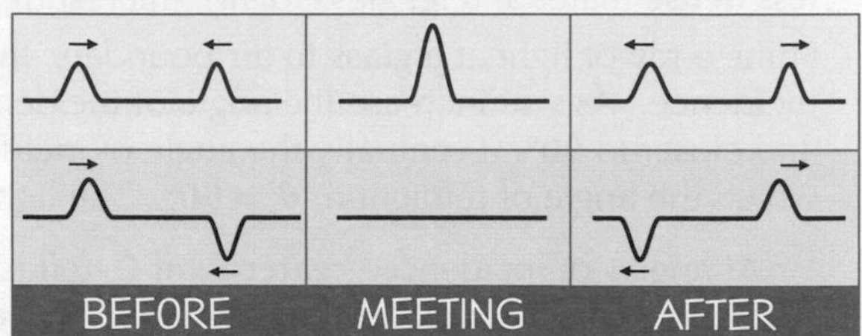

"Superposition" means "one thing on top of another thing". You can use the same idea in reverse — a complex wave can be separated out mathematically into several simple sine waves of various sizes.

Interference can be **Constructive** or **Destructive**

1) When two or more waves **superpose** with each other, the effect is called **interference**.
2) A **crest** plus a **crest** gives a **bigger crest**. A **trough** plus a **trough** gives a **bigger trough**. These are both examples of **constructive interference**.
3) A **crest** plus a **trough** of **equal size** gives... **nothing**. The two displacements **cancel each other out** completely. This is called **destructive interference**.
4) If the **crest** and the **trough** aren't the **same size**, then the destructive interference **isn't total**. For the interference to be **noticeable**, the two **amplitudes** should be **nearly equal**.

Graphically, you can superimpose waves by adding the individual displacements at each point along the *x*-axis, and then plotting them.

In **Phase** Means In **Step** — Two Points **In Phase** Interfere **Constructively**

1) Two points on a wave are **in phase** if they are both at the **same point** in the **wave cycle**. Points in phase have the **same displacement** and **velocity**.
2) On the graph on the right, points **A** and **B** are **in phase**; points **A** and **C** are **out of phase**.
3) It's mathematically **handy** to show one **complete cycle** of a wave as an **angle of 360° (2π radians)**.
4) **Two points** with a **phase difference** of **zero** or a **multiple of 360°** are **in phase**.
5) **Points** with a **phase difference** of **odd-number multiples** of **180° (π radians)** are **exactly out of phase**.
6) You can also talk about two **different waves** being **in phase**. **In practice** this happens because **both** waves came from the **same oscillator**. In **other** situations there will nearly always be a **phase difference** between two waves.

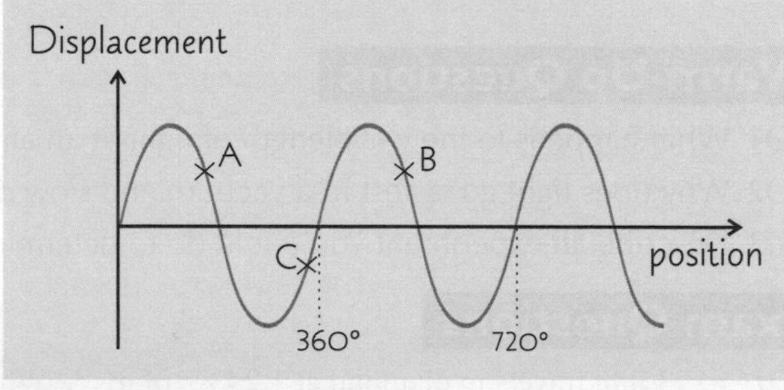

To Get **Interference Patterns** the **Two Sources** Must Be **Coherent**

Interference **still happens** when you're observing waves of **different wavelength** and **frequency** — but it happens in a **jumble**. In order to get clear **interference patterns**, the two or more sources must be **coherent**.

Two sources are **coherent** if they have the **same wavelength** and **frequency** and a **fixed phase difference** between them.

In exam questions at AS, the 'fixed phase difference' is almost certainly going to be zero. The two sources will be in phase.

Superposition and Coherence

Constructive or Destructive Interference Depends on the Path Difference

1) Whether you get **constructive** or **destructive** interference at a **point** depends on how **much further one wave** has travelled than the **other wave** to get to that point (assuming the sources are coherent and in phase).
2) The **amount** by which the path travelled by one wave is **longer** than the path travelled by the other wave is called the **path difference**.
3) At **any point an equal distance** from both sources you will get **constructive interference**. You also get constructive interference at any point where the **path difference** is a **whole number of wavelengths**. At points where the path difference is an odd number of **half wavelengths**, the waves arrive **out of phase** and you get **destructive interference**.

Constructive interference occurs when: **path difference = $n\lambda$ (where n is an integer)**

Destructive interference occurs when: **path difference $= \frac{(2n+1)\lambda}{2} = (n + \frac{1}{2})\lambda$**

You Can Observe Interference With Sound Waves

1) Connect two **speakers** to the same oscillator (so they're **coherent**) and place them in line with each other.
2) Walk slowly across the room in front of them.
3) You will hear varying volumes of sound. At the points where the sound is **loudest**, the **path difference** is a **whole** wavelength.
4) The sound will be quietest at points where the path difference is an **odd** number of **half wavelengths**.

You may still hear some sound at the quietest points due to sound being reflected off walls and around the room.

You could use a microphone and an oscilloscope to investigate how interference varies with position along this line.

Warm-Up Questions

PRACTICE QUESTIONS

Q1 What is the principle of superposition?

Q2 What happens when a crest of one wave meets a slightly smaller trough of another wave?

Q3 If two points on a wave have a phase difference of 1440°, are they in phase?

Q4 If there was a path difference of 5λ between two in phase waves, what kind of interference would occur?

Exam Questions

Q1 a) Two wave sources are coherent. Explain what this means. [2 marks]

b) Explain why you might have difficulty in observing interference patterns in an area affected by two waves from two sources even though the two sources are coherent. [1 mark]

Q2 Two waves from coherent sources meet and interfere. Which row of the table shows the correct type of interference that would occur with the stated phase and path difference? [1 mark]

	Phase Difference	Path Difference	Type of Interference
A	180°	λ	Constructive
B	180°	λ/2	Constructive
C	360°	λ	Destructive
D	360°	λ/2	Constructive

Learn this and you'll be in a super position to pass your exam... ...I'll get my coat.

A few crucial concepts here: a) interference can be constructive or destructive, b) you get constructive interference when the path difference is a whole number of wavelengths (for sources in phase), c) the sources must be coherent.

Two-Source Interference

Yeah, I know, fringe spacing doesn't really sound like a Physics topic — just trust me on this one, OK.

Demonstrating Two-Source Interference in **Water** and **Sound** Waves is Easy

1) It's **easy** to demonstrate **two-source interference** for either **sound** or **water** waves because they've got **wavelengths** of a handy **size** that you can **measure**.
2) You need **coherent** sources, which means the **wavelength** and **frequency** have to be the **same**. The trick is to use the **same oscillator** to drive **both sources**. For **water**, one **vibrator drives two dippers**. For sound, **one oscillator** is connected to **two loudspeakers**. (See diagram on page 87.)

Demonstrating **Two-Source** Interference for **EM Radiation** is Harder

Light is more difficult to demonstrate two-source interference with — you can either use **two coherent light sources**, or use a single **laser** and shine it through **two slits**... clever, huh. It's called **Young's double-slit experiment**, and you need to learn it...

1) Laser light is **coherent** and **monochromatic** (there's only **one wavelength** present).
2) The slits have to be about the same size as the wavelength of the laser light so that it is **diffracted** — then the light from the slits acts like **two coherent point sources**.
3) You get a pattern of light and dark **fringes**, depending on whether constructive or destructive **interference** is taking place.

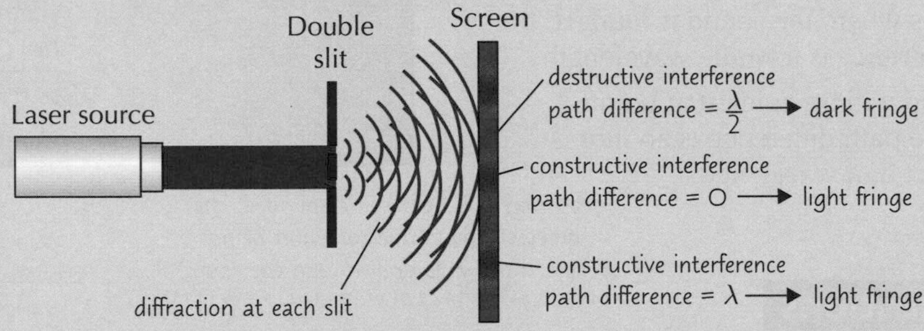

4) Thomas Young — the first person to do this experiment (with a lamp rather than a laser) — came up with an **equation** to **work out** the **wavelength** of the **light** from this experiment (see p.89).
5) To find the wavelength, you'll need to measure the **fringe spacing** — the distance from the **centre** of one **minimum** to the centre of the next minimum (or from one **maximum** centre to the next maximum centre).
6) The **fringes** are so **tiny** that it's very hard to get an accurate value for their **spacing** (x). It's easier to measure across **several fringes** and then divide by the number of **fringe spacings** between them. Doing this helps to lower the **percentage error** — see p.8 for more about this.

You Can Do a **Similar** Experiment with **Microwaves**

1) To see interference patterns with **microwaves**, you can **replace** the laser and slits with two microwave **transmitter cones** attached to the **same** signal generator.
2) You also need to replace the screen with a microwave **receiver probe** (like the one used in the stationary waves experiment on page 93).
3) If you move the probe along the path of the green arrow, you'll get an **alternating pattern** of **strong** and **weak** signals — just like the light and dark fringes on the screen.

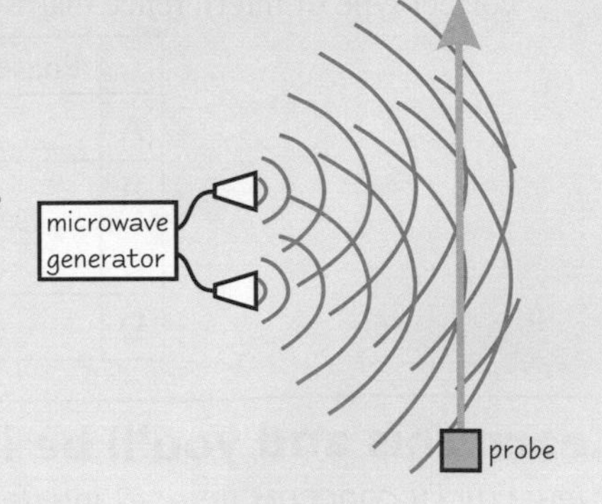

Two-Source Interference

Work Out the Wavelength with **Young's Double-Slit Formula**

The fringe spacing (***x***), wavelength (**λ**), spacing between slits (***a***) and the distance from slits to screen (***D***) are all related by **Young's double-slit formula**, which works for all waves when $a << D$.

Fringe Spacing, $x = \frac{\lambda D}{a}$

a has to be **much** smaller than *D* so you can use trigonometry to find this equation — including a small angle approximation of $\sin\theta \approx \theta$. Thankfully, you don't need to derive this equation.

Always check your fringe spacing.

Since the wavelength of light is so small you can see from the formula that a high ratio of ***D* / *a*** is needed to make the fringe spacing **big enough to see**.

You can rearrange the equation to **calculate the wavelength** of light.

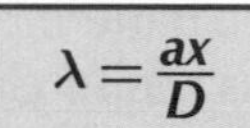

$$\lambda = \frac{ax}{D}$$

Young's Experiment was **Evidence** for the **Wave Nature** of Light

1) Towards the end of the **17th century**, two important **theories of light** were published — one by Isaac Newton and the other by a chap called Huygens. **Newton's** theory suggested that light was made up of tiny particles, which he called "**corpuscles**". And **Huygens** put forward a theory using **waves**.
2) The **corpuscular theory** could explain **reflection** and **refraction**, but **diffraction** and **interference** are both **uniquely** wave properties. If it could be **shown** that light showed interference patterns, that would help settle the argument once and for all.
3) **Young's** double-slit experiment (over 100 years later) provided the necessary evidence. It showed that light could both **diffract** (through the narrow slits) and **interfere** (to form the interference pattern on the screen).

Of course, this being Physics, nothing's ever simple — give it another 100 years or so and the debate would be raging again.

Warm-Up Questions

Q1 In Young's double-slit experiment, why do you get a bright fringe at a point equidistant from both slits?

Q2 Write down the formula you'd use to calculate the wavelength of light in Young's double-slit experiment.

Q3 What does Young's double-slit experiment show about the nature of light?

Exam Questions

Q1 a) The diagram on the right shows waves from two coherent light sources, S_1 and S_2. Sketch the interference pattern, marking on constructive and destructive interference. [2 marks]

b) In practice if interference is to be observed, S_1 and S_2 must be slits in a screen behind which there is a source of laser light. Explain why this is so. [2 marks]

Q2 In an experiment to study sound interference, two loudspeakers are connected to an oscillator emitting sound at 1320 Hz and set up as shown in the diagram below. They are 1.5 m apart and 7 m away from the line AC. A listener moving from A to C hears minimum sound at A and C and maximum sound at B. (You may assume that Young's double-slit formula can be used in this calculation.)

a) Calculate the wavelength of the sound waves if the speed of sound in air is taken to be 330 ms^{-1}. [1 mark]

b) Calculate the separation of points A and C. [2 marks]

I used to have a ridiculous fringe spacing...

... thankfully I stopped trying to cut my own hair. Seriously, leave it to the professionals. Be careful when you're calculating the fringe spacing by averaging over several fringes. Don't just divide by the number of bright lines. Ten bright lines will only have nine fringe-widths between them, not ten. It's an easy mistake to make, but you have been warned.

Diffraction Gratings

What could possibly be more exciting than shining a laser through two slits? Shining a laser through more than two slits of course. Jeez, ask a stupid question...

Interference Patterns Get **Sharper** When You Diffract Through **More Slits**

1) You can repeat **Young's double-slit** experiment (see p.88) with **more than two equally spaced** slits. You get basically the **same shaped** pattern as for two slits — but the **bright bands** are **brighter** and **narrower** and the **dark areas** between are **darker**.
2) When **monochromatic light** (one wavelength) is passed through a **grating** with **hundreds** of slits per millimetre, the interference pattern is **really sharp** because there are so **many beams reinforcing** the **pattern**.
3) Sharper fringes make for more **precise** measurements as they are easier to tell apart and so are **easier** to measure.

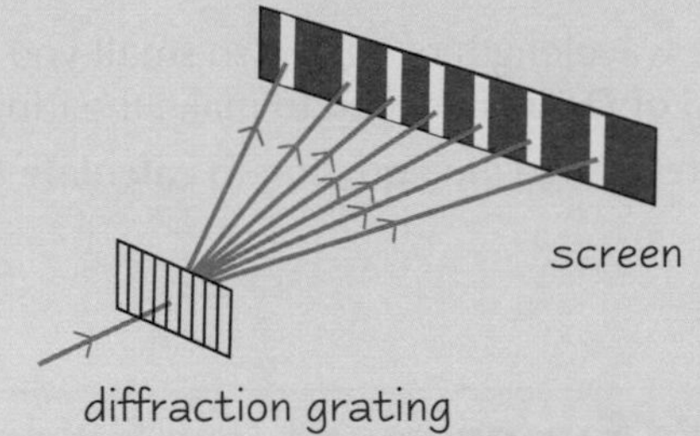

You can **Measure** the **Wavelength** of Light using a **Diffraction Grating**

1) For monochromatic light, all of the maxima are sharp lines. (It's different for white light — see the next page).
2) This means the distance between the maxima can be easily measured (**fringe width**).
3) There's a line of **maximum brightness** at the centre called the **zero order** line.
4) The lines just **either side** of the central one are called **first order lines**. The **next pair out** are called **second order** lines and so on.

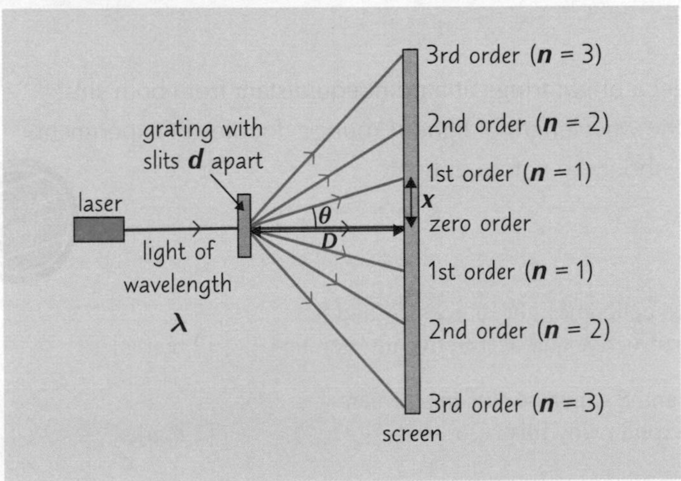

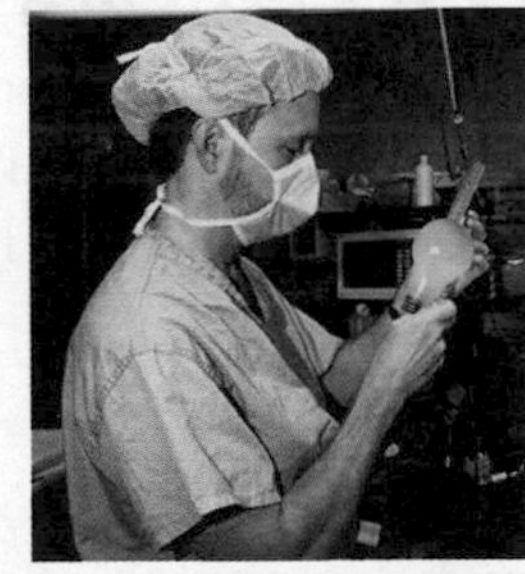

Graham's attempt to measure the wavelength of light was proving to be less than successful.

5) Using the **fringe width**, x, and the distance to the screen, D, the angle the 1st order fringe makes with the zero order line can be calculated using **small angle approximations**.

$$\tan\theta \approx \theta \text{ and } \tan\theta = \frac{x}{D}, \text{ so } \boldsymbol{\theta \approx \frac{x}{D}}$$

6) The slit separation, d, for the diffraction grating is given.
7) If the grating has N slits per metre, then the slit separation, d, is just $1/N$ metres.
8) If you know the slit separation, d, what order maximum you're observing, n, and the angle between this maximum and the incident light, θ, you can find the **wavelength** of the incident light.

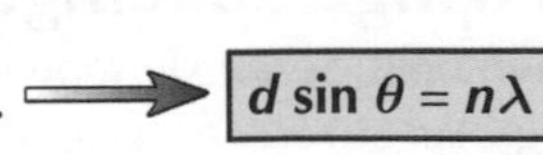

$$d \sin\theta = n\lambda$$

You don't need to know this equation unless you're doing the full A level Physics course, but it's useful for understanding the experiment (which you do need to know) and how the wavelength affects the diffraction pattern.

Diffraction Gratings

You can Draw General Conclusions from $d \sin \theta = n\lambda$

1) If λ is **bigger**, **sin θ** is **bigger**, and so θ is **bigger**. This means that the larger the **wavelength**, the more the pattern will **spread out**.
2) If d is **bigger**, **sin θ** is **smaller**. This means that the **coarser** the **grating**, the **less** the pattern will **spread out**.
3) Values of **sin θ** greater than **1** are **impossible**. So if for a certain n you get a result of **more than 1** for **sin θ** you know that that order **doesn't exist**.

Shining White Light Through a Diffraction Grating Produces Spectra

1) **White light** is really a **mixture** of **colours**. If you **diffract** white light through a **grating** then the patterns due to **different wavelengths** within the white light are **spread out** by **different** amounts.
2) Each **order** in the pattern becomes a **spectrum**, with **red** on the **outside** and **violet** on the **inside**. The **zero order maximum** stays **white** because all the wavelengths just pass straight through.

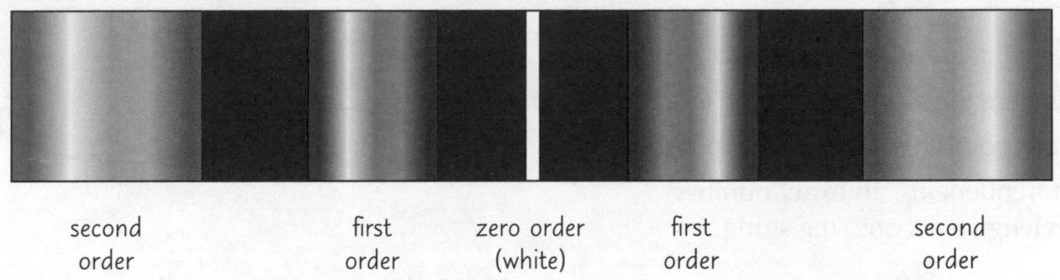

Astronomers and **chemists** often need to study spectra to help identify elements. They use diffraction gratings rather than prisms because they're **more accurate**.

Warm-Up Questions

Q1 What is the formula for finding the wavelength of light incident on a diffraction grating?

Q2 Why do more slits in a diffraction grating lead to a sharper diffraction pattern?

Q3 What equation is used to find the angle between the nth order maximum and the incident beam for a diffraction grating interference pattern?

Exam Questions

Q1 Yellow laser light of wavelength 6.00×10^{-7} m is transmitted through a diffraction grating of 4.0×10^{5} lines per metre.

a) State the angle to the normal where the first and second order bright lines are seen. [4 marks]

b) State whether there is a fifth order line. Explain your answer. [1 mark]

Q2 Visible, monochromatic light is transmitted through a diffraction grating of 3.70×10^{5} lines per metre. The first order maximum is at an angle of 14.2° to the incident beam.

Calculate the wavelength of the incident light. [2 marks]

Ooooooooooooo — pretty patterns...

Yes, it's the end of another beautiful topic. Three important points for you to take away — the more slits you have, the sharper the image, monochromatic light leads to sharp fringes and one lovely equation to get to know. Make sure you get everything in this topic — there's some good stuff waiting in the next one and I wouldn't want you to be distracted.

Stationary (Standing) Waves

Stationary waves are waves that... er... stand still... well, not still exactly... I mean, well... they don't go anywhere... um...

You get Stationary Waves When a **Progressive Wave** is **Reflected** at a **Boundary**

A stationary wave is the **superposition** of **two progressive waves** with the **same wavelength**, moving in **opposite directions**.

1) Unlike progressive waves, **no energy** is transmitted by a stationary wave.
2) You can demonstrate stationary waves by attaching a **vibration transducer** at one end of a **stretched string** with the other end fixed. The transducer is given a wave frequency by a **signal generator** and creates that wave by vibrating the string.
3) The wave generated by the vibration transducer is **reflected** back and forth.
4) For most frequencies the resultant **pattern** is a **jumble**. However, if you alter the **signal generator** so the **transducer** produces an **exact number of waves** in the time it takes for a wave to get to the **end** and **back again**, then the **original** and **reflected** waves **reinforce** each other.

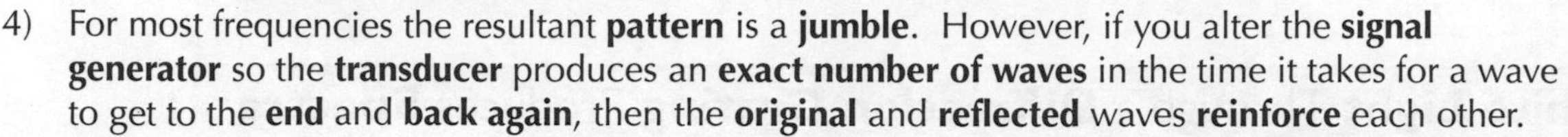

A sitting wave.

5) At these **"resonant frequencies"** you get a **stationary wave** where the **pattern doesn't move** — it just sits there, bobbing up and down. Happy, at peace with the world...

Stationary waves are also known as standing waves.

Stationary Waves in **Strings** Form **Oscillating "Loops"** Separated by **Nodes**

1) Each particle vibrates at **right angles** to the string.
2) **Nodes** are where the **amplitude** of the vibration is **zero**.
3) **Antinodes** are points of **maximum amplitude**.
4) At resonant frequencies, an **exact number** of **half wavelengths** fits onto the string.

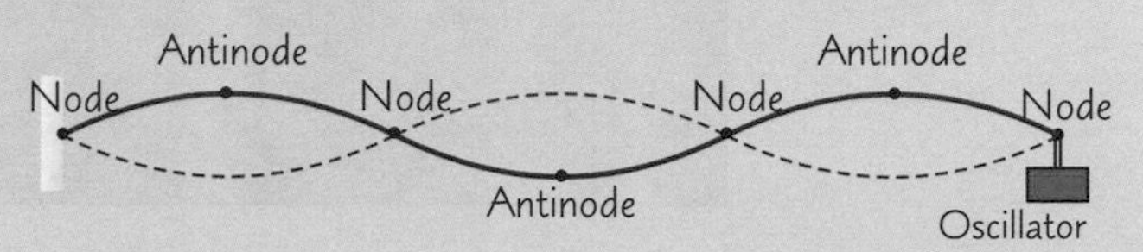

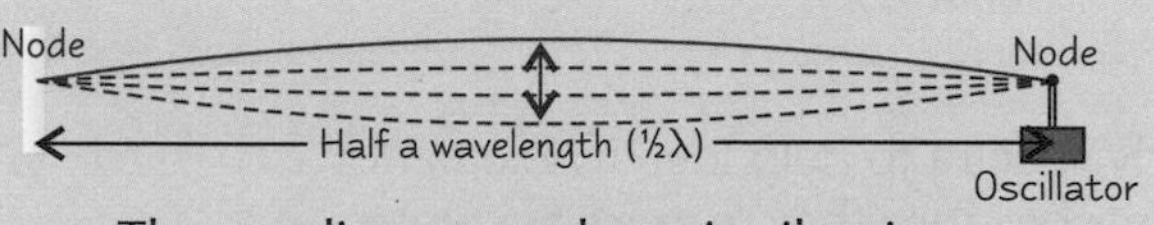

The standing wave above is vibrating at the **lowest possible** resonant frequency (the **fundamental mode of vibration** — also called the **first harmonic**). It has **one "loop"** with a **node at each end**.

This is the **second harmonic**. It is **twice** the **fundamental mode of vibration**. There are two **"loops"** with a **node** in the **middle** and **one at each end**.

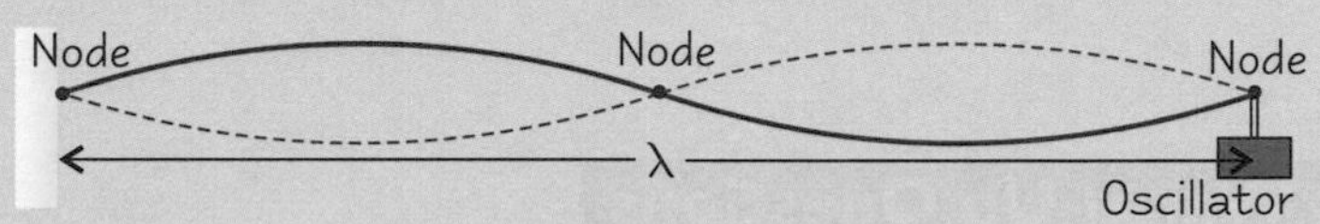

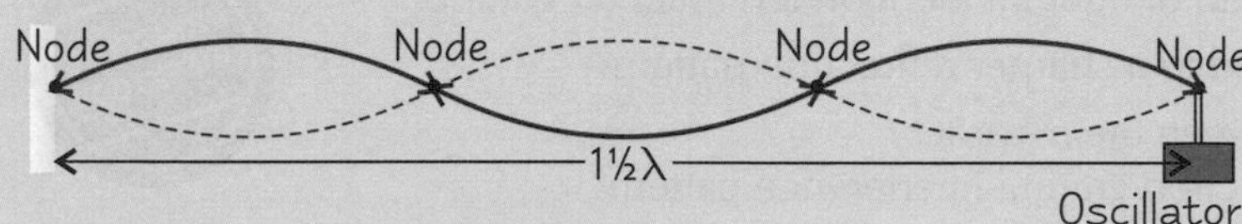

The **third harmonic** is **three times** the fundamental mode of vibration. **1½ wavelengths** fit on the string.

The **Notes** Played by **Stringed** and **Wind Instruments** are Stationary Waves

Transverse stationary waves form on the strings of **stringed instruments** like **violins** and **guitars**. Your finger or the bow sets the **string vibrating** at the point of contact. Waves are sent out in **both directions** and **reflected** back at both ends.

Longitudinal Stationary Waves Form in a **Wind Instrument** or Other Air **Column**

1) If a source of sound is placed at the open end of a flute, piccolo, oboe or other column of air, there will be some **frequencies** for which **resonance** occurs and a stationary wave is set up.
2) If the instrument has a **closed end**, a **node** will form there. You get the lowest resonant frequency when the length, l, of the pipe is a **quarter wavelength**.

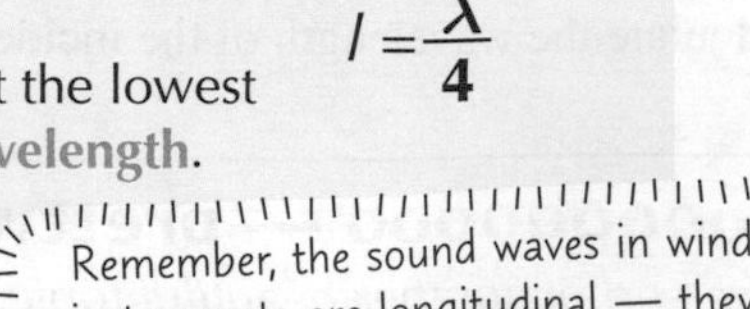

$$l = \frac{\lambda}{4}$$

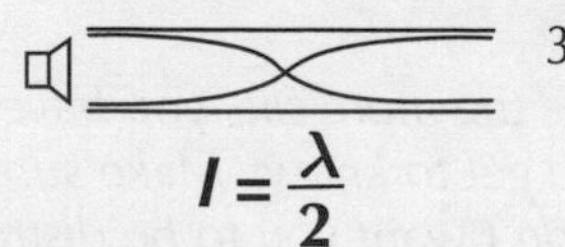

$$l = \frac{\lambda}{2}$$

3) **Antinodes** form at the **open ends** of pipes. If both ends are open, you get the lowest resonant frequency when the length, l, of the pipe is a **half wavelength**.

Remember, the sound waves in wind instruments are longitudinal — they don't actually look like these diagrams.

Stationary (Standing) Waves

You can Demonstrate Stationary Waves with Microwaves

1) Microwaves are produced by a **microwave transmitter**.
2) They are **reflected** off a metal reflecting plate back towards the transmitter.
3) The reflected and incoming waves interfere and set up **stationary waves**.
4) You can find the **nodes** and **antinodes** by moving the **microwave receiver** between the **transmitter** and the **reflecting** plate.
5) Whenever a **node** is detected, the meter will read a minimum value. The meter will show a **maximum** reading when an **antinode** is detected.

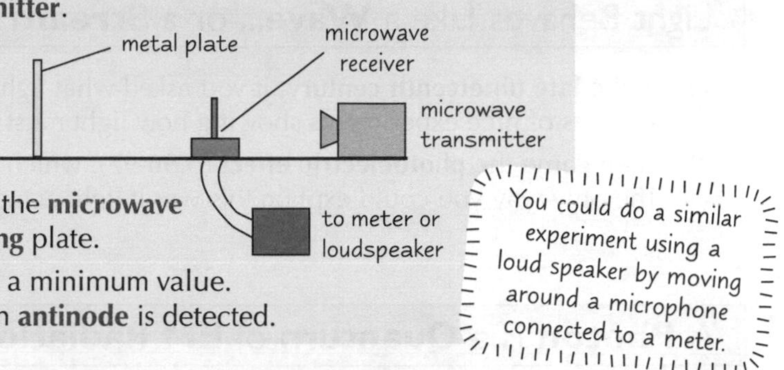

You could do a similar experiment using a loud speaker by moving around a microphone connected to a meter.

You can Use Stationary Waves to Measure the Speed of Sound

PRACTICAL SKILLS

1) You can create a closed-end pipe by placing a **hollow tube** into a measuring cylinder of water.
2) Choose a tuning fork and note down the frequency of sound it produces (it'll be stamped on the side of it).
3) Gently tap the tuning fork and hold it just above the hollow tube. The sound waves produced by the fork travel down the tube and get reflected (and form a **node**) at the air/water surface.
4) Move the tube up and down until you find the **shortest distance** between the top of the tube and the water level that the sound from the fork **resonates** at (when the sound is at its loudest).
5) Just like with any closed pipe, this distance is a **quarter** of the **wavelength** of the stationary sound wave.
6) Once you know the frequency and wavelength of the stationary sound wave, you can work out the speed of sound (in air), v, using the equation $v = f\lambda$.

tuning fork

$\frac{\lambda}{4}$

node

water

hollow plastic tube

measuring cylinder

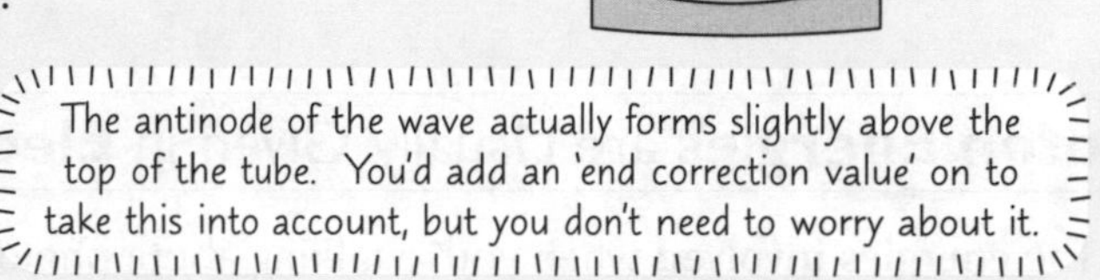

The antinode of the wave actually forms slightly above the top of the tube. You'd add an 'end correction value' on to take this into account, but you don't need to worry about it.

Warm-Up Questions

Q1 How do stationary waves form?

Q2 At four times the first harmonic, how many half wavelengths fit on a violin string?

Q3 Describe an experiment to find the speed of sound in air using stationary waves.

Exam Questions

Q1 a) A stationary wave of three times the first harmonic is formed on a stretched string of length 1.2 m. Sketch a diagram showing the form of the wave. [2 marks]

b) Calculate the wavelength of the stationary wave. [1 mark]

c) Explain how the amplitude varies along the string. How is that different from the amplitude of a progressive wave? [2 marks]

Q2 A stationary wave microwave experiment is set up, using microwaves of 1.00 GHz. At a certain position x, the meter connected to the microwave receiver reads 0.00. The receiver is moved 15.0 cm along the line of the stationary wave until the meter once again reads 0.00. Calculate the speed at which the microwaves are travelling. [4 marks]

CGP — putting the FUN back in FUNdamental mode of vibration...

Resonance was a big problem for the Millennium Bridge in London. The resonant frequency of the bridge was roughly normal walking pace, so as soon as people started using it they set up a huge stationary wave. An oversight, I feel...

Light — Wave or Particle

You probably already thought light was a bit weird — but oh no... being a wave that travels at the fastest speed possible isn't enough for light — it has to go one step further and act like a particle too...

Light Behaves Like a **Wave...** or a **Stream of Particles**

1) In the **late nineteenth century**, if you asked what light was, scientists would happily show you lots of nice experiments showing how light must be a **wave** (see Module 4: Section 2).
2) Then came the **photoelectric effect** (p.96-97), which mucked up everything. The only way you could explain this was if light acted as a **particle** — called a **photon**.

A **Photon** is a **Quantum** of **EM Radiation**

1) When Max Planck was investigating **black body radiation** (don't worry — you don't need to know about that right now), he suggested that **EM waves** can **only** be **released** in **discrete packets**, called **quanta.** A single packet of **EM radiation** is called a **quantum**. The **energy carried** by one of these **wave-packets** had to be:

$$E = hf = \frac{hc}{\lambda}$$

where h = Planck constant = 6.63×10^{-34} Js, f = frequency (Hz), λ = wavelength (m) and c = speed of light in a vacuum = 3.00×10^{8} ms^{-1}

2) So, the **higher** the **frequency** of the electromagnetic radiation, the more **energy** its wave-packets carry.
3) **Einstein** went **further** by suggesting that **EM waves** (and the energy they carry) can only **exist** in discrete packets. He called these wave-packets **photons**.
4) He believed that a photon acts as a **particle**, and will either transfer **all** or **none** of its energy when interacting with another particle, e.g. an electron.
5) Photons have **no charge** — they are **neutral**, like neutrons.

Photon Energies are Usually Given in **Electronvolts**

1) The **energies involved** when you're talking about photons are **so tiny** that it makes sense to use a more **appropriate unit** than the **joule**. Bring on the **electronvolt**...
2) When you **accelerate** an electron between two electrodes, it transfers some electrical potential energy (eV) into kinetic energy.

$$eV = \frac{1}{2}mv^2$$

e is the charge on an electron: 1.60×10^{-19} C. See page 60.

3) An electronvolt is defined as:

   The kinetic energy gained by an electron when it is accelerated through a potential difference of 1 volt.

4) So 1 electron volt = $e \times V = 1.60 \times 10^{-19}$ C $\times$ 1 JC^{-1}. ⟹ **1 eV = 1.60×10^{-19} J**

The **Threshold Voltage** is Used to Find the **Planck Constant**

1) The Planck constant comes up everywhere — but it's not just some random number plucked out of the air. You can find its value by doing a simple experiment with **light-emitting diodes** (**LEDs**).
2) Current will only pass through an LED after a **minimum voltage** is placed across it — **the threshold voltage V_0**.
3) This is the voltage needed to give the electrons the **same energy** as a photon emitted by the LED. **All** of the electron's **kinetic energy** after it is accelerated over this potential difference is **transferred** into a **photon**.
4) So by finding the threshold voltage for a particular wavelength LED, you can estimate the Planck constant.

$$E = \frac{hc}{\lambda} = eV_0 \Rightarrow h = \frac{(eV_0)\lambda}{c}$$

Light — Wave or Particle

You can Use LEDs to Estimate the Planck Constant

You've just seen the **theory** of how to find the **Planck constant** — now it's time for the **practicalities**.

Experiment to Measure the Planck Constant

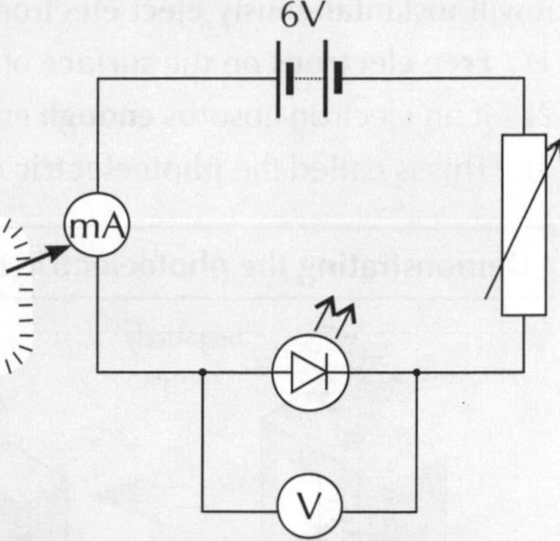

1) Connect an LED of known wavelength in the electrical circuit shown.
2) Start off with no current flowing through the circuit, then adjust the variable resistor until a current just begins to flow through the circuit and the LED lights up.
3) Record the voltage (V_0) across the LED, and the wavelength of light the LED emits.
4) Repeat this experiment with a number of LEDs of different colours that emit light at different wavelengths.

This is a milliammeter — used for measuring small currents.

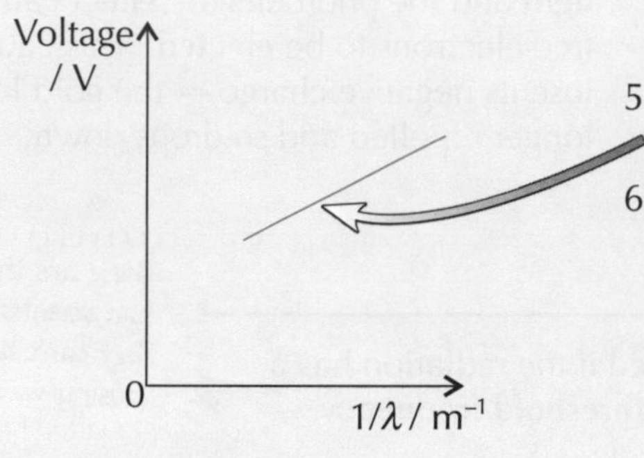

5) Plot a graph of threshold voltages (V_0) against $1/\lambda$ (where λ is the wavelength of light emitted by the LED in metres).
6) You should get a straight line graph with a gradient of hc/e — which you can then use to find the value of h.

E.g. gradient $= \frac{hc}{e} = 1.24 \times 10^{-6}$

$$\text{so } h = \frac{1.24 \times 10^{-6} e}{c} = \frac{(1.24 \times 10^{-6}) \times (1.6 \times 10^{-19})}{3 \times 10^{8}}$$

$$= \mathbf{6.6 \times 10^{-34}\ Js\ (to\ 2\ s.f.)}$$

Warm-Up Questions

Q1 Give two different ways to describe the nature of light.

Q2 What is a photon?

Q3 Write down the two formulas you can use to find the energy of a photon. Include the meanings of all the symbols you use.

Q4 What is an electronvolt? What is 1 eV in joules?

Q5 Describe an experiment to determine the Planck constant using different coloured LEDs.

After careful measurements, Fluffles determined that her plank was indeed constant.

Exam Question

Q1 An LED is tested and found to have a threshold voltage of 1.70 V.

a) Calculate the energy of the photons emitted by the LED. Give your answer in joules. [2 marks]

b) The LED emits light with a wavelength of 700 nm, given to 3 significant figures.
Use your answer from a) to calculate an estimate for the value of the Planck constant. [2 marks]

Millions of light particles are hitting your retinas as you read this... PANIC...

*I hate it in physics when they tell you lies, make you learn it, and just when you've got to grips with it they tell you it was all a load of codswallop. It just makes me doubt all the other things they say. I bet the Earth isn't even round. *Adjusts tin foil hat.* Ahem. This actually is the real deal folks — light isn't just the nice wave you've always known...*

The Photoelectric Effect

The photoelectric effect was one of the original troublemakers in the light-is-it-a-wave-or-a-particle problem...

Shining Light on a **Metal** can **Release Electrons**

If you shine **electromagnetic waves** (e.g. light) of a **high enough frequency** onto the **surface of a metal**, it will **instantaneously eject electrons**. For **most** metals, this **frequency** falls in the **U.V.** range.

1) **Free electrons** on the **surface** of the metal **absorb energy** from the light.
2) If an electron absorbs **enough** energy, the **bonds** holding it to the metal **break** and it is **emitted from the surface**.
3) This is called the **photoelectric effect** and the electrons emitted are called **photoelectrons**.

Demonstrating the photoelectric effect with a gold-leaf electroscope

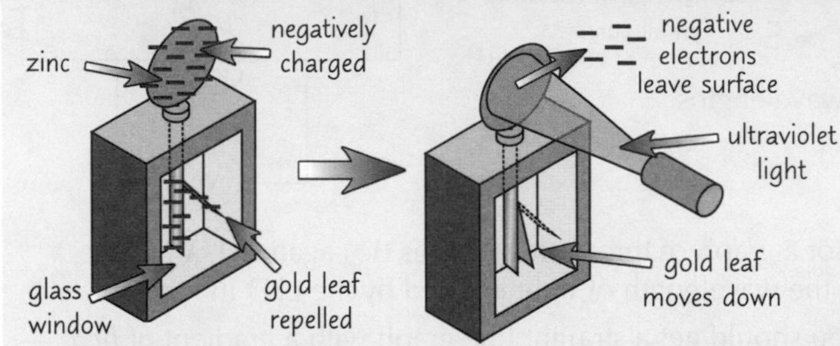

1) The electroscope plate is initially **negatively** charged, so the gold leaf is **repelled**.
2) The zinc plate is then exposed to **ultraviolet light** and the photoelectric effect causes its free electrons to be **ejected**. This causes it to lose its negative charge — the gold leaf is no longer repelled and so drops down.

These are the two that had scientists puzzled. They can't be explained using wave theory.

Conclusion 1: For a given metal, **no photoelectrons are emitted** if the radiation has a frequency **below** a certain value — called the **threshold frequency**.

Conclusion 2: The photoelectrons are emitted with a variety of kinetic energies ranging from zero to some maximum value. This value of **maximum kinetic energy** increases with the **frequency** of the radiation, and is **unaffected** by the **intensity** of the radiation.

Conclusion 3: The **number** of photoelectrons emitted per second is **proportional** to the **intensity** of the radiation.

The **Photoelectric Effect Couldn't** be Explained by **Wave Theory**

According to wave theory:

1) For a particular frequency of light, the **energy** carried is **proportional** to the **intensity** of the beam.
2) The energy carried by the light would be **spread evenly** over the wavefront.
3) **Each** free electron on the surface of the metal would gain a **bit of energy** from each incoming wave.
4) Gradually, each electron would gain **enough energy** to leave the metal.

SO... The **higher the intensity** of the wave, the **more energy** it should transfer to each electron — the kinetic energy should increase with **intensity**. There's **no explanation** for the **kinetic energy** depending only on the **frequency**.

There is also **no explanation** for the **threshold frequency**. According to **wave theory**, the electrons should be emitted **eventually**, no matter what the **frequency** is.

The **Photon Model** Explained the **Photoelectric Effect** Nicely

According to the photon model (see page 94):

1) When light hits its surface, the metal is **bombarded** by photons.
2) If one of these photons is **absorbed** by a free electron, the electron will gain energy equal to hf.

Before an electron can **leave** the surface of the metal, it needs enough energy to **break the bonds holding it there**. This energy is called the **work function energy** (symbol ϕ, phi) and its **value** depends on the **metal**.

The Photoelectric Effect

The **Photon Model** Explains the **Threshold Frequency**...

1) If the energy **gained** by an electron (on the surface of the metal) from a photon is **greater** than the **work function**, the electron is **emitted**.
2) If it **isn't**, the metal will heat up, but **no electrons** will be emitted.
3) Since, for **electrons** to be released, $hf \geq \phi$, the **threshold frequency** must be:

$$f = \frac{\phi}{h}$$

... and the **Maximum Kinetic Energy**

1) The **energy transferred** to an electron is hf.
2) The **kinetic energy** it will be carrying when it **leaves** the metal will be hf **minus** any energy it's **lost** on the way out (there are loads of ways it can do that, and so the emitted electrons have a **range** of energies).
3) The **minimum** amount of energy an electron can lose is the **work function energy**, so the **maximum kinetic energy** is given by **Einstein's photoelectric equation**:

$$hf = \phi + KE_{max} \quad \text{where} \quad KE_{max} = \frac{1}{2}mv_{max}^2$$

$hf = \phi + KE_{max}$ can be rearranged to $KE_{max} = hf - \phi$. This is the same format as $y = mx + c$, so if you plot a graph of KE_{max} against f, the gradient of the line will be h.

4) The **kinetic energy** of the electrons is **independent of the intensity** of the radiation, because they can **only absorb one photon** at a time. A **higher intensity** just means **more** photons hitting a given area per second.
5) But, the **rate of photoelectron emission** is **directly proportional** to the **intensity** of radiation provided it's above the **threshold frequency** — more photons per second means more collisions.

Warm-Up Questions

Q1 Describe an experiment that demonstrates the photoelectric effect.

Q2 What is meant by the term threshold frequency?

Q3 Write down the equation that relates the work function of a metal and the threshold frequency.

Q4 Write down an equation that relates the maximum kinetic energy of a photoelectron released from a metal surface and the frequency of the incident light on the surface.

Exam Questions

$h = 6.63 \times 10^{-34}$ Js; $e = 1.60 \times 10^{-19}$ C

Q1 The work function of calcium is 2.9 eV. Calculate the threshold frequency of radiation needed for the photoelectric effect to take place. [2 marks]

Q2 The surface of a copper plate is illuminated with monochromatic ultraviolet light, with a frequency of 2.0×10^{15} Hz. The work function for copper is 4.7 eV.

a) Calculate the energy in eV carried by one photon of the ultraviolet light. [2 marks]

b) Calculate the maximum kinetic energy of a photoelectron emitted from the copper surface. [2 marks]

Q3 Explain why the photoelectric effect only occurs after the incident light has reached a certain frequency. [2 marks]

I'm so glad we got that all cleared up...

Yep, the photoelectric effect is a bit tricky. The most important bits here are why wave theory doesn't explain the phenomenon, and why the photon theory does. A good way to learn conceptual stuff like this is to try to explain it to someone else. You'll get most formulas in your handy data sheet, but it's probably a good idea to learn them too...

Wave-Particle Duality

Is it a wave? Is it a particle? No, it's a wave. No, it's a particle. No it's not, it's a wave. No don't be daft, it's a particle. (etc.)

Interference and **Diffraction** show **Light** as a **Wave**

1) Light produces **interference** and **diffraction** patterns — **alternating bands** of **dark** and **light**.
2) These can **only** be explained using **waves interfering constructively** (when two waves overlap in phase) or **interfering destructively** (when the two waves are out of phase). (See p.86.)

The **Photoelectric Effect** Shows **Light** Behaving as a **Particle**

1) **Einstein** explained the results of **photoelectricity experiments** (see p.96) by thinking of the **beam of light** as a series of **particle-like photons**.
2) If a **photon** of light is a **discrete** bundle of energy, then it can **interact** with an **electron** in a **one-to-one way**.
3) **All** the **energy** in the **photon** is **given** to one **electron**.

De Broglie Came up With the **Wave-Particle Duality Theory**

1) Louis de Broglie made a **bold suggestion** in his **PhD thesis**:

   If **'wave-like' light** showed **particle properties** (photons), **'particles'** like **electrons** should be expected to show **wave-like properties**.

2) The **de Broglie equation** relates a **wave property** (**wavelength**, λ) to a **moving particle property** (momentum, p). h = Planck constant = 6.63×10^{-34} Js.

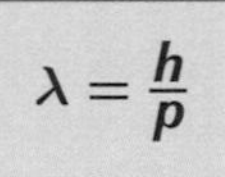

$$\lambda = \frac{h}{p}$$

I'm not impressed — this is just speculation. What do you think Dad?

3) The de Broglie wave of a particle can be interpreted as a **'probability wave'** — the **likelihood** of finding a particle at a point is **directly proportional** to the **square** of the **amplitude** of the wave at that point.
4) Many physicists at the time **weren't very impressed** — his ideas were just **speculation**. But later experiments **confirmed** the wave nature of electrons.

Electron Diffraction shows the **Wave Nature** of **Electrons**

1) In **1927**, two American physicists, **Clinton Davisson** and **Lester Germer**, succeeded in diffracting **electrons**.
2) **Diffraction patterns** are observed when **accelerated electrons** in a vacuum tube **interact** with the **spaces** between **carbon atoms** in **polycrystalline graphite**.
3) This **confirms** that electrons show **wave-like** properties.
4) According to wave theory, the **spread** of the **lines** in the diffraction pattern **increases** if the **wavelength** of the wave is **greater**.
5) In electron diffraction experiments, a **smaller accelerating voltage**, i.e. **slower** electrons, gives **widely spaced** rings.
6) **Increase** the **electron speed** and the diffraction pattern circles **squash together** towards the **middle**. This fits in with the **de Broglie** equation above — if the **momentum** is **higher**, the **wavelength** is **shorter** and the **spread** of lines is **smaller**.
7) Electron diffraction was a **huge** discovery — this was the first **direct evidence** for de Broglie's theory.

In general, λ for **electrons** accelerated in a **vacuum tube** is about the **same size** as **electromagnetic waves** in the **X-ray** part of the spectrum.

Wave-Particle Duality

Particles Don't show Wave-Like Properties All the Time

1) You **only** get **diffraction** if a particle interacts with an object of about the **same size** as its **de Broglie wavelength**.
2) A **tennis ball**, for example, with **mass 0.058 kg** and **speed 100 ms^{-1}** has a **de Broglie wavelength** of **10^{-34} m**. That's **10^{19} times smaller** than the **nucleus** of an **atom**! There's nothing that small for it to interact with.

Example: An electron of mass 9.11×10^{-31} kg is fired from an electron gun at 7.00×10^{6} ms^{-1}. What size object will the electron need to interact with in order to diffract?

Momentum of electron = $p = mv = (9.11 \times 10^{-31}) \times (7.00 \times 10^{6}) = 6.377 \times 10^{-24}$ kg ms^{-1}

$$\lambda = \frac{h}{p} = \frac{6.63 \times 10^{-34}}{6.377 \times 10^{-24}} = \mathbf{1.04 \times 10^{-10}\ m\ (to\ 3\ s.f.)}$$

Electrons with a wavelength of around **1×10^{-10} m** are **likely** to be diffracted by the atoms in **polycrystalline structures**.

3) A **shorter wavelength** gives **less diffraction effects**. This fact is used in the **electron microscope**.
4) **Diffraction** effects **blur detail** on an image. If you want to **resolve tiny detail** in an **image**, you need a **shorter wavelength**. **Light** blurs out detail more than **'electron-waves'** do, so an **electron microscope** can resolve **finer detail** than a **light microscope**. They can let you look at things as tiny as a single strand of DNA... which is nice.

Warm-Up Questions

Q1 Which observations show light to have a 'wave-like' character?
Q2 Which observations show light to have a 'particle' character?
Q3 What happens to the de Broglie wavelength of a particle if its velocity increases?
Q4 Describe the experimental evidence that shows electrons have a 'wave-like' character.

Exam Questions

proton mass, $m_p = 1.673 \times 10^{-27}$ kg; electron mass, $m_e = 9.11 \times 10^{-31}$ kg

Q1 a) State what is meant by the wave-particle duality of electromagnetic radiation. [1 mark]

b) Calculate the momentum of an electron with a de Broglie wavelength of 590 nm. [2 marks]

Q2 Electrons travelling at a speed of 3.50×10^{6} ms^{-1} exhibit wave properties.

a) Calculate the wavelength of these electrons. [2 marks]

b) Calculate the speed of protons which would have the same wavelength as these electrons. [2 marks]

c) Some electrons and protons were accelerated from rest by the same potential difference, giving them the same kinetic energy. Explain why they will have different wavelengths. [3 marks]

Q3 Electrons are directed at a thin slice of graphite at high speed and a diffraction pattern is observed. Which of the following statements correctly describe a conclusion that this observation supports? [1 mark]

1 Electrons can show particle-like behaviour.
2 Waves can show particle-like behaviour.
3 Photons can show wave-like behaviour.
4 Electrons can show wave-like behaviour.

A 1, 2 and 4 B 4 only C 3 only D 1 and 4 only

Don't hide your wave-particles under a bushel...

Right — I think we'll all agree that quantum physics is a wee bit strange when you come to think about it. What it's saying is that electrons and photons aren't really waves, and they aren't really particles — they're both... at the same time. It's what quantum physicists like to call a 'juxtaposition of states'. Well they would, wouldn't they...

Extra Exam Practice

Well that's Module 4 settled. These questions test if you can apply it all together to unfamiliar contexts.

- Have a look at this example of how to answer a tricky exam question.
- Then check how much you've understood from Module 4 by having a go at the questions on the next page.

When you've finished these, there's some synoptic questions covering content from AS/Year 1 of A level on pages 192-195.

1 **Figure 1** shows two monochromatic rays of light incident on the surface of a material. One ray is red and one ray is blue. Both rays are directed into the material at the same angle to the normal, θ. **Table 1** shows the frequency and the material's refractive index for each ray of light. The material is surrounded by air, which has a refractive index of 1.

Figure 1

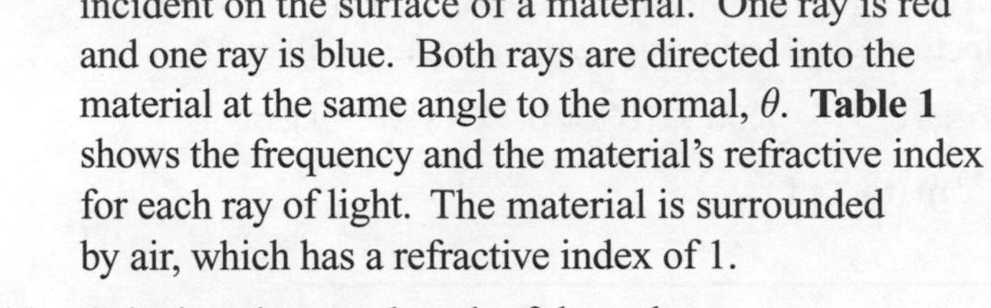

(a) Calculate the wavelength of the red ray in the material. ($c = 3.00 \times 10^8$ ms^{-1})

(2 marks)

Table 1

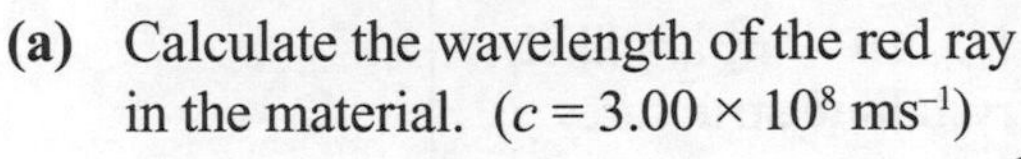

Colour	Frequency / $\times 10^{14}$ Hz	Refractive index of material (n_m)
Red	4.57	1.224
Blue	6.59	1.231

(b) Both rays fully reflect when they meet the upper boundary of the material. The angle θ in **Figure 1** is slowly increased for both rays of light. Determine by calculation which ray of light will begin to refract out of the upper boundary of the material first as θ is increased.

(4 marks)

1(a)

It's not immediately obvious how to use what you've got to find the wavelength. You know $v = f\lambda$ and you've got f, so chances are you'll need to set about trying to find the speed, v.

First, calculate the speed of red light in the material:

$n_m = \frac{c}{v_m}$, so $v_m = \frac{c}{n_m} = (3.00 \times 10^8) \div 1.224 = 2.450... \times 10^8$ ms^{-1}

$v = f\lambda$, so the wavelength of red light in the material is:

$\lambda = v_m \div f_{red} = (2.450... \times 10^8) \div (\mathbf{4.57 \times 10^{14}}) = 5.363... \times 10^{-7}$ m

$= 5.36 \times 10^{-7}$ m (to 3 s.f.)

Remember, frequency doesn't change during refraction, so the frequency in the material is just the value given in Table 1.

You'd get 2 marks for the correct answer, otherwise it's 1 mark for calculating v_m for red light.

1(b)

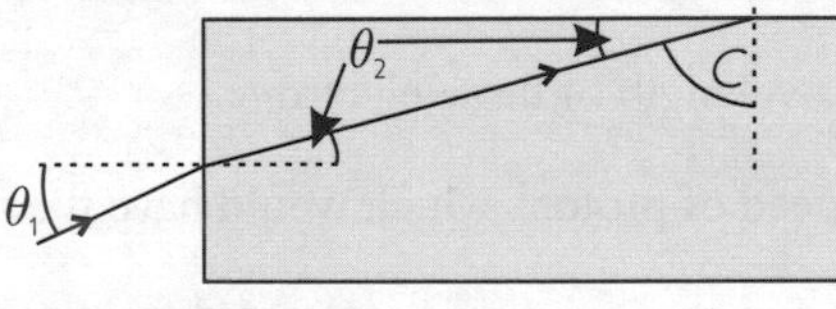

It's handy to draw a diagram before you start — this makes it easier to keep track of angles and what's going on.

For each ray, calculate the angle of incidence, θ_1, when C is equal to the critical angle, as shown in the diagram:

At the critical angle, $\sin C = \frac{1}{n_m}$, so $C = \sin^{-1}\left(\frac{1}{n_m}\right)$.

The angle of refraction: $\theta_2 = 90 - C$, so $\theta_2 = 90 - \sin^{-1}\left(\frac{1}{n_m}\right)$

$n\sin\theta$ = constant, so $n_1\sin\theta_1 = n_2\sin\theta_2$.

When the light enters the material, $n_1 = n_{air} = 1$, and n_2 equals n_m:

$\sin\theta_1 = n_m\sin\theta_2 = n_m\sin\left(90 - \sin^{-1}\left(\frac{1}{n_m}\right)\right)$, so $\theta_1 = \sin^{-1}\left(n_m\sin\left(90 - \sin^{-1}\left(\frac{1}{n_m}\right)\right)\right)$

For red: $\theta_1 = \sin^{-1}\left(1.224 \times \sin\left(90 - \sin^{-1}\left(\frac{1}{1.224}\right)\right)\right) = 44.895...°$

For blue: $\theta_1 = \sin^{-1}\left(1.231 \times \sin\left(90 - \sin^{-1}\left(\frac{1}{1.231}\right)\right)\right) = 45.880...°$

There's a lot of equations going on here — for this question it's easier to wait until the end to substitute any numbers in.

The red light will be the first ray to refract out of the material as it reaches the critical angle at a smaller angle of θ_1 than the blue light.

Don't forget to write a conclusion once you've done all the calculations, otherwise you won't have fully answered the question.

You'd get 1 mark for the correct equation for θ_1, 1 mark for calculating θ_1 for red light, 1 mark for calculating θ_1 for blue light, and 1 mark for a correct conclusion linking to the calculations.

Extra Exam Practice

2 A student investigates the electronic systems inside a car.

(a) The main purpose of a car battery is to start the engine. To start the engine a very large current is supplied to the starter motor for a short amount of time. The starter motor will not start the engine unless a minimum potential difference, V, is applied across it. Most car batteries have an e.m.f. rated at approximately this minimum value, V. Explain why a car battery must have a very low internal resistance in order to start the engine.

(2 marks)

(b)* Describe an experiment that the student could carry out to investigate the internal resistance of a car battery. In your answer you should include an explanation of how the student can ensure valid and accurate results.

(6 marks)

Figure 2

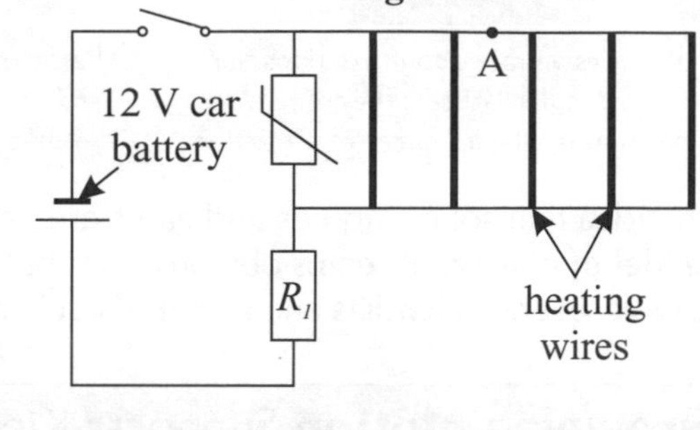

A student is designing a circuit that keeps a car's rear window glass mist-free when the temperature outside is low. **Figure 2** shows a simplified circuit that the student uses to model the five heating wires that are embedded in the glass. The greater the current flowing through the heating wires, the hotter they get. **Figure 3** shows how the resistance of the thermistor changes with the outside temperature. The resistance of resistor R_1 is 2.50 Ω.

Figure 3

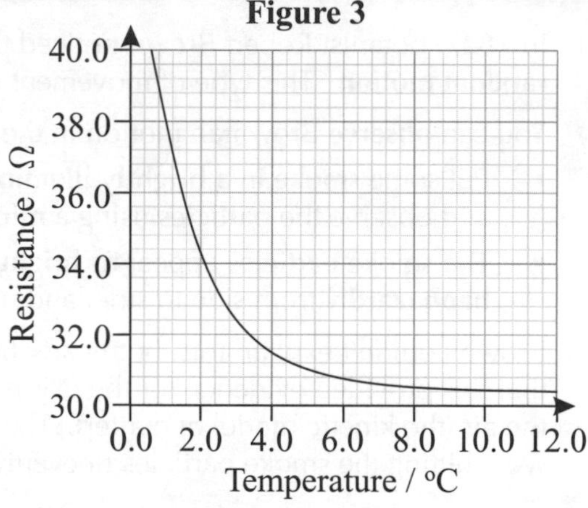

(c) Each wire has a diameter of 0.102 mm and a length of 1.25 m. The resistivity of each wire is 3.86×10^{-8} Ωm. Show that when the outside temperature is 1.0 °C, the potential difference across each heating wire is 3.8 V.

(4 marks)

(d) Calculate the current at point A on the circuit, shown in **Figure 2**, when the outside temperature is 1.0 °C.

(2 marks)

Figure 4

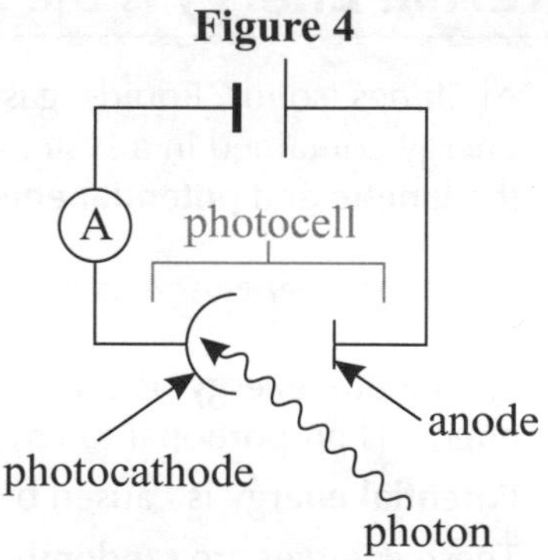

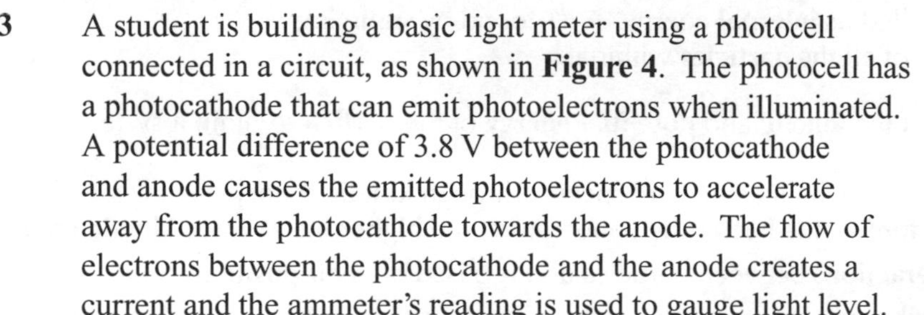

3 A student is building a basic light meter using a photocell connected in a circuit, as shown in **Figure 4**. The photocell has a photocathode that can emit photoelectrons when illuminated. A potential difference of 3.8 V between the photocathode and anode causes the emitted photoelectrons to accelerate away from the photocathode towards the anode. The flow of electrons between the photocathode and the anode creates a current and the ammeter's reading is used to gauge light level.

(a) For a certain frequency of incident photons, the maximum speed of a photoelectron reaching the anode is 1.5×10^{6} ms^{-1}. Calculate the maximum kinetic energy of photoelectrons emitted from the photocathode. ($e = 1.60 \times 10^{-19}$ C, $m_e = 9.11 \times 10^{-31}$ kg)

(3 marks)

(b) The work function of the photocathode is 4.1 eV. Calculate the momentum of the photons incident on the photocathode. ($c = 3.00 \times 10^{8}$ ms^{-1}, $h = 6.63 \times 10^{-34}$ Js)

(3 marks)

(c) The intensity of the incident light on the photocathode increases. State the effect this has, if any, on the current in the circuit. Explain your answer.

(2 marks)

* The quality of your extended response will be assessed in this question.

Phases of Matter and Temperature

You need energy to heat something up, and to change its state. Everything comes down to energy. Pretty much always.

The Three Phases of Matter are Defined by the Arrangement of Particles

You'll remember these **three phases** (or states) **of matter** (**solid**, **liquid** and **gas**) from GCSE — but here's a quick recap just in case.

Particles vibrate about fixed positions in a regular lattice. They're held in position by strong forces of attraction.

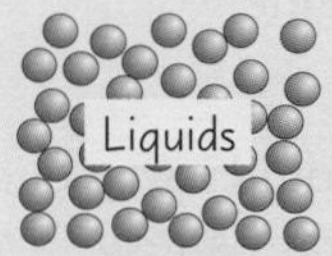

Particles are constantly moving around and are free to move past one another, but are attracted to each other.

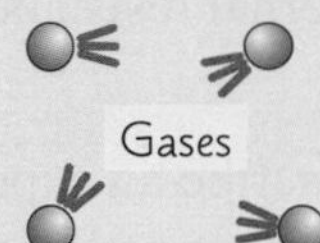

Particles are free to move around with constant random motion. There are no forces of attraction between particles in an ideal gas.

The idea that solids, liquids and gases are made up of **tiny** moving or vibrating **particles** is called the **kinetic model of matter**. It seems obvious now, but this **wasn't** always accepted by the scientific community. It took **several scientists** and **hundreds of years** to **develop** a **controversial idea** into an **accepted theory**.

Brownian Motion Supports Kinetic Theory

1) In 1827, botanist Robert Brown noticed that tiny particles of pollen suspended in water moved with a **zigzag, random motion**. This type of movement of any particle suspended in a fluid is known as **Brownian motion**.
2) You can **observe** Brownian motion in the lab:
   - Put some **smoke** in a **brightly illuminated** glass jar and observe the particles using a **microscope**.
   - The smoke particles appear as **bright specks** moving **haphazardly** from side to side, and up and down.
3) Brown couldn't explain this, but nearly 80 years later Einstein showed that this provided evidence for the existence of atoms or **molecules** in the air (the kinetic model of matter). The **randomly moving** air particles were hitting the smoke particles unevenly, causing this motion.

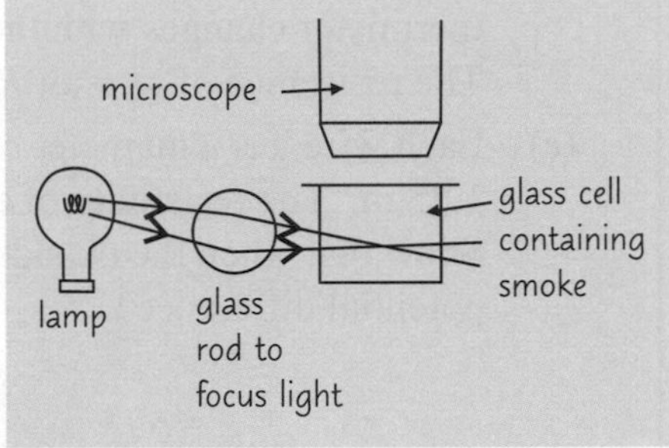

Internal Energy is the Sum of Kinetic and Potential Energy

1) All things (solids, liquids, gases) have **energy** contained within them. The amount of **energy** contained in a system is called its **internal energy** — it's found by **summing** the **kinetic** and **potential energies** of all the **particles** within it.

> **Internal energy** is the **sum** of the **kinetic** and **potential energy** of the **particles** within a system.

2) The **kinetic energy** of a particle depends on its **mass** and **speed**. Through **kinetic theory**, the average kinetic energy is proportional to **temperature** — the **hotter** the temperature, the **higher** the **average kinetic energy**.
3) **Potential energy** is caused by **interactions** between particles and is based on their **positions** relative to each other.
4) These energies are **randomly distributed** amongst the particles.

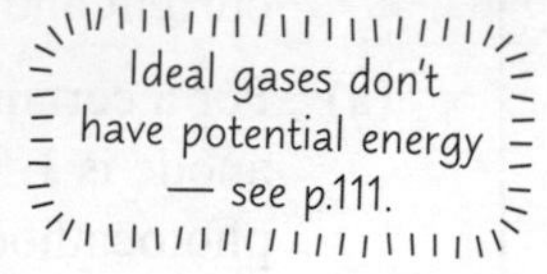

A Change of Phase Means a Change of Internal Energy

1) When you **heat** a substance, you **increase** its **temperature** — thereby **increasing** the **kinetic energy** of the particles within it and its **internal energy**.
2) When a substance **changes phase**, its **internal energy** changes, but its **kinetic energy** (and temperature) **doesn't**. This is because the change of phase is altering the bonds and therefore **potential energy** of the particles.
3) For example, in a pan of **boiling water**, the **potential energy** of the water molecules **increases** as they break free of the liquid. But the water in both phases is at **100 °C**.

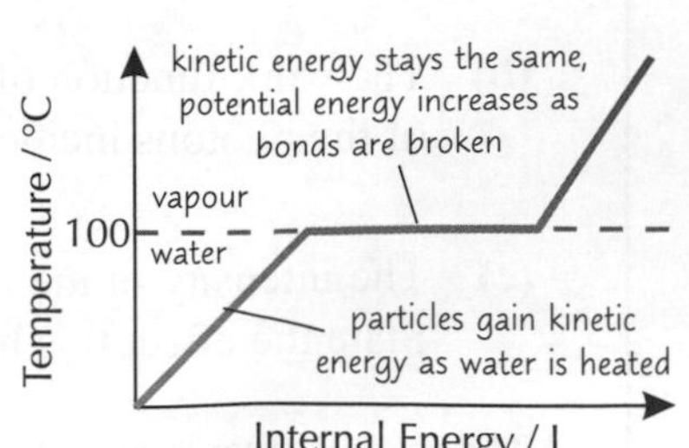

Phases of Matter and Temperature

There's an Absolute Scale of Temperature

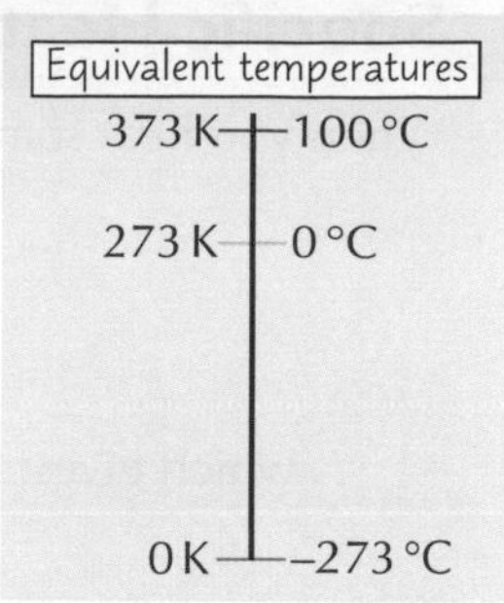

*It's true. –273 °C is the lowest temperature theoretically possible. Weird, huh. You'd kinda think there wouldn't be a minimum, but there is.

The **Celsius scale** uses the **freezing** and **boiling points** of **water** (0 °C and 100 °C) to make a temperature scale which can be easily used for **day to day** activities. However, scientists use the **kelvin** scale (**the absolute scale of temperature**) for **all equations** in **thermal physics**.

It's also known as the **thermodynamic scale**, and it does not **depend** on the properties of any **particular substance**, unlike the **Celsius** scale.

Zero kelvins is the **lowest possible temperature** and is called **absolute zero***.

At **0 K** all particles have the **minimum** possible **internal energy** — everything theoretically stops — at higher temperatures, particles have more energy. In fact, with the **Kelvin scale**, a particle's **energy** is **proportional** to its **temperature** (see page 111).

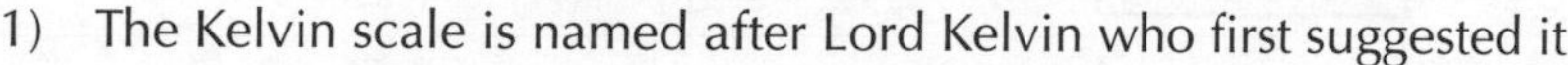

1) The Kelvin scale is named after Lord Kelvin who first suggested it.
2) A change of **1 K** equals a change of **1 °C**.
3) To change from degrees Celsius into kelvins you **add 273** (or subtract 273 to go the other way).

$$T(\text{K}) \approx \theta(^\circ\text{C}) + 273$$

If A and B are in Thermal Equilibrium with C, A is in Equilibrium with B

If **body A** and **body B** are both in **thermal equilibrium** with **body C**, then **body A** and **body B** must be in thermal equilibrium with **each other**.

1) Suppose A, B and C are three identical metal blocks. A has been in a **warm oven**, B has come from a **refrigerator** and C is at **room temperature**.
2) **Thermal energy** flows from A to C and C to B until they all reach **thermal equilibrium** and the net flow of energy stops. This happens when the three blocks are at the **same temperature**.

Thermal energy is **always** transferred from regions of **higher temperature** to regions of **lower temperature**.

Warm-Up Questions

Q1 What is internal energy?

Q2 What happens to the kinetic and potential energies of water molecules as water boils?

Q3 Explain the difference between the Celsius and Kelvin scales.

Q4 What is the boiling point of water in kelvins?

Q5 State in degrees Celsius the lowest possible temperature that a substance could theoretically be cooled to and explain why it cannot be cooled any further.

Q6 Describe what will happen to the thermal energy and temperatures of a hot metal tray and a cold metal spoon when they are placed touching each other.

Exam Questions

Q1 Describe the spacing, ordering and motion of particles in solids, liquids and gases. [3 marks]

Q2 Brownian motion provides evidence for the continual random motion of particles in a gas.

a) Describe an experiment you could use to demonstrate Brownian motion. [2 marks]

b) Explain how Brownian motion supports the theory of the random movement of particles. [2 marks]

Brownieaan motion — we collided, then I dropped the cake down the stairs...

Celsius, I'm sorry — it's not you it's me, I just need someone more absolute and proportional, who is always positive. We'll still be friends and see each other in weather forecasts and ovens, we just can't be together in thermal physics...

Thermal Properties of Materials

This couple of pages has more heat than Guy Fawkes on bonfire night. Phwoar...

Specific Heat Capacity is how much Energy it Takes to Heat Something

When you heat something, the amount of energy needed to raise its **temperature** depends on its **specific heat capacity**.

The **specific heat capacity** (c) of a substance is the amount of **energy** needed to **raise** the **temperature** of **1 kg** of the substance by **1 K** (or 1°C).

which gives: **energy change = mass × specific heat capacity × change in temperature**

in symbols: $E = mc\Delta\theta$ ← Q is sometimes used instead of E for the change in thermal energy.

E is the energy change in J, m is the mass in kg and $\Delta\theta$ is the temperature change in K or °C.
Units of c are $\text{J kg}^{-1}\text{ K}^{-1}$ or $\text{J kg}^{-1}\ ^\circ\text{C}^{-1}$.

You can Measure Specific Heat Capacity in the Laboratory

The **method** is the same for **solids** and **liquids**, but the **set-up** is a little bit different:

Specific Heat Capacity of a Solid

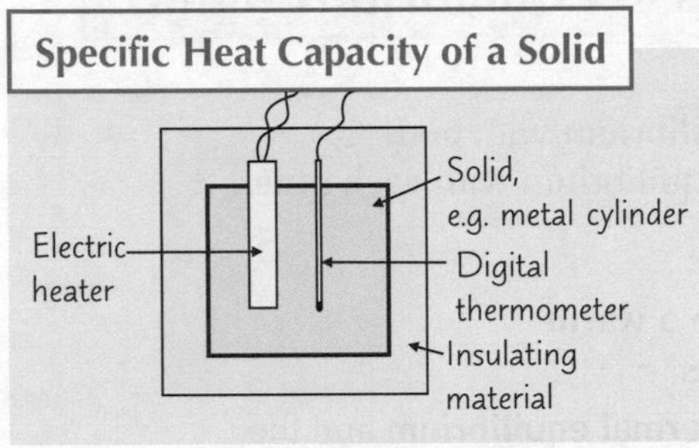

Specific Heat Capacity of a Liquid

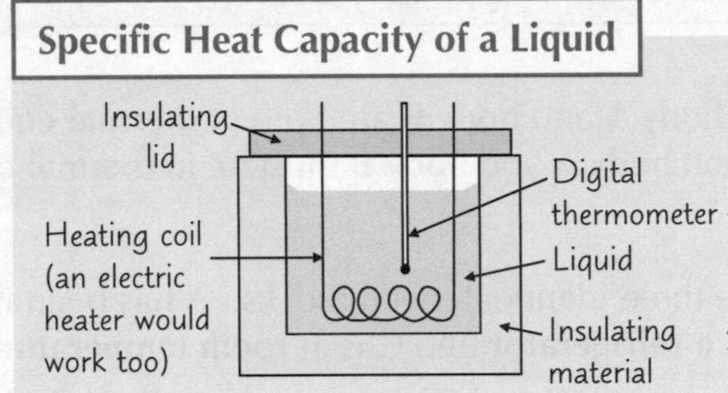

The value you end up with for c will probably be too high by quite a long way. That's because some of the energy from the heater gets transferred to the air and the container. If you're really keen, start below and finish above room temperature to cancel out gains and losses.

Method for both experiments:

1) **Heat** the substance with the heater. You need a **temperature rise** of about 10 K to get an **accurate** value of c.
2) With an ammeter and voltmeter attached to your **electric heater** you can work out the energy supplied. Calculate the energy (E) using: $E = W = VIt$ (V is the heater voltage, I is the current and t is the time in seconds)
3) Plug your data into: $E = mc\Delta\theta$ to calculate c.

Example: You heat 0.250 kg of water from 12.1 °C to 22.9 °C with an electric immersion heater. The heater has a voltage of 11.2 V and a current of 5.30 A, and is switched on for 205 s. Calculate the specific heat capacity of water.

$E = VIt = 11.2 \times 5.30 \times 205 = 12\,168.8$ J $\qquad \Delta\theta = 22.9 - 12.1 = 10.8$ °C

$$E = mc\Delta\theta \text{ so } c = \frac{E}{m\Delta\theta} = \frac{12168.8}{0.250 \times 10.8} = 4506.9... = \mathbf{4510\ J\,kg^{-1}\,^\circ C^{-1}}\ (\text{or } 4510\ \text{J kg}^{-1}\text{K}^{-1})\ \textbf{(to 3 s.f.)}$$

Estimating the Specific Heat Capacity of a Metal Block Using the Method of Mixtures

1) Heat a metal block of known mass, m_b, up to a temperature T_b.
2) Quickly transfer this block into a container containing a mass of water, m_w, at a temperature T_w.
3) The hot block will heat the water. Measure the temperature of the water once it has reached a **steady** value, T_s.
4) The **heat (energy) gained** by the water is **equal** to the **heat lost** by the block, so:
   $m_w c_w \Delta\theta_w = m_b c_b \Delta\theta_b$ which becomes: $m_w c_w (T_s - T_w) = m_b c_b (T_b - T_s)$
5) Rearrange for c_b: $c_b = \dfrac{m_w c_w (T_s - T_w)}{m_b (T_b - T_s)}$

Thermal Properties of Materials

Specific Latent Heat is the Energy Required to Change State per kg

To **melt** a **solid**, you need to **break the bonds** that hold the particles in place. The **energy** needed for this is called the **latent heat of fusion**. Similarly, when you **boil or evaporate a liquid**, **energy is needed** to **pull the particles apart** completely. This is the **latent heat of vaporisation**.

The **larger** the **mass** of the substance, the **more energy** it takes to **change** its **state**. That's why the **specific latent heat** is defined per kg:

> The **specific latent heat** (*L*) of **fusion** or **vaporisation** is the quantity of **thermal energy** required to **change the state** of **1 kg** of a substance.

You wouldn't be laughing if it was your bum stuck to the ice. I need some latent heat energy, pronto.

which gives: **energy change = mass of substance changed × specific latent heat**

or in symbols: $E = mL$

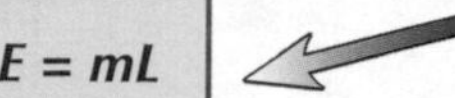

You'll usually see the latent heat of vaporisation written L_v and the latent heat of fusion written L_f

Where E is the energy change in J and m is the mass in kg. The units of L are J kg^{-1}.

Measuring the Specific Latent Heat of a Solid or Liquid

PRACTICAL SKILLS

For a **solid**, e.g. ice:

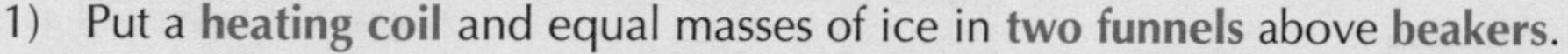

1) Put a **heating coil** and equal masses of ice in **two funnels** above **beakers**.

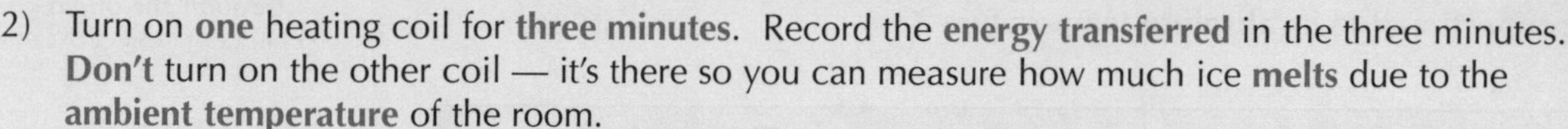

2) Turn on **one** heating coil for **three minutes**. Record the **energy transferred** in the three minutes. **Don't** turn on the other coil — it's there so you can measure how much ice **melts** due to the **ambient temperature** of the room.
3) At the end of the three minutes, **measure** the **mass of water** collected in the beakers. Subtract one from the other to get the mass of ice, *m*, that melted **solely** due to the presence of the **heater**.
4) $E = mL$, so to find the **specific latent heat of fusion** for water just **divide** the energy supplied by the mass of ice that melted: $L = E \div m$

For a **liquid**, you can do a very similar experiment — use a heating coil to **boil** water in a **beaker**, then **divide** the **energy transferred** by the coil while the water is boiling by the **change in mass** of the water.

Warm-Up Questions

Q1 Define specific heat capacity.

Q2 Show that the thermal energy needed to heat 2 kg of water from 20 °C to 50 °C is ~250 kJ (c_{water} = 4180 Jkg^{-1}K^{-1}).

Q3 Describe an experiment to determine the specific heat capacity of olive oil.

Q4 Describe two ways you could measure the specific heat capacity of a metal block.

Q5 Define the specific latent heats of fusion and vaporisation and describe experiments to find them for water.

Exam Questions

Q1 A 2.0 kg metal cylinder is heated uniformly from 4.5 °C to 12.7 °C in 3.0 minutes. The electric heater supplies energy at a rate of 90.0 Js^{-1}. Assuming that heat losses are negligible, calculate the specific heat capacity of the metal. State a correct unit for your answer. [3 marks]

Q2 A 4.0 kg metal block is heated to 100 °C (correct to 2 significant figures). It is then transferred into a container holding 2.0 kg of water (c = 4180 J kg^{-1} K^{-1}) at a temperature of 19 °C. The water warms to a steady temperature of 26 °C. Find an estimate for the specific heat capacity of the metal. [2 marks]

Q3 A 3.00 kW electric kettle contains 0.500 kg of water already at its boiling point. Neglecting heat losses, calculate the length of time it will take to boil dry. (L_v (water) = 2.26 × 10^6 J kg^{-1}) [3 marks]

My specific eat capacity — 24 pies...

This stuff's a bit dull, but hey... make sure you're comfortable using those equations. Interesting(ish) fact for the day — the huge difference in specific heat capacity between the land and the sea is one of the causes of monsoons in Asia.

Ideal Gases

Aaahh... great... another one of those 'our equation doesn't work properly with real gases, so we'll invent an ideal gas that it does work for and they'll think we're dead clever' situations. Hmm. Physicists, eh...

There are **Three Gas Laws...**

A (theoretical) **ideal gas** obeys all three gas laws

The three gas laws were each worked out **independently** by **careful experiment**. Each law applies to a **fixed mass** of gas.

Boyle's Law: pV = constant

At a **constant temperature**, the **pressure** p and **volume** V of a gas are **inversely proportional.**

The higher the temperature of the gas, the further the curve is from the origin.

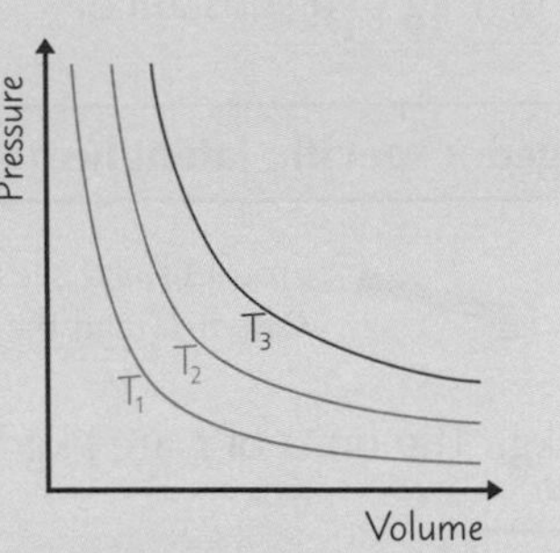

The Pressure Law: $p \div T$ = constant

At a constant **volume**, the **pressure** p of a gas is **directly proportional** to its **absolute temperature** T.

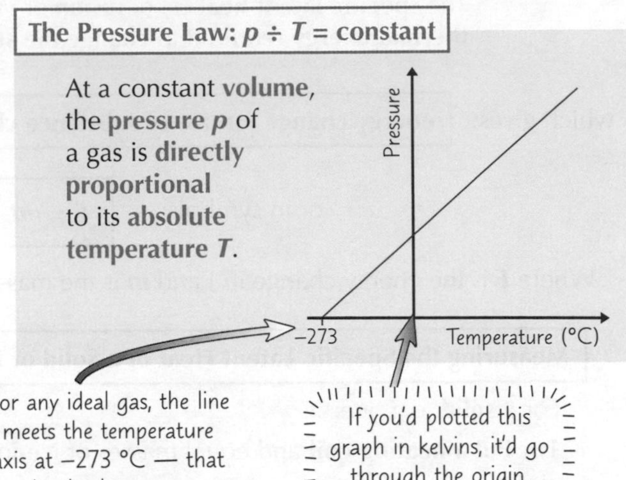

The third gas law, **Charles's Law**, says that at a constant **pressure**, the **volume** V of a gas is **directly proportional** to its **absolute temperature** T.

...which you can **Demonstrate** with these **Experiments**

PRACTICAL SKILLS

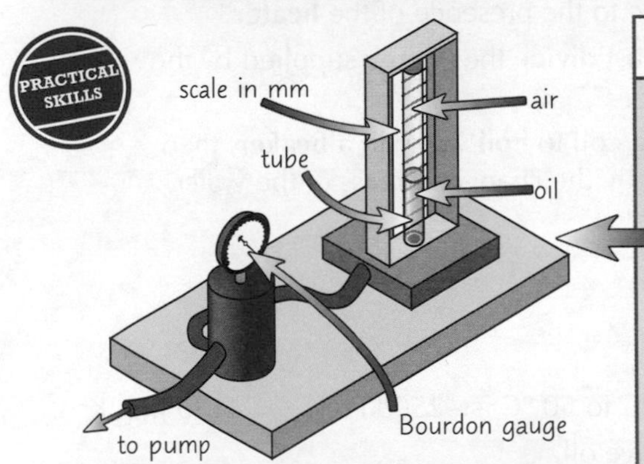

Experiment to investigate pressure and volume (Boyle's Law)

1) You can investigate the effect of **pressure** on **volume** by setting up the experiment shown. The **oil** confines a parcel of air in a sealed **tube** with **fixed dimensions**. A **tyre pump** is used to **increase** the pressure in the tube and the **Bourdon gauge** records the **pressure**. As the pressure increases the air will **compress** and the volume occupied by air in the tube will **reduce**.
2) Measure the volume of air when the system is at **atmospheric pressure**, then gradually increase the pressure noting down **both** the pressure and the volume of air. Multiplying them together at any point should give a **constant**.

Experiment to estimate absolute zero (Pressure Law)

1) Immerse a stoppered flask of **air** in a beaker of water so that as much as possible of the flask is **submerged**. Connect the stopper to a **Bourdon gauge** using a short length of tube — the volume of the tubing must be **much smaller** than the volume of the flask. Record the **temperature** of the water and the **pressure** on the gauge.
2) **Heat** the water for a few minutes then remove the heat, **stir** the water to ensure it is at a **uniform temperature** and allow some time for the heat to be **transferred** from the water to the air. Record the **pressure** on the gauge and the **temperature**, then heat the water again and **repeat** until the water boils.
3) **Repeat** your experiment **twice** more with **fresh cool water**.
4) Plot your results on a graph of **pressure** against **temperature**. Draw a **line of best fit**. Estimate the value of **absolute zero** by **continuing** (extrapolating) your line of best fit until it crosses the ***x*-axis**.

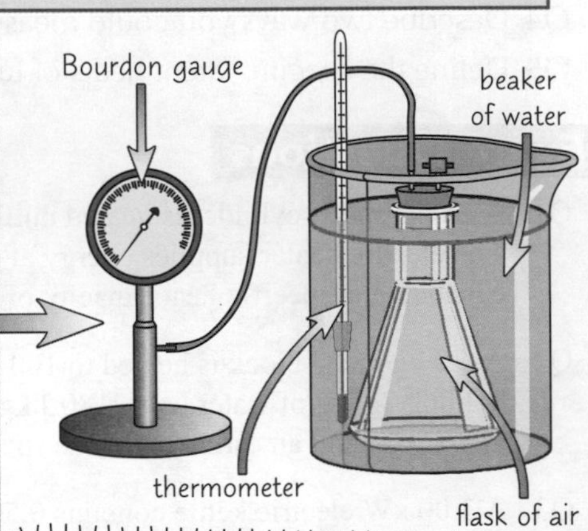

If the markings on your measuring equipment are quite far apart, you can often interpolate between them (e.g. if the temperature is halfway between the markings for 24 °C and 25 °C you could record it as 24.5 °C). But it's better to use something with a finer scale if you can.

Ideal Gases

If you Combine All Three you get the Equation of State

Combining all three gas laws gives the equation: $p\frac{V}{T}$ **= constant**

1) The constant in the equation depends on the amount of gas used. The amount of **gas** can be **measured** in **moles**, ***n***.
2) The constant then becomes ***nR***, where ***R*** is called the **molar gas constant**. Its value is 8.31 J mol^{-1} K^{-1}. Plugging this into the equation gives:

$p\frac{V}{T} = nR$ or rearranging, $pV = nRT$ — ***the equation of state of an ideal gas***

p is pressure (Pa), *V* is volume (m^3), *T* is temperature (K), *n* is amount of gas in moles (see below)

3) This equation works well (i.e., real gases approximate to an ideal gas) for gases at **low pressures** and fairly **high temperatures**.

The Boltzmann Constant k is like a Gas Constant for One Particle of Gas

One mole of **any** material contains the same **number of particles**, no matter what the material is. This number is called **Avogadro's constant** and has the symbol N_A. The value of N_A is **6.02 × 10^{23} particles per mole.**

1) The **number of particles**, *N*, in an amount of gas is given by the **number of moles**, ***n***, multiplied by **Avogadro's constant**, N_A. → $N = nN_A$
2) The **Boltzmann constant**, ***k***, is given by $k = \frac{R}{N_A}$ — you can think of the Boltzmann constant as the **gas constant** for **one particle of gas**, while ***R*** is the gas constant for **one mole of gas.**
3) The value of the Boltzmann constant is **1.38 × 10^{-23} JK^{-1}.**
4) If you combine $N = nN_A$ and $k = R/N_A$ you'll see that $Nk = nR$ — which can be substituted into the equation of state to give this alternative form (in terms of number of particles *N*, rather than moles, *n*). → $pV = NkT$

Warm-Up Questions

PRACTICE QUESTIONS

Q1 State Boyle's Law and describe an experiment you could use to investigate it.

Q2 Describe an experiment you could use to find an estimate for the value of absolute zero.

Q3 The pressure of a gas is 100 000 Pa and its temperature is 27.0 °C. The gas is heated — its volume stays fixed but the pressure rises to 150 000 Pa. Show that its new temperature is 177 °C.

Q4 Give the equation of state of an ideal gas and use the Boltzmann constant to derive an alternative form.

Exam Questions

Q1 The pressure inside a gas cylinder is 1.04 × 10^6 Pa at 10.0 °C. It is heated in a fire to 62.3 °C. Calculate the new pressure inside the cylinder. [2 marks]

Q2 The mass of one mole of nitrogen gas is 0.0280 kg. $R = 8.31$ J mol^{-1} K^{-1}.

a) A flask contains 0.0140 kg of nitrogen gas.

i) Calculate the number of moles of nitrogen gas in the flask. [1 mark]

ii) Calculate the number of nitrogen molecules in the flask. [1 mark]

b) The flask has a volume of 0.0100 m^3 and is at a temperature of 27.0 °C. Calculate the pressure inside. [2 marks]

c) Describe the effect on the pressure if the number of molecules of nitrogen in the flask was halved. [1 mark]

Q3 A large helium balloon has a volume of 10.0 m^3 at ground level. The temperature of the gas in the balloon is 293 K and the pressure is 1.00 × 10^5 Pa. The balloon is released and rises to a height where its volume becomes 25.0 m^3 and its temperature is 261 K. Calculate the pressure inside the balloon at its new height. [3 marks]

Ideal revision equation: marks = (pages read × questions answered)^2...

All this might sound a bit theoretical, but most gases you'll meet in the everyday world come fairly close to being 'ideal'. They only stop obeying these laws when the pressure's too high or they're getting close to their condensing point.

The Pressure of an Ideal Gas

Kinetic theory tries to explain the gas laws. It basically models a gas as a series of hard balls that obey Newton's laws.

You Can Use Newton's Laws to **Explain** the **Pressure** of an **Ideal Gas**

Imagine a cubic box containing ***N*** particles of an ideal gas, each with a mass ***m***.

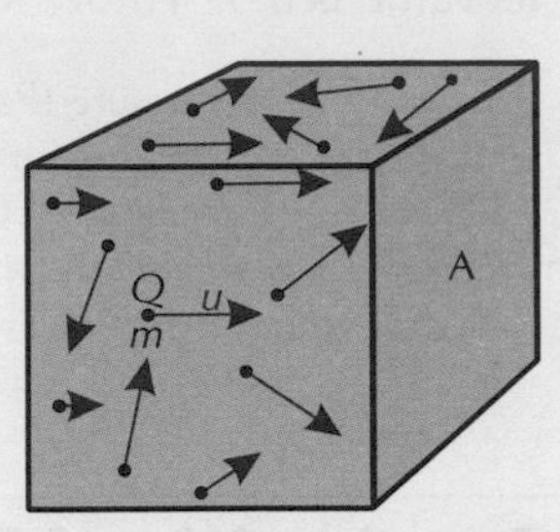

1) The particles of the gas are **free to move** around with **constant random motion**. There are **no forces of attraction** between the particles, so according to **Newton's 1st law**, they continue to move with **constant velocity** until they collide with another particle or the box itself.
2) When a particle **collides** with a **wall** of the box, it exerts a **force** on the wall, and the wall exerts an **equal and opposite force** on the particle. This is **Newton's 3rd law** in action.

See pages 54-55 for a recap of Newton's laws.

3) The **size of the force** exerted by the particle on the wall can be **calculated** using **Newton's 2nd law**, which says the **force is equal to the rate of change of momentum**.
4) For example, if particle ***Q*** is travelling directly towards wall *A* with velocity ***u***, its momentum is ***mu***. When it **hits** the wall, the force of the **impact** causes it to rebound in the **opposite direction**, at the same speed. Its **momentum** is now ***–mu***, which means the **change in momentum** is 2***mu***.
5) So, the **force** a particle exerts is **proportional** to its **mass** and its velocity. The **mass** of a single **gas particle** is **tiny** (for example, an atom of helium gas is only 6.6×10^{-27} kg), so each particle can only exert a **minuscule force**.
6) But, there **isn't** just **one particle** in the box — there's probably **millions of billions** of them. The **combined force** from so many tiny particles is **much bigger** than the contribution from any individual particle.

Imagine putting a single grain of sugar into a lunchbox and shaking it around — the box might as well be empty. Now put a couple of spoonfuls of sugar in, and shake that around — this time you'll hear the sugar thumping against the walls of the box as it collides. You don't notice the effect of the individual grains, only the combined action of loads of them.

7) Because there are so many particles in the box, a **significant number** will be **colliding** with each wall of the box at **any given moment**. And because the particles' motion is **random**, the **collisions** will be **spread** all over the surface of each wall. The result is a **steady**, **even force** on all the walls of the box — this is **pressure**.

Pressure is **Proportional** to the **Number of Particles**, their **Mass** and **Speed**

So, the pressure in a gas is a result of all the **collisions** between particles and the **walls** of the container. Using a method similar to that above you can obtain this equation for the pressure of an ideal gas:

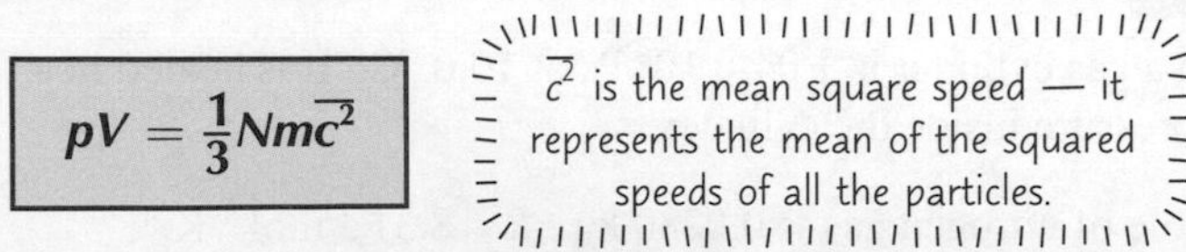

$$pV = \frac{1}{3}Nm\overline{c^2}$$

$\overline{c^2}$ is the mean square speed — it represents the mean of the squared speeds of all the particles.

The equation shows that the pressure exerted by a gas depends on **four** things:

1) The **volume**, *V*, of the container — increasing the volume of the container decreases the **frequency of collisions** because the particles have **further to travel** in between collisions. This decreases the pressure.
2) The **number of particles**, *N* — increasing the number of particles increases the **frequency of collisions** between the particles and the container, so increases the **total force** exerted by all the collisions.
3) The **mass**, ***m***, of the particles — according to Newton's 2nd law, **force is proportional to mass**, so **heavier** particles will exert a **greater force**.
4) The **speed**, ***c***, of the particles — the **faster** the particles are going when they hit the walls, the **greater** the **change in momentum** and **force** exerted.

The Pressure of an Ideal Gas

Lots of **Simplifying Assumptions** are Used in **Kinetic Theory**

In **kinetic theory**, physicists picture gas particles moving at **high speed** in **random directions**. To get relations like the one on the previous page, some **simplifying assumptions** are needed:

1) The gas contains a **large number of particles**.
2) The particles **move rapidly** and **randomly**.
3) The **volume** of the **particles** is **negligible** when compared to the volume of the **gas**.
4) **Collisions** between particles themselves or between particles and the walls of the container are **perfectly elastic**.
5) The duration of each collision is **negligible** when compared to the time **between collisions**.
6) There are **no forces** between particles except for the moment when they are in a collision.

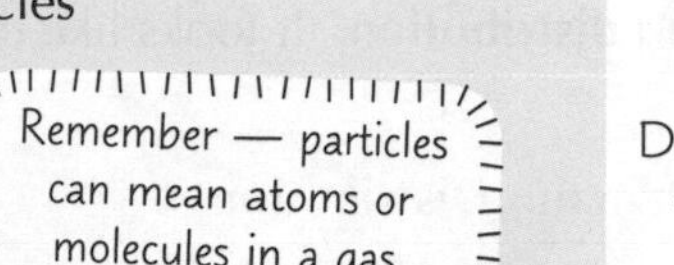

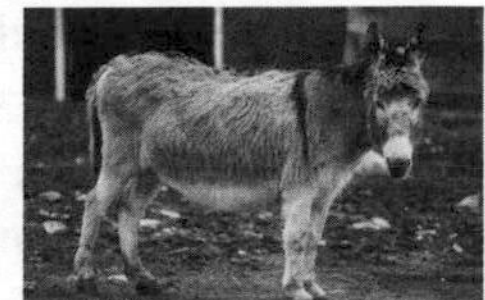

Don't make an ass of yourself — learn the assumptions.

A **gas obeying** these **assumptions** is called an **ideal** gas. Real gases behave like ideal gases as long as the **pressure isn't too big** and the **temperature** is **reasonably high** (compared with their boiling points).

The **Root Mean Square Speed** or c_{rms} is a **Useful Quantity**

As you saw on the previous page, it often helps to think about the motion of a **typical particle** in kinetic theory.

1) $\overline{c^2}$ is the **mean square speed** and has **units m^2s^{-2}**.
2) $\overline{c^2}$ is the average of the **squared speeds** of **all** the particles, so the square root of it gives you the typical speed.
3) This is called the **root mean square speed** or, usually, the **r.m.s. speed**. It's often written as c_{rms}. The **unit** is the same as any speed — **ms^{-1}**.

$$c_{rms} = \sqrt{\text{mean square speed}} = \sqrt{\overline{c^2}}$$

Warm-Up Questions

Q1 Describe how Newton's laws can be used to explain the pressure in an ideal gas.

Q2 Write down the equation linking pressure of an ideal gas with the mean square speed of the gas particles.

Q3 List the assumptions made about ideal gas behaviour.

Q4 What is the 'mean square speed'? What are its units?

Exam Questions

Q1 Describe and explain the factors that influence the pressure exerted by a gas. [4 marks]

Q2 Some helium gas is contained in a flask of volume 7.00×10^{-5} m^3.
Each helium atom has a mass of 6.65×10^{-27} kg, and there are 2.17×10^{22} atoms present.
The pressure of the gas is 1.03×10^5 Pa.

a) Calculate the mean square speed of the atoms. [2 marks]

b) Calculate the r.m.s. speed of a typical helium atom in the flask. [1 mark]

So that's mean square speed, next up: cantankerous hexagon velocity...

Crikey, if that's kinetic theory after a load of simplifying assumptions I'd hate to see the uncensored version. Speaking of assumptions, if you can't name all six of them right now you'd better go back and learn the lot pronto. Go on, just see if you can write them down. Yes, now. I'm watching you. Don't believe me? Nice... er... jumper...

Internal Energy of an Ideal Gas

Particles in gases all have different amounts of kinetic energy, and it all depends on the absolute temperature...

Molecules in a Gas **Don't** all have the **Same Amount of Energy**

Imagine looking down on **Oxford Street** when it's teeming with people. You'll see some people ambling along **slowly**, some hurrying **quickly**, but most of them will be walking with a **moderate speed**.

It's the same with the **molecules** in a **gas**. Some **don't have much kinetic energy** and move **slowly**. Others have **loads of kinetic energy** and **whizz** along. But most molecules are somewhere **in between**.

If you plot a **graph** of the **numbers of molecules** in a **gas** with different **kinetic energies** you get a **Maxwell-Boltzmann distribution**. It looks like this:

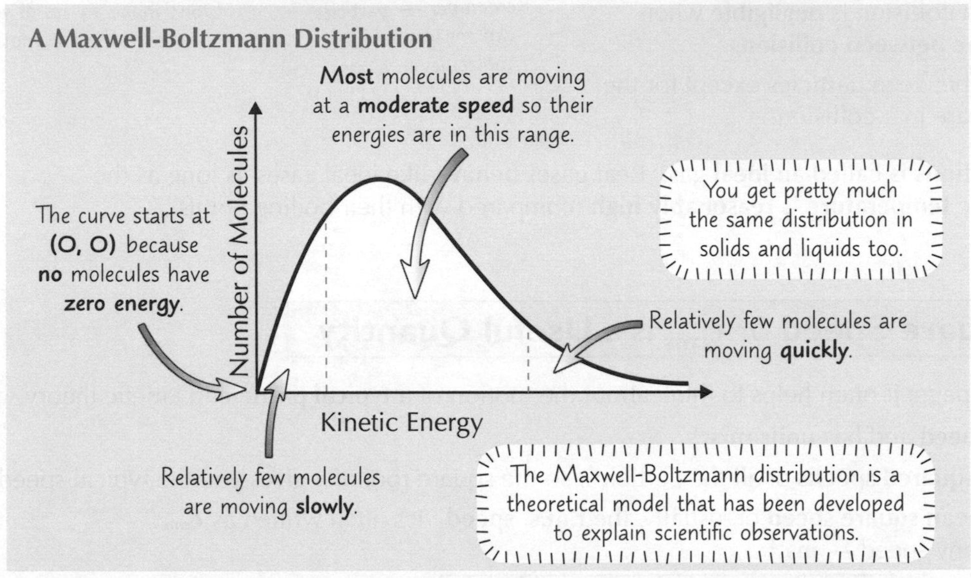

Nave's energy levels on a Monday morning are always towards the lower end of the distribution.

The **Speed Distribution** of **Gas Particles** Depends on **Temperature**

The shape of the **speed distribution** depends on the **temperature** of the gas.

Both the curves on the right represent the **same number of particles**, but the cooler curve has a higher, steeper peak at a lower speed.

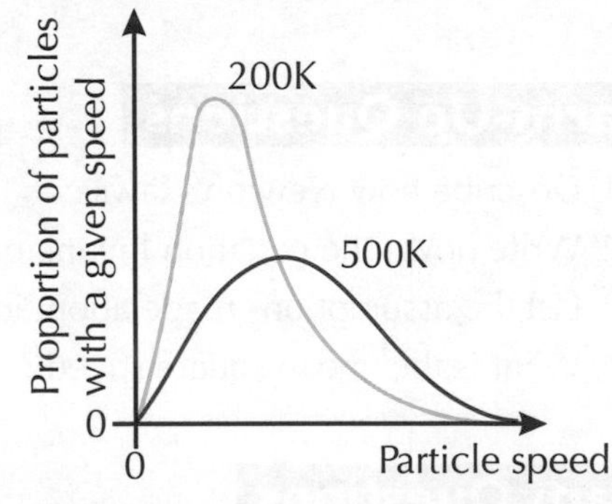

As the temperature of the gas increases:
1) the **average** particle speed increases.
2) the **maximum** particle speed increases.
3) the distribution curve becomes more **spread out**.

Energy Changes Happen Between Particles

The particles of a gas **collide** with each other **all the time**. Some of these collisions will be **'head-on'** (particles moving in **opposite directions**) while others will be **'shunts from behind'** (particles moving in the **same direction**).

1) As a result of the collisions, **energy** will be **transferred** between particles.
2) Some particles will **gain speed** in a collision and others will **slow down**.
3) **Between collisions**, the particles will travel at **constant speed**.
4) Although the energy of an individual particle changes at each collision, the collisions **don't alter** the **total energy** of the **system**.
5) So, the **average** speed of the particles will stay the same provided the **temperature** of the gas **stays the same**.

Internal Energy of an Ideal Gas

Average Kinetic Energy is Proportional to Absolute Temperature

If you've been paying attention to this section, you'll know that $pV = NkT$ (from page 107) and that $pV = \frac{1}{3}Nm\overline{c^2}$ (page 108). You can **combine** these to **derive** the **kinetic energy** of gas particles.

1) $\boldsymbol{pV = NkT}$
2) The **pressure** of an **ideal gas** given by kinetic theory is $\boldsymbol{pV = \frac{1}{3}Nm\overline{c^2}}$
3) **Equating** these two gives: $\boldsymbol{\frac{1}{3}Nm\overline{c^2} = NkT}$
4) And you can **cancel** N to give: $\boldsymbol{\frac{1}{3}m\overline{c^2} = kT}$
   which you can rearrange to give $\boldsymbol{m\overline{c^2} = 3kT}$
5) $\frac{1}{2}m\overline{c^2}$ is the **average kinetic energy** of an **individual particle**. (Remember $\overline{c^2}$ is a measure of speed squared, so this is just like the equation for kinetic energy, $KE = \frac{1}{2}mv^2$, that you'll know already.)
6) So multiplying both sides by $\frac{1}{2}$ gives you $\boldsymbol{\frac{1}{2}m\overline{c^2} = \frac{3}{2}kT}$
7) So the **average kinetic energy**, E, of **one gas particle** is given by: $\boldsymbol{E = \frac{3}{2}kT}$

$\overline{c^2}$ = mean square speed of particles
N = number of particles in the gas
m = mass of one particle
T = absolute temperature
$k = 1.38 \times 10^{-23}$ JK^{-1} (Boltzmann const.)

The kinetic energy of gas particles is always an average value because the particles are all travelling at different speeds.

8) Now for a **bonus equation** — multiplying by the number of gas particles, N, gives you an equation for the **internal energy**, U, of an ideal gas: $\boldsymbol{U = \frac{3}{2}NkT}$

In an ideal gas the potential energy is 0 J because there are no forces between the particles. This means that the internal energy is equal to the total random kinetic energy only (see p.102).

The equations above show that **average kinetic energy** and **internal energy** are both directly proportional to the **absolute temperature** — a **rise** in **absolute temperature** will cause an **increase** in the kinetic energy of the particles, meaning a rise in **internal energy**.

Warm-Up Questions

Q1 Sketch a graph of a Maxwell-Boltzmann distribution and label the key characteristics.

Q2 Describe the changes in the distribution of gas particle speeds as the temperature of a gas increases.

Q3 Show how $pV = NkT$ and the equation for the pressure of an ideal gas can be combined to derive an equation for the average kinetic energy of particles in an ideal gas.

Q4 What happens to the average kinetic energy of a particle if the temperature of a gas doubles?

Exam Questions

Q1 A flask contains one mole of nitrogen at 300 K (correct to three significant figures).

a) State the number of molecules of nitrogen in the flask. [1 mark]

b) Calculate the average kinetic energy of a nitrogen molecule in the flask. [2 marks]

c) Explain why all the nitrogen molecules in the flask will not have the same kinetic energy. [1 mark]

Q2 A container of neon gas is heated from 300 K to 500 K (correct to three significant figures). There are 3.00×10^{23} neon molecules in the container. *($k = 1.38 \times 10^{-23}$ JK^{-1})*

a) Calculate the change in the internal energy of the gas. [2 marks]

b) After heating, the pressure inside the container is 1.66×10^4 Pa. Calculate the volume of the container. [2 marks]

I wish I could distribute all my energy to the weekend...

*Just to clarify — I said "**imagine**" Oxford Street. This isn't one of those practicals you need to know for the exam so no, you can't have a day out shopping while "revising physics". Unfortunately, you have to spend your time learning the derivation above — you could be tested on it. Then make sure you can use it to explain changes in kinetic energy.*

Circular Motion

*It's probably worth putting a bookmark in here — this stuff is needed **all over** the place.*

Angles can be Expressed in **Radians**

1) The angle in **radians**, θ, is defined as the **arc-length** divided by the radius of the circle.
2) For a **complete circle** (360°), the arc-length is just the circumference of the circle ($2\pi r$). Dividing this by the radius (r) gives 2π. So there are 2π radians in a complete circle.

Moving between degrees and radians is pretty easy — you just need to remember this handy formula:

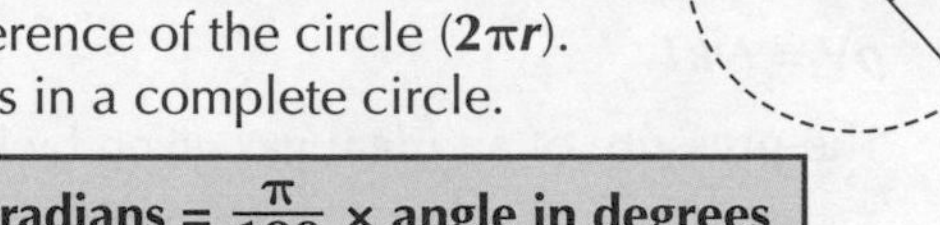

$$\textbf{angle in radians} = \frac{\pi}{180} \times \textbf{angle in degrees}$$

The **Angular Velocity** is the **Angle** an Object Rotates Through **per Second**

1) Just as **linear velocity**, v, is defined as displacement ÷ time, the **angular velocity**, ω, is defined as **angle ÷ time**. The unit of angular velocity is rad s^{-1} — radians per second.

$$\omega = \frac{\theta}{t}$$

ω = angular velocity (rad s^{-1}) — the symbol for angular velocity is the little Greek 'omega', not a w. θ = angle (radians) turned through in a time, t (seconds).

Angular velocity is a vector quantity. It has a size and a direction (see page 14).

2) The **linear velocity**, v, and **angular velocity**, ω, of a rotating object are linked by the equation:

$$v = r\omega$$

v = linear velocity (ms^{-1}), r = radius of the circle (m), ω = angular velocity (rad s^{-1})

Circular Motion has a **Frequency** and **Period**

1) The **frequency**, f, is the number of complete **revolutions per second** (rev s^{-1} or hertz, Hz).
2) The **period**, T, is the **time taken** for a complete revolution (in seconds). Frequency and period are **linked** by the equation:

$$f = \frac{1}{T}$$

f = frequency in rev s^{-1}, T = period in s

3) For a complete circle, an object turns through 2π radians in a time T, so frequency and period are related to ω by:

$$\omega = \frac{2\pi}{T} \quad \text{and} \quad \omega = 2\pi f$$

ω = angular velocity in rad s^{-1}

Objects Travelling in Circles are **Accelerating** since their **Velocity is Changing**

1) Even if the car shown on the right is going at a **constant speed**, its **velocity** is changing since its **direction** is changing.
2) Since acceleration is defined as the **rate of change of velocity**, the car is accelerating even though it isn't going any faster.
3) This acceleration is called the **centripetal acceleration** and is always directed towards the **centre of the circle**.

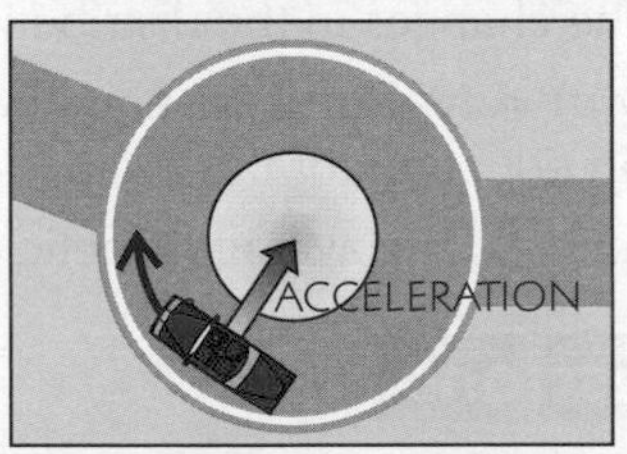

There are two formulas for centripetal acceleration:

$$a = \frac{v^2}{r} \quad \text{and} \quad a = \omega^2 r$$

a = centripetal acceleration in ms^{-2}, v = linear velocity in ms^{-1}, ω = angular velocity in rad s^{-1}, r = radius in m

The **Centripetal Acceleration** is produced by a **Centripetal Force**

From Newton's 1st law (see page 54), if an object has an **acceleration**, there must be a **net force** acting on it. An object will travel in a circular path if there is a constant net force acting on it perpendicular to its velocity. This is called a **centripetal force** and it **always acts towards the centre of the circle.** Since $F = ma$ (Newton's 2nd law), the centripetal force is:

$$F = \frac{mv^2}{r} \quad \text{and} \quad F = m\omega^2 r$$

The centripetal force is what keeps the object moving in a circle — remove the force and the object would fly off at a tangent.

Although the force changes the **direction** of the motion, the object's **velocity remains perpendicular** to the direction of the force. The object **never moves towards or away from** the centre of the circle, so there is no motion in the direction of the force. Hence **no work is done** on the object, and the object's **kinetic energy** (and therefore **speed**) remains **constant**.

Circular Motion

You Can Investigate Circular Motion With a Whirling Bung

1) You'll need a **rubber bung**, some **washers**, some **string** and a **glass tube**. Measure the **mass** of the bung (m_b) and the mass of the washers (m_w), then attach the bung to the string. Thread the string through the glass tube, and weigh down the free end using the washers.
2) Make a **reference mark** on the string, then measure the **distance** from the mark to the centre of the bung. Pull the string taut to make sure this measurement is as accurate as possible.
3) Line the mark up with the top of the glass tube, then begin to **spin** the bung in a **horizontal circle**, as shown in the diagram on the right. You'll need to spin it at the right speed to **keep the reference mark level** with the top of the glass tube (spin too quickly and it'll move outwards, too slowly and it'll move down). Try to keep your hand as **still as possible** whist you spin.
4) Measure the **time taken** for the bung to make **one complete circle**. This is the **time period**, ***T***. In practice, this may be too small to time accurately, so you might need to measure the time taken to complete ten circles and divide to get an average.
5) You can then use the formula $\omega = \frac{2\pi}{T}$ to find the **angular velocity** of the bung, and $F = m_b\omega^2 r$ to find the **centripetal force**. In this equation, r is the radius of the circle, which should be the distance from the reference mark on the string to the centre of the bung.
6) The centripetal force should be equal to the **weight of the washers** ($W = m_w g$, p.32). This weight is what causes the tension in the string, which acts as the centripetal force.
7) Repeat this experiment for different distances between the bung and the reference mark — you should find that as r gets bigger, the **time period gets longer** but the **centripetal force stays the same**.

Make sure that the bung and the washers are securely fastened to the string, that you're not standing too close to anyone and that there's nothing breakable nearby. And remember to wear safety goggles.

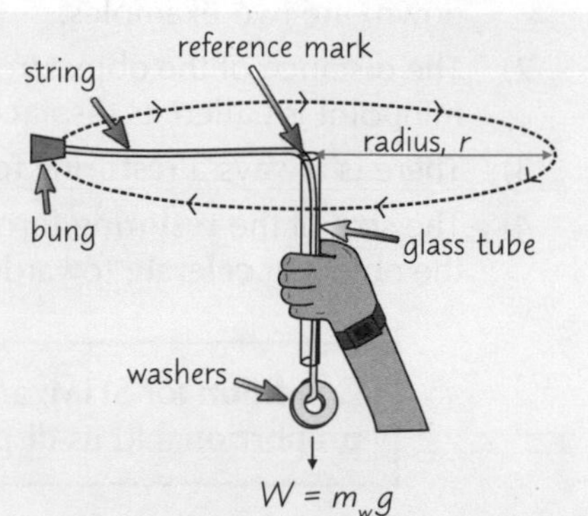

Stopping the string from slipping is a bit of an art, so you may need a lot of repeats.

Warm-Up Questions

Q1 How many radians are there in a complete circle?

Q2 How is angular velocity defined? What is the relationship between angular velocity and linear velocity?

Q3 Define the period and frequency of circular motion. State the relationship between period and angular velocity.

Q4 Write down two formulas for centripetal acceleration, a, in terms of radius, r, for an object with circular motion.

Q5 In which direction does the centripetal force act, and what happens when this force is removed?

Q6 Describe an experiment to investigate the relationship between radius and time period for an object moving in a circle.

Exam Questions

Q1 a) The Earth takes 3.2×10^7 s to orbit the Sun. Assuming its orbit is a perfect circle, calculate the Earth's angular and linear velocity (the distance from the Earth to the Sun is approximately 1.5×10^{11} m). [2 marks]

b) Given that the mass of the Earth is 6.0×10^{24} kg, calculate the centripetal force needed to keep the Earth in its orbit. State the cause of this force. [2 marks]

Q2 A bucket full of water, tied to a rope, is being swung around in a vertical circle (so it is upside down at the top of the swing). The radius of the circle is 1 m.

a) By considering the acceleration due to gravity at the top of the swing ($g = 9.81$ ms^{-2}), what is the minimum frequency with which the bucket can be swung without any water falling out? [3 marks]

b) The bucket is now swung with a constant angular speed of 5 rad s^{-1}. What will be the tension in the rope when the bucket is at the top of the swing if the total mass of the bucket and water is 10 kg? [2 marks]

My head is spinning after all that...

"Centripetal" just means "centre-seeking". The centripetal force is what actually causes circular motion. What you feel when you're spinning, though, is the reaction (centrifugal) force. Don't get the two mixed up.

Simple Harmonic Motion

Something simple at last — I like the sound of this. And colourful graphs too — you're in for a treat here.

SHM is Defined in Terms of Acceleration and Displacement

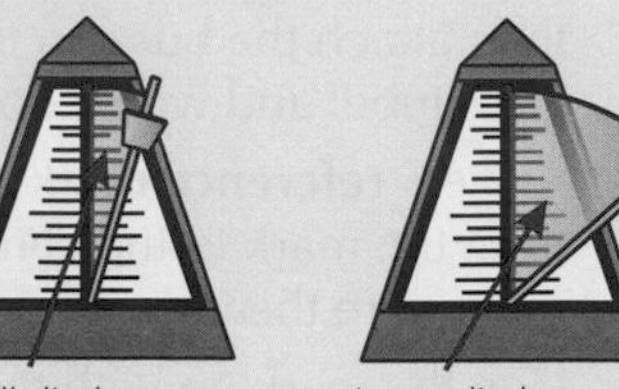

1) An object moving with **simple harmonic motion** (SHM) **oscillates** to and fro, either side of a **midpoint**. **Pendulums** and **mass-spring systems** (e.g. a mass hanging on a spring that's free to move up and down) are two examples.
2) The distance of the object from the midpoint is called its **displacement**.
3) There is always a **restoring force** pulling or pushing the object back **towards** the **midpoint**.
4) The **size** of the **restoring force** depends on the **displacement**, and the force makes the object **accelerate** towards the midpoint.

Condition for SHM: an oscillation in which the **acceleration** of an object is **directly proportional** to its **displacement** from the **midpoint**, and is directed **towards the midpoint**.

The Restoring Force Makes the Object Exchange PE and KE

1) The **type of potential energy** (*PE*) depends on **what it is** that's providing the **restoring force** — e.g. **gravitational *PE*** for pendulums or **elastic *PE*** (elastic stored energy) for masses on springs moving horizontally.
2) As the object moves **towards the midpoint**, the restoring force **does work** on the object and so **transfers** some ***PE*** to ***KE***. When the object is moving **away from the midpoint**, the object's *KE* is transferred **back to** *PE* again.
3) As the object passes the **midpoint**, its *PE* is **zero** and its *KE* is **maximum**.
4) At the **maximum displacement** (the **amplitude**) on both sides of the midpoint, the object's *KE* is **zero** and its *PE* is at its **maximum**.

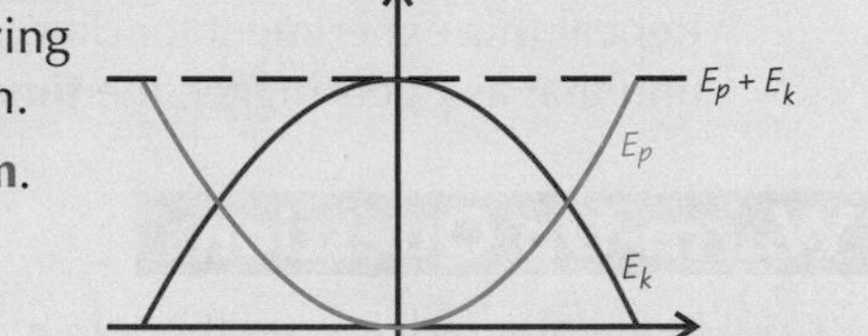

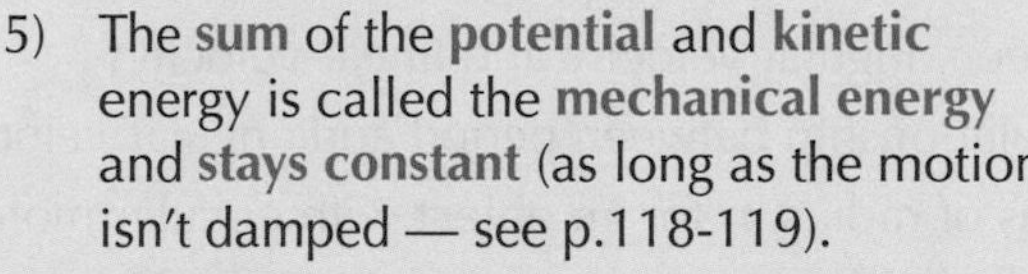

5) The **sum** of the **potential** and **kinetic** energy is called the **mechanical energy** and **stays constant** (as long as the motion isn't damped — see p.118-119).

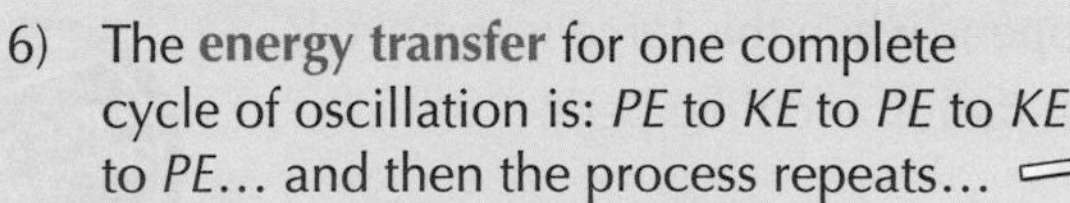

6) The **energy transfer** for one complete cycle of oscillation is: *PE* to *KE* to *PE* to *KE* to *PE*... and then the process repeats...

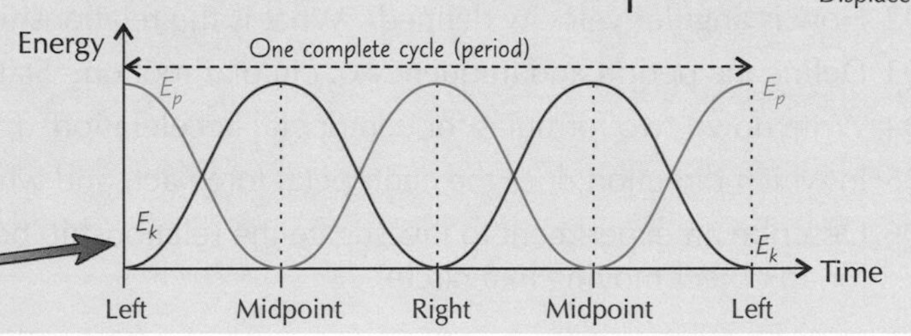

You can Draw Graphs to Show Displacement, Velocity and Acceleration

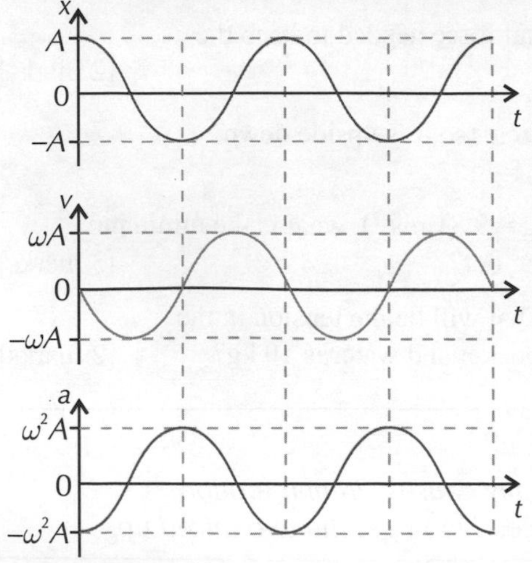

Displacement, ***x***, varies with time, *t*, as a cosine (or sine) wave with a maximum value, ***A*** (the amplitude).

Velocity, ***v***, is the gradient of the **displacement-time** graph. It is a **quarter of a cycle** in front of the **displacement** (a phase difference of $\pi/2$) and has a maximum value of ωA.

Acceleration, ***a***, is the gradient of the **velocity-time** graph. It has a maximum value of $\omega^2 A$, and is in **antiphase** with the **displacement**.

ω is the **angular frequency** of the oscillation (in rad s^{-1}). It is the **magnitude** of the vector quantity angular velocity:

$$\omega = 2\pi f \text{ and } \omega = \frac{2\pi}{T}$$

Where T is the time taken for one oscillation and f is the number of oscillations per second (see next page).

Simple Harmonic Motion

The **Frequency** and **Period** Don't Depend on the **Amplitude**

1) From **maximum positive displacement** (e.g. maximum displacement to the right) to **maximum negative displacement** (e.g. maximum displacement to the left) and **back again** is called a **cycle** of oscillation.
2) The **frequency**, ***f***, of the SHM is the **number of cycles per second** (measured in Hz).
3) The **period**, ***T***, is the **time** taken for a **complete cycle** (in seconds).

> In SHM, the **frequency** and **period** are independent of the **amplitude** (they're constant for a given oscillation), so a **pendulum clock** will keep ticking in **regular** time **intervals** even if its swing becomes very **small**. This kind of oscillator is called an **isochronous oscillator.**

Learn the SHM Equations

Make sure your calculator is set to radians before you use these equations.

1) According to the definition of SHM, the **acceleration**, *a*, is directly proportional to the **displacement**, *x*. The **constant of proportionality** is equal to $-\omega^2$. There's a minus sign in the equation because the acceleration is always in the **opposite direction** to the displacement.

Acceleration: 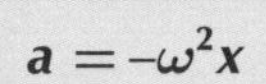 $a = -\omega^2 x$ Maximum acceleration: 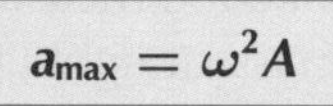 $a_{max} = \omega^2 A$

Don't forget, A is the maximum displacement — it's not acceleration.

2) **Velocity** is a vector quantity, so the **direction** of motion matters as well as the **speed** — that's why there's a ± sign.

Velocity: $v = \pm\omega\sqrt{A^2 - x^2}$ Maximum velocity: $v_{max} = \omega A$

When $v = v_{max}$, $x = 0$.

3) The **displacement** varies with time according to one of two equations, depending on **where** the object was when the timing was started. This determines whether the displacement-time graph is a cosine or sine wave.

If you began timing when the displacement was at its **maximum**: $x = A\cos(\omega t)$

If you began timing as the object passed through the **midpoint**: $x = A\sin(\omega t)$

These are solutions of the equation $a = -\omega^2 x$.

Warm-Up Questions

PRACTICE QUESTIONS

Q1 Sketch a graph to show how both the kinetic and potential energy vary with displacement for an object oscillating with simple harmonic motion. Explain the shape of the graph you've drawn.

Q2 Sketch a graph of how the velocity of an object oscillating with SHM varies with time.

Q3 A mass on a spring oscillates with simple harmonic motion. A timer is started as it passes the midpoint. Write formulas for the displacement, velocity and acceleration of the mass.

Exam Questions

Q1 a) Define simple harmonic motion. [2 marks]

b) Explain why the motion of a ball bouncing off the ground is not simple harmonic motion. [1 mark]

Q2 A pendulum is pulled 0.05 m to the left and released.
It oscillates with simple harmonic motion with a frequency of 1.5 Hz. Calculate:

a) its maximum velocity, [1 mark]

b) its displacement 0.1 s after it is released, [1 mark]

c) the time it takes for its displacement to fall to 0.01 m after it is released. [2 marks]

Q3 Two pendulums, X and Y, are oscillating with simple harmonic motion. Pendulum X has the same maximum displacement as pendulum Y, but twice the angular speed. Which option correctly describes the maximum acceleration of pendulum X with respect to pendulum Y?

A half B the same C double D quadruple [1 mark]

"Simple" harmonic motion — hmmm, I'm not convinced...

Don't let all the 'ω's confuse you, this stuff's actually not too bad. Make sure you can remember the shapes of all the graphs on page 114. And make sure you're comfortable with all the formulas on these pages too.

Investigating Simple Harmonic Motion

You can investigate simple harmonic motion in a few different ways — make sure you've read pages 114-115 before you tackle this lot, or it won't make much sense.

You Can Investigate Simple Harmonic Motion Using a **Data Logger**...

Data loggers and **sensors** are a great way of investigating simple harmonic motion, as they allow you to make **precise measurements** (p.8). You still need to know what you're doing though.

To investigate the simple harmonic motion of a **mass on a spring** using a data logger and a position sensor:

1) Set up the equipment as shown in the diagram (if you don't have a long spring you could connect a few shorter ones together).
2) Lift the mass slightly and release it — this will cause the mass-spring system to start **oscillating** with **simple harmonic motion**. To make sure your experiment is **repeatable**, place a ruler behind the spring to measure how far you raise the mass. Make sure your eye is **level** with the mass when you take the measurement. You should also try to lift the mass straight up, to stop the mass from swinging from side to side.
3) As the mass oscillates, the **position sensor** will measure the **displacement** of the mass over **time**. The computer can be set to record this data automatically.
4) Let the experiment run until you've got a good amount of data (at least ten complete oscillations).
5) Once you've collected your data, you can use the computer to generate a **displacement-time** graph.
6) From the graph, you can measure T, the **time period** of the oscillation, and A, the **amplitude** of the oscillation. You should find that the amplitude of the oscillations gets **smaller** over time, but the time period remains **constant**:

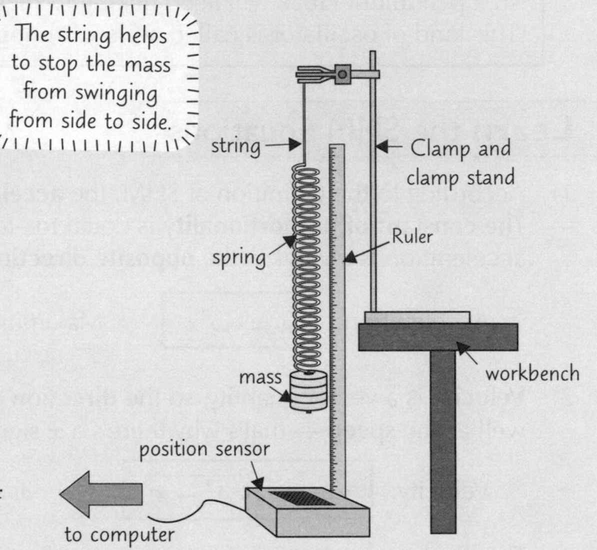

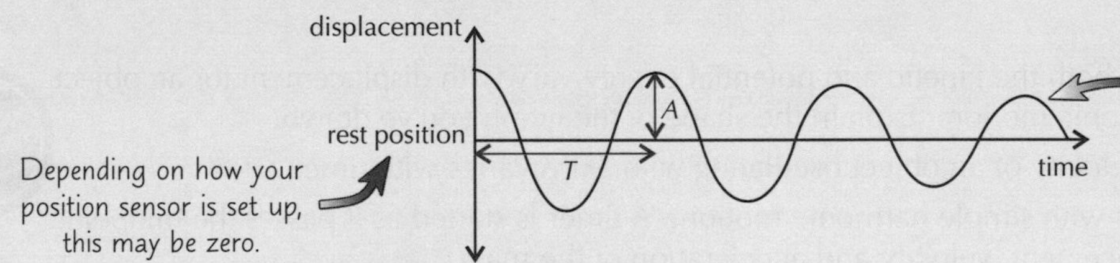

You can use this system to investigate how **different variables** affect the time period of the oscillation.

You could investigate the effect of changing:

- the **weight** of the mass,
- the **stiffness** of the spring,
- the size of the **initial displacement**.

If you're investigating the effect of changing one of these factors, you need to be careful to **control all the others**. You'll need to repeat the experiment for each value of every independent variable you investigate.

You should find:

- the **heavier** the mass, the **longer** the time period,
- the **stiffer** the spring, the **shorter** the time period,
- the **initial displacement** has **no effect** on the time period.

Sorry everyone, not that kind of spring...

Investigating Simple Harmonic Motion

... or **Without One**

If you don't have a data logger, you won't be able to generate a displacement-time graph, but you can still investigate the **time period** of an oscillation. For example, you can investigate the simple harmonic motion of a pendulum using the equipment in the diagram below and a **stopwatch**:

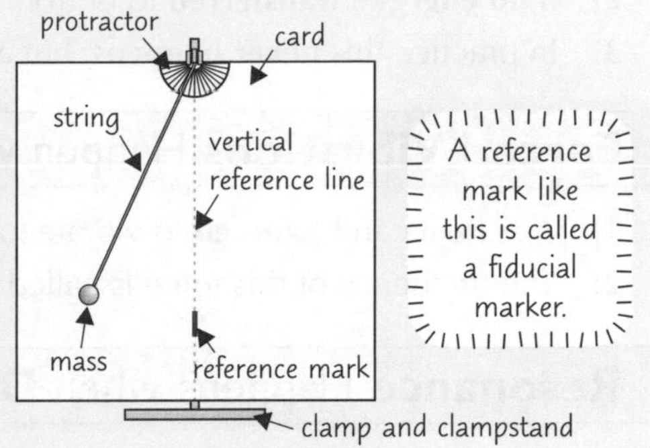

A reference mark like this is called a fiducial marker.

1) Set up the equipment as shown on the right. Measure the **weight** of the mass, and use a ruler to find the **length** of the string.
2) Move the mass to the side, keeping the string **taut**. Measure the **angle** between the string and the vertical using the protractor. Make sure it's **less than 10°**, or the mass won't swing with simple harmonic motion when you release it.
3) Release the mass. Position your eye **level with the mark on the card**, and start the stopwatch when the mass passes in front of it.
4) Record the time when the mass passes the mark again, **moving from the same direction**. This is the **time period** of the oscillator. Depending on your pendulum, T might be too short to measure accurately from one swing. If so, measure the total time for a number of complete oscillations combined (say 5 or 10) and take an average.
5) Keep recording T at regular intervals as the motion dies away. You should find that T **remains constant** as the amplitude of the swing decreases.
6) You can investigate how different factors affect the motion of the pendulum by changing the weight of the **mass** on the string, the **length** of the string, and the **angle** that you turn the string through before you first release it (still keeping it below 10°). Measure all the variables as **accurately** as possible, and only change **one variable at a time**.
7) You should find that the **angle** of the initial displacement and the **weight of the mass** have **no effect** on the time period of the pendulum, but as the **length** of the string increases the **time period increases**.

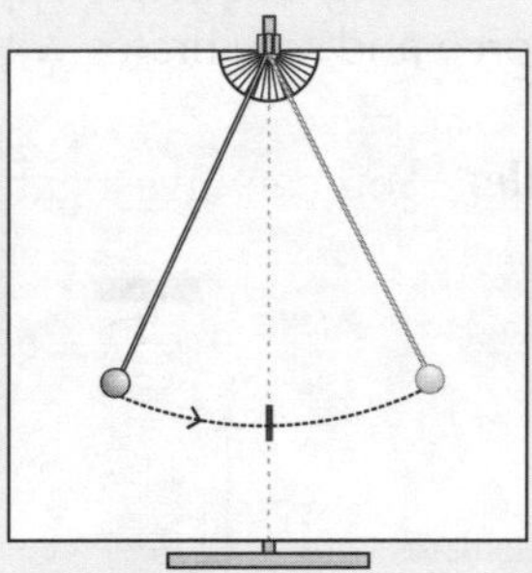

Only record the times when the mass passes in front of the mark from the same direction (e.g. from left to right), or you won't get the time period of a complete oscillation.

Your data will contain more random errors (p.12) if you don't use a data logger, so you'll need to do more repeats.

Warm-Up Questions

Q1 Give one advantage of using a data logger instead of a stopwatch to investigate simple harmonic motion.

Q2 Describe an experiment to investigate the simple harmonic motion of a mass on a spring.

Q3 What effect does increasing the weight of the mass have on:
a) the simple harmonic motion of a mass on a spring?
b) the simple harmonic motion of a mass on a pendulum?

Exam Question

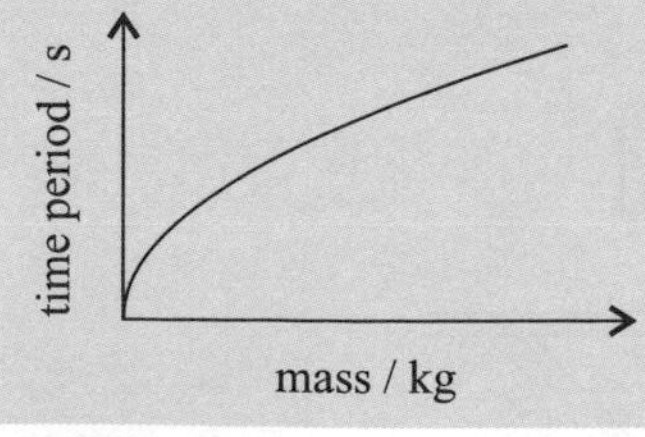

Q1 The graph on the left shows the results of an experiment to investigate how the time period of an object oscillating vertically on a spring is affected by its mass.

a) Describe how the experiment might have been conducted. [4 marks]

b) Describe the relationship shown by the graph. [2 marks]

I keep oscillating between confusion and bewilderment...

Two lovely experiments here for you to learn — make sure you understand how to swap them round, too. You can measure the time period of a spring using a stopwatch and reference mark, and you can use a data logger and a sensor to investigate the SHM of a pendulum. (You'd use an angle sensor where the protractor is instead of a position sensor.)

Free and Forced Vibrations

Resonance... tricky little beast. The Millennium Bridge was supposed to be a feat of British engineering, but it suffered from a severe case of the wobbles caused by resonance. How was it sorted out? By damping, of course — read on...

Free Vibrations — No Transfer of Energy To or From the Surroundings

1) If you stretch and release a mass on a spring, it oscillates at its **natural frequency**.
2) If **no energy's transferred** to or from the surroundings, it will **keep** oscillating with the **same amplitude forever**.
3) In practice this **never happens**, but a spring vibrating in air is called a **free vibration** (or oscillation) anyway.

Forced Vibrations Happen when there's an External Driving Force

1) A system can be **forced** to vibrate (or oscillate) by a periodic **external force**.
2) The frequency of this force is called the **driving frequency**.

Resonance Happens when Driving Frequency = Natural Frequency

When the **driving frequency** approaches the **natural frequency**, the system gains more and more energy from the driving force and so vibrates with a **rapidly increasing amplitude**. When this happens the system is **resonating**.

Example: You can investigate how amplitude varies with driving frequency using a system like the one below.

PRACTICAL SKILLS

Mass oscillates with very large amplitude at the resonant frequency

Mass

Signal Generator

Frequency

Sets driving frequency

Vibration Generator

If you vary the driving frequency using the signal generator, and plot amplitude against driving frequency, you get a graph like this:

amplitude

natural frequency

driving frequency

Here are some examples of resonance:

a) organ pipe
The column of air resonates, driven by the motion of air at the base.

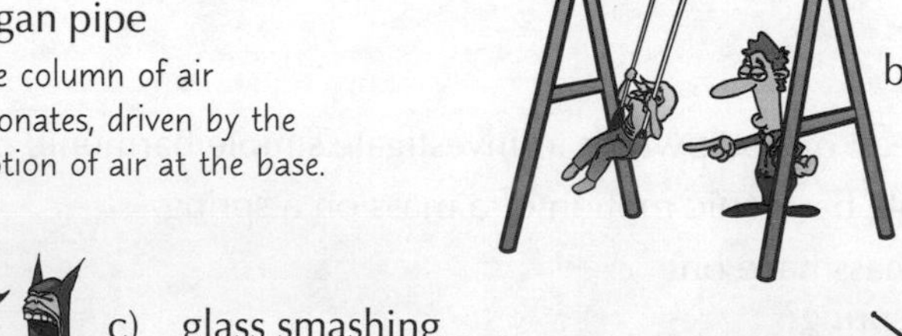

b) swing
A swing resonates if it's driven by someone pushing it at its natural frequency.

Armies deliberately march 'out of step' when they cross a bridge. This reduces the risk of the bridge resonating and breaking apart.

c) glass smashing
A glass resonates when driven by a sound wave of the right frequency. This can make the glass break.

d) radio
A radio is tuned so the electric circuit resonates at the same frequency as the radio station you want to listen to.

Damping Happens when Energy is Lost to the Surroundings

1) In practice, **any** oscillating system **loses energy** to its surroundings.
2) This is usually down to **frictional forces** like air resistance.
3) These are called **damping forces**.
4) Systems are often **deliberately damped** to **stop** them oscillating or to **minimise** the effect of **resonance**.

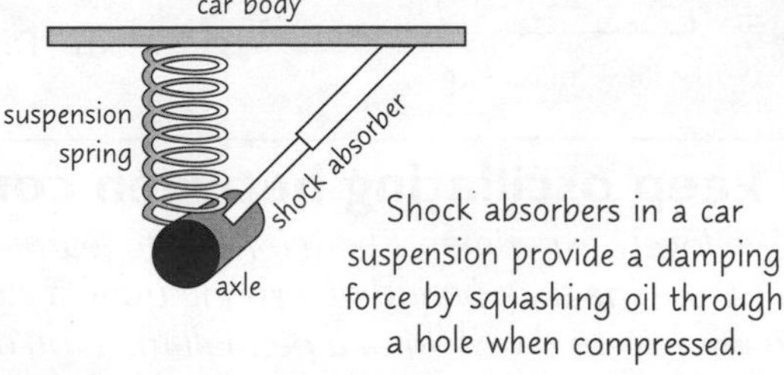

Shock absorbers in a car suspension provide a damping force by squashing oil through a hole when compressed.

Free and Forced Vibrations

Different Amounts of Damping have **Different Effects**

1) The **degree** of damping can vary from **light** damping (where the damping force is small) to **overdamping**.
2) Damping **reduces** the **amplitude** of the oscillation over time. The **heavier** the damping, the **quicker** the amplitude is reduced to zero.
3) **Critical damping** reduces the amplitude (i.e. stops the system oscillating) in the **shortest possible time**.
4) Car **suspension systems** and moving coil **meters** (which control the arm in analogue voltmeters and ammeters) are critically damped so that they **don't oscillate** but return to equilibrium as quickly as possible.

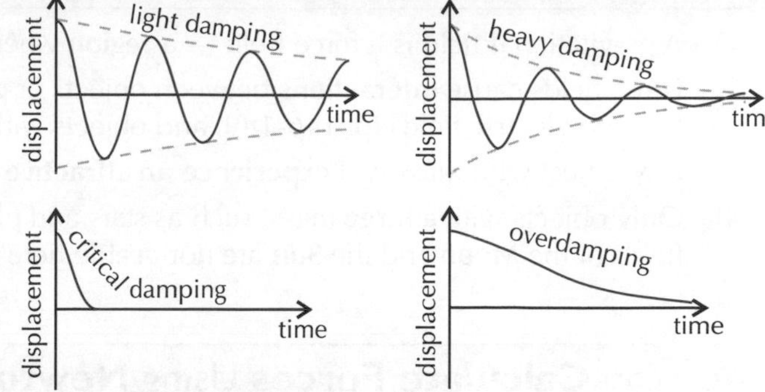

5) Systems with **even heavier damping** are **overdamped**. They take **longer** to return to equilibrium than a critically damped system.

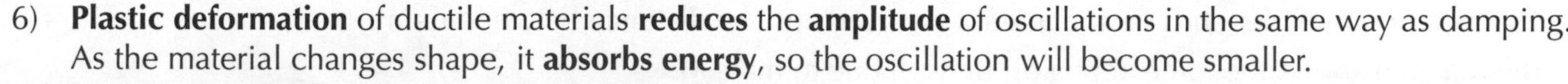

6) **Plastic deformation** of ductile materials **reduces** the **amplitude** of oscillations in the same way as damping. As the material changes shape, it **absorbs energy**, so the oscillation will become smaller.

Damping Affects **Resonance** too

1) **Lightly damped** systems have a **very sharp** resonance peak. Their amplitude only increases dramatically when the **driving frequency** is **very close** to the **natural frequency**.
2) **Heavily damped** systems have a **flatter response**. Their amplitude doesn't increase very much near the natural frequency and they aren't as **sensitive** to the driving frequency.

Structures are damped to avoid being damaged by resonance. Loudspeakers are also made to have as flat a response as possible so that they don't 'colour' the sound.

PRACTICAL SKILLS

Example: You can show how damping affects resonance using the experiment on the previous page.

The mass oscillates at a smaller amplitude at the resonant frequency than a free oscillator.

Adding a disc increases air resistance.

Signal Generator
Frequency

Here's how increasing the damping affects resonance in this system:

amplitude
sharp
increasing degree of damping
flat
driving frequency
natural frequency

In general, the more damped a system is, the flatter the graph of amplitude of oscillation against driving frequency.

Warm-Up Questions

Q1 What is a free vibration? What is a forced vibration?

Q2 Give an example of resonance.

Exam Questions

Q1 a) Define resonance. [2 marks]

b) Draw a diagram to show how the amplitude of a lightly damped system varies with driving frequency. [2 marks]

c) On the same diagram, show how the amplitude of the system varies with driving frequency when it is heavily damped. [1 mark]

Q2 Define critical damping and state a situation where it is used. [2 marks]

Physics — it can really put a damper on your social life...

Resonance can be really useful (radios, organ pipes, swings — yay) or very, very bad...

Gravitational Fields

Gravity's all about masses attracting each other. If the Earth didn't have a gravitational field, apples wouldn't fall to the ground and you'd probably be floating off into space instead of sitting here reading this page...

Masses in a **Gravitational Field** Experience a **Force of Attraction**

1) A gravitational field is a force field — a **region** where an object will experience a **non-contact force**.
2) Force fields cause **interactions** between objects or particles — e.g. **static** or **moving charges** interact through **electric** fields (p. 146-149) and objects with **mass** interact through **gravitational** fields.
3) Any object with mass will **experience an attractive force** if you put it in the **gravitational field** of another object.
4) Only objects with a **large** mass, such as stars and planets, have a significant effect. E.g. the gravitational fields of the **Moon** and the **Sun** are noticeable here on Earth — they're the main cause of our **tides**.

You can **Calculate Forces** Using **Newton's Law of Gravitation**

1) The **force** experienced by an object in a gravitational field is always **attractive**. It's a **vector** which depends on the **masses** involved and the **distance** between them.
2) The diagram shows the force acting on mass m due to mass M. (The force on M due to m is equal but in the opposite direction.)
3) M and m are **uniform spheres**, which behave as **point masses** — as if all their mass is concentrated at the centre.
4) It's easy to work out the **force** experienced by a **point mass** in a **gravitational field** — you just put the numbers into this **equation**, known as **Newton's law of gravitation**:

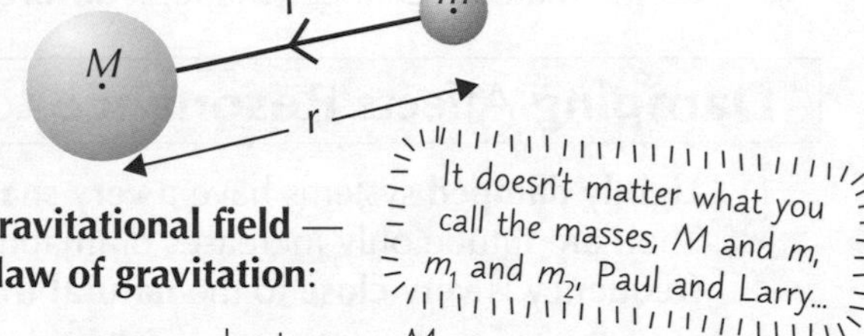

It doesn't matter what you call the masses, M and m, m_1 and m_2, Paul and Larry...

The negative sign shows that the vector F is in the opposite direction to r (displacement of m from M).

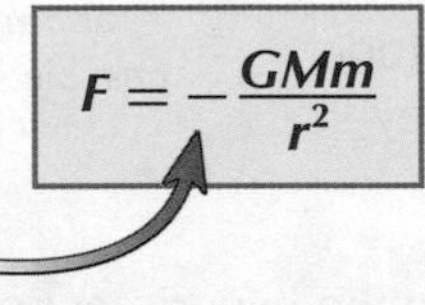

$$F = -\frac{GMm}{r^2}$$

where F is the force acting on mass m due to mass M,
M and m behave as point masses,
G is the gravitational constant — 6.67×10^{-11} $\text{Nm}^2\text{kg}^{-2}$ and
r is the distance (in metres) between the centres of the two masses.

Newton's Law of Gravitation is an **Inverse Square Law**

The law of gravitation is an **inverse square law** so:

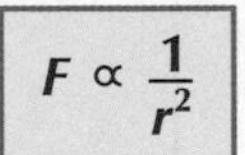

$$F \propto \frac{1}{r^2}$$

1) If the distance r between the masses **increases** then the force F will **decrease**.
2) If the **distance doubles** then the **force** will be one **quarter** the strength of the original force.

The officers weren't sure how to enforce the inverse square law.

You can Draw **Field Lines** to Show the **Field** Around an Object

Gravitational field lines (or **lines of force**) are arrows showing the **direction of the force** that masses would feel in a gravitational field.

1) If you put a small mass, ***m***, anywhere in the Earth's gravitational field, it will always be attracted **towards** the Earth.
2) The Earth's gravitational field is **radial** — the lines of force meet at the centre of the Earth.
3) If you move mass m further away from the Earth — where the **lines** of force are **further apart** — the **force** it experiences **decreases**.
4) The small mass, m, has a gravitational field of its own. This doesn't have a noticeable effect on the Earth though, because the Earth is so much **more massive**.
5) Close to the Earth's surface, the field is (almost) uniform — the **field lines** are (almost) **parallel** and **equally spaced**. You can usually **assume** that the field is perfectly uniform.

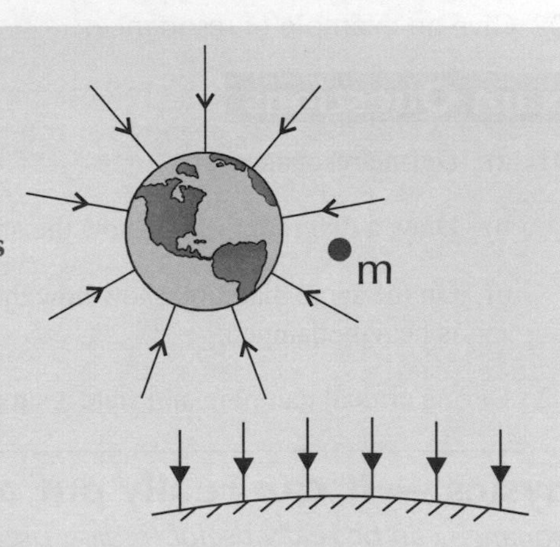

Gravitational Fields

The **Field Strength** is the **Force per Unit Mass**

Gravitational field strength, g, is the **force per unit mass**. Its value depends on **where you are** in the field. There's a really simple equation for working it out:

$$g = \frac{F}{m}$$

g has units of newtons per kilogram (Nkg^{-1})

The **value** of g at the **Earth's surface** is approximately **9.81 Nkg^{-1}** (or 9.81 ms^{-2}).

1) F is the force experienced by a mass m when it's placed in the gravitational field. Divide F by m and you get the **force per unit mass**.
2) g is a **vector** quantity, always pointing towards the centre of the mass whose field you're describing. Depending on the direction **defined** to be positive, it **could** be negative.
3) Since the gravitational field is **almost uniform** at the Earth's surface, you can assume g is a **constant** if you don't go too **high**.
4) g is just the **acceleration** of a mass in a gravitational field. It's often called the **acceleration due to gravity**.

In a **Radial Field**, g is **Inversely Proportional** to r^2

Point masses have **radial** gravitational fields (see previous page).
The value of g depends on the distance r from the point mass M.

$$g = -\frac{GM}{r^2}$$

where g is the gravitational field strength (Nkg^{-1})

And it's an **inverse square law** again — as r **increases**, g **decreases**.

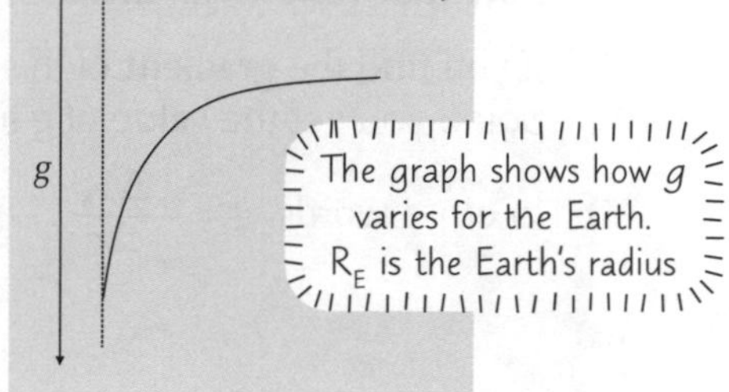

The graph shows how g varies for the Earth. R_E is the Earth's radius

Example: The graph shows how the gravitational field strength, g, varies with distance, r, from the centre of the planet Mars. The radius of Mars is approximately 3.4×10^3 km. Estimate the mass of Mars.

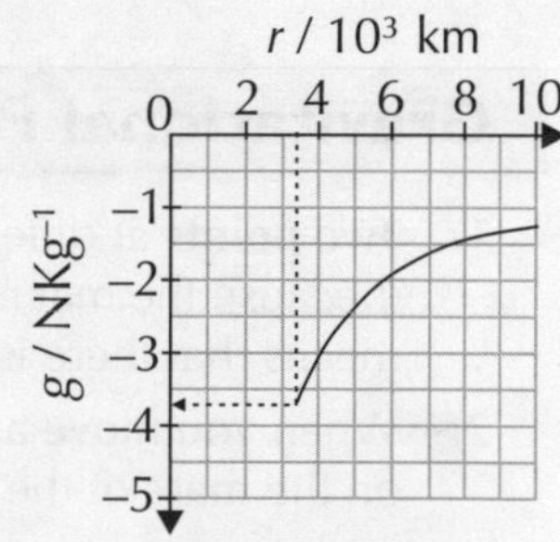

You can see from the graph that the value of g at the surface of Mars is about -3.7 Nkg^{-1}.

Rearrange the formula: $g = -\frac{GM}{r^2}$ to find M, then stick the values in — don't forget to convert to standard units first.

So, $M = -\frac{gr^2}{G} = -\frac{-3.7 \times (3.4 \times 10^6)^2}{6.67 \times 10^{-11}}$ = **6.4×10^{23} kg (to 2 s.f.)**.

Warm-Up Questions

Q1 Draw a diagram showing the Earth's gravitational field close to its surface. State the assumption made.

Q2 Define gravitational field strength and write an equation linking it to force.

Exam Questions

PRACTICE QUESTIONS

Acceleration due to gravity on Earth $g = 9.81\ ms^{-2}$, $R_E = 6400$ km

Q1 Calculate the mass of Earth. [2 marks]

Q2 The Moon has a mass of 7.35×10^{22} kg and a radius of 1740 km.

a) Calculate the value of g at the Moon's surface. [1 mark]

b) Calculate the gravitational force on a 25 kg object 10 m (to 2 s.f.) above the surface of the Moon. [2 marks]

Q3 A satellite is orbiting Earth and experiences a gravitational field strength of $g = 4$ Nkg^{-1}. The radius of its orbit is then increased until it experiences a gravitational field strength of $g = 2$ Nkg^{-1}. Choose the option which describes the factor by which the radius of orbit has been increased, correct to 2 s.f.

A 1.2 B 1.4 C 1.6 D 1.8 [1 mark]

If you're really stuck, put 'Inverse Square Law'...

Clever chap, Newton, but famously tetchy. He got into fights with other physicists, mainly over planetary motion and calculus... the usual playground squabbles. Then he spent the rest of his life trying to turn scrap metal into gold. Weird.

Gravitational Potential and Energy

Gravitational potential is all to do with the energy something has based on where it is in a gravitational field.

Gravitational Potential is the Work Done to Move a Unit Mass from 'Infinity'

1) The **gravitational potential**, V_g, at a point is the work done in moving a **unit mass** from **infinity** to that **point**.
2) In a **radial field** (like the Earth's), the equation for gravitational potential is:

$$V_g = -\frac{GM}{r}$$

V_g is gravitational potential (Jkg^{-1}), G is the gravitational constant, M is the mass of the object causing the gravitational field (kg), and r is the distance from the centre of the object (m).

Gravitational potential is **negative** — you have to **do work against** the **gravitational field** to move an object out of it. The **further** you are from the centre of a radial field, the **smaller** the magnitude of V_g. At an **infinite distance** from the mass, the gravitational potential will be **zero**.

3) The graph on the right shows how **gravitational potential** varies with **distance** from the Earth.
4) If you find the **gradient** of this graph at a particular point, you get the value of **g** at that point.
5) In other words, $g = -\frac{\Delta V_g}{\Delta r}$.

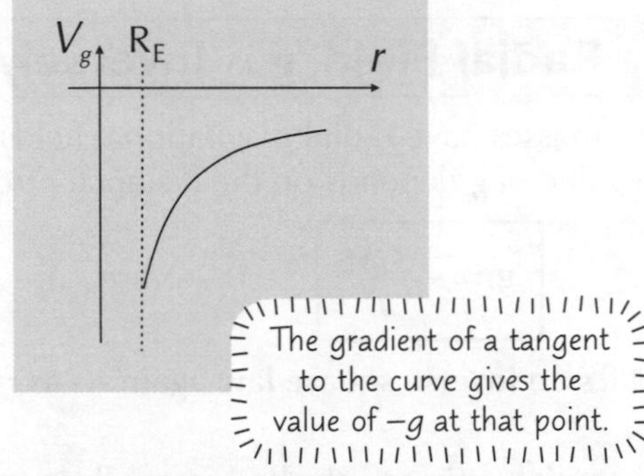

Gravitational Potential Difference is the Work Done Moving a Unit Mass

1) **Two points** at different distances from a mass will have **different** gravitational potentials (because the magnitude of the gravitational potential decreases with distance) — this means that there is a **gravitational potential difference** between these two points.
2) When you **move** an object you do **work** against **gravity** — the **amount of energy** you need depends on the **mass** of the object and the **gravitational potential difference** you move it through:

$$\Delta W = m\Delta V_g$$

where ΔW is the work done (J), m is the mass of the object (kg) and ΔV_g is the gravitational potential difference (Jkg^{-1}).

3) The graph shows how the **size of the force** on an object, due to the **gravitational field** of a **point mass**, varies with the object's **distance, r,** from the point mass.
4) The **area** under the curve between two values of r gives the **work done** to **move** the object from one point to the other.

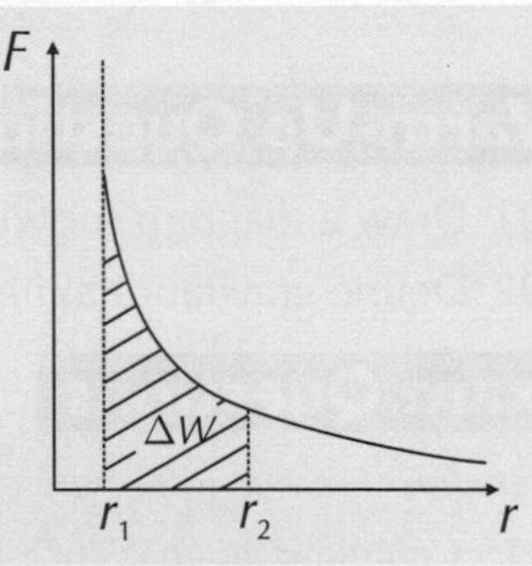

Since F is usually defined to be negative (see page 120), you might see a graph of F against r. It would have the same shape as this graph, but reflected in the r axis.

An Object's Gravitational Potential Energy Depends on its Mass

1) **Gravitational potential** is work done per unit mass, so the **gravitational potential energy** (E) of an object at a point in a gravitational field is:

$$E = mV_g$$

2) Substituting in the formula for V_g, the gravitational potential energy of an object of mass m is:

$$E = m\left(-\frac{GM}{r}\right) = -\frac{GMm}{r}$$

E is gravitational potential energy (J), and r is the distance from the centre of M to the centre of m (m).

Gravitational Potential and Energy

To Escape a **Gravitational Field**, a Mass must Travel at the **Escape Velocity**

The **escape velocity** is defined as the velocity needed so an object has **just enough** kinetic energy to escape a gravitational field. This is when an object's **kinetic energy** is **equal** and **opposite** to its **gravitational potential energy** — so the **total energy** is **zero**. The formula for **escape velocity** is:

$$v = \sqrt{\frac{2GM}{r}}$$

v is escape velocity (ms^{-1})

Deriving Escape Velocity

1) As you know total energy (kinetic energy + gravitational potential energy) is **zero**:

$$\frac{1}{2}mv^2 + \left(-\frac{GMm}{r}\right) = 0 \text{ so } \frac{1}{2}mv^2 = \frac{GMm}{r}$$

2) **Cancel** the m's.

$$\frac{1}{2}v^2 = \frac{GM}{r}$$

The escape velocity is the same for all masses in the same gravitational field.

3) **Rearrange** for velocity, v:

$$v^2 = \frac{2GM}{r} \longrightarrow v = \sqrt{\frac{2GM}{r}}$$

No matter how fast he ran, Luke couldn't escape exams.

Example: Find the escape velocity on Earth. Mass of Earth = 5.98×10^{24} kg, radius of Earth = 6.37×10^6 m and $G = 6.67 \times 10^{-11}$ Nm^2kg^{-2}.

Simply substitute in the given values.

$$v = \sqrt{\frac{2GM}{r}} = \sqrt{\frac{2 \times 6.67 \times 10^{-11} \times 5.98 \times 10^{24}}{6.37 \times 10^6}} = 11\,190.7... = \mathbf{11\,200\ ms^{-1}} \text{ (to 3 s.f.)}$$

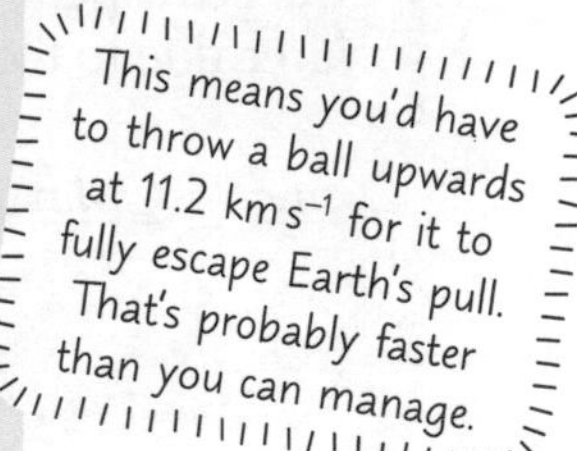

This means you'd have to throw a ball upwards at 11.2 kms^{-1} for it to fully escape Earth's pull. That's probably faster than you can manage.

Warm-Up Questions

Q1 What is gravitational potential? Write an equation for it.

Q2 Sketch a graph of gravitational potential against distance for the Earth. What does the gradient of this graph describe?

Q3 Write down the equation for calculating the work done by moving a unit mass through a gravitational potential.

Q4 Describe how you get from the gravitational potential to gravitational potential energy.

Q5 What is the escape velocity? Write an equation for it.

Exam Question

Q1 A 300 kg probe is sent to an asteroid to collect rock samples before returning to Earth. The asteroid has a mass of 2.67×10^{19} kg.

a) The gravitational potential, V_g, at the surface of the asteroid is -1.52×10^4 Jkg^{-1}. Calculate the radius of the asteroid. [2 marks]

b) Calculate the speed at which an object would need to be launched from the surface of the asteroid for it to fully escape its gravitational field. [1 mark]

c) Calculate the work done by the probe as it travels from the surface to a point 2000 m above the surface. [3 marks]

With enough work you have the potential for brilliance...

So quite a lot of new stuff here, but hopefully you can see how everything links together. It's all to do with energy — you do work to change your gravitational potential energy, and you need to make your kinetic energy equal your gravitational potential energy in order to escape a gravitational field. Now time to start learning all of those equations.

Motion of Masses in Gravitational Fields

Planets just go round and round in circles. Well, ellipses really, but I won't tell if you don't...

Planets are **Satellites** which **Orbit** the **Sun**

1) A **satellite** is just any **smaller mass** which **orbits** a **much larger mass** — the **Moon** is a satellite of the Earth.
2) In our Solar System, the planets have **nearly circular orbits**... so you can use the **equations of circular motion**.

The **Speed** of an Orbit depends on its **Radius** and the Mass of the **Larger Body**

1) Earth feels a force due to the gravitational 'pull' of the **Sun**. This force is given by Newton's law of gravitation...

$$F = -\frac{GMm}{r^2}$$

(see p.120)

2) The Earth has velocity v. Its linear speed is constant but its **direction** is not — so it's accelerating. The **centripetal force** (p.112) causing this acceleration is:

$$F = \frac{mv^2}{r}$$

3) The **centripetal force** on the Earth must be a result of the **gravitational force** due to the Sun, and so these forces must be **equal**...

$$\frac{mv^2}{r} = \frac{GMm}{r^2}$$ and rearranging...

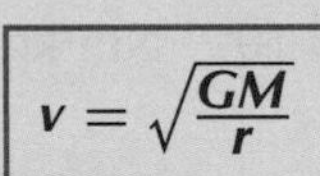

v is orbital speed (ms^{-1}),
G is the gravitational constant, 6.67×10^{-11} Nm^2kg^{-2},
M is the mass of the object being orbited (kg),
r is the distance from the centre of the object being orbited to the centre of the orbiting satellite (m).

And the **Period** does too

The **time** taken **for one orbit** is called the **period, T**. For circular motion $T = \frac{2\pi r}{v}$.

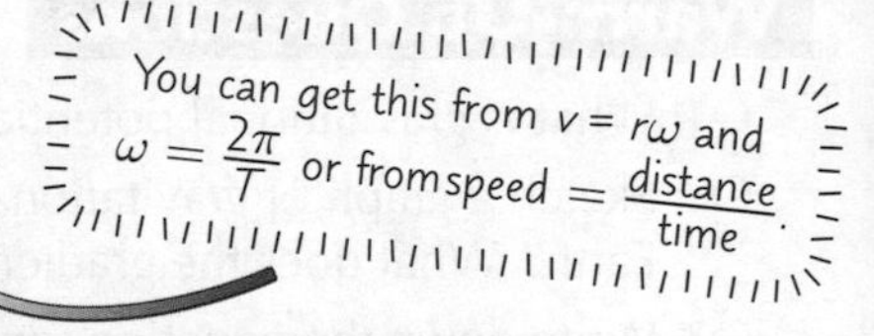

Substitute $v = \sqrt{\frac{GM}{r}}$ and rearrange...

$$T^2 = \left(\frac{4\pi^2}{GM}\right)r^3$$

T is the period (s).

Example: The Moon takes 27.3 days (2.36×10^6 s) to orbit the Earth. Calculate its distance from the Earth. Take the mass of the Earth to be 5.975×10^{24} kg.

You're trying to find the radius of the orbit, r. Use the formula for the period, T, and rearrange it for r^3:

$$r^3 = \frac{T^2GM}{4\pi^2} = \frac{(2.36 \times 10^6)^2 \times 6.67 \times 10^{-11} \times 5.975 \times 10^{24}}{4\pi^2} = 5.62... \times 10^{25}$$

Then take the cube root: $r = \sqrt[3]{5.62... \times 10^{25}} = 3.830... \times 10^8 =$ **3.83×10^8 m (to 3 s.f.)**

(this is the distance between the centre of the Earth and the centre of the Moon)

Geostationary Satellites Orbit the Earth once in **24 Hours**

1) Geostationary satellites orbit directly over the **equator** and are **always above the same point** on Earth.
2) A geostationary satellite travels at the **same angular speed as the Earth** turns below it.
3) Their orbit takes exactly **one day**.
4) These satellites are really useful for sending TV and telephone signals and have improved **communication** around the world. The satellite is **stationary** relative to a certain point on the **Earth**, so you don't have to alter the angle of your receiver (or transmitter) to keep up.
5) There are downsides though — they are **expensive** and pose a **small** risk of something going **wrong** and the satellite **falling** back to Earth.

Motion of Masses in Gravitational Fields

Kepler's Laws are about the Motion of Planets in the Solar System

Kepler came up with these three laws around 1600, about 80 years before Newton developed his law of gravitation. They're usually used to describe the planets in our solar system, but can be used for **any** object and its satellite.

FIRST LAW: Each planet moves in an **ellipse** around the Sun, with the Sun at one **focus** (a circle is just a special kind of ellipse).

SECOND LAW: A line joining the Sun to a planet will sweep out **equal areas in equal times**. (So if moving from A to B takes the same amount of time as moving from C to D, the two shaded sections will have equal areas.)

THIRD LAW: The **period** of the orbit and the **mean distance** between the Sun and the planet are related by **Kepler's third law**: $T^2 \propto r^3$

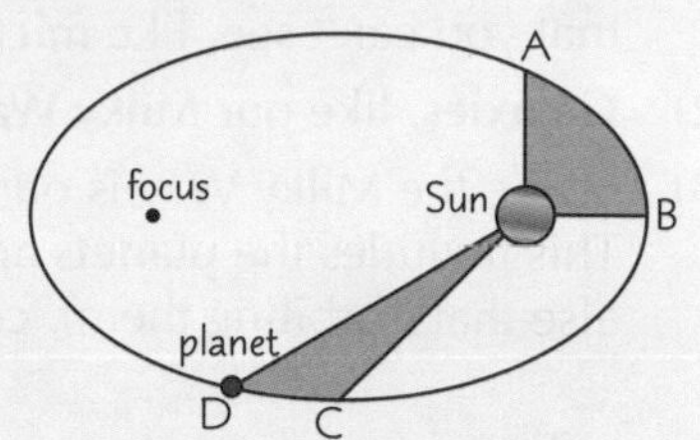

Example: The diagram shows the orbits of two exoplanets around a star in a nearby solar system. Exoplanet A completes one orbit of the star in 42.5 hours. Find the orbital period of exoplanet B to the nearest hour, assuming both orbits are circular.

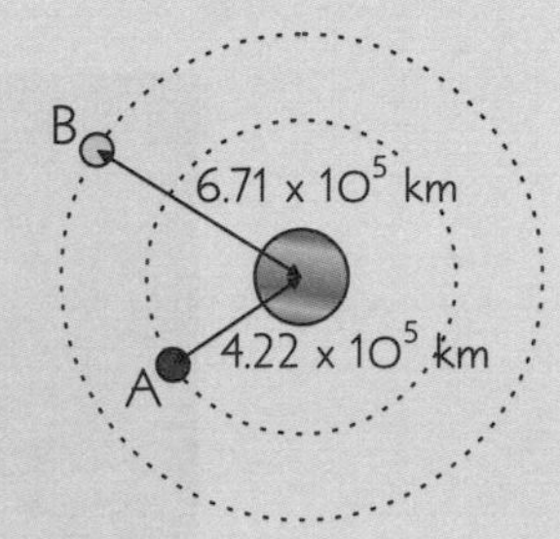

Using Kepler's third law: $\frac{T_A^2}{r_A^3} = \frac{T_B^2}{r_B^3}$ so $T_B = \sqrt{\frac{T_A^2 r_B^3}{r_A^3}} = \sqrt{\frac{(42.5)^2 \times (6.71 \times 10^5)^3}{(4.22 \times 10^5)^3}}$

= 85 hours to the nearest hour

Atmospheric Thickness is also Linked to Gravity

1) As well as predicting the motion of satellites, **Newton's law of gravitation** can also help to explain how **thick** a planet's **atmosphere** is.
2) The planet's gravitational field exerts a **force** on everything around it, including the particles which make up its atmosphere. Otherwise, the particles would float off into **space**.
3) For a planet of a fixed density, the more **massive** the planet is, the **larger** the force is further away from it's surface — so the more atmosphere particles it can stop escaping into space, leading to a **thicker atmosphere**.

Warm-Up Questions

Q1 The International Space Station orbits the Earth with velocity v. If another vehicle docks with it, increasing its mass, what difference, if any, does this make to the speed or radius of the orbit?

Q2 Derive an expression for the radius of the orbit of a planet around the Sun, in terms of the period of its orbit.

Q3 State Kepler's three laws of planetary motion.

Q4 Explain why a massive planet would generally have a thicker atmosphere than a less massive planet of the same radius.

Exam Questions

$G = 6.67 \times 10^{-11}$ Nm²kg⁻², mass of Earth = 5.98×10^{24} kg, radius of Earth = 6400 km

Q1 a) A satellite orbits 200.0 km above the Earth's surface. Calculate the period of the satellite's orbit. [2 marks]

b) What is the linear speed of the satellite? [1 mark]

Q2 At what height above the Earth's surface would a geostationary satellite orbit? [3 marks]

Q3 The Sun has a mass of 2.0×10^{30} kg, but loses mass at a rate of around 6×10^9 kgs^{-1}. Discuss whether this will have had any significant effect on the Earth's orbit over the past 50 000 years, supporting your answer with calculations. [2 marks]

All this talk of orbits is putting my head in a spin...

Kepler is sometimes proclaimed as the first science fiction writer. He wrote a tale about a fantastic trip to the Moon, where the book narrator's mum asks a demon the secret of space travel, to boldly go where — oh wait, different story. Unfortunately Kepler's book might have sparked an actual witch-hunt on Kepler's mum, whoops-a-daisy...

The Solar System & Astronomical Distances

Space is big. I mean, really big...

Our Solar System Contains More than just the Sun and Planets

1) The **universe** is **everything** that exists — this includes plenty you can see, like **stars** and **galaxies**, and plenty that you can't see, like **microwave radiation** (page 135), **dark energy** and **dark matter** (pages 136-137).
2) **Galaxies**, like our **Milky Way galaxy**, are clusters of **stars** and **planets** that are held together by gravity.
3) Inside the Milky Way is our **Solar System**, which consists of the **Sun** and all of the objects that **orbit** it. This includes the **planets** and their **planetary satellites** (including moons, artificial satellites and anything else that's orbiting them), **comets**, and **asteroids**.

The planets (in order) are: **Mercury**, **Venus**, **Earth**, **Mars**, **Jupiter**, **Saturn**, **Uranus** and **Neptune**. The planets (and the asteroid belt) all have nearly **circular** orbits. Pluto is a dwarf planet beyond Neptune.

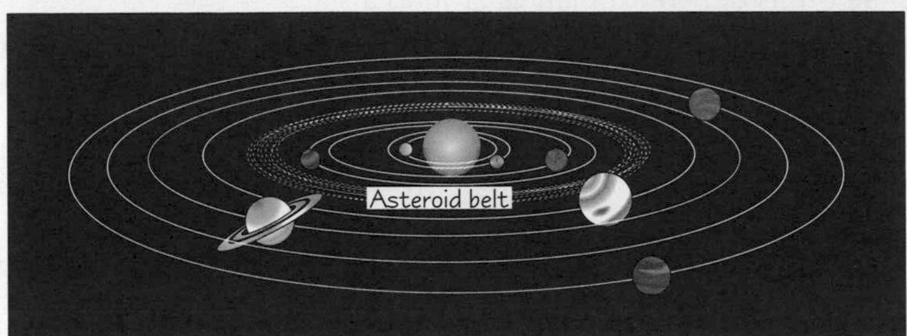

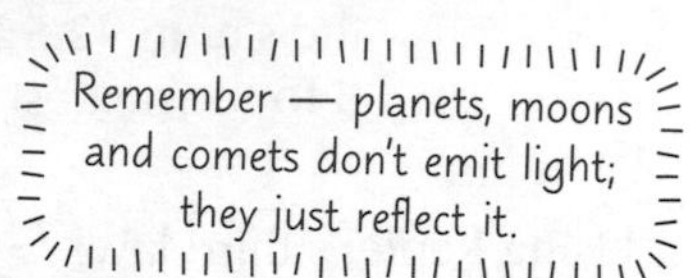

4) The orbits of the **comets** we see are **highly elliptical**. Comets are "**dirty snowballs**" that we think usually orbit the Sun about **1000 times further away** than **Pluto** does (in the "Oort cloud"). Occasionally one gets **dislodged** and heads towards the Sun. It follows a new elliptical orbit, which can take **millions of years** to complete. Some comets (from closer in than the Oort cloud) follow a **smaller orbit** and they return to swing round the Sun more regularly. The most famous is **Halley's comet**, which orbits in **76 years**.

Distances in the Solar System can be Measured in Astronomical Units (AU)

1) From **Copernicus** onwards, astronomers were able to work out the **distance** the **planets** are from the Sun **relative** to the Earth, using **astronomical units** (AU). But they could not work out the **actual distances**.

One **astronomical unit** (AU) is defined as the **mean distance** between the **Earth** and the **Sun**.

2) The **size** of the AU wasn't known accurately until 1769 — when it was carefully **measured** during a **transit of Venus** (when Venus passed between the Earth and the Sun).
3) We now know that 1 AU is equal to about **150 million km**.

Another Measure of Astronomical Distance is the Light-Year (ly)

1) All **electromagnetic waves** travel at the **speed of light**, c, in a vacuum ($c = 3.00 \times 10^8$ ms^{-1}). The **distance** that electromagnetic waves travel through a vacuum in **one year** is called a **light-year** (ly). **1 ly** is equivalent to about **9.5×10^{15} m**.
2) If you see the light from a star that is, say, **10 light-years away** then you're actually seeing it as it was **10 years ago**. The further away the object is, the further **back in time** you are actually seeing it. So when we look at the stars we're looking **back in time**, and we can only see as far back as the **beginning of the universe**. This means we can work out the **size** of the **observable universe** (p.136).

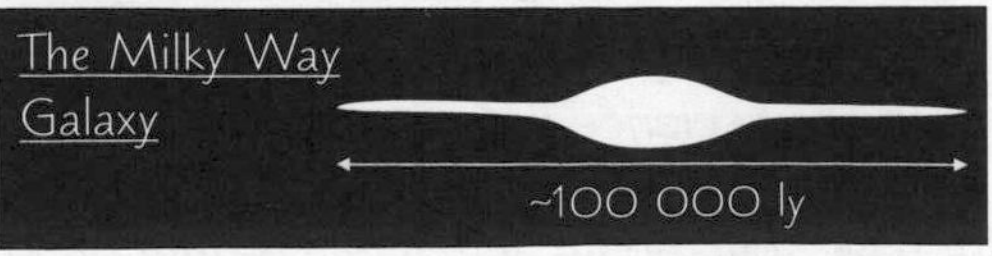

Though technically correct, Ida felt Karl's promise they'd be looking back in time had been slightly misleading.

The Solar System & Astronomical Distances

The **Distance** to **Nearby Stars** can be Measured in **Parsecs**

1) Imagine you're in a **moving car**. You see that (stationary) objects in the **foreground** seem to be **moving faster** than objects in the **distance**. This **apparent motion** is called **parallax**. Parallax is measured in terms of the **angle of parallax**. The **greater** the **angle**, the **nearer** the object is to you.
2) The same thing happens as the Earth orbits the Sun. At different points in the Earth's orbit, nearby stars appear to **move** relative to very distant stars.
3) By **measuring** the angle that a nearby star seems to move through as the Earth moves round its orbit, you can work out how far away the star is:

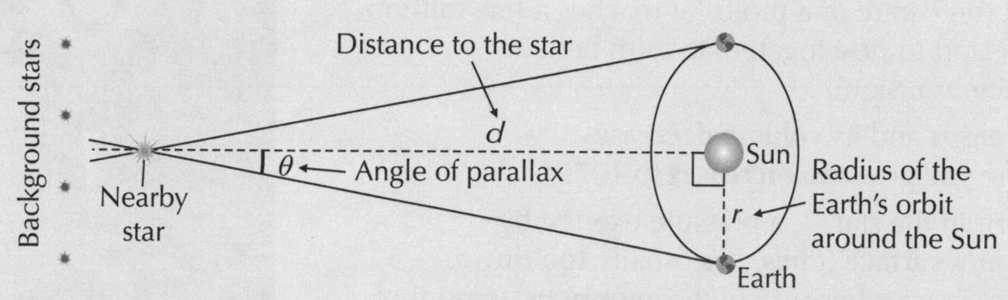

Using trig: $d = \frac{r}{\tan\theta}$.

For stars, θ is really small, so you can use the small angle approximation: $\tan\theta \approx \theta$ (where θ is in radians).

So $d \approx \frac{r}{\theta}$.

4) Calculating d in metres, or in AU, would give you some really big numbers. Instead, astronomers have defined a unit of distance from the angle of parallax. This unit is called a **parsec**.

> A star is exactly **one parsec (pc)** away from Earth if the **angle of parallax**, θ, as the Earth moves through 1 AU, is **1 second of arc** — that's $(1/3600)^\circ$.

5) This means the distance to a nearby star, in parsecs, is given by:

$$d = \frac{1}{p} \quad \text{so} \quad p = \frac{1}{d}$$ where p is the parallax, in arcseconds

The clue's in the name: an object is 1 parsec away if the parallax is 1 arcsecond.

6) One parsec is about 3.1×10^{16} m. The nearest star to Earth (other than the Sun) is about 1.3 parsecs away.

Warm-Up Questions

Q1 Describe what is meant by: a) the universe, b) the Milky Way.

Q2 Apart from the planets, what other components make up our Solar System?

Q3 Define an astronomical unit.

Q4 Describe what parallax is and explain how it allows us to measure the distances to nearby stars.

Exam Questions

Q1 Describe the main differences between the orbits of planets and comets in our Solar System. [2 marks]

Q2 a) State the definition of a light-year. [1 mark]

b) Explain why looking at distant stars is like looking back in time. [2 marks]

Q3 A star has an angle of parallax of $(5 \times 10^{-5})^\circ$ when the Earth moves through 1 AU.

a) Calculate the distance from the star to the Sun in parsecs. [2 marks]

b) Calculate the distance from the star to the Sun in light years. [2 marks]

So — using a ruler's out of the question then...

Welcome to astrophysics, the best bit of Physics. Shame it starts with the maths, really. Make sure you know why we need the different measures used in astronomy (and you get how parsecs work — they're a bit tricky). You're given conversion factors for light-years and parsecs in the exam, but not AU, so repeat after me: 1 AU = 150 million kilometres.

Stellar Evolution

Stars go through several different stages in their lives — from clouds of dust and gas, to red giants to white dwarfs...

Stars Begin as Clouds of **Dust and Gas**

1) Stars are born in a **cloud** of interstellar **dust** and **gas**, most of which was left when previous stars blew themselves apart in **supernovae**. The denser clumps of the cloud **contract** (very slowly) under the force of **gravity**.
2) When these clumps get dense enough, the cloud fragments into regions called **protostars**, that continue to contract and **heat up**.
3) Eventually the **temperature** at the centre of a protostar reaches a **few million degrees**, and **hydrogen nuclei** start to **fuse** together to form helium (see page 179 for more on nuclear fusion).
4) As the star's **temperature increases** and its **volume decreases** (remember, its contracting), the **gas pressure increases** (p.107)
5) There is also **radiation pressure** in the star — a pressure exerted by electromagnetic radiation on **any surface** it hits. It's usually **too tiny** to notice, but becomes significant in stars because of the **enormous** amount of **electromagnetic radiation** released by **fusion**.
6) The combination of gas pressure and radiation pressure counteract the force of gravity, preventing the star from contracting further.
7) The star has now reached the **MAIN SEQUENCE** and will stay there, relatively **unchanged**, while it fuses hydrogen into helium.

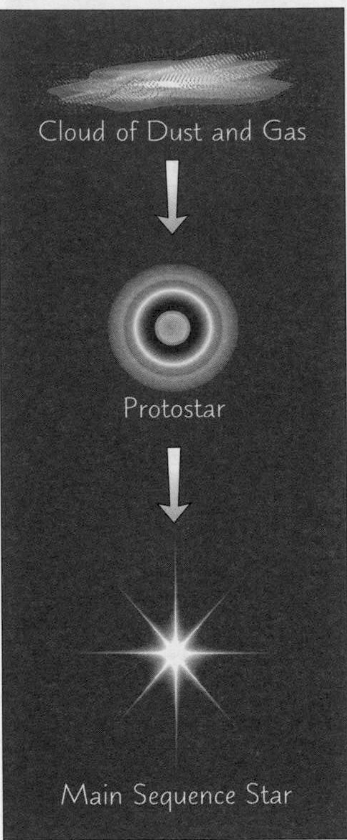

Main Sequence Stars become **Red Giants** when they **Run Out** of **Fuel**

1) Stars spend most of their lives as **main sequence** stars. The **pressure** produced from **hydrogen fusion** in their **core balances** the **gravitational force** trying to compress them. This stage is called **core hydrogen burning**.
2) When the **hydrogen** in the **core** runs out, nuclear fusion **stops**, and with it the **outward pressure stops**. The core **contracts** and **heats up** under the **weight** of the star. The outer layers expand and cool, and the star becomes a **RED GIANT**.
3) The material **surrounding** the core still has **plenty of hydrogen**. The **heat** from the contracting **core** raises the **temperature** of this material enough for the hydrogen to **fuse**. This is called **shell hydrogen burning**. (Very low-mass stars stop at this point. They use up their fuel and slowly fade away...)
4) The core continues to contract until, eventually, it gets **hot** enough and **dense** enough for **helium** to **fuse** into **carbon** and **oxygen**. This is called **core helium burning**. This releases a **huge** amount of energy, which **pushes** the **outer layers** of the star outwards.
5) When the **helium** runs out, the carbon-oxygen core **contracts again** and heats a **shell** around it so that helium can fuse in this region — **shell helium burning**.

Low Mass Stars (like the Sun) **Eject** their Shells, leaving behind a **White Dwarf**

1) In low-mass stars, the **carbon-oxygen core isn't hot enough** for any further **fusion** and so it continues to **contract** under its own **weight**. Once the core has shrunk to about **Earth-size**, **electrons** exert enough pressure (**electron degeneracy pressure**) to stop it collapsing any more (fret not — you don't have to know how).
2) This only works for stars with a core mass under about 1.4 times the mass of the sun though — in bigger stars the electron degeneracy pressure **isn't enough** to counteract the gravitational force and the star collapses (see next page). The maximum mass for which the electron degeneracy pressure can counteract the gravitational force is called the **Chandrasekhar limit**.
3) For stars below the Chandrasekhar limit, the **helium shell** becomes increasingly **unstable** as the core contracts. The star **pulsates** and **ejects** its outer layers into space as a **planetary nebula**, leaving behind the dense core.
4) The star is now a very **hot**, **dense solid** called a **WHITE DWARF**, which will simply **cool down** and **fade away**.

Stellar Evolution

The Sun is a Main Sequence Star

The **Sun** might seem quite **special** to us on Earth — it's the reason we're all here after all. But it's just like any other **low mass star** — it started off as a **cloud of dust and gas** and evolved to be the **main sequence star** we see today. Of course, this means it will most likely become a **red giant** and then finally fizzle out as a **white dwarf** — sob.

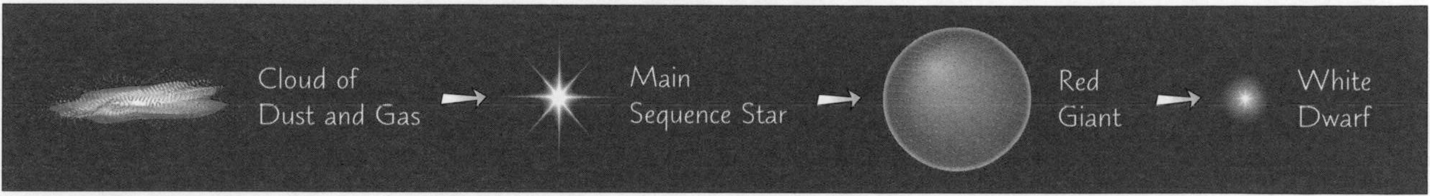

Massive Stars have a Shorter Life and a more Exciting Death

The **mass** of a star will determine how it **evolves**. **Low to medium mass** stars (like the **Sun**) follow the sequence above. **High mass stars** follow the **sequence below**.

1) Stars with a **large mass** have a **lot of fuel**, but they use it up **more quickly** and don't spend so long as main sequence stars.
2) When they are **red giants** the **'core burning to shell burning'** process can continue beyond the fusion of helium, building up layers in an **onion-like structure** to become **SUPER RED GIANTS** (or red super giants).
3) For **really massive** stars, fusion can go all the way up to **iron**. Nuclear fusion **beyond iron** isn't **energetically favourable** (p.176), so once an iron core is formed then very quickly it's goodbye star...
4) When the core of a star runs out of fuel, it starts to **contract**, forming a **white dwarf** core.
5) If the star's core is larger than the **Chandrasekhar limit, electron degeneracy pressure** can't stop the core contracting. This happens when the mass of the core is more than **1.4 times** the mass of the **Sun**. The core of the star continues to **contract**, and as it does, the **outer layers fall in** and **rebound** off the core, setting up huge **shockwaves**. These shockwaves cause the star to **explode** cataclysmically in a **SUPERNOVA**, leaving behind a **NEUTRON STAR** or (if the star was massive enough) a **BLACK HOLE**. The light from a supernova can briefly outshine an entire galaxy.

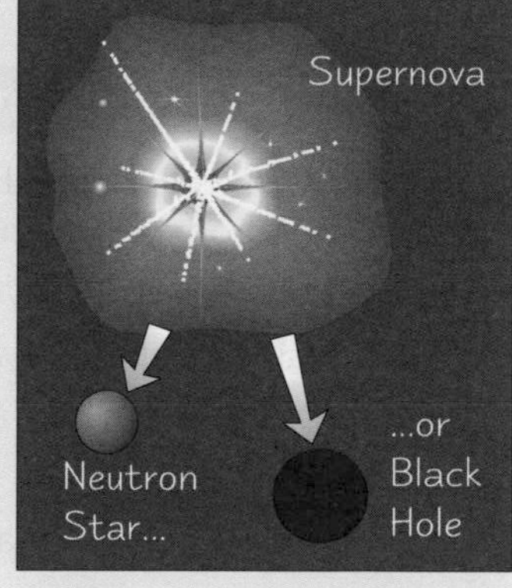

Neutron Stars are Very Dense...

1) As the core of a massive star contracts, electrons get squashed onto the atomic **nuclei**, combining with protons to form **neutrons** and **neutrinos** (hence the name 'neutron star'). If a white dwarf's core is 1.4 to 3 times the mass of the Sun then this is as far as the star can contract. The core suddenly collapses to a **neutron star**, causing a **supernova**.
2) **Neutron stars** are incredibly **dense** (about 4×10^{17} kgm^{-3}). They're also **very small**, typically about 20 km across, and they can **rotate very fast** (up to 600 times a second).
3) They emit **radio waves** in two beams as they rotate. These beams sometimes sweep past the Earth and can be observed as **radio pulses** rather like the flashes of a lighthouse. These rotating neutron stars are called **PULSARS**.

... But Not as Dense as Black Holes

1) If the **core** of a star is more than **3 times** the **Sun's mass**, the neutrons can't withstand the gravitational forces and the star continues to **collapse**.
2) For something of this size, there are **no known mechanisms** left to stop the core collapsing to an **infinitely dense** point called a **singularity**. At that point, the **laws of physics** break down completely.
3) Up to a certain distance away the gravitational pull is **so strong** that nothing, not even **light**, can escape its grasp — it's called a **black hole**. The **boundary** of this region is called the **event horizon**.

Elle wasn't sure she wanted to be the star player anymore if this was how it would end...

Stellar Evolution

Luminosity vs Temperature — the H-R Diagram

1) **Luminosity** is a measure of how **bright** an object is (p.132). If you plot **luminosity** against **temperature** for stars, you don't just get a random collection of dots. The stars appear to group in **distinct areas** on the plot.
2) The distinct areas show the main stages of a star's life cycle: the **main sequence**, **red giants**, **super red giants** and **white dwarfs** (see previous pages). This is called the **Hertzsprung-Russell diagram.**
3) The reason you can see these areas is because stars exist in these **stable** stages of their life cycle for **long periods of time**. You don't see groups of stars in any transitional period on the H-R diagram because they are unstable and the transitions happen **quickly** (compared with the life of the star).

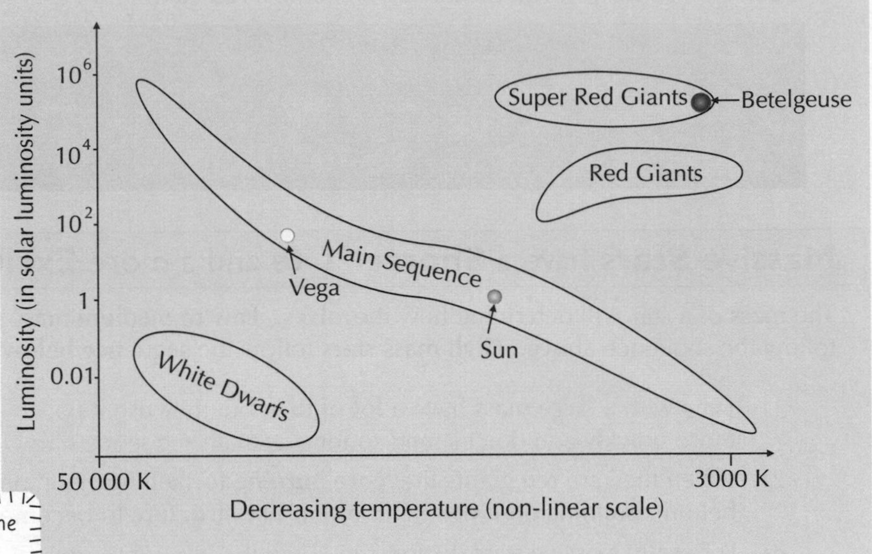

Temperature goes the "wrong way" along the horizontal axis — from hotter to cooler.

Warm-Up Questions

Q1 How are stars formed? Describe the two forms of pressure that prevent a star at the beginning of its main sequence from collapsing due to gravity and explain what causes them.
Q2 What causes a star to evolve from the main sequence to become a red giant?
Q3 What causes a supernova?
Q4 Describe a white dwarf and a neutron star. What are the main differences between them?
Q5 Describe briefly what is meant by a black hole.
Q6 What is a H-R diagram a plot of? What four main types of star are shown on a H-R diagram?

PRACTICE QUESTIONS

Exam Questions

Q1 a) Describe what is meant by the Chandrasekhar limit. [1 mark]

b)* Describe and explain the main similarities and differences between the evolution of high mass and low mass stars, starting from the beginning of their main sequence. [6 marks]

Q2 Antares is a super red giant in the constellation Scorpius.

State the letter (A, B, C, D or E) on the Hertzsprung-Russell diagram on the right that represents Antares.

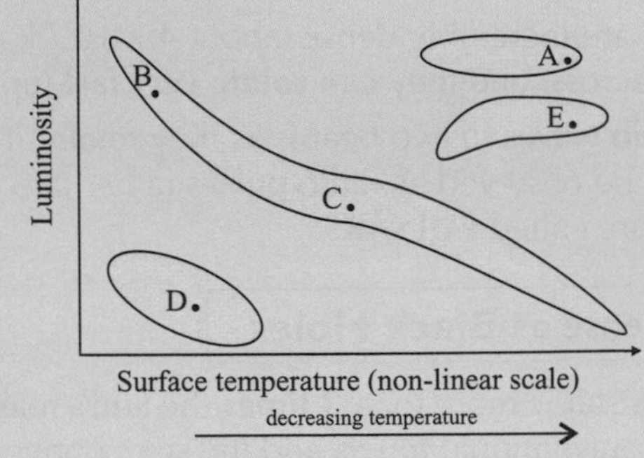

[1 mark]

*The quality of your extended response will be assessed in this question.

Live fast, die young, burn bright...

The more massive a star, the more spectacular its life cycle. The most massive stars burn up the hydrogen in their core so quickly that they only live for a fraction of the Sun's lifetime — but when they go, they do it in style. Make sure you know all the stages in the life cycles of stars of different sizes, and where they all fit in on the H-R diagram.

Spectra from Stars

'Twinkle, twinkle little star, how I wonder what you are'... well if you really want to know, you can look at the star's spectrum. It'll help if you know the regions of the EM spectrum before you start, so flick back to p.79 if you're rusty.

You Can Use a **Diffraction Grating** to find the **Wavelength** of Light

1) If you shine **monochromatic light** (light with a single wavelength or frequency) through a diffraction grating, you'll get a pattern of **bright lines** (maxima) on a dark background. This is a result of the light **interfering** with itself constructively and destructively (see pages 86-90).
2) The line of **maximum brightness** at the centre is called the **zero order** line, the next lines on **each side** are called **first order lines**, and so on.
3) Using the **fringe width** (the distance **between** the maxima), x, and the distance to the screen, D, the angle the first order line makes with the zero order line can be calculated using the **small angle approximation**: $\theta \approx \tan\theta = \frac{x}{D}$
4) If you know the slit separation, d, the order of the maximum you're observing, n, and the angle between this maximum and the incident light, θ, you can find the **wavelength** of the incident light:

$$d \sin\theta = n\lambda$$

If $\sin\theta > 1$, then that maximum doesn't exist.

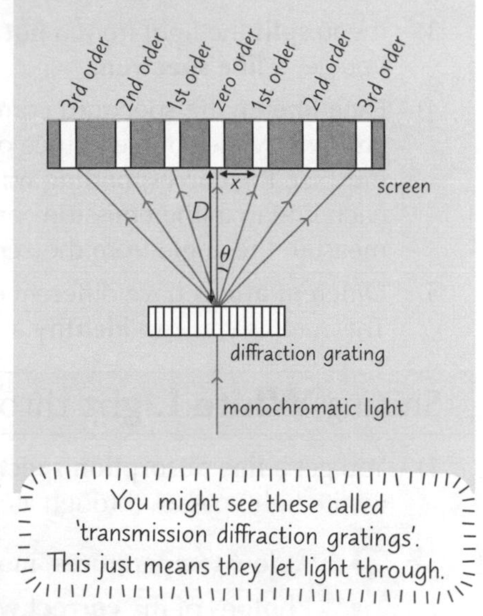

You might see these called 'transmission diffraction gratings'. This just means they let light through.

Continuous Spectra Contain **All** Possible **Wavelengths**

1) The **spectrum** of **white light** is **continuous**.
2) If you **split** white **light** up with a **diffraction grating**, the **different wavelengths** within the white light are **diffracted** by **different** amounts.
3) Each **order** in the pattern becomes a **spectrum**, with **red** on the **outside** and **violet** on the **inside**. The **zero order maximum** stays **white** because all the wavelengths just pass straight through.
4) **Hot things** emit a **continuous spectrum** in the visible and infrared regions. If an object is hot enough, the spectrum can reach into shorter wavelengths, like **ultraviolet**.

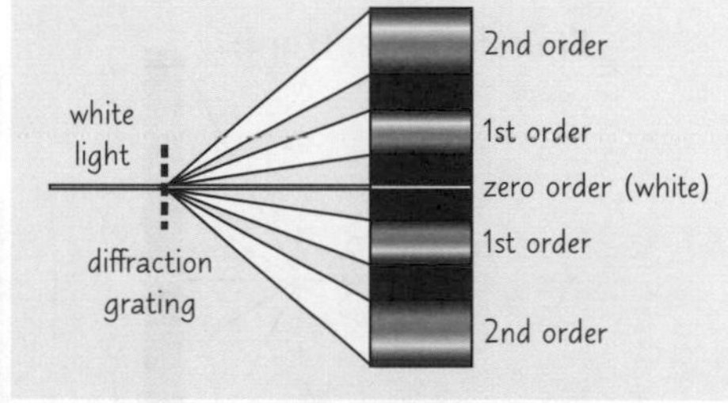

Electrons in **Atoms** Exist in **Discrete Energy Levels**

1) **Electrons** in an **atom** can **only exist** in certain **well-defined energy levels.** Each level is given a **number**, with **n = 1** representing the **ground state**.
2) Electrons can **move down** an energy level by **emitting** a **photon**.
3) Since these **transitions** are between **definite energy levels**, the **energy** of **each photon** emitted can **only** take a **certain allowed value**.
4) The diagram on the right shows the **energy levels** for **atomic hydrogen** (the energies are all negative because of how 'zero energy' is defined.)
5) The **energy** carried by each **photon** is **equal** to the **difference in energies** between the **two levels**. It's given by the equation:

$$\Delta E = hf = \frac{hc}{\lambda}$$

where h is the Planck constant, 6.63×10^{-34} Js (see page 94), c is the speed of light, 3.00×10^{8} ms^{-1}, λ is the photon's wavelength and f is the photon's frequency

$1 \text{ eV} = 1.60 \times 10^{-19}$ J

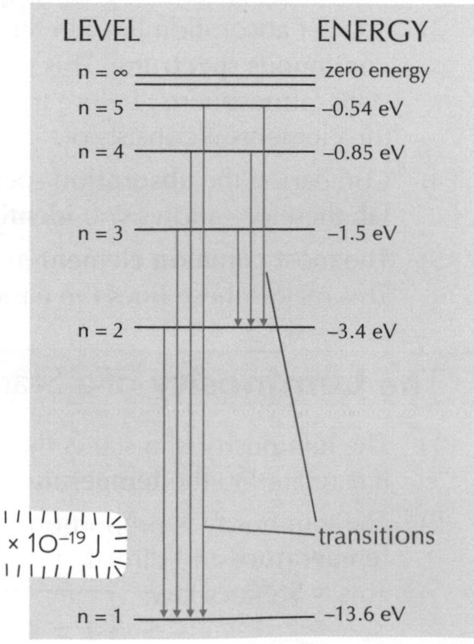

Spectra from Stars

Hot Gases Produce Line Emission Spectra

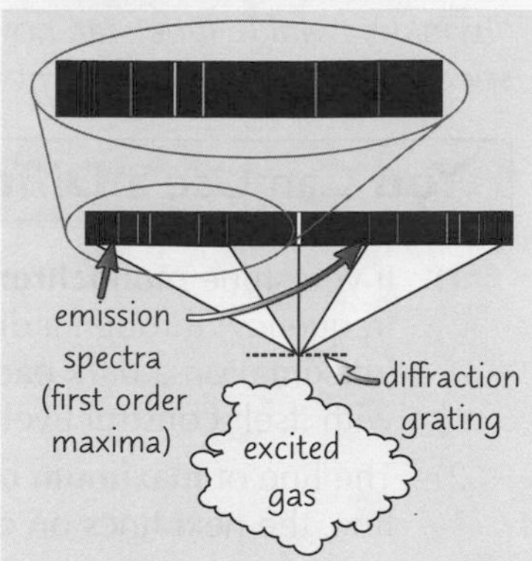

1) If you heat a gas to a high temperature, many of its electrons move to **higher energy levels**.
2) As they fall back to the ground state, these electrons emit energy as **photons**.
3) If you **split** the light from a **hot gas** with a **diffraction grating**, you get a **line spectrum**.
4) Each **line** on the spectrum corresponds to a **particular wavelength** of light **emitted** by the source. Since only **certain photon energies** are **allowed**, you only see the **corresponding wavelengths**. You can calculate the wavelength of each line in a line emission spectrum using the formula on page 90 if you measure the angle from the zero order line and you know which order maxima the spectrum is.
5) Different **atoms** have different electron **energy levels** and so different sets of **emission spectra**. This means you can **identify** a gas from its **emission spectrum**.

Shining White Light through a Cool Gas gives an Absorption Spectrum

1) You get a **line absorption spectrum** when **light** with a **continuous spectrum** of **energy** (white light) passes through a cool gas:

- At **low temperatures**, **most** of the **electrons** in the **gas atoms** will be in their **ground states**.
- **Photons** of the **correct wavelength** are **absorbed** by the **electrons** to **excite** them to **higher energy levels**.
- These **wavelengths** are **missing** from the **continuous spectrum** when it **comes out** on the other side.
- You see a **continuous spectrum** with **black lines** in it corresponding to the **absorbed wavelengths**.

2) If you **compare** the **absorption** and **emission spectra** of a **particular gas**, the **black lines** in the **absorption spectrum match up** to the **bright lines** in the **emission spectrum**.

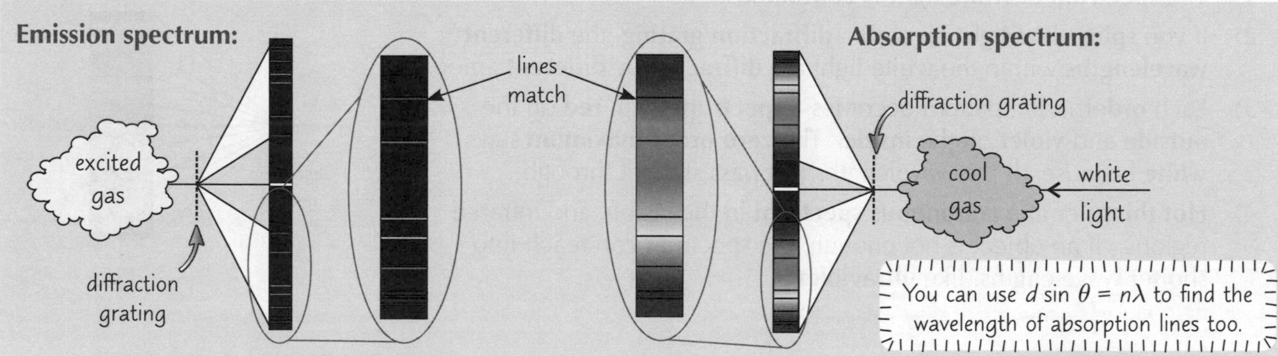

3) You get absorption lines in the spectra of light from **stars**. Stars can be assumed to emit radiation in a **continuous spectrum**. This radiation has to pass through a **large amount** of gas at the surface of the star (the star's 'atmosphere') before travelling to Earth. This gas **absorbs** particular wavelengths of light depending on the elements it consists of.
4) Comparing the **absorption** spectra of **stars** to sets of **emission** spectral lines from the **lab** therefore allows you **identify elements** within a star.
5) The most **common element** in most stars is **hydrogen**, so the spectral lines for hydrogen are usually the **clearest**. This makes these lines the **easiest** to identify and measure.

The Luminosity of a Star Depends on its Temperature and Surface Area

1) The **luminosity** of a star is the **total energy** it emits **per second** i.e. its **power output**. It is related to the **temperature** of the star and its **surface area**.
2) The luminosity is proportional to the **fourth power** of the star's **temperature** and directly proportional to its surface area. This is **Stefan's law**:

$$L = 4\pi r^2 \sigma T^4$$

Where L is the luminosity of the star (in W), r is its radius (in m), T is its surface temperature (in K) and σ (a lower case 'sigma') is the Stefan constant.

3) Measurements give the Stefan constant as $\sigma = 5.67 \times 10^{-8}$ $\text{Wm}^{-2}\text{K}^{-4}$.

Spectra from Stars

The **Peak Wavelength** of a Star Depends on its **Temperature**

1) Objects emit **electromagnetic radiation** due to their **temperature**. At everyday temperatures this is mostly in the **infrared** part of the spectrum (which we can't see). But heat something up enough and it will start to **glow**.
2) **Stars** can be assumed to emit radiation in a **continuous spectrum**.
3) The relationship between **intensity** ('power per unit area', see p.78) and **wavelength** for this radiation varies with **temperature**, as shown in the graph:
4) The most common wavelength becomes shorter as the surface temperature of the star increases. This is called the **peak wavelength**, λ_{max}.
5) You can use λ_{max} to estimate a star's **peak surface temperature** using **Wien's displacement law**:

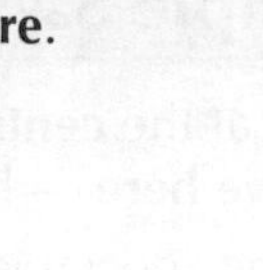

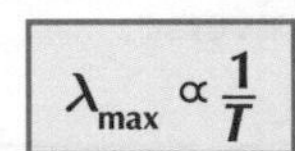

$$\lambda_{max} \propto \frac{1}{T}$$ Where T is the temperature in kelvins.

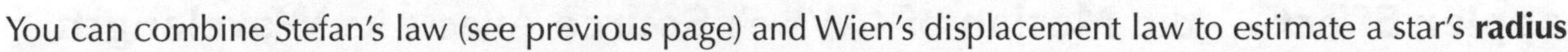

You can combine Stefan's law (see previous page) and Wien's displacement law to estimate a star's **radius**:

Example: Sirius A is a main sequence star, and Sirius B is a white dwarf. Sirius A has a surface temperature of 9800 K and produces electromagnetic radiation with a peak wavelength of 300 nm (to 2 s.f.). Sirius B has a luminosity of 9.4×10^{24} W and produces electromagnetic radiation with a peak wavelength of 115 nm. Estimate the radius of Sirius B.

First, find the temperature of Sirius B. $\lambda_{max} \propto \frac{1}{T}$, so $T\lambda_{max}$ = constant.

This means $T_A \lambda_{max\,A} = T_B \lambda_{max\,B}$ so $9800 \times 300 \times 10^{-9} = (115 \times 10^{-9})T_B$. So $T_B = \frac{9800 \times (300 \times 10^{-9})}{115 \times 10^{-9}} = 25\,565.2...$ K

Then use Stefan's law to find the star's radius:

$L = 4\pi r^2 \sigma T^4$ so $r = \sqrt{\frac{L}{4\pi\sigma T^4}} = \sqrt{\frac{9.4 \times 10^{24}}{4\pi \times (5.67 \times 10^{-8}) \times 25\,565.21...^4}}$ = **5.6×10^6 m (to 2 s.f.)**

Warm-Up Questions

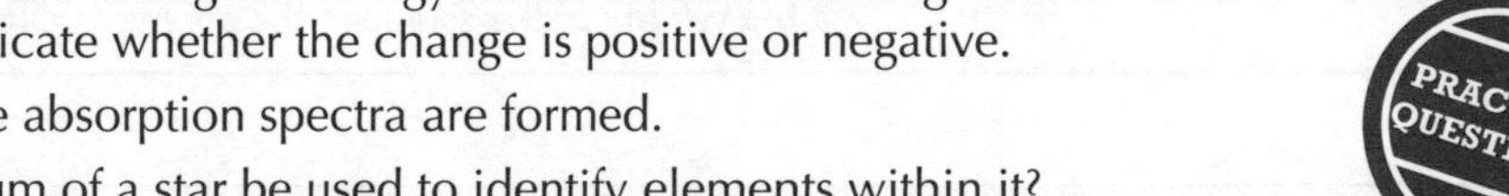

Q1 Using the diagram on page 131 find the change in energy for an electron moving from n = 2 to n = 3 in an atom of atomic hydrogen. Indicate whether the change is positive or negative.

Q2 Describe how line emission and line absorption spectra are formed.

Q3 How can the line absorption spectrum of a star be used to identify elements within it?

Q4 Describe how the radiation emitted by a star varies with its temperature.

Exam Question

Q1 A scientist is investigating light from the Sun. She uses a telescope to pass light from the Sun through a diffraction grating with a slit separation of 8.3×10^{-7} m, and observes a first order absorption line at 30.0° from the zero order line.

a) Calculate the wavelength of light that this absorption line corresponds to. [1 mark]

b) Explain why photons of certain wavelengths are absorbed by atoms in the Sun's atmosphere. [2 marks]

c) Calculate the energy of the photon that has been absorbed to produce the line observed at 30.0°. [1 mark]

d) The scientist records the peak wavelength in sunlight as 490 nm. Given that the star Rigel has a surface temperature of 12 000 K, and a peak wavelength of 240 nm, estimate the peak temperature of the surface of the Sun. [2 marks]

e) The diameter of the Sun is about 1.4×10^9 m. Estimate the Sun's luminosity. [1 mark]

Who knew light could tell you so much...

This is some pretty tricky stuff, but it's also pretty cool. Just by looking at a star, you can tell what it's made of, how hot it is, and how big it is. Not too shabby. This is one of the hardest bits in this section, so take your time, and make sure you really understand it before you move on.

The Big Bang Theory

Everyone's heard of the Big Bang theory — well here's some evidence for it.

The **Cosmological Principle** Says the Whole **Universe** Obeys the **Same Laws**

It's easy to imagine that the Earth is at the **centre of the universe**, or that there's something really **special** about it. **Earth** is special to us because we **live here** — but on a **universal scale**, it's just like any other lump of rock.

The **demotion** of **Earth** from anything special is taken to its logical conclusion with the **Cosmological principle**:

> **COSMOLOGICAL PRINCIPLE**: on a **large scale** the universe is **homogeneous** (every part is the same as every other part) and **isotropic** (it looks the same in every direction), and the laws of physics are **universal** (the same everywhere).

This is a powerful idea — it means we can apply what we know about physics on the Earth and in our Solar System to the **rest of the universe**.

The **Doppler Effect** — the **Motion** of a Wave's **Source** Affects its **Wavelength**

1) Imagine an ambulance driving past you. As it moves **towards you**, its siren sounds **higher-pitched**, but as it **moves away**, its **pitch** is **lower**. This change in **frequency** and **wavelength** is called the **Doppler shift**.
2) The frequency and the wavelength **change** because the waves **bunch together** in **front** of the source and **stretch out behind** it. The **amount** of stretching or bunching together depends on the **velocity** of the **source**.
3) This happens with light too — when a **light source** moves **away** from us, the wavelengths become **longer** and the frequencies become lower. This shifts the light towards the **red** end of the spectrum and is called **red shift**.
4) When a light source moves **towards** us, the **opposite** happens and the light undergoes **blue shift**.
5) The amount of red shift or blue shift is determined by the following formula:

Putting that sock in with the white wash had caused a definite red shift in the girls' football kits.

$$\frac{\Delta\lambda}{\lambda} \approx \frac{\Delta f}{f} \approx \frac{v}{c}$$

$\Delta\lambda$ is the difference between the observed and emitted wavelengths, λ is the emitted wavelength, Δf is the difference between the observed and emitted frequencies, f is the emitted frequency, v is the velocity of the source in the observer's direction and c is the speed of light.

Red Shift Shows That the **Universe** is **Expanding**

1) Until the early 20th century, cosmologists believed that the Universe was **infinite** in both **space** and **time** (that is, it had always existed) and **static**. This seemed the **only way** it could be **stable.**
2) This changed when Edwin Hubble realised that the **spectra** from **galaxies** (apart from a few very close ones) all show **red shift** — so they're all **moving away** from us. The amount of **galactic red shift** gives the **recessional velocity** — how fast the galaxy is moving away.
3) Plotting **recessional velocity** against **distance** shows that they're **proportional** — i.e. the **speed** that **galaxies move away** from us depends on **how far** away they are.
4) This suggests that the universe is **expanding**, and gives rise to **Hubble's law**:

Some nearby galaxies are moving towards us due to gravitational attraction. The light from these galaxies shows blue shift.

$$v = H_0 d$$

Where v = recessional velocity in kms^{-1}, d = distance in Mpc and H_0 = Hubble's constant in kms^{-1}Mpc^{-1}.

5) Since distance is very difficult to measure, astronomers used to **disagree** greatly on the value of H_0, with measurements ranging from 50 to 100 km s^{-1} Mpc^{-1}. It's now generally accepted that H_0 lies **between 65 and 80 km s^{-1} Mpc^{-1}** and most agree it's around the **mid to low 70s**. You'll be given a value to use in the exam.
6) The **SI unit** for $\boldsymbol{H_0}$ is s^{-1}. To get $\boldsymbol{H_0}$ in SI units, you need $\boldsymbol{v}$ in ms^{-1} and $\boldsymbol{d}$ in m (1 Mpc = 3.1×10^{22} m).

The Big Bang Theory

The **Expanding Universe** gives rise to the **Big Bang Model**

The universe is **expanding** (as you know from the previous page) and **cooling down**. So further back in time it must have been **smaller** and **hotter**. If you trace time back **far enough**, you get a **Big Bang**.

THE BIG BANG THEORY:
The universe started off **very hot** and **very dense** (perhaps as an **infinitely hot**, **infinitely dense** singularity) and has been **expanding** ever since.

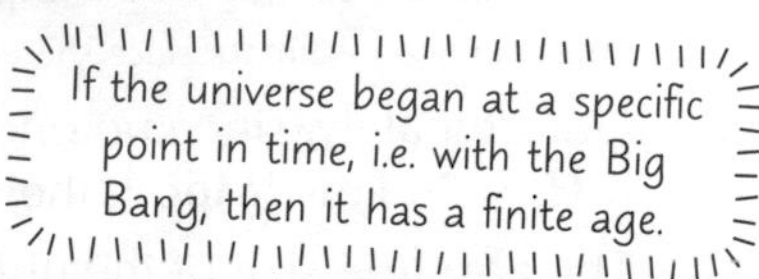

1) According to the Big Bang theory, **before** the Big Bang, there was **no space or time** — space-time **began** with the Big Bang, (when time = 0 and the radius of the universe = 0) and has been expanding ever since.
2) The red shift of light from other galaxies isn't caused by them flying away from us through space — they are moving away from us because **space itself** is **expanding**. You'd see the same thing looking from anywhere else in the universe.

Cosmic Microwave Background Radiation is Evidence for the Big Bang

1) The Big Bang model predicts that loads of **gamma radiation** was produced in the **very early universe**. This radiation should **still** be observed today (it hasn't had anywhere else to go).
2) Because the universe has **expanded**, the wavelengths of this cosmic background radiation have been **stretched** and are now in the **microwave** region.
3) Cosmic microwave background radiation (CMBR) was picked up **accidentally** by Penzias and Wilson in the 1960s.
4) In the late 1980s a satellite called the **Cosmic Background Explorer** (**COBE**) was sent up to have a **detailed look** at the radiation. It found a **continuous spectrum** corresponding to a **temperature** of about **2.7 K**.

5) The radiation is largely the same everywhere (**homogeneous**) and in all directions (**isotropic**), in line with the **Cosmological principle**.
6) There are **very tiny fluctuations** in temperature, which were at the limit of COBE's detection. These are due to tiny energy-density variations in the early universe, and are needed for the initial '**seeding**' of a star or galaxy formation.
7) The background radiation also shows a **Doppler shift**, indicating the Earth's motion through space. It turns out that the **Milky Way** is rushing towards an unknown mass (the **Great Attractor**) at over a **million miles an hour**.

Warm-Up Questions

Q1 What is the Cosmological principle?
Q2 Describe and explain the Doppler effect on waves. What observable effect does it have on EM waves?
Q3 State Hubble's law, in symbols and in words.
Q4 Give two units for measuring H_0.
Q5 Explain how the discovery of cosmic microwave background radiation supports the Big Bang theory.

Exam Questions

Q1 a) An astronomer observes that the spectral line corresponding to a wavelength of 650 nm has been shifted to 890 nm in the spectra from a distant object. Estimate the speed at which the object is moving, giving a direction. *($c = 3.00 \times 10^8$ ms^{-1})* [2 marks]

b) Use Hubble's law to estimate the distance (in light years) that the object is from us. (Use $H_0 = 2.4 \times 10^{-18}$ s^{-1}, 1 ly = 9.5×10^{15} m) [2 marks]

Q2 Explain why the red shift of light from other galaxies provides evidence for the Big Bang model of the universe. [3 marks]

So it's not just about socially awkward physicists trying to get a date then...

I love this stuff, but it's pretty bizarre trying to get your head around it, particularly the stuff about space-time expanding. Just take it nice and slow, and go back over it a few times to let it sink in.

The Evolution of the Universe

If you thought expanding space-time was weird, just wait till we get to dark energy...

The **Age** and **Observable Size** of the **Universe** Depend on H_0

1) If the universe has been **expanding** at the **same rate** for its whole life, the **age** of the universe is: $t = H_0^{-1}$
This is only an estimate since the universe probably hasn't always been expanding at the same rate.
2) Unfortunately, since no one knows the **exact value** of H_0 we can only guess the universe's age.
If $\mathbf{H_0 = 70\ kms^{-1}Mpc^{-1}}$, then the age of the universe $\approx 1/(2.2... \times 10^{-18}\ s^{-1}) = 4.4... \times 10^{17}$ s = **14 billion years**.
3) The **absolute size** of the universe is **unknown** but there is a limit on the size of the **observable universe**.
This is simply a **sphere** (with the Earth at its centre) with a **radius** equal to the **maximum distance** that **light** can travel during its **age**. So if $\mathbf{H_0 = 70\ kms^{-1}Mpc^{-1}}$ then this sphere will have a radius of **14 billion light years**.
Taking into account the **expansion** of the universe (p.134), it is thought to be more like 46-47 billion light years.

The **Story So Far** (as far as we know)...

Before 10^{-4} seconds after the Big Bang, this is mainly guesswork. There are plenty of theories around, but not much experimental evidence to back them up. The general consensus at the moment goes something like this:

1) **Big Bang to 10^{-43} seconds.** Well, it's anybody's guess, really. At this sort of size and energy, even general relativity stops working properly. This is the "infinitely hot, infinitely small, infinitely dense" bit.
2) **10^{-43} seconds to 10^{-4} seconds.** At the start of this period, there's no distinction between different types of force — there's just one grand unified force. Then the universe expands and cools, and the unified force splits into gravity, strong nuclear, weak nuclear and electromagnetic forces. Many cosmologists believe the universe went through a rapid period of expansion called inflation at about 10^{-34} s.
The universe is a sea of quarks, antiquarks, leptons and photons. The quarks aren't bound up in particles like protons and neutrons, because there's too much energy around.
At some point, matter-antimatter symmetry gets broken, so slightly more matter is made than antimatter.
Nobody knows exactly how or when this happened, but most cosmologists like to put it as early as possible in the history of the universe.

Now we're onto more solid ground

3) **10^{-4} seconds.** This corresponds to a temperature of about 10^{12} K. The universe is cool enough for quarks to join up to form particles like protons and neutrons. They can never exist separately again. Matter and antimatter annihilate each other, leaving a small excess of matter and huge numbers of photons (resulting in the cosmic background radiation that we observe today).
4) **About 100 seconds.** Temperature has cooled to 10^9 K. The universe is similar to the interior of a star. Protons are cool enough to fuse to form helium nuclei.
5) **About 300 000 years.** Temperature has cooled to about 3000 K. The universe is cool enough for electrons (that were produced in the first millisecond) to combine with helium and hydrogen nuclei to form atoms. The universe becomes transparent since there are no free charges for the photons to interact with. This process is called recombination.
6) **About 14 billion years (now).** Temperature has cooled to about 2.7 K. Slight density fluctuations in the universe mean that, over time, clumps of matter have been condensed by gravity into galactic clusters, galaxies and individual stars.

Dark Matter Makes Things More **Complicated**

1) In the 1930s, the Swiss astronomer Fritz Zwicky calculated the mass of a **cluster of galaxies** (the COMA cluster) based on the **velocity** of its outer galaxies and compared this figure to the mass of the cluster as estimated from its **luminosity**. The mass calculated from the velocity was **much bigger**, suggesting there was 'extra' mass in the cluster that couldn't be **seen**.
2) In the 1970s, Vera Rubin observed that stars at the edges of **galaxies** were moving **faster** than they should given the mass and distribution of stars in the galaxy. For Newton's laws to hold, there needed to be **extra matter** in the galaxies that hadn't been accounted for.
3) These observations suggest there is something **extra** in the universe, giving mass to galaxies, that we **can't see**.
4) This theoretical substance has been called '**dark matter**'. Astrophysicists now estimate that there is about **five times** as much dark matter as ordinary matter in the universe, and that dark matter makes up about **25% of the universe** in total.

The Evolution of the Universe

No One Knows What Dark Matter Is

1) One explanation is that dark matter is made up of **MACHOs** (Massive Compact Halo Objects). These are objects made of **normal matter** in a very **dense** form, that don't give off light and so are hard to detect, e.g. **black holes** (p.129) and **brown dwarfs** (stars that aren't massive enough for nuclear fusion to take place). Astronomers looking for evidence of these kinds of objects have had **some success**, but it's **unlikely** that MACHOs made of normal matter account for **all the dark matter** in the universe, as this would require more protons and neutrons to exist than is compatible with our current understanding of the **Big Bang**.
2) Another idea is that dark matter is made of **WIMPs** (Weakly Interacting Massive Particles). These are exotic particles that don't interact with the **electromagnetic force**, but do interact with **gravity**. As yet, though, no particle like this has ever been detected, and WIMPs are currently **purely theoretical**.
3) There's also the possibility that dark matter **doesn't really exist at all**, and is an illusion caused by **mistakes** in other theories. But most scientists **agree that it is there**, even if we don't know what it is yet.

Dark Energy is making the Universe Expand More Quickly

1) Everything in the universe is attracted to everything else by **gravity**. This means the expansion of the universe should be **slowing down**.
2) Historically, astronomers debated whether this would slow the expansion of the universe enough to cause it to contract back in on itself (in a so called 'Big Crunch'), or if the universe would go on expanding forever.
3) In the late 1990s, astronomers discovered something entirely **unexpected**. Rather than slowing down, the expansion of the universe appears to be **accelerating**. Astronomers are trying to explain this acceleration using **dark energy** — a type of energy that fills the whole of space.
4) There are various theories of what this dark energy is, but it's really hard to test them. So like dark matter, it's currently a **mystery.**

Based on current observations, **dark energy** makes up about **70%** of the universe. As **dark matter** makes up another **25%**, this means that only about **5%** of the universe is made up of **ordinary matter**. Or to put it another way, we have very little idea what 95% of the universe is made up of.

Warm-Up Questions

Q1 Using the Big Bang theory, describe the evolution of the universe from the beginning up to the present day.
Q2 Explain what is meant by the terms MACHOs and WIMPs.
Q3 What discovery led scientists to think that 70% of the universe is made up of dark energy?
Q4 What percentage of the universe is thought to be made up of ordinary matter?

PRACTICE QUESTIONS

Exam Questions

Q1 Assume $H_0 = 50$ kms^{-1}Mpc^{-1} (to 2 s.f.). (*1 year ≈ 3.16 × 10⁷ s, 1 pc = 3.1 × 10¹⁶ m*)

a) Calculate H_0 in SI units. [2 marks]

b) Calculate an estimate of the age of the universe, and hence the radius of the observable universe, ignoring expansion. [3 marks]

Q2 Some scientists believe that weakly interacting massive particles (WIMPs) are a candidate for the dark matter which makes up around 25% of the universe. Explain why scientists believe dark matter must exist, and give a reason why it cannot be ordinary matter that emits little or no radiation. [4 marks]

So, this book only applies to about 5% of the universe?...

Dark matter and dark energy represent a huge hole in our knowledge — trying to understand the universe without studying them is like trying to revise for your exams by only reading 5% of this book (not a good idea, by the way). This stuff is a great example of how science works though — we have a theory, make some observations, find something that doesn't fit in with our predictions, then look for a new way of explaining it. Ach, science, don't you just love it?

Extra Exam Practice

Hasta la vista Module 5... almost — here's a mix of questions from this module for you to have a crack at.

- Have a look at this example of how to answer a tricky exam question.
- Then check how much you've understood from Module 5 by having a go at the questions on the next page.

1 A waitress warms a pot of milk for a coffee by passing steam through it. The steam condenses in the milk to form hot water and cools, transferring thermal energy to the milk.

(a) The steam has a temperature of 100.0 °C. Calculate the mass of steam needed to warm 225 g of milk from 7.5 °C to 80.0 °C. The specific heat capacity of milk is 3.93×10^3 J kg^{-1}K^{-1}. The specific heat capacity of water is 4.20×10^3 J kg^{-1}K^{-1}. The specific latent heat of vaporisation of water is 2.26×10^6 J kg^{-1}. You may assume there is no heat transferred to the surroundings.

(5 marks)

(b) The waitress sprinkles some cocoa powder on top of the coffee. Describe the motion of the cocoa particles on the surface of the coffee, and explain how this will change as the coffee cools.

(3 marks)

1(a)

Energy is conserved, so all of the heat energy transferred from the steam **condensing** and **cooling** to 80.0 °C will be transferred to the milk to **heat** it from 7.5 °C to 80.0 °C.

There's a lot going on here, with the steam condensing and cooling, and the milk warming up. Make sure you're clear on what's going on before starting on any calculations.

Mass of milk = 225 g = 0.225 kg. Mass of steam needed = m_s.

Energy transferred from the steam as it condenses = $mL = 2.26 \times 10^6 m_s$

Energy transferred from the water as it cools from 100.0 °C to 80.0 °C = $mc\Delta\theta = m_s \times (4.20 \times 10^3) \times$ **(100.0 – 80.0)** $= 8.4 \times 10^4 m_s$

To calculate $\Delta\theta$, you don't have to convert both of the temperatures to kelvin, as a change of 1 °C is the same as a change of 1 K.

Energy transferred to the milk = $mc\Delta\theta$

$= 0.255 \times (3.93 \times 10^3) \times$ **(80.0 – 7.5)**

= 72 655.875 J

So $(2.26 \times 10^6 m_s) + (8.4 \times 10^4 m_s) = 72\ 655.875$

$2.344 \times 10^6 m_s = 72\ 655.875$

$m_s = 72\ 655.875 \div (2.344 \times 10^6) = 0.03099...$ kg = **0.031 kg (to 2 s.f.)**

Round your final answer to the lowest number of significant figures given in the question. In this case it's 2, but don't round until the end.

You'd get 5 marks for the correct answer. If you got the answer wrong, you'd still get 1 mark for writing an expression for the energy transferred from the steam as it condenses, 1 mark for writing an expression for the energy transferred from the water as it cools, 1 mark for calculating the energy transferred to the milk and 1 mark for equating the energy transferred away from the steam/water and the energy transferred to the milk.

1(b)

The cocoa particles are suspended in a fluid, so will move with a zigzag, random motion known as Brownian motion as a result of collisions with fast, randomly-moving particles in the fluid. As the coffee cools, the kinetic energy of the fluid particles decreases, so less energy is transferred to the cocoa particles during collisions with the fluid particles. So the average kinetic energy of the cocoa particles, and therefore their average speed, will decrease as the coffee cools.

You'd get 1 mark for describing the Brownian motion of the particles, 1 mark for saying the kinetic energy transferred in collisions decreases, and 1 mark for saying the average speed of the cocoa particles therefore decreases.

You might not have realised that 1(b) is about Brownian motion. If you find yourself struggling to apply the physics you know, search the question for clues. Particles are mentioned, so particle theory is a good place to start.

Don't forget that 'explain' means you need to say why something happens. Make sure someone could follow your explanation all the way through, with no unexplained leaps between points.

Extra Exam Practice

2 A loudspeaker is a device that converts electrical energy into sound energy. An alternating current with frequency f forces a loudspeaker cone to vibrate back and forth at the same frequency. This forces air molecules to vibrate, causing a sound wave of frequency f. The loudness of the sound produced will depend on the amplitude of the sound wave, and the pitch depends on its frequency. A higher amplitude means a louder sound and a higher frequency means a higher pitched sound.

(a) The back and forth movement of the loudspeaker cone can be modelled as simple harmonic motion. At time $t = 0$ s, the cone is at the midpoint of an oscillation. The cone is oscillating at 28 Hz and with an amplitude of 4.2 mm. Calculate the acceleration of the cone at $t = 0.21$ s. You can assume that energy losses are negligible.

(3 marks)

Many loudspeaker units use two cones to produce sounds. The large cone has a low natural frequency and the small cone has a high natural frequency. The input signal is filtered to ensure that the small cone produces the high frequency sounds and the large cone produces the low frequency sounds. Both cones are usually critically damped. **Figure 1** shows how the amplitude of vibration varies with the driving frequency of a fixed amplitude signal for two different cones.

Figure 1

(b)* Explain why the quality of the sound of a loudspeaker unit is improved by using critical damping and by using different-sized cones.

(6 marks)

3 Data about two planets is shown in **Table 1**.

(a) Calculate the mass of planet 1 in terms of M.

(3 marks)

Table 1

Planet	Radius	g at surface of planet	Mass
1	$5r$	$2g$	—
2	r	g	M

(b) In the absence of any other bodies, the gravitational potential at a point between two planets, which is 3.10×10^{10} m from the centre of planet 1, is $V_g = -\frac{GM}{6.65 \times 10^8}$, where V_g is in Jkg^{-1}, G is in $\text{Nm}^2\text{kg}^{-2}$ and M is in kg. Calculate the distance between the centres of the two planets.

(4 marks)

The two planets in **Table 1** are orbiting a distant star, star A.

(c) A scientist is observing the spectra of electromagnetic radiation coming from star A. He measures the peak wavelength of this radiation to be 645 nm as it reaches Earth. The scientist uses the peak wavelength received at Earth and Wien's displacement law to calculate a surface temperature of 4487 K for star A. He does not take into account the Doppler shift of the electromagnetic radiation. Star A has an actual surface temperature of 4553 K. Estimate the speed at which star A is moving away from the Earth. ($c = 3.00 \times 10^8$ ms^{-1})

(3 marks)

(d) The age of the universe is approximately 4.4×10^{17} s (14 billion years). Suggest why it would be difficult to measure the distance to star A using parallax. Justify your answer with a calculation. (1 parsec $\approx 3.1 \times 10^{16}$ m)

(4 marks)

* The quality of your extended response will be assessed in this question.

Capacitors

Capacitors are things that store electrical charge — like a charge bucket. The capacitance of one of these things tells you how much charge the bucket can hold. Sounds simple enough... ha... ha, ha, ha...

Capacitors Build Up Charge on Plates

1) A **capacitor** is an electrical component that can **store electrical charge.**
2) Capacitors are made up of two **conducting plates** separated by a **gap** or a **dielectric** (an insulating material).
3) The **circuit symbol** for a capacitor is two **parallel lines.**
4) When a capacitor is connected to a **power source**, **positive** and **negative** charge build up on **opposite** plates. The insulating material (which could be an **air gap**) stops charge moving between the two plates, so a **potential difference** is created.
5) This creates a **uniform electric field** (p.147) between the plates.

Remember, the potential difference between two points is the work done in moving a unit charge between them.

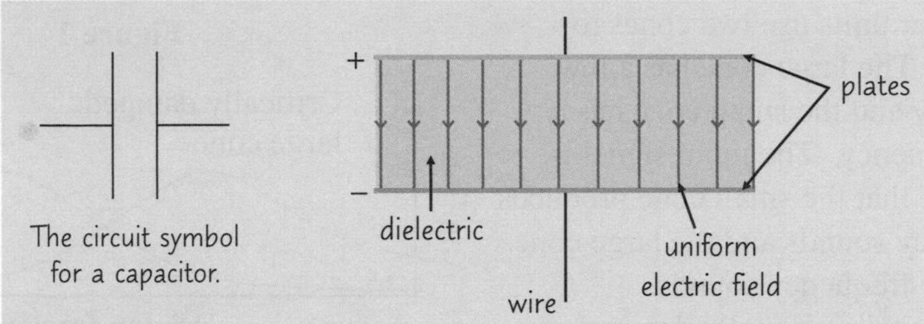

The circuit symbol for a capacitor.

6) The amount of **charge per unit voltage** stored by a capacitor is called its **capacitance.**

$$C = \frac{Q}{V}$$

where Q is the charge in coulombs, V is the potential difference in volts and C is the capacitance in farads (F) — 1 farad = 1 CV^{-1}.

7) A farad is a **huge** unit so you'll usually see capacitances expressed in terms of:

μF — microfarads (× 10^{-6}) **nF** — nanofarads (× 10^{-9}) **pF** — picofarads (× 10^{-12})

Combined Capacitance Increases in Parallel, but Decreases in Series

Depending on how you place **capacitors** in a **circuit**, you can increase or decrease the amount of **charge stored.**

You could be asked to solve circuit problems using these equations.

If you put two or more **capacitors** in a **parallel circuit**, the **potential difference** across each one is the **same**.

Each capacitor can store the **same** amount of **charge** as it would if it was the **only component** in the circuit.

So, the **total capacitance** is just the **sum** of the individual capacitances:

$$C_{total} = C_1 + C_2$$

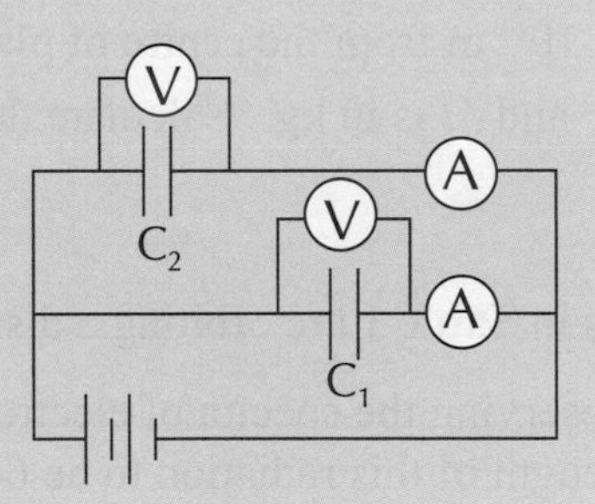

When you put capacitors in a **series circuit**, the **potential difference** is **shared** between them.

Each capacitor stores the **same charge.**

It can be shown that:

$$\frac{1}{C_{total}} = \frac{1}{C_1} + \frac{1}{C_2} + \frac{1}{C_3}$$

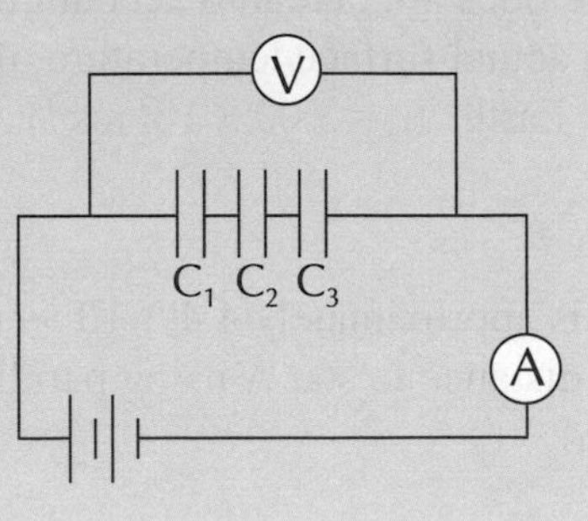

You can keep adding as many capacitors you want like this — the formula will just be: $\frac{1}{C_{total}} = \frac{1}{C_1} + \frac{1}{C_2} + \frac{1}{C_3} + \frac{1}{C_4} + ...$

Capacitors

You Can Investigate Capacitors in Series and Parallel

PRACTICAL SKILLS

1) Set up a **test series circuit** to measure current and potential difference. Add a **variable resistor** and a switch. Close the switch.
2) Constantly adjust the **variable resistor** to keep the charging current **constant** for as long as you can (it's impossible when the capacitor is nearly fully charged).
3) A **data logger** connected to the **voltmeter** can be used to record the **potential difference** over **time**. Once the capacitors are fully charged, open the **switch**.
4) Rearrange the circuit so the capacitors are in **parallel** (like the diagram on the previous page, but now with a variable resistor). Make sure they have been discharged first (see p.143). Close the switch and repeat step 2.
5) Once both circuits have been tested, you can plot graphs of **current against time** and **charge against potential difference** (using $\Delta Q = I\Delta t$).

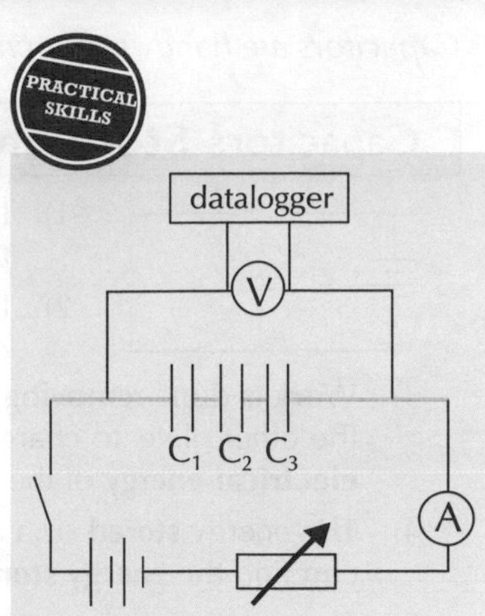

Assuming all three capacitors have the same **capacitance** C, and can hold a **charge** of Q, your graphs will look like:

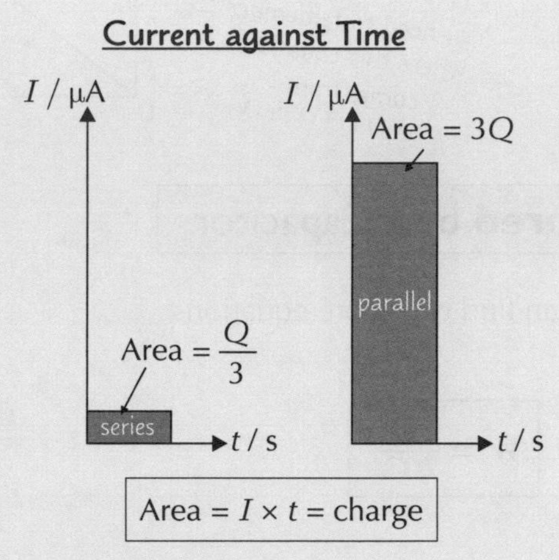

The area under each graph gives the **total charge** stored by the three capacitors.

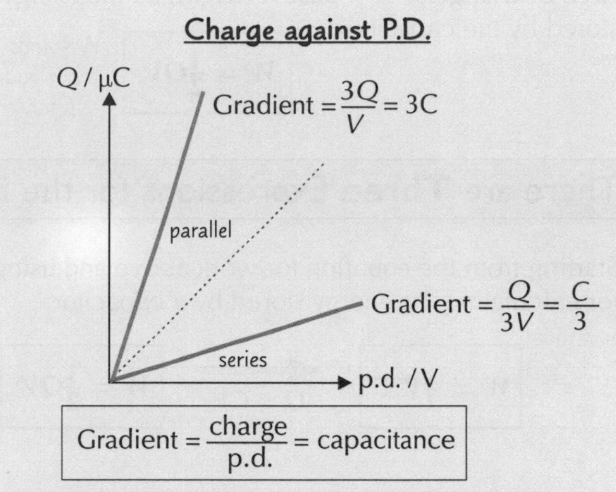

The gradient of each graph gives the **total capacitance** of the three capacitors.

Warm-Up Questions

PRACTICE QUESTIONS

Q1 What is a capacitor?

Q2 Define capacitance and write down the formula for calculating it.

Q3 How do you find the total capacitance of a circuit if the capacitors are placed in parallel?

Q4 Describe an experiment you could do to show how capacitance changes for a parallel and series circuit.

Exam Questions

Q1 From the graphs shown on the right, calculate the capacitance of the capacitor and the charge stored on its plates after 66 seconds.

[4 marks]

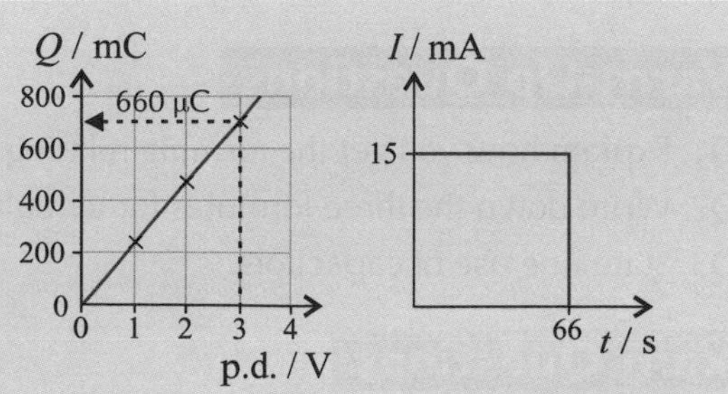

Q2 a) Two capacitors are connected in series and a potential difference of 12 V is applied to them. Calculate the total charge stored in the circuit. The capacitance of the first capacitor is 12 pF and for the second is 7.0 pF.

[2 marks]

b) The same potential difference is applied but now the capacitors are connected in parallel. Calculate the new total charge stored in the circuit.

[2 marks]

Capacitance — fun, it's not...

Capacitors are really useful in the real world. Pick an appliance, any appliance, and it'll probably have a capacitor or several. If I'm being honest, though, the only saving grace of these pages for me is that they're not especially hard...

Energy Stored by Capacitors

Capacitors are handy for storing small amounts of energy that can be accessed quickly.

Capacitors **Store Energy**

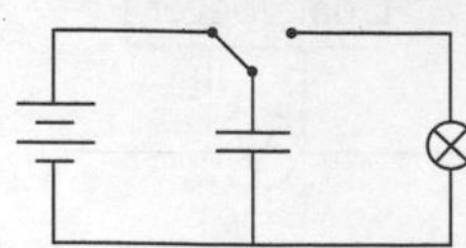

1) In this circuit, when the switch is flicked to the **left**, **charge** builds up on the plates of the **capacitor**. **Electrical energy**, provided by the battery, is **stored** by the capacitor.
2) If the switch is flicked to the **right**, the energy stored on the plates will **discharge** through the **bulb**, converting electrical energy into light and heat.
3) **Work** is done **removing negative charge** from **one plate** and depositing it onto the other plate (to charge the capacitor). The energy for this must come from the **electrical energy** of the **battery**, and is given by **charge × average p.d.**
4) The energy **stored** by a capacitor is **equal** to the **work done** to deposit the charge on the plate. So, you can find the **energy stored** from the **area** under a **graph** of **p.d.** against **charge stored** on the capacitor.
5) The p.d. across the capacitor is **proportional** to the charge stored on it, so the graph will be a **straight line** through the origin. The **energy stored** is given by the **yellow triangle**.

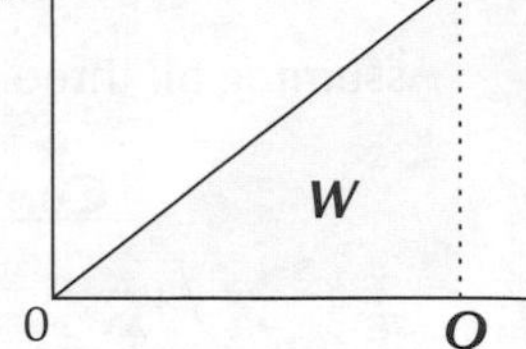

Area of triangle = ½ × base × height, so the energy stored by the capacitor is:

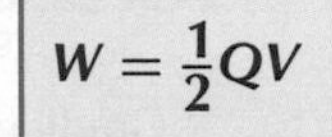

W stands for 'work done', but you can also use *E* for 'energy stored'.

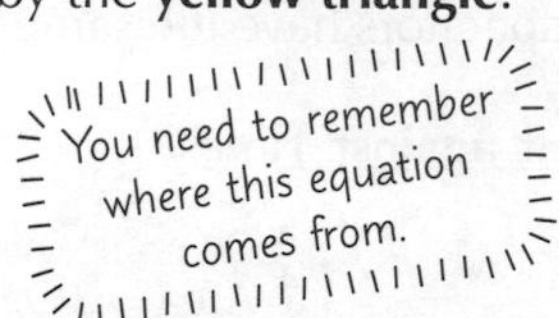

There are **Three** Expressions for the **Energy Stored** by a Capacitor

Starting from the equation for work above and using $C = \frac{Q}{V}$ you can find two more equations for calculating the energy stored by a capacitor:

$$W = \frac{1}{2}V^2C \quad \xleftarrow{Q = CV} \quad W = \frac{1}{2}QV \quad \xrightarrow{V = \frac{Q}{C}} \quad W = \frac{1}{2}\frac{Q^2}{C}$$

Different Capacitors Have Different **Uses**

Capacitors are found in loads of **electronic devices**. They don't store much charge, so can't replace **batteries**, but they can discharge **quicker** than batteries, which makes them very useful. What's more, the **amount of charge** that can be stored and the **rate** at which it's **released** can be controlled by the capacitor chosen. Some uses for them are:

1) **Flash photography** — when you take a picture, the capacitor has to discharge really quickly to give a **short pulse** of high current to create a brief, bright flash.
2) **Back-up power supplies** — these often use lots of large capacitors that can release charge for a **short period** if the power supply goes off — e.g. for keeping computer systems running if there's a brief power outage.
3) **Smoothing out p.d.** — when converting an **a.c. power** supply to **d.c. power**, capacitors charge up during the **peaks** and discharge during the **troughs**, helping to maintain a **constant output**.

Warm-Up Questions

Q1 Explain how you get the formula relating work, charge and voltage for a capacitor.

Q2 Write down the three formulas for calculating the energy stored by a capacitor.

Q3 State one use of capacitors.

Exam Questions

Q1 Calculate the energy stored by a capacitor if it is charged from a 12 V source and holds a charge of 0.6 nC. [1 mark]

Q2 Calculate the capacitance of a capacitor that stores 2.5×10^{-10} J of energy if it is charged from a 5 V supply. [1 mark]

Short and sweet — just how I like my physics...

Make sure you can explain how to get the energy equations as well as how to use them and you're pretty much sorted.

Charging and Discharging

Charging and discharging — sounds painful...

You can Investigate what Happens when you Charge a Capacitor

1) Set up the test circuit shown in the circuit diagram.
2) Close the switch to connect the **uncharged** capacitor to the power supply.
3) Let the capacitor **charge** whilst the **data logger** records both the **potential difference** (from the voltmeter) and the **current** (from the ammeter) over time.
4) When the current through the ammeter is **zero**, the capacitor is fully charged.
5) You can then use a computer to plot a graph of **charge, p.d.** or **current against time**, as shown below (remember $\Delta Q = I\Delta t$).

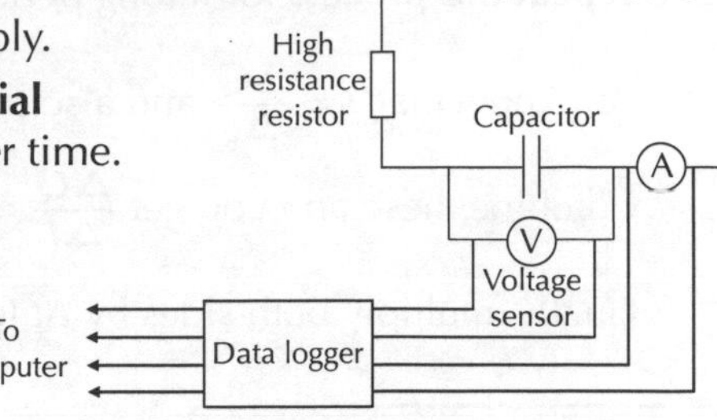

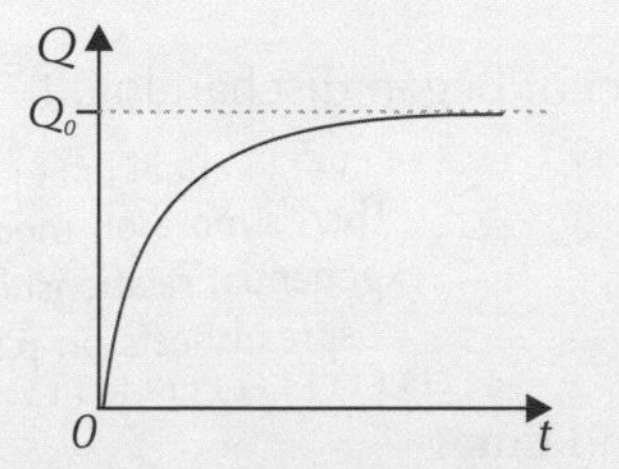

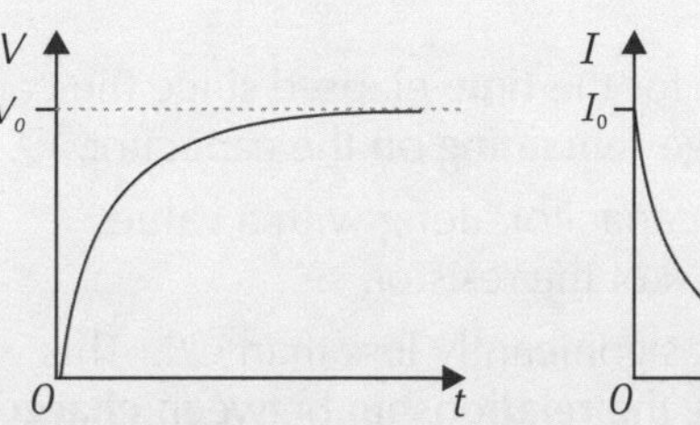

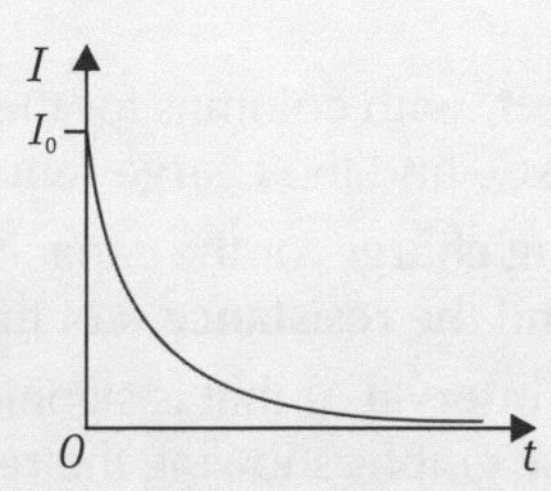

These circuits charge and discharge capacitors through a fixed resistor. You'll see on p.145 that resistance slows down the charge/discharge. In practice, using a resistor makes the process slower and easier to investigate.

1) As soon as the switch closes, current starts to flow. The electrons flow onto the plate connected to the **negative terminal** of the power supply, so a **negative charge** builds up.
2) This build-up of negative charge **repels** electrons off the plate connected to the **positive terminal** of the power supply, making that plate positive. These electrons are attracted to the positive terminal of the power supply.
3) An **equal** but **opposite** charge builds up on each plate, causing a **potential difference** between the plates. Remember that **no charge** can flow **between** the plates because they're **separated** by an **insulator** (gap or dielectric).
4) Initially the **current** through the circuit is **high**. But, as **charge** builds up on the plates, **electrostatic repulsion** makes it **harder** and **harder** for more electrons to be deposited. When the p.d. across the **capacitor** is equal to the p.d. across the **power supply**, the **current** falls to **zero**. The capacitor is **fully charged**.

An equal but opposite charge

To Discharge a Capacitor, Disconnect the Power and Reconnect the Circuit

1) **Disconnect** the power supply from the test circuit above, reconnect the circuit and close the **switch**.
2) Let the capacitor **discharge** whilst the data logger records **potential difference** and **current** over time.
3) When the **current** through the ammeter and the **potential difference** across the plates fall to **zero**, the capacitor is fully discharged.
4) You can once more plot **graphs** of **p.d.**, **charge** and **current** against **time**:

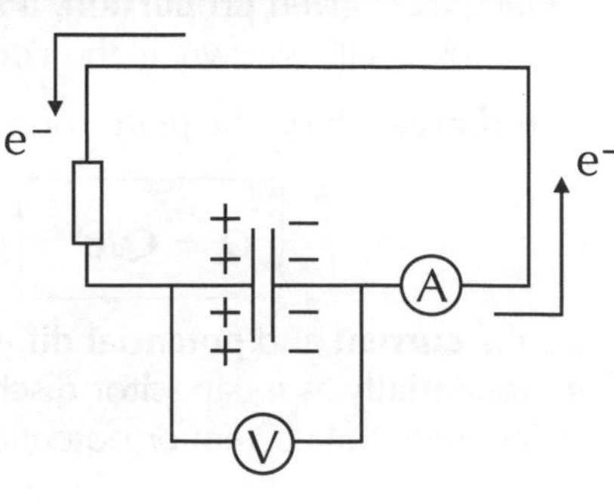

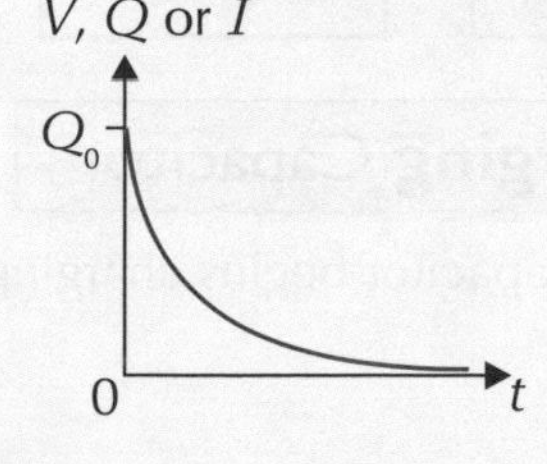

OR

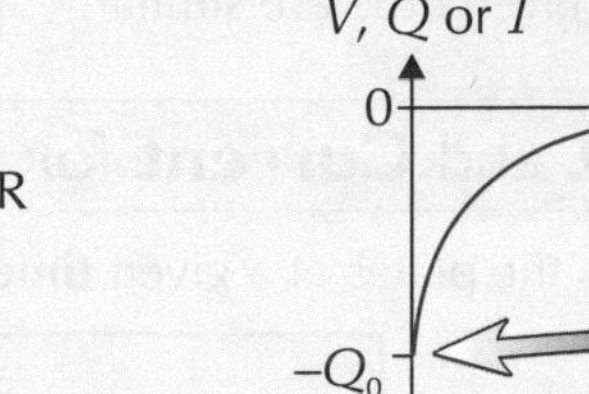

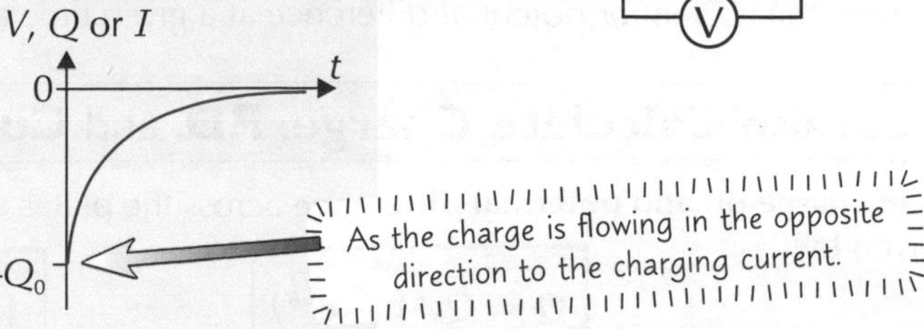

The electrons (current) flow from the **negative** plate to the **positive** plate (shown above). Initially, the current is **high**, but as the charge leaves the plates, the **potential difference** across the plates **decreases**. So the **electrostatic repulsion** decreases, reducing the flow of current.

Charging and Discharging

You Can Model Discharging Capacitors with a Spreadsheet

You can predict **roughly** how the stored **charge** will **change over time** for any **discharging** capacitor with capacitance C and initial charge Q, in a circuit with resistance R. You need to find the change in charge over a **tiny time interval** and **repeat** this process for a long period of time. To do this, you'll need an equation which relates ΔQ and Δt.

You know that $I = \frac{\Delta Q}{\Delta t}$ and also that $I = \frac{V}{R}$, so $\frac{\Delta Q}{\Delta t} = \frac{V}{R}$. For capacitors, $Q = CV$ so $V = \frac{Q}{C}$.

Combine these and you get $\frac{\Delta Q}{\Delta t} = -\frac{Q}{RC}$.

There's a minus sign here because the charge is decreasing over time.

Finally, multiply both sides by Δt to get $\Delta Q = -\frac{Q}{RC}\Delta t$.

Spreadsheet Modelling

1) Create a new **spreadsheet**, with columns for the **time** elapsed since the capacitor began discharging, t, the **change in charge**, ΔQ, and the **charge remaining** on the capacitor, Q.
2) Choose an **initial starting charge** for the capacitor along with a value for the **capacitance** C and the **resistance** R of the resistor.
3) Choose a sensible **time interval** Δt that is significantly less than CR. This will let you plot more **precise** graphs showing the **relationship** between **charge** and **time**.
4) In the initial row, $t_0 = 0$ and Q_0 = **initial charge**. Leave ΔQ blank in this row.
5) In the next row:
   - The **new time** $t_1 = t_0 + \Delta t$.
   - You can write a formula for the **change in charge**, ΔQ, over the time interval by using the equation $\Delta Q = -\frac{Q}{RC}\Delta t$ above. I'll call it $(\Delta Q)_1$.
   - The **new charge** is given by $Q_1 = Q_0 + (\Delta Q)_1$ so write a formula for that too.
6) **Repeat** this process of calculating the values in each row from Q and t in the **row above**. If you write the formulas correctly, you can use the spreadsheet program to **automatically fill** in as many rows as you want.
7) Once you have enough points, plot a **graph** of **charge** against **time**. It should be similar to the graph for a **discharging capacitor** shown on page 143.

There's more on modelling exponential relationships with spreadsheets on p.173.

The Charge on a Discharging Capacitor Decreases Exponentially

The **shape** of the graph you plot from the model above is actually one of **exponential decay** (p.190). This means that when a capacitor is **discharging**, the amount of **charge** left on the plates falls **exponentially with time**.

It always takes the **same length of time** for the charge to **halve**, no matter **how much charge** you start with — like radioactive decay (see p.174-175).

In fact, for a given **proportion**, it always takes the same time for that proportion of the charge to be lost — it's known as the **constant ratio property** of exponential relationships.

See p.143 for the graphs showing the exponential relationships of Q, V and I.

The **charge** left on the plates of a capacitor discharging from full is given by the equation:

$$Q = Q_0 e^{\frac{-t}{CR}}$$

where Q_0 is the charge of the capacitor when it's fully charged (C), t is time since discharging began (s), R is the resistance (Ω) and C is the capacitance (F).

As the **current** and **potential difference** also decrease **exponentially** as a capacitor discharges, the formulas for calculating the current or potential difference at a given time are similar:

$$I = I_0 e^{\frac{-t}{CR}} \qquad V = V_0 e^{\frac{-t}{CR}}$$

You can also Calculate Charge, P.D. and Current for a Charging Capacitor

1) The **charge** on and **potential difference** across the plates at a given **time** after a capacitor begins charging are given by:

$$Q = Q_0(1 - e^{\frac{-t}{CR}}) \qquad V = V_0(1 - e^{\frac{-t}{CR}})$$

2) The **charging current decreases exponentially** (it just travels in the **opposite direction** to the discharging current). So the formula for the charging current at a given time is the **same** as for a **discharging** capacitor:

$$I = I_0 e^{\frac{-t}{CR}}$$

Charging and Discharging

The **Time Taken** to **Charge** or **Discharge** Depends on **Two Factors**

The **time** it takes to charge up or discharge a capacitor depends on:

1) The **capacitance** of the capacitor (**C**). This affects the amount of **charge** that can be transferred at a given **voltage**.
2) The **resistance** of the circuit (**R**). This affects the **current** in the circuit.

Time Constant $\tau = CR$

τ is the Greek letter 'tau'

If $t = \tau = CR$ is put into the equation for the charge on a discharging capacitor, then $Q = Q_0 e^{-1}$.
So when $t = \tau$: $\frac{Q}{Q_0} = \frac{1}{e} \approx \frac{1}{2.718} \approx 0.37$.

1) So τ, the **time constant**, is the time taken for the **charge**, **potential difference** or **current** on a discharging capacitor to **fall** to **37%** of its initial value.
2) It's also the time taken for the **charge** or **potential difference** of a **charging** capacitor to **rise** to **63%** of it's maximum value.
3) The **larger** the **resistor** in series with the capacitor, the **longer it takes** to charge or discharge.
4) In practice, the time taken for a capacitor to charge or discharge **fully** is taken to be about $5CR$.

To find CR, you can plot a graph of $\ln Q$ against t while discharging — p.190-191 (p.d. or current would work too). The gradient of the line gives you $\frac{-1}{CR}$.

τ can be found experimentally by using a voltmeter and timing how long it takes a discharging capacitor to reach 37% of its starting potential difference.

Warm-Up Questions

Q1 Describe an experiment you could do to investigate how charge changes over time for a charging capacitor.

Q2 Sketch graphs to show how the p.d. across the plates of a capacitor changes with time for:
a) charging a capacitor, b) discharging a capacitor,
and explain what effect the p.d. has on the current, in terms of electron flow.

Q3 Describe how you could model the change of charge across a discharging capacitor with a spreadsheet.

Q4 Describe what effect the initial charge on a capacitor has on the time taken for the charge to half.

Q5 State the formula for calculating the p.d. across a charging capacitor at a time t after charging began.

Q6 What two factors affect the rate of charge of a capacitor?

Q7 What is meant by the 'time constant' of a capacitor and how could you find it from a graph of $\ln Q$ against t?

PRACTICE QUESTIONS

Exam Question

Q1 A 250 μF capacitor is fully charged from a 6 V battery and then discharged through a 1 kΩ resistor.

a) Calculate the time taken for the charge on the capacitor to fall to 37% of its original value. [2 marks]

b) Calculate the percentage of the initial charge remaining on the capacitor after 0.7s. [2 marks]

c) If the charging voltage is increased to 12 V, what effect will this have on:

i) the total charge stored, [1 mark]

ii) the capacitance of the capacitor, [1 mark]

iii) the time taken to fully charge. [1 mark]

An analogy — consider the lowly bike pump...

A good way to think of the charging process is like pumping air into a bike tyre. To start with, the air goes in easily, but as the pressure in the tyre increases, it gets harder and harder to squeeze any more air in. The tyre's 'full' when the pressure of the air in the tyre equals the pressure of the pump. The analogy works just as well for discharging...

Electric Fields

*Electric fields can be attractive or repulsive, so they're different from gravitational ones. It's all to do with **charge**.*

There is an Electric Field around a Charged Object

Any object with **charge** has an **electric field** around it — the region where it can attract or repel other charges.

1) Electric charge, Q, is measured in **coulombs** (C) and can be either positive or negative.
2) **Oppositely** charged particles **attract** each other. **Like** charges **repel**.
3) If a **charged object** is placed in an electric field, then it will experience a **force**.
4) If the charged object is a **sphere**, and the charge is evenly distributed (it's spherically symmetrical), you can assume all of its **charge** is at its **centre**.
5) Just like with gravitational fields, **electric fields** can be represented by **field lines**.

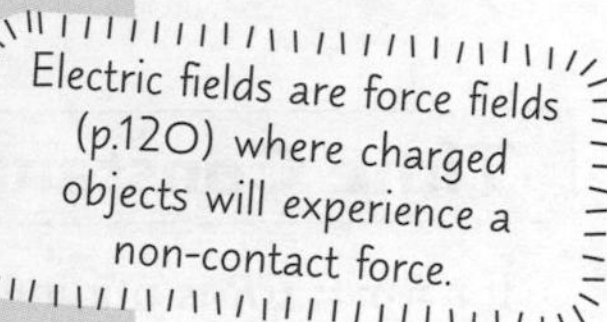

You can Calculate Forces using Coulomb's Law

You'll need **Coulomb's law** to work out F — the force of attraction or repulsion between two point charges.

$$F = \frac{Qq}{4\pi\varepsilon_0 r^2}$$

ε_0 ("epsilon-nought") is the permittivity of free space, Q and q are the charges, r is the distance between Q and q.

If the charges are **opposite** then the force is **attractive**. F will be **negative**.

If Q and q are **like** charges then the force is **repulsive**, and F will be **positive**.

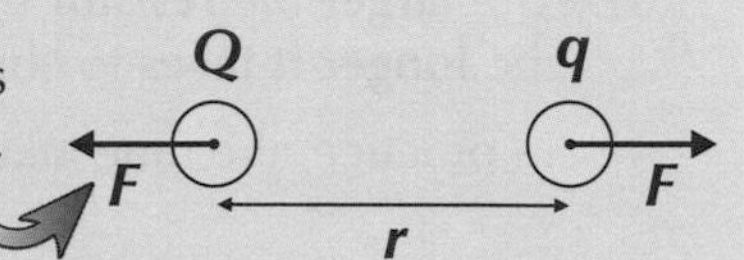

1) The force on Q is always **equal** and **opposite** to the force on q.
2) It's an **inverse square law** (again — see p.120). The further apart the charges are, the weaker the force between them.
3) The size of the **force** F also depends on the **permittivity**, ε, of the **material** between the two charges. For **free space** (a vacuum), the permittivity is $\varepsilon_0 = 8.85 \times 10^{-12}\ C^2N^{-1}m^{-2}$.

You can also give the units as Fm^{-1}.

Electric Field Strength is Force per Unit Charge

Electric field strength, E, is defined as the **force per unit positive charge** — the force that a charge of +1 C would experience if it was placed in the electric field.

$$E = \frac{F}{Q}$$

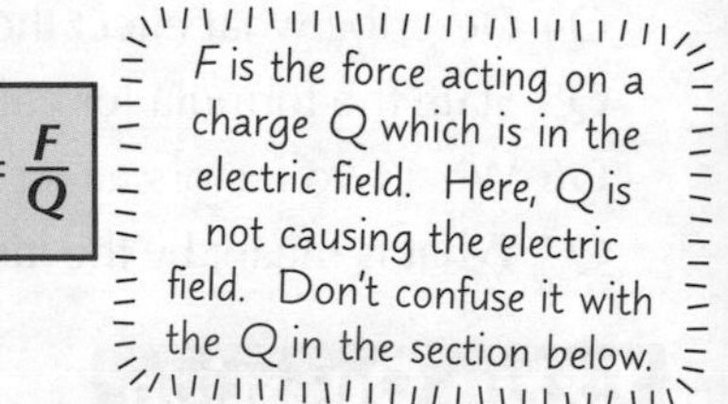

1) E **is a vector** pointing in the **direction** that a **positive charge** would **move**.
2) The units of E are **newtons per coulomb** (NC^{-1}).
3) Field strength depends on **where you are** in the field.

4) A **point charge** — or any body which behaves as if all its charge is concentrated at the centre — has a **radial** field.

In a Radial Field, *E* is Inversely Proportional to r^2

1) When the electric field is being generated by a **point charge**, we call the charge generating the field **Q** and **redefine** the charge experiencing the **force** as **q**. In a **radial field**, E depends on the **distance** r from the point charge Q.

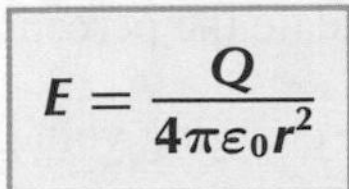

$$E = \frac{Q}{4\pi\varepsilon_0 r^2}$$

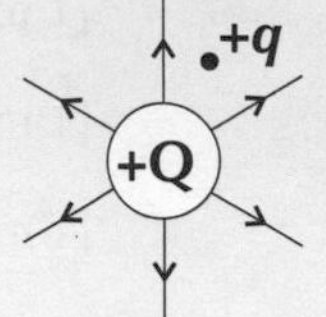

For a positive Q, the small positive 'test' charge q would be repelled, so the field lines point away from Q.

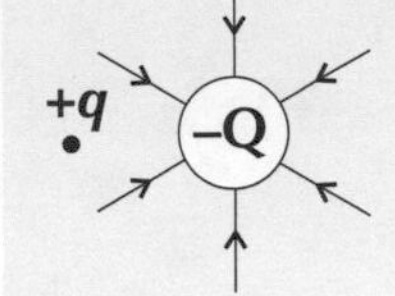

For a negative Q, the small positive charge q would be attracted, so the field lines point towards Q.

Electric field lines always go from + to –.

2) It's another **inverse square law** — $E \propto \frac{1}{r^2}$

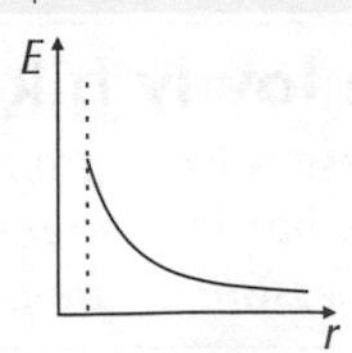

3) Field strength **decreases** as you go **further away** from Q — on a diagram, the **field lines** get **further apart**.

Electric Fields

Field Strength is the Same Everywhere in a Uniform Field

A **uniform field** can be produced by connecting two **parallel plates** to the opposite poles of a battery.

1) **Field strength** E is the **same** at **all points** between the two plates and is given by:

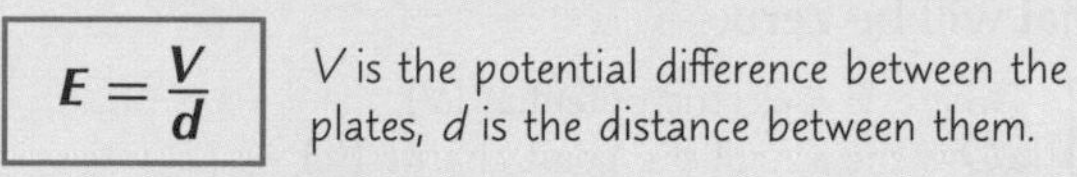

$$E = \frac{V}{d}$$

V is the potential difference between the plates, d is the distance between them.

2) E can also be measured in volts per metre (Vm^{-1}).

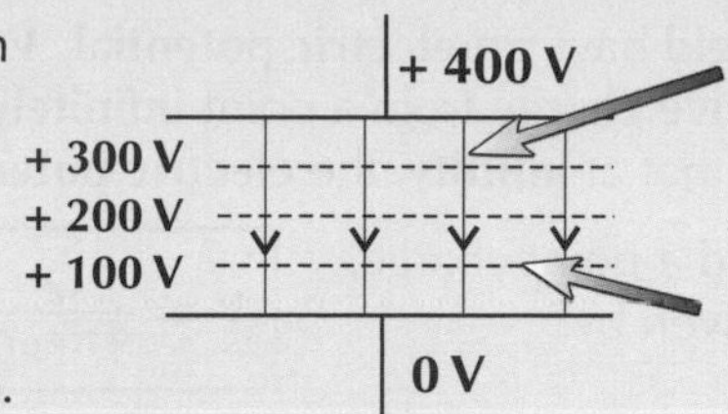

The **field lines** are **parallel** to each other.

Areas with the **same potential** are **parallel** to the **plates**, and **perpendicular** to the **field lines**.

Parallel Plate Capacitors Generate a Uniform Field

C is measured in farads (F). This is a large unit though, so you'll often see nano- or picofarad capacitors.

1) The **capacitance** (p.140) of a capacitor depends on how easy it is to generate an **electric field** between its two plates.
2) It also depends on the **dimensions** of the capacitor, and can be calculated by using:

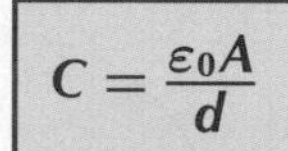

$$C = \frac{\varepsilon_0 A}{d}$$

Where A is the area of the plates (m^2), ε_0 is the permittivity of free space (Fm^{-1}), and d is the separation of the plates (m).

3) If the plates have a **material** in between them instead of a **vacuum**, ε_0 is replaced with **permittivity**, ε, where:

$$\varepsilon = \varepsilon_r \varepsilon_0$$

Where ε_r is the relative permittivity (a ratio of the size of the electric field generated in a vacuum, compared to if it was generated in a material).

Charged Particles Move Through Uniform Electric Fields Like Projectiles

You'll probably remember that **projectiles** move through a **uniform gravitational field** along a curved path (p.20). **Charged particles** do a similar thing when they move through **uniform electric fields**.

1) A particle of charge Q will experience a **constant force**, given by $F = EQ$, acting **parallel** to the **electric field lines**.
2) If the particle is **positively charged** then the force is in the **same direction** as the field lines. If it's **negatively charged** (e.g. an **electron**), the force is in the **opposite direction** to the field lines.
3) The **work done** on the particle by this force ($W = Fd$) increases its **kinetic energy** and causes it to **accelerate at a constant rate** in the direction of the force (**Newton's second law**).
4) If the particle's **velocity** has a **component** at **right angles** to the field lines, this **component** will remain **unchanged** and the **velocity** in **this direction** will be **uniform**. That's **Newton's first law**.
5) The combined effect of constant acceleration and constant velocity at right angles to one another is a **curved path**.

Warm-Up Questions

Q1 Describe the force field that surrounds a positively charged sphere with evenly distributed charge. State the assumption made.

Q2 Write down Coulomb's law.

Q3 Define electric field strength. Write an equation for the electric field strength of any electric field.

Q4 Describe the path a charged particle would take as it travels at an angle through a uniform electric field.

Exam Questions

Q1 The diagram shows two electric charges with equal but opposite charge, Q. Draw electric field lines to show the electric field in the area surrounding the charges. (+Q ● ● -Q) [3 marks]

Q2 Find the electric field strength at a distance of 1.75×10^{-10} m from a 1.60×10^{-19} C point charge. [2 marks]

Q3 Two parallel plates are separated by an air gap of 4.5 mm. The plates are connected to a 1500 V dc supply. Calculate the electric field strength between the plates. State the direction of the field. [2 marks]

Q4 A parallel plate capacitor, P, has square plates of side length 5.0 mm which are separated by a gap of 2.0 mm. This gap is fully filled by a material with a relative permittivity of 4.1. Calculate the capacitance of P. [3 marks]

Electric fields — one way to roast beef...

At least you get a choice here — uniform or radial, positive or negative, attractive or repulsive, chocolate or strawberry...

Electric Potential

Electric potential is all to do with how much energy a charge has based on where it is in an electric field.

Electric Potential is Potential Energy per Unit Charge

All points in an **electric field** have an **electric potential**, ***V***. This is equal to the **work done** bringing a **unit positive charge** from a point **infinitely** far away to that point in the electric field. This means that at **infinity**, the **electric potential** will be **zero**.

In a **radial field** around a point charge, **electric potential** is given by:

$$V = \frac{Q}{4\pi\varepsilon_0 r}$$

where V is electric potential (V), Q is the size of the point charge (C) and r is the distance from the point charge (m).

1) The **sign** of V depends on the charge Q — i.e. V is **positive** when Q is **positive** and the force is **repulsive** (when acting on a unit positive charge), and **negative** when Q is negative and the force is **attractive**.
2) The **absolute magnitude** of V is **greatest** on the **surface of the charge**, and **decreases** as the **distance** from the charge **increases**.

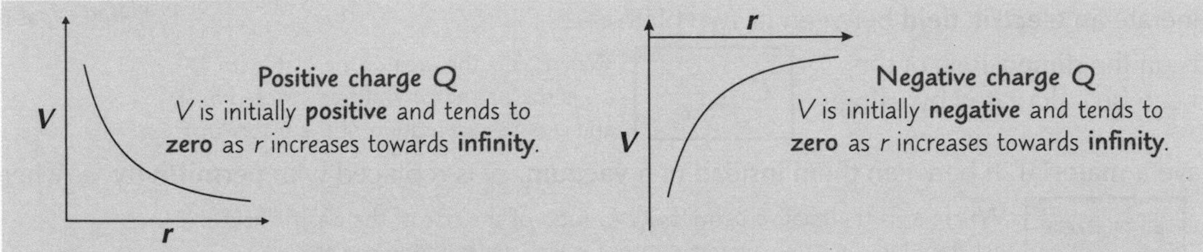

If you **move** a unit charge and **change** its **electric potential**, you have to apply a **force** and do **work**. For a point charge (and therefore also for a spherical charge, see p.146) you can plot the **force** applied, ***F***, **against** the distance, ***r***, from the charge producing the **electric field**.

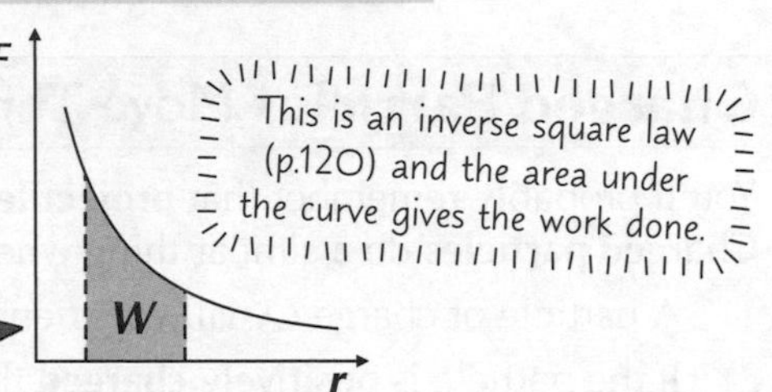

This is an inverse square law (p.120) and the area under the curve gives the work done.

From Electric Potential you can find Electric Potential Energy...

Electric potential is the **electric potential energy** that a **unit positive charge** (+1 C) would have at a certain point. This means you can find the electric potential energy for **any charge** at that point in the electric field by multiplying the **electric potential** by the **value** of the charge.

$$\text{electric potential energy} = Vq \qquad \text{electric potential energy} = \frac{Qq}{4\pi\varepsilon_0 r}$$

where V is electric potential (V), and q is the size of the charge in the electric field (C).

... And Capacitance

You can use the formula for the **electric potential** of a **radial** field and the fact that $Q = CV$ (p.140) for capacitors to **derive** an expression for the **capacitance** of an **isolated charged sphere**, assuming the charge is evenly distributed.

1) As it is a charged sphere, you can assume all of its charge is at its **centre** and treat it like a **point charge**.
2) Substitute $V = \frac{Q}{C}$ into $V = \frac{Q}{4\pi\varepsilon_0 R} \Longrightarrow \frac{Q}{C} = \frac{Q}{4\pi\varepsilon_0 R}$

   Here, R is the radius of the sphere.
3) Cancel out the Q's: $\frac{1}{C} = \frac{1}{4\pi\varepsilon_0 R}$
4) Rearrange for C, which gives: $C = 4\pi\varepsilon_0 R$

   The unit for C is farads.

Electric Potential

There are Similarities between Gravitational and Electric Fields...

If a lot of the stuff on the previous couple of pages sounded strangely familiar it could be because it's very similar to the stuff on gravitational fields (or it could be because you've learnt it before — this is a revision book after all). Anyway, there are **four** big **similarities** between **electric** and **gravitational fields** that you need to know — read on.

Gravitational field strength, g, is **force** per **unit mass**.	Electric field strength, E, is **force** per **unit positive charge**.
Newton's law of gravitation for the **force** between two point masses is an **inverse square law**.	Coulomb's law for the electric **force** between two point charges is also an **inverse square law**.
The **field lines** for a spherical mass... (m)	The **field lines** for a **negative** spherically symmetric charge... (+q, –Q)
Gravitational potential, V, is **potential energy** per **unit mass** and is **zero** at **infinity**.	Electric potential, V, is **potential energy** per **unit positive charge** and is **zero** at **infinity**.

... and Three Differences too

Gravitational and electric fields aren't all the same — you need to know the **three main differences**:

1) Gravitational forces are always **attractive**. Electric forces can be either **attractive** or **repulsive**.
2) Objects can be **shielded** from **electric** fields, but not from gravitational fields.
3) The size of an **electric** force depends on the **medium** between the charges, e.g. plastic or air. For gravitational forces, this makes no difference.

Warm-Up Questions

PRACTICE QUESTIONS

Q1 What is meant by 'electric potential'?

Q2 State the formula for finding the electric potential in a radial field.

Q3 Sketch a graph of force against distance for a unit charge being moved out of a radial electric field. How would you calculate work done from the graph?

Q4 Derive the equation for the capacitance of an isolated charged sphere.

Exam Questions

$e = 1.60 \times 10^{-19}$ C, $\varepsilon_0 = 8.85 \times 10^{-12}$ $C^2N^{-1}m^{-2}$ (Fm^{-1})

Q1 Point A is 1.00 mm away from an electron.

a) Calculate the electric potential at point A. [2 marks]

b) A positron has an equal but opposite charge to an electron. A positron is placed at point A. Calculate the electric potential energy of the positron. [1 mark]

c) The positron is then placed at a point B, where the electric potential is -1.0×10^{-6} V. Calculate the distance from the electron to point B. [2 marks]

Q2 Calculate the capacitance of an isolated sphere which has a diameter of 10.0 cm. [1 mark]

Q3 State two similarities and one difference between gravitational and electric fields. [3 marks]

I prefer gravitational fields — electric fields are repulsive...

Revising fields is a bit like a buy-one-get-one-free sale — you learn all about gravitational fields and they throw electric fields in for free. You just have to remember to change your ms for Qs and your Gs for $1/4\pi\varepsilon_0$s... okay, so it's not quite a BOGOF sale. Maybe more like a buy-one-get-one-half-price sale... anyway, you get the point — go learn some stuff.

Magnetic Fields

Magnetic fields — making pretty patterns with iron filings before spending an age trying to pick them off the magnet.

A Magnetic Field is a Region Where a Force is Exerted on Magnetic Materials

Magnetic fields exist around **permanent magnets** and **moving charges**.

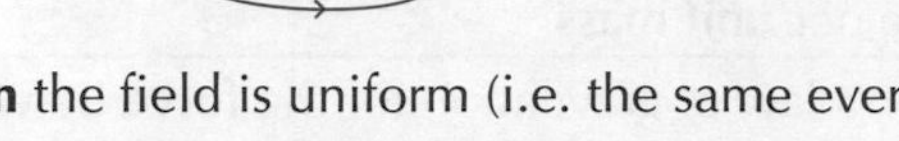

1) Magnetic fields can be represented (mapped) by **field lines**.
2) Field lines go from **north** to **south**.
3) The **closer** the lines, the **stronger** the field.
If the field lines are **equally spaced** and **in the same direction** the field is uniform (i.e. the same everywhere).

There is a Magnetic Field Around a Wire Carrying Electric Current

When **current** flows in any conductor, there's a **magnetic field** around the conductor. For a long straight wire:

1) The **field lines** are **concentric circles** centred on the wire.
2) The **direction** of the **field** can be worked out with the **right-hand rule**.
3) You also need to know the fields formed around **flat coils** and **solenoids**:

Right-hand Rule

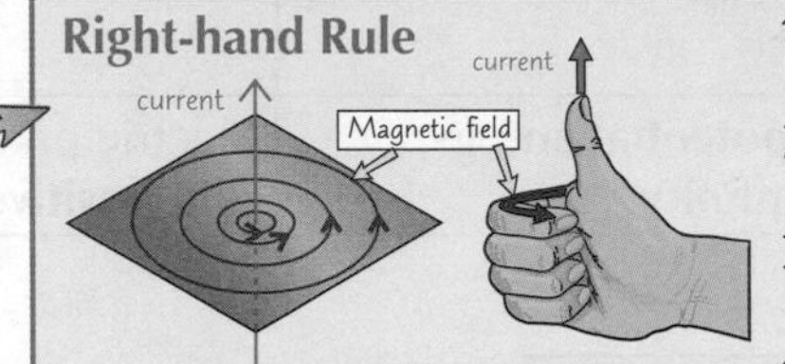

1) Stick your right thumb up, like you're hitching a lift.
2) Your thumb points in the direction of conventional current...
3) ...and your curled fingers point in the direction of the field.
4) This also works for a flat coil.

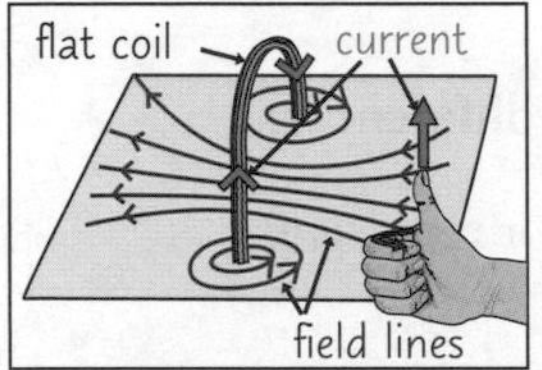

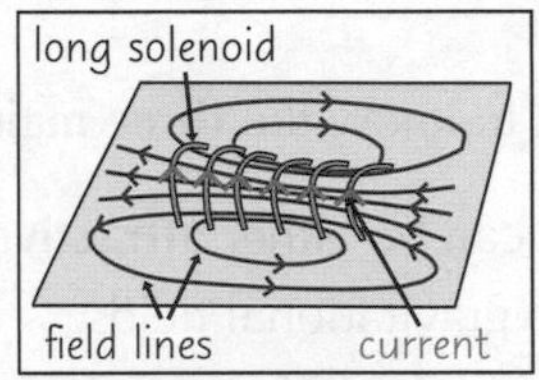

In each case, there's a sort of 'ring doughnut' field around the coil and a strong field inside it.

Learn these types of coil:

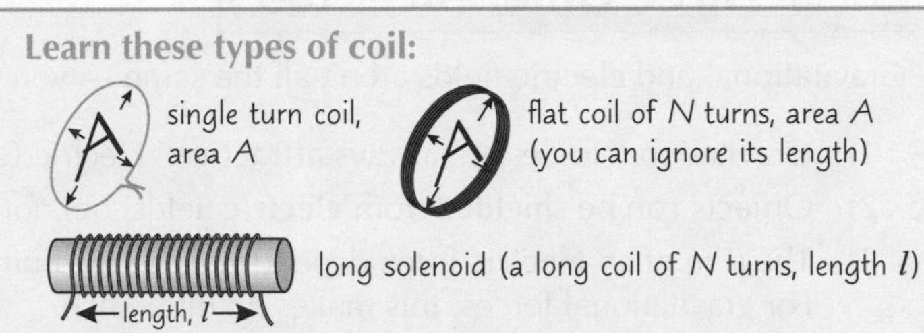

A Current Perpendicular to a Uniform Magnetic Field will Induce a Force

For a current in a conductor that's **perpendicular** to the field lines in a **uniform** magnetic field:

1) The field around the wire and the external magnetic field will interact causing a **force** on the wire.
2) The **direction** of the force is always **perpendicular** to both the **current** direction and the **magnetic field** — it's given by **Fleming's left hand rule**...

Fleming's Left Hand Rule

The First finger points in the direction of the external uniform magnetic Field, the seCond finger points in the direction of the conventional Current. Then your thuMb points in the direction of the force (in which Motion takes place).

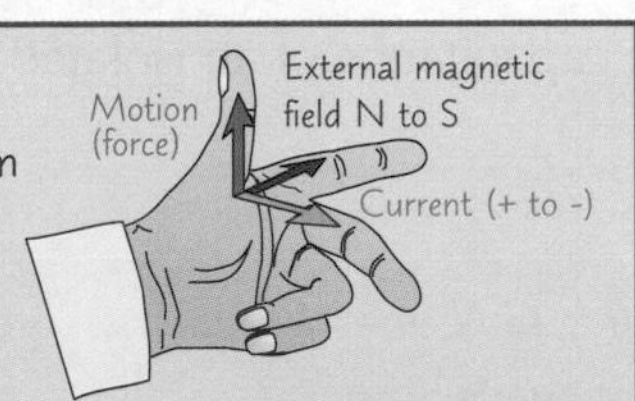

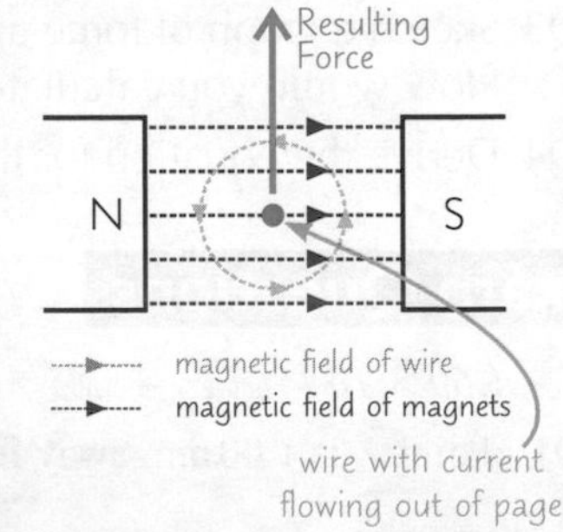

The Force on a Conductor is Proportional to Flux Density

1) The size of the **force** on a **current-carrying** conductor at a **right angle** to an external magnetic field is proportional to the **magnetic flux density**, B. Magnetic flux density is used as a measure of the **strength** of a magnetic field.
2) **Magnetic flux density**, B, is **defined** as:

> The **force on one metre** of wire carrying a **current of one amp** at **right angles** to the **magnetic field.**

3) When current is at 90° to the magnetic field, the size of the **force**, F is proportional to the **current**, I, the **length of wire** in the field, l, as well as the **flux density**, B. This gives the equation:

$$F = BIl$$

4) **Flux density** is a **vector** quantity with both a **direction** and **magnitude**. It's measured in **teslas, T**:

$$1 \text{ tesla} = \frac{\text{Wb}}{\text{m}^2}$$

It helps to think of flux density as the number of field lines (measured in webers (Wb), see p.154) per unit area.

Magnetic Fields

The Force is Greatest when the Wire and Field are Perpendicular...

1) The **force** on a current-carrying wire in a magnetic field is caused by the **component** of the magnetic field which is **perpendicular** to the wire — $B \sin \theta$.
2) So, for a wire at an **angle** θ to the field, the **force** acting on the wire is given by: Notice that when the current and field are parallel, there's no force.

$$F = BIl \sin\theta$$

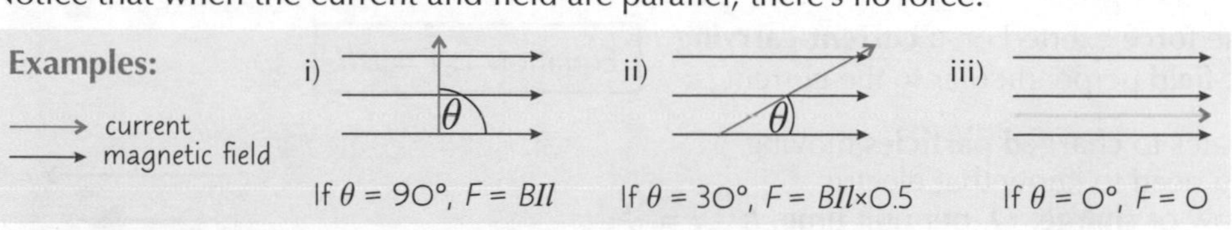

Use a Digital Balance to Investigate Flux Density

PRACTICAL SKILLS

You can use the set-up shown to investigate the **uniform magnetic field** between the poles of a magnet and obtain a value for **flux density**, ***B***. You should use magnets with **poles** on their **largest** faces.

1) A **square hoop** of metal wire is positioned so that the **top** of the hoop, **length *l***, passes through the magnetic field, **perpendicular** to it. When a current flows, the **length of wire** in the magnetic field will experience a downwards **force** (Fleming's left hand rule).
2) The power supply should be connected to a **variable resistor** so that you can **alter** the **current**. Zero the digital balance when there is **no** current through the wire so that the mass reading is due to the electromagnetic force only. Then turn on the power supply.
3) Note the **mass** and the **current**. Use the variable resistor to **change** the current and record the new mass — do this for a **large range** of currents. Repeat this twice to give 3 mass readings for each current.
4) Calculate the **mean** for each mass reading, then convert your mass readings into **force** using $F = mg$. **Plot** the data on a graph of **force *F*** against **current *I***, and draw a line of best fit.
5) Because $F = BIl$, the **gradient** of your graph is equal to $B \times l$. Measure the gradient, then divide by length l to **get a value for *B***.

Warm-Up Questions

Q1 What two things can cause a magnetic field?

Q2 Sketch the magnetic fields around a long straight current-carrying wire, a flat coil and a solenoid. Show the direction of the current and magnetic field on each diagram.

Q3 A copper bar can roll freely on two copper supports, as shown in the diagram. When current is applied in the direction shown, which way will the bar roll?

Q4 What is the definition of magnetic flux density? What are its units?

Q5 Describe an experiment you could carry out to determine the uniform magnetic flux density between the poles of a magnet.

Exam Question

Q1 A 4.00 cm length of wire carrying a current of 3.00 A runs perpendicular to a magnetic field of strength 2.00×10^{-5} T.

a) Calculate the magnitude of the force on the wire. [1 mark]

b) The wire is rotated so that it is at 30.0° to the direction of the field. Calculate the size of the force. [1 mark]

I revised the right hand rule by the A69 and ended up in Newcastle...

Fleming's left hand rule is the key to this section — so make sure you know how to use it and understand what it all means. Remember that the direction of the magnetic field is from N to S, and that the current is from +ve to –ve — this is as important as using the correct hand. You need to get those right or it'll all go to pot...

Charged Particles in Magnetic Fields

Magnetic fields are used a lot when dealing with particle beams.

Forces Act on **Charged Particles** in Magnetic Fields

Electric current in a wire is caused by the **flow** of negatively **charged** electrons. These charged particles are affected by **magnetic fields** — so a current-carrying wire can experience a **force** in a magnetic field (see pages 150–151).

1) The equation for the **force** exerted on a **current-carrying wire** in a **magnetic field** perpendicular to the current is: Equation 1: $F = BIl$

2) To see how this relates to **charged particles** moving through a wire, you need to know that electric **current**, I, is the flow of **charge**, Q, per unit **time**, t: $I = \frac{Q}{t}$

In many exam questions, Q is the size of the charge on the electron, which is 1.60×10^{-19} coulombs.

3) A charged particle which moves a **distance** l in **time** t has a **velocity**, v, given by $v = \frac{l}{t}$ (speed = dist ÷ time), so:

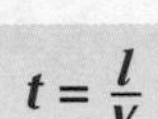

$t = \frac{l}{v}$

4) Putting the two equations **together** gives the **current** in terms of the **charge** flowing through the **wire**:

Equation 2: $I = \frac{Qv}{l}$

5) Putting **equation 2** back into **equation 1** gives the **electromagnetic force** on the wire as:

$F = BQv$

6) You can use this equation to find the **force** acting on a **single charged particle moving through a magnetic field.**

Example: An electron is travelling at 2.00×10^4 ms^{-1} perpendicular to the field lines of a uniform magnetic field of strength 2.00 T. Calculate the size of the force acting on the electron. (The magnitude of the charge on an electron is 1.60×10^{-19} C.)

$F = BQv$

so $F = 2.00 \times 1.60 \times 10^{-19} \times 2.00 \times 10^4$

$F = \mathbf{6.40 \times 10^{-15}}$ **N**

Charged Particles in a **Magnetic Field** are Deflected in a **Circular Path**

1) By **Fleming's left hand rule** the force on a **moving charge** in a magnetic field is always **perpendicular** to its **direction of travel.** Mathematically, that is the condition for **circular motion** (p.112).
2) This effect is used in **particle accelerators** such as **cyclotrons** and **synchrotrons**, which use **magnetic fields** to accelerate particles to very **high energies** along circular paths.
3) It's also used in **mass spectrometers** to analyse chemical samples. **Ions** (charged particles) with the **same velocity** are made to enter a **magnetic field** which deflects them in a curved path towards a detector. The **radius of curvature** depends on the **charge** and **mass** of the particles (see equation below). The **identity** of the ions reaching the detector can be deduced from their **mass to charge** ratio.

Centripetal Force Tells Us About a Particle's **Path**

The centripetal force (see p.112) and the force due to the magnetic field are equivalent for a charged particle travelling along a circular path.

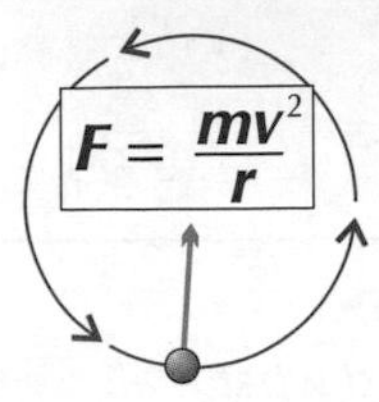

Centripetal force

$F = BQv$

Electromagnetic force

1) For uniform circular motion **Newton's second law** gives: $F = \frac{mv^2}{r}$
2) So, for a **charged particle** following a **circular** path in a **magnetic field** (where $F = BQv$): $BQv = \frac{mv^2}{r}$
3) Rearranging gives:

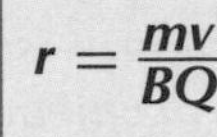

$r = \frac{mv}{BQ}$

Where: m is the mass of the particle, v is its speed and r is the radius of the circular path.

Charged Particles in Magnetic Fields

Velocity Selectors Use Both Magnetic and Electric Fields

Velocity selectors are used to **separate** out particles of a **certain velocity** from a stream of **accelerated charged particles** moving at a **range of speeds**. They do this by applying **both** a magnetic and an electric field at the **same time** perpendicular to each other, while a stream of particles is fired perpendicularly to both fields at a device with a narrow gap called a **collimator**.

For the examples on this page:
The **electric** field, *E*, goes **top** to **bottom** (i.e. down the page). The **magnetic** field, *B*, goes straight **into** the page.

1) Particles fired into the velocity selector experience **opposing forces** from the electric and magnetic fields:

- The **magnetic** field tries to deflect particles **upwards** — check this with Fleming's left hand rule. The force on each particle is $F = BQv$ (see previous page).
- The **electric** field tries to deflect particles **downwards** (opposite charges attract, like charges repel). The force on the particle is $F = EQ$ (see p.146).

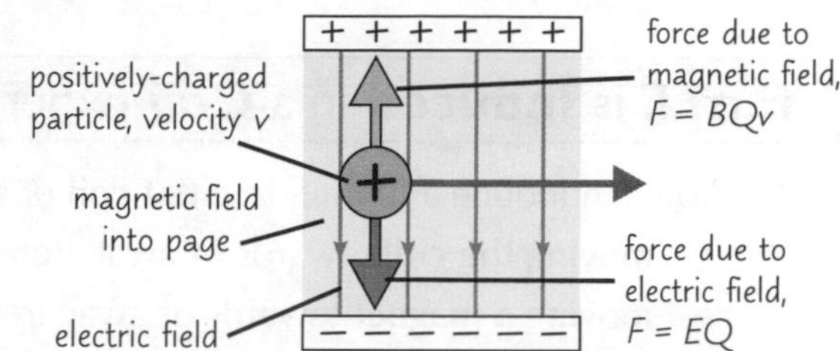

2) Particles will be **deflected** unless the forces balance (i.e. $BQv = EQ$). Cancelling *Q*s and rearranging gives:

$$v = \frac{E}{B}$$

3) So **only** particles with **velocity** $v = \frac{E}{B}$ as given above will travel in a **straight line** to pass through the gap in the **collimator**.
4) You can select and vary the **velocity** of the particles that get through the collimator by **changing** the **strength** of the magnetic or electric fields.

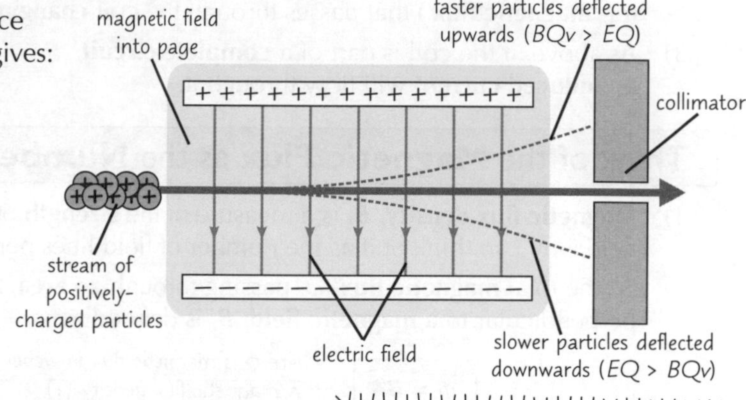

The directions of deflection are reversed for negatively-charged particles.

5) Velocity selectors are often used in **mass spectrometers** to ensure that the accelerated particles entering the magnetic field have the same velocity.

Warm-Up Questions

Q1 Derive the formula for the force on a charged particle in a magnetic field, $F = BQv$, from $F = BIl$.
Q2 Briefly describe two applications of charged particles being deflected in a circular field in a magnetic field.
Q3 Describe how a velocity selector works, including the roles of the electric and magnetic fields.

Exam Questions

PRACTICE QUESTIONS

Elementary charge $= 1.60 \times 10^{-19}$ *C, electron rest mass* $= 9.11 \times 10^{-31}$ *kg,*

Q1 a) An electron is travelling at a velocity of 5.00×10^{6} ms^{-1} through a perpendicular magnetic field of 0.770 T. Calculate the magnitude of the force acting on the electron. [2 marks]

b) Explain why the electron follows a circular path while in the field. [1 mark]

Q2 Calculate the radius of the circular path of an electron with a velocity of 2.30×10^{7} ms^{-1} moving perpendicular to a magnetic field of 0.600 mT. [3 marks]

Q3 A sample of sodium chloride is analysed using a mass spectrometer. The magnetic field is initially set to 0.200 T and ions of the isotope Cl-35 (mass 35 u) reach the same point on the detector. Calculate the magnetic field strength you would need for Cl-37 ions (mass 37 u) to reach the same point on the detector. Assume that both types of ion have the same charge as an electron and that all ions enter the magnetic field with the same velocity. [3 marks]

Hold on to your hats folks — this is starting to get tricky...

Basically, the main thing you need to know here is that both electric and magnetic fields will exert a force on a charged particle. There's even a handy equation to work out the force on a charged particle moving through a magnetic field.

Electromagnetic Induction

Producing electricity by waggling a wire about in a magnetic field sounds like magic — but it's real physics...

E.m.f. is Induced in a Conducting Rod Moving Through a Magnetic Field

1) If there is relative motion between a **conducting rod** and a magnetic field, the **electrons in the rod** will experience a **force** (see p.150), which causes them to **accumulate** at one end of the rod.
2) This **induces** an **electromotive force (e.m.f.)** across the ends of the rod exactly as connecting a battery to it would — this is called **electromagnetic induction**.
3) If the rod is part of a complete **circuit**, then an induced current will **flow** through it.

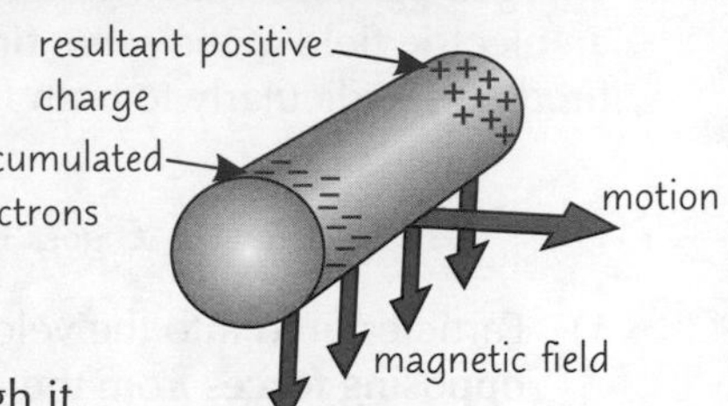

E.m.f. is Induced in a Coil experiencing a Changing Magnetic Field

1) You can induce an e.m.f. in a **flat coil** or **solenoid** by:
   - **moving the coil** towards or away from the poles of a magnet.
   - **moving a magnet** towards or away from the coil.
2) In either case, the e.m.f. is caused by the **magnetic field** (or '**magnetic flux**') that passes through the coil **changing**.
3) As above, if the coil is part of a **complete circuit**, an **induced current** will flow through it.

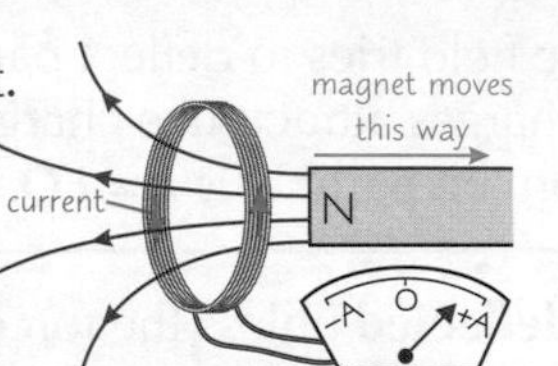

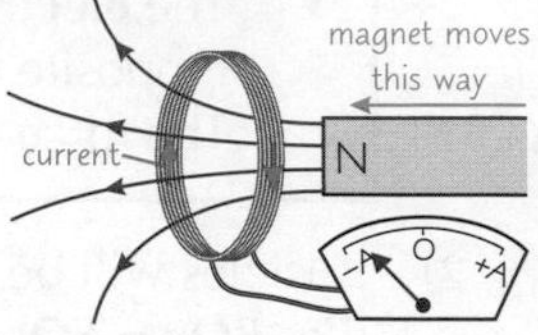

Think of the Magnetic Flux as the Number of Field Lines

1) **Magnetic flux density, *B***, is a measure of the **strength** of the magnetic field (you can think of it as the number of field lines per unit area).
2) So the total **magnetic flux**, ϕ, passing through an **area**, ***A***, perpendicular to a **magnetic field**, ***B***, is defined as:

$$\phi = BA$$

where ϕ is magnetic flux in webers (Wb), B is magnetic flux density (T) and A is area (m^2).

3) You can think of **flux** as the **number of field lines**. But remember that flux is **continuous** — field lines are just a way of **drawing it**.
4) The diagram to the right shows magnetic flux inside a **single loop coil**. The flux inside the coil is $\phi = BA$, where A = area of coil.
5) If you have a **coil of *N* turns**, rather than a single loop, you need to talk about **flux linkage** instead which is just flux multiplied by N:

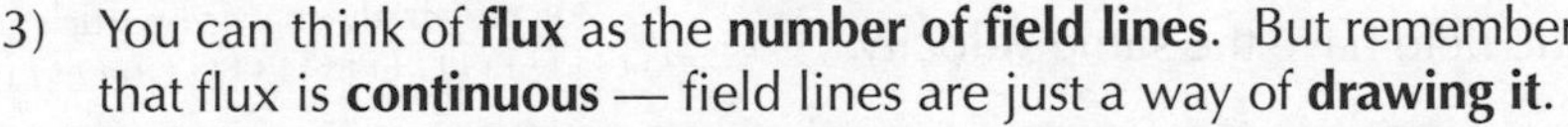

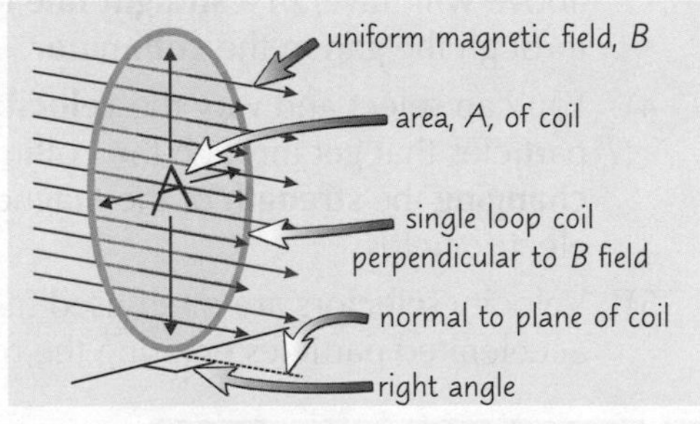

flux linkage = $N\phi$ units of flux linkage are also Wb

Use Trig if the Magnetic Flux Isn't Perpendicular to the Area

1) When the magnetic flux **isn't perpendicular** to the area of the coil you're interested in, you need to use **trigonometry** to find the component of the flux that is **perpendicular** to the area (see p.14-15).
2) If θ is the **angle** between the **magnetic flux** and the **normal to the plane** of the coil, you get:

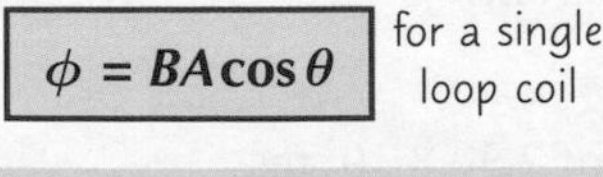

$\phi = BA\cos\theta$ for a single loop coil

flux linkage = $N\phi = BAN\cos\theta$ for a coil of N turns

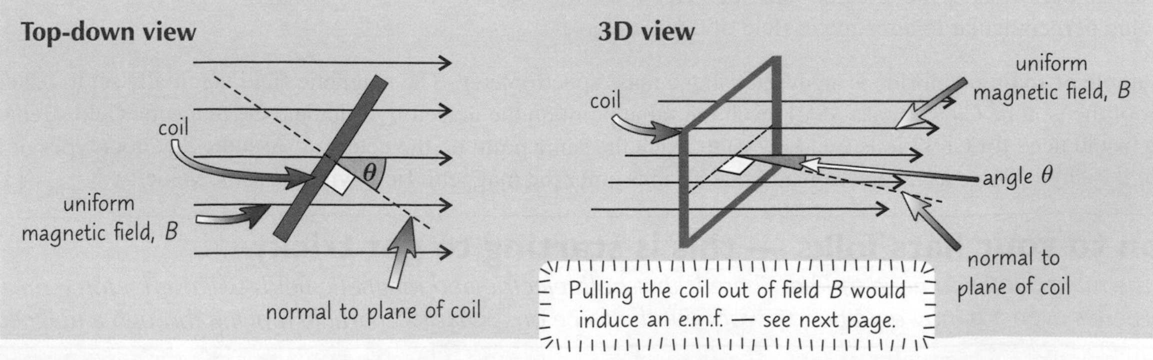

Electromagnetic Induction

Faraday's Law Links the Rate of Change of Flux Linkage with E.m.f.

FARADAY'S LAW: The **induced e.m.f.** is **directly proportional** to the **rate of change of flux linkage**.

It can be written as:

$$\text{Induced e.m.f., } \varepsilon = -\frac{\textbf{flux linkage change}}{\textbf{time taken}} = -\frac{\Delta(N\phi)}{\Delta t} = -\frac{N\Delta\phi}{\Delta t}$$

The minus sign is Lenz's law — see next page. $N = 1$ if it's just a single loop or rod.

1) The formula above can be applied to a **coil** or **conducting rod**.
2) For a coil, induced e.m.f. depends on the number of turns and **how fast** flux through the coil is changing.
3) For a conducting rod, think of flux change as field lines being 'cut' as the rod moves (see next page).
4) The unit of flux, the **weber** (**Wb**), is defined in terms of the e.m.f. induced:

A **change** in **flux linkage** of **one weber per second** will induce an **electromotive force** of **1 volt** in a loop of wire.

Faraday's Law on Graphs:

1) The **size** of the **e.m.f.** is shown by the **gradient** of a graph of flux linkage against time.
2) The **area under** the graph of e.m.f. against time gives the **flux linkage change**.

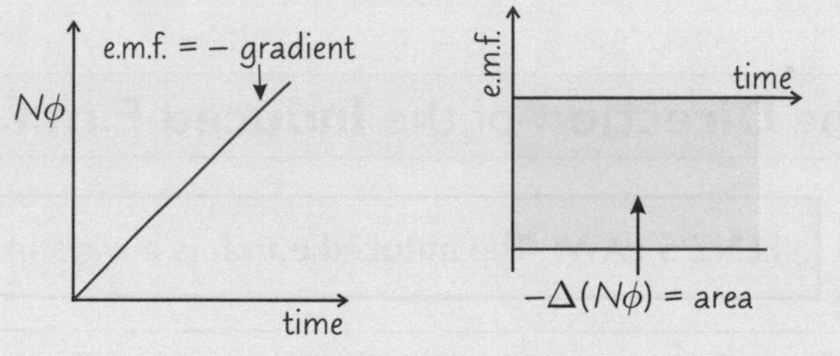

Warm-Up Questions

Q1 What is the difference between magnetic flux density, magnetic flux and magnetic flux linkage?
Q2 Give the equations for flux linkage in an N-turn coil at right angles and at angle θ to a magnetic field.
Q3 State Faraday's law and give the definition of the weber.
Q4 What does the gradient of a graph of flux linkage against time tell you?
Q5 How can you find the change in flux linkage from a graph of e.m.f. against time?

Exam Questions

Q1 The magnetic flux density of a uniform magnetic field is 2.00×10^{-3} T.

a) Calculate the magnetic flux passing through an area of 0.230 m^2 at right angles to the field lines. [1 mark]

b) A coil of area 0.230 m^2 with 151 turns is placed in the field at right angles to the field lines. Calculate the magnetic flux linkage in the coil. [1 mark]

c) Over a period of 2.50 seconds the magnetic field is reduced uniformly to 1.50×10^{-3} T. Calculate the e.m.f. induced across the ends of the coil. [3 marks]

Q2 A 0.010 m^2 coil of 550 turns is perpendicular to a magnetic field of strength 0.92 T generated.

a) Calculate the magnetic flux linkage in the coil. [1 mark]

b) The coil is rotated until the normal to the plane of the coil is at 90° to the magnetic field. The movement is uniform and takes 0.5 s. Calculate the e.m.f. induced by this movement. [2 marks]

Q3 The graph shows how the flux linkage through a coil varies over time. Sketch a graph to show how the induced e.m.f. in the coil varies over this same time period. [3 marks]

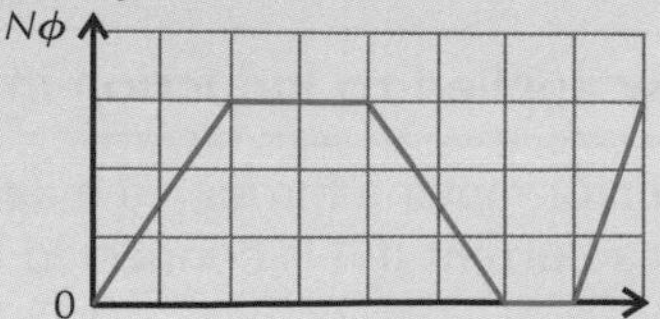

Beware — physics can induce extreme confusion...

Make sure you know the difference between flux and flux linkage, and that you can calculate both even when they aren't perpendicular to area and you have to get some pesky trigonometry involved. This is a tricky topic so if I were you, I'd head back to the start and go through it all again even more carefully — don't let it catch you out in the exams.

Electromagnetic Induction

A bit more on Faraday's Law, then we move on to his partner in crime, Lenz...

Faraday's Law Gives E.m.f. of a Conducting Rod in terms of Velocity

1) For a rod moving across a **magnetic field**, e.m.f. is induced as the rod '**cuts**' magnetic flux (field lines).
2) Remember that magnetic flux $\phi = BA$ (see p.154) — here, think of A as the **area of flux cut** in a certain time.
3) Faraday's equation can be **used** to find the **e.m.f.** in terms of the rod's speed:

Example: A conducting rod of length l moves through a perpendicular uniform magnetic field, B, at a constant velocity, v. Show that the e.m.f. induced in the rod is equal to $-Blv$.

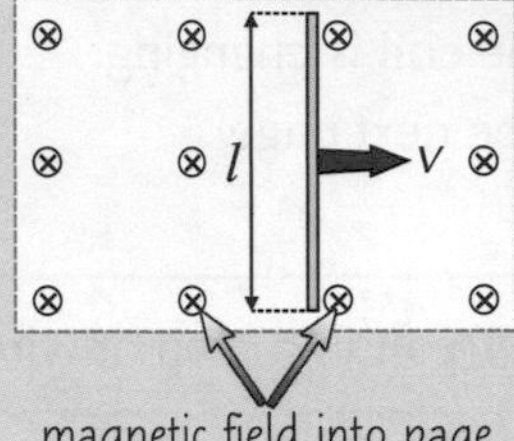

Distance travelled, $s = v\Delta t$ (distance = speed × time)

Area of flux it cuts, $A = lv\Delta t$

Total magnetic flux cut through, $\Delta\phi = BA = Blv\Delta t$

Faraday's law gives $\varepsilon = -\frac{\Delta(N\phi)}{\Delta t} = -\frac{\Delta\phi}{\Delta t}$ (since $N = 1$)

So induced e.m.f., $\varepsilon = -\frac{\Delta\phi}{\Delta t} = -\frac{Blv\Delta t}{\Delta t} = \mathbf{-Blv}$

You might be asked to find the e.m.f. induced on something more interesting than a rod, e.g. the Earth's magnetic field across the wingspan of a plane. Just think of it as a moving rod and use the equation as usual.

The Direction of the Induced E.m.f. and Current are given by Lenz's Law

LENZ'S LAW: The **induced e.m.f.** is always in such a **direction** as to **oppose** the **change** that caused it.

This is why there's a **minus sign** in Faraday's Law.

Lenz's Law applied to Induction in a Coil

1) A changing magnetic field **induces an e.m.f.** in a coil (see previous page).
2) If the coil is part of a **complete** circuit, a **current** is induced in the **same direction** as the induced **e.m.f.**
3) The **induced current** then produces its own **magnetic field** (p.150).
   Lenz's law says:

- If the **original** magnetic field is getting **stronger**, the **induced** magnetic field will be in the **opposite direction** to try to **weaken** it.
- If the **original** magnetic field is getting **weaker** (collapsing), the **induced** magnetic field will be in the **same direction** to try to **maintain** it.

Example: The area of a flat coil is perpendicular to a magnetic field as it collapses by 50% as shown below. What will be the direction of the current induced in the loop?

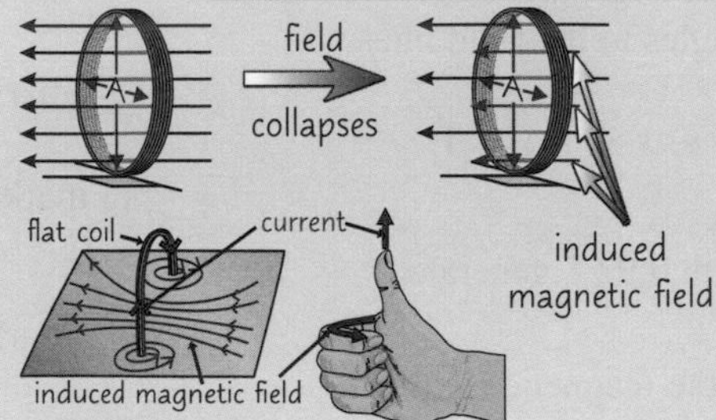

A **collapsing** field means the field is getting **weaker** and the field lines are getting **further apart** (p.150). So by Lenz's law the current induced in the coil will **induce** a **magnetic field** in the **same direction** as the **collapsing** field to try to **maintain** the **original** field.

Use the **right-hand rule** (p.150) to find the direction of the induced current. The induced **field** is to the **left**, so the induced **current** is **clockwise** when viewed from the right.

Lenz's Law applied to Induction in a Conducting Rod

- A conductor moving through a magnetic field **induces a current** if it is connected to a circuit.
- **Lenz's law** says that the **induced current** will produce a **force to oppose** the motion of the conductor (a **resistance**).
- You know the directions of the **magnetic field** and the induced **resistance force**, so you can use **Fleming's left hand rule** (see p.150) to find the direction of the **induced current** and so the direction of the **induced e.m.f.**

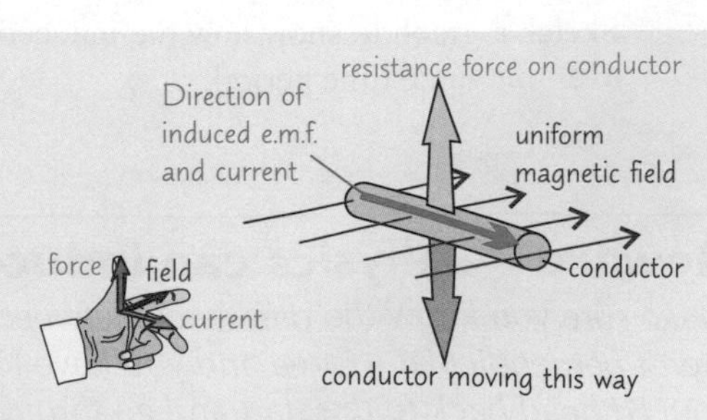

Electromagnetic Induction

You can use **Faraday's Law** to **Investigate Magnetic Flux**

This set up shows how you can find the magnetic flux density, *B*, using a search coil and a data logger...

1) Place two **bar magnets** a small distance apart with **opposite poles facing** each other — they should be far enough apart not to snap together, but otherwise as close as possible to give a uniform field.
2) Get a **search coil** — this is a small coil of wire with a **known number of turns** (*N*) and a **known area** (*A*). Connect it to a **data recorder** and set the recorder to measure the **induced e.m.f.** with a **very small time interval** between readings.
3) Place the search coil in the **middle** of the magnetic field so that the area (*A*) of the coil is parallel to the surface of the magnets. Start the data recorder. Keeping the coil in the **same orientation**, immediately move the coil out of the field.
4) An e.m.f. will be induced due to the magnetic flux density through the coil changing from **maximum** to **zero** as you **remove** the coil from the **field**.
5) Use your data or the data recorder to plot a graph of **induced e.m.f.** against **time**.
6) Using Faraday's Law, estimating the **area under the graph** of e.m.f. against time gives you an estimate for the **total flux linkage change** (p.155).
7) **Flux linkage = $N\phi$ = BAN** (p.154), so to **find *B***, divide the total flux linkage change by coil area (*A*) and number of turns (*N*).
8) **Repeat** this experiment several times and find the mean of your values for *B*.

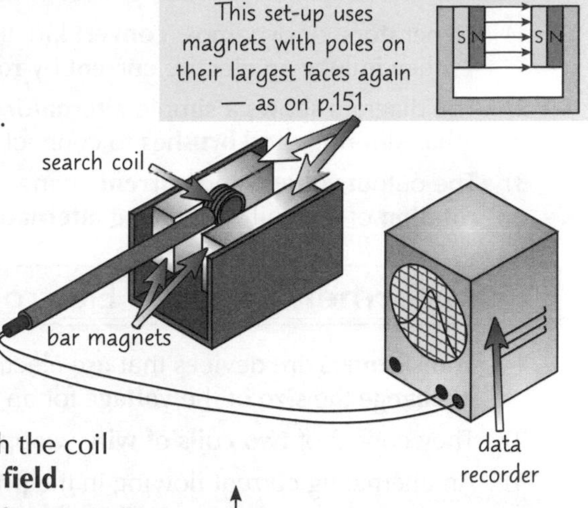

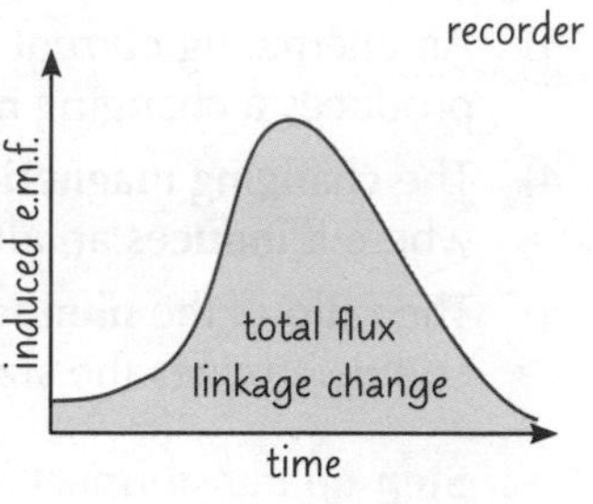

Warm-Up Questions

Q1 State Lenz's law.

Q2 Describe how to determine the direction of the induced current when:
   a) a coil moves perpendicularly through the field lines of a magnetic field, with the area of the coil perpendicular to the field lines.
   b) a conducting rod moves through a magnetic field with the length of the rod perpendicular to the field lines.

Q3 Describe an experiment you could carry out to investigate magnetic flux using a search coil.

PRACTICE QUESTIONS

Exam Questions

Q1 An aeroplane with a wingspan of 33.9 m flies at a speed of 148 ms^{-1} perpendicular to the Earth's magnetic field, as shown. The Earth's magnetic field at the aeroplane's location is 6.00×10^{-5} T. The magnetic field in the diagram goes into the page.

a) Calculate the induced e.m.f. between the wing tips. [3 marks]

b) Copy and complete the diagram to show the direction of the induced e.m.f. between the wing-tips. [1 mark]

Q2 A flat coil of 75 turns with an area of 0.030 m^2 is placed in a uniform magnetic field generated by an electromagnet. The area of the coil is perpendicular to the field lines.

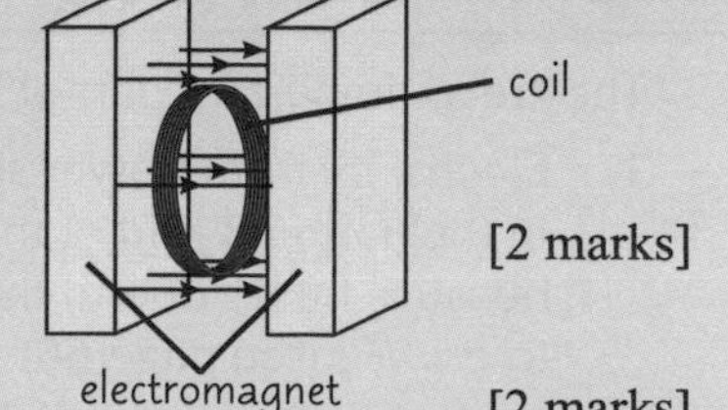

a) The electromagnet is initially turned off. The power supply is switched on and the current is increased so that the magnetic field strength linearly increases from 0 to 150 mT in 7.5 seconds. Calculate size of the e.m.f. induced in the coil. [2 marks]

b) The coil is part of a complete circuit. State the direction the induced current will flow through the coil and explain why this is the case. [2 marks]

Don't steal camera Lenzs — the law will catch you before you get Far away...

Far away... Far aday... Faraday... geddit? No? I really don't know why I bother sometimes. Anyway, don't worry if this stuff doesn't make complete (or any) sense at first... Lenz's law is particularly horrible. Just keep going over the page until slowly but surely the penny begins to drop. Then pick up the penny and err... add it to your coin collection.

Uses of Electromagnetic Induction

Faraday's law of electromagnetic induction turns up all over the place — from phone chargers to power stations...

An **Alternator** is a **Generator** of **Alternating Current**

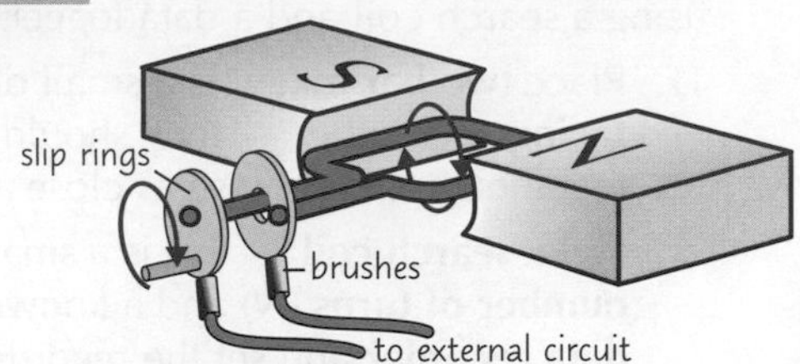

1) **Generators**, or dynamos, **convert** kinetic energy into **electrical energy** — they **induce** an electric **current** by **rotating** a **coil** in a magnetic field.
2) The diagram shows a simple **alternator** — a generator of **a.c.** It has **slip rings** and **brushes** to connect the coil to an external circuit.
3) The output **voltage** and **current** change direction with every **half rotation** of the coil, producing **alternating current** (a.c.).

Transformers Work by Electromagnetic **Induction**

1) **Transformers** are devices that use electromagnetic induction to **change** the size of the **voltage** for an **alternating current**.
2) They consist of **two coils of wire** wrapped around an **iron core**.
3) An alternating current flowing in the **primary** (or input) **coil** produces a changing **magnetic field** in the **iron core**.
4) The **changing magnetic field** is passed through the **iron core** to the **secondary** (or output) coil, where it **induces** an alternating **voltage** (e.m.f.) of the same frequency as the input voltage.
5) The **ratio** of the **number of turns** on each coil along with the voltage across the primary coil determines the **size of the voltage** induced in the secondary coil.

Step-up transformers **increase** the **voltage** by having **more turns** on the **secondary** coil than the primary.
Step-down transformers **reduce** the voltage by having **fewer** turns on the secondary coil.

6) Real-life transformers **aren't 100% efficient** — some power is always lost. Using a **laminated core** reduces losses.

You Can **Calculate** the **Induced E.m.f.s** in **Each Coil**

From Faraday's law (page 155), the **induced** e.m.f.s in both the **primary** (*p*) and **secondary** (*s*) coils can be calculated:

Primary coil	Secondary coil
$V_p = -\frac{n_p \Delta\phi}{\Delta t}$	$V_s = -\frac{n_s \Delta\phi}{\Delta t}$

(where *n* is the number of turns in a coil)

Ideal transformers are **100% efficient**, so **power in** equals the **power out**.

Power is **current × voltage**, so for an ideal transformer $I_p V_p = I_s V_s$, or $\frac{I_p}{I_s} = \frac{V_s}{V_p}$.

Combine this with the equations for induced e.m.f. in each coil to get the **transformer equation**...

$$\frac{n_s}{n_p} = \frac{V_s}{V_p} = \frac{I_p}{I_s}$$

Example: What is the output voltage for a transformer with a primary coil of 120 turns, a secondary coil of 350 turns and an input voltage of 230 V?

$\frac{n_s}{n_p} = \frac{V_s}{V_p}$ $\quad V_s = \frac{V_p \times n_s}{n_p} = \frac{230 \times 350}{120}$ = 670.83... = **670 V (to 2 s.f.)**

Transformers are Everywhere

They're an important part of the national grid...

1) **Electricity** from power stations is sent round the country in the **national grid** at the **lowest** possible current. This is because **losses** due to the **resistance** in the cables is equal to $P = I^2R$ (see page 66) — so if you double the transmitted current, you **quadruple** the power lost.
2) Since **power = current × voltage** (p.66), a **low current** means a **high voltage**.
3) **Transformers** allow us to **step up** the voltage to around **400 000 V** for **transmission** through the national grid, and then **reduce** it again in substations to **230 V** for home use.

...and are in loads of your devices.

1) Lots of **electronic devices** like laptops, mobiles, monitors and speakers **can't function** using a standard **230 V** mains supply — they need a **much lower voltage** (and usually a d.c. supply too).
2) The **chargers** for these devices contain **transformers** to adjust the voltage — they're contained in the **plug** or a **box** in the cable.

Uses of Electromagnetic Induction

Investigate the **Number of Turns, Voltage** and **Current** in a Transformer

To investigate the relationship between **number of turns** and the **voltages** across the coils:

1) Set up the equipment as shown. Put two C-cores together and wrap wire around each to make the coils. Begin with 5 turns in the primary coil and 10 in the secondary coil (a **ratio** of 1:2).
2) Turn on the a.c. supply to the primary coil. **Use a low voltage** — remember transformers **increase voltage**, so make sure you keep it at a safe level. Record the voltage across each coil.
3) Keeping V_p the same so it's a fair test, repeat the experiment with different ratios of turns. Try 1:1 and 2:1. Divide n_s by n_p and V_s by V_p. You should find that for each ratio of turns, $\frac{n_s}{n_p} = \frac{V_s}{V_p}$.

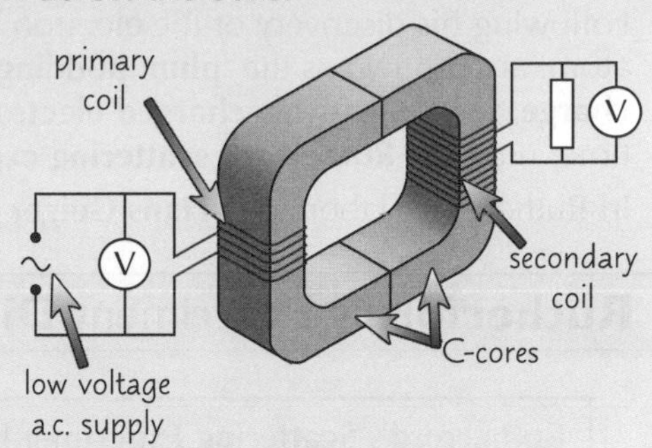

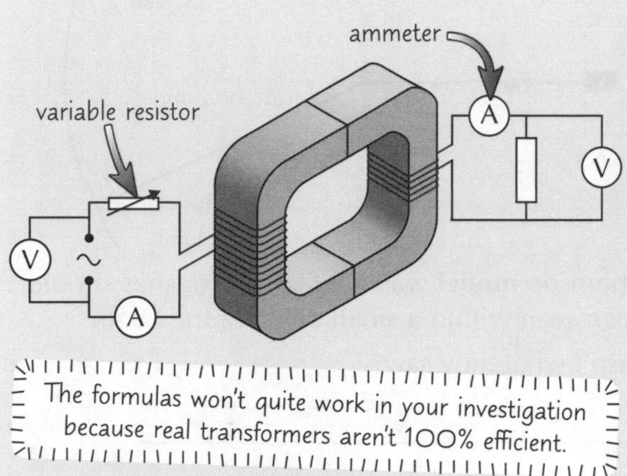

The formulas won't quite work in your investigation because real transformers aren't 100% efficient.

To investigate the relationship between **number of turns**, **voltage** across and **current** of the transformer coils:

1) Use the same equipment as above, but add a **variable resistor** to the primary coil circuit and an **ammeter** to both circuits.
2) Turn on the power supply and **record** the **current through** and **voltage across** each coil.
3) Leaving the number of turns **constant**, adjust the variable resistor to change the input current. Record the current and voltage for each coil, then **repeat** this process for a **range** of input currents.
4) You should find that for each current, $\frac{n_s}{n_p} = \frac{V_s}{V_p} = \frac{I_p}{I_s}$.

Warm-Up Questions

Q1 Sketch and label a diagram of an a.c. generator. How does it work?

Q2 Draw a diagram of a simple transformer. What is meant by a step-down transformer?

Q3 Describe the role of transformers in the national grid.

Q4 Describe an experiment to investigate how the ratio of number of turns in the primary and secondary coils of a transformer affects the current and voltage in the secondary coil.

Exam Questions

Q1 A transformer with 158 turns in the primary coil has an input voltage of 9.30 V.

a) i) Calculate the number of turns needed in the secondary coil to step up the voltage to 45.0 V. [1 mark]

ii) The secondary coil actually has 90.0 turns. Calculate the voltage induced in the secondary coil. [1 mark]

b) The input current for the transformer is 1.50 A. Assuming the transformer is ideal, calculate the output current. [1 mark]

Q2 A substation receives 943 kW of electricity from a power station through wires with a total resistance 132 Ω. The input current was 15.6 A.

a) Calculate the electrical power originally transmitted from the power station. [2 marks]

b) Describe how transformers are used in the transmission of electricity at a low current, explaining why this is important. [2 marks]

Aaaaaand — relax...

Breathe a sigh of relief, pat yourself on the back and make a brew — well done, you've reached the end of the section. That was pretty nasty stuff (the section, not your tea), but don't let all of those equations get you down — once you've learnt the main ones and can use them blindfolded, even the trickiest looking exam question will be a walk in the park.

Atomic Structure

We have a pretty good idea of atomic structure these days — but it's been anything but plain sailing...

The **Thomson Model** said **Electrons** were **Spread Out** Inside an **Atom**

Following his discovery of the electron in the late 19th century, **J.J. Thomson** proposed the **Thomson model** of the atom, also known as the '**plum pudding**' model. This model said that atoms were made up of a globule of **positive charge**, with **negatively charged electrons sprinkled** in it, like fruit in a plum pudding. It was widely accepted at the time, until the **Rutherford scattering experiment** of 1909.

In Rutherford's laboratory, **Hans Geiger** and **Ernest Marsden** studied the scattering of **alpha particles** by **thin metal foils**.

Rutherford's Experiment **Disproved** the **Thomson Model**...

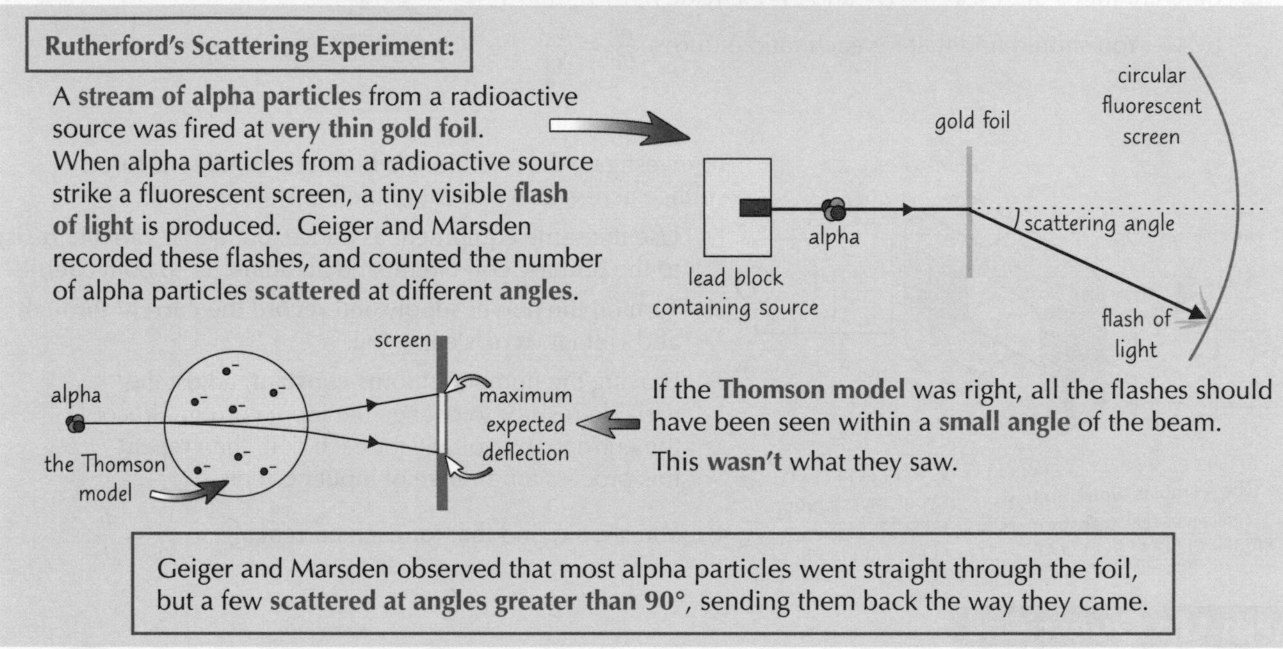

...and Supported the Idea of a **Small, Positively Charged Nucleus**

This experiment led Rutherford to some **important conclusions**:

1) Most of the fast, charged alpha particles went **straight through** the foil. So the atom is mainly **empty space**.
2) **Some** of the alpha particles were **deflected** through **large angles**, so the **centre** of the atom must have a **large**, **positive charge** to repel them. Rutherford named this the **nucleus**.
3) Very few particles were deflected by angles greater than **90 degrees**, so the nucleus must be **tiny**.
4) Most of the **mass** must be in the nucleus, since the fast alpha particles (with high momentum) are deflected by the nucleus.

So most of the **mass** and the **positive charge** in an atom must be contained within a **tiny**, **central nucleus**.

The **Nuclear Model** Explained **Rutherford Scattering**

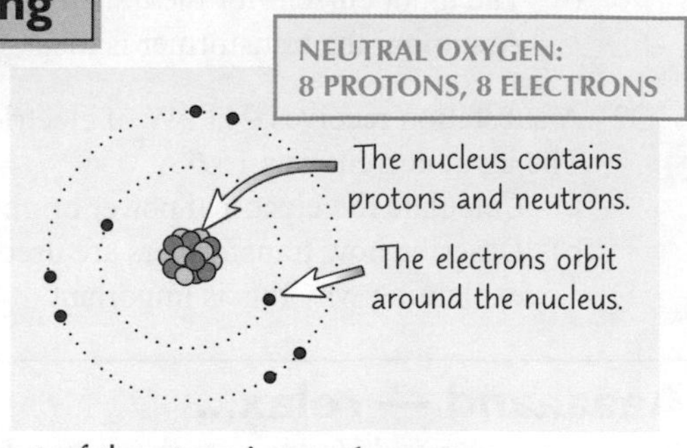

1) Inside **every atom**, there's a **positive nucleus** containing **neutrons** (which have no charge) and **positively charged protons**. **Protons** and **neutrons** are both known as **nucleons**. **Orbiting** this core are the **negatively charged electrons**.
2) The **charge** on an **electron**, $-e$, is **equal and opposite** to the charge on a **proton**, $+e$. e is the **elementary charge** 1.60×10^{-19} C.
3) The **nucleus** only makes up a tiny proportion of an atom — it's only about **one 10 000th of the size** of the whole atom. The electrons orbit at relatively **vast distances** from the nucleus, so most of the atom is **empty space**.
4) The **proton** and **neutron** are roughly **2000 times** more **massive** than the **electron**, so the nucleus makes up **nearly all** of the **mass** of the atom.

Atomic Structure

The Proton Number is the Number of Protons in the Nucleus

No... really.

The **proton number** is sometimes called the **atomic number**, and has the **symbol** ***Z*** (don't ask me why). ***Z*** is just the **number of protons** in the nucleus.

It's the **proton number** that **defines** the **element** — **no two elements** will have the **same** number of protons.

In a **neutral atom**, the number of **electrons equals** the number of **protons**. The element's **reactions** and **chemical behaviour** depend on the number of **electrons**. So the **proton number** tells you a lot about its **chemical properties**.

The Nucleon Number is the Total Number of Protons and Neutrons

The **nucleon number** is also called the **mass number**, and has the **symbol** ***A*** (*shrug*).
It tells you how many **protons** and **neutrons** are in the nucleus.

Each **proton or neutron** has a **mass** of (approximately) **1 atomic mass unit** (1.661×10^{-27} kg, see p.176).
The mass of an electron compared with a nucleon is virtually nothing, so the **number** of **nucleons** is about the same as the **atom's mass** (in atomic mass units).

Nuclei can be Represented Using Standard Notation

Standard notation summarises the important information about an element's **atomic structure**:

$$^{12}_{6}\mathrm{C}$$

The **nucleon number** or **mass number** (*A*) — there are a total of 12 protons and neutrons in a carbon-12 atom.

The symbol for the element carbon.

The **proton number** or **atomic number** (*Z*) — there are six protons in a carbon atom.

Isotopes have the Same Proton Number, but Different Nucleon Numbers

Atoms with the **same number of protons** but **different numbers of neutrons** are called **isotopes**.

1) **Changing** the number of **neutrons doesn't affect** the atom's **chemical** properties.
2) The **number of neutrons** affects the **stability** of the nucleus though (see p.170).
3) **Unstable nuclei** may be **radioactive**.
4) Isotopes are often named using their **nucleon number**, e.g. carbon's isotopes include carbon-12 and carbon-13. Other isotopes have **special names** e.g. deuterium and tritium.

Example: Hydrogen has three naturally occurring isotopes: hydrogen, deuterium and tritium.

Hydrogen has **1 proton** and **0 neutrons.**
Deuterium has **1 proton** and **1 neutron.**
Tritium has **1 proton** and **2 neutrons.**

Warm-Up Questions

Q1 List the particles that make up the atom and give their charges and relative masses.
Q2 Define the proton number and nucleon number.
Q3 What is an isotope?

Exam Questions

Q1 In 1911, Ernest Rutherford proposed the nuclear model of the atom after experiments using alpha-particle scattering.

a) Describe the nuclear model of the atom. [3 marks]

b) Explain how the alpha-particle scattering experiment provided evidence for Rutherford's model. [3 marks]

Q2 State how many protons, neutrons and electrons there are in a (neutral) $^{139}_{57}\mathrm{La}$ atom. [2 marks]

Alpha scattering — it's positively repulsive...

The important things to learn from these two pages are the nuclear model for the structure of the atom (i.e. a large mass nucleus surrounded by orbiting electrons) and how the alpha particle scattering experiment provides evidence that supports this model. Once you know that, take a deep breath — it's about to get a little more confusing.

The Nucleus

The tiny nucleus — such a weird place, but one that you need to become ultra familiar with. Lucky you. There's a nice graph coming up on page 164 though, so at least there's something to look forward to...

The **Nucleus** is a **Very Small Part** of a Whole **Atom**

1) By **probing atoms** using scattering and diffraction methods, we know that the **diameter of an atom** is about 0.1 nm (1×10^{-10} m) and the diameter of the smallest **nucleus** is a few fm ($1 \text{ fm} = 1 \times 10^{-15}$ m — pronounced "femtometres").
2) So basically, **nuclei** are really, really **tiny** compared with the size of the **whole atom**.
3) To make this **easier to visualise**, try imagining a **large Ferris wheel** (which is pretty darn big) as the size of **an atom**. If you then put a **grain of rice** (which is rather small) in the centre, this would be the size of the atom's **nucleus**.
4) **Molecules** are just a number of **atoms joined together**. As a rough guide, the size of a molecule equals the number of atoms in it multiplied by the size of one atom.

I've seen bigger...

Nuclear Radius is **Proportional** to the **Cube Root** of the **Nucleon Number**

1) As you know from p.161, the **particles** that make up the nucleus (i.e. **protons** and **neutrons**) are called **nucleons**. The **number of nucleons** in an atom is called the **nucleon** (or **mass**) **number, *A***.
2) Unsurprisingly, as **more nucleons** are added to the nucleus, it gets **bigger**.
3) You can measure the size of a nucleus by firing particles at it. If you plot the **radius of the nucleus**, ***R***, against the **nucleon number**, you get a graph like this:

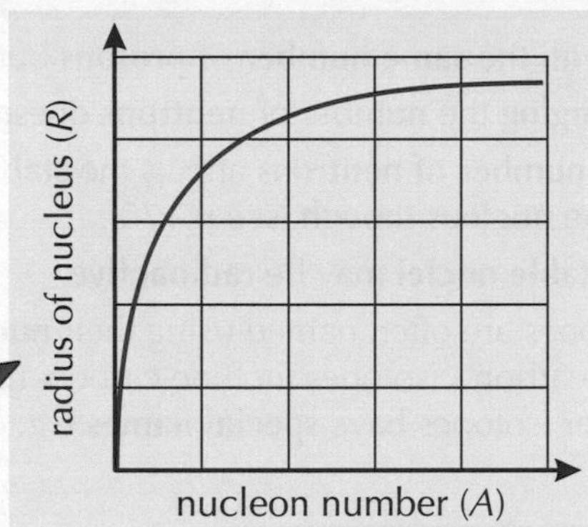

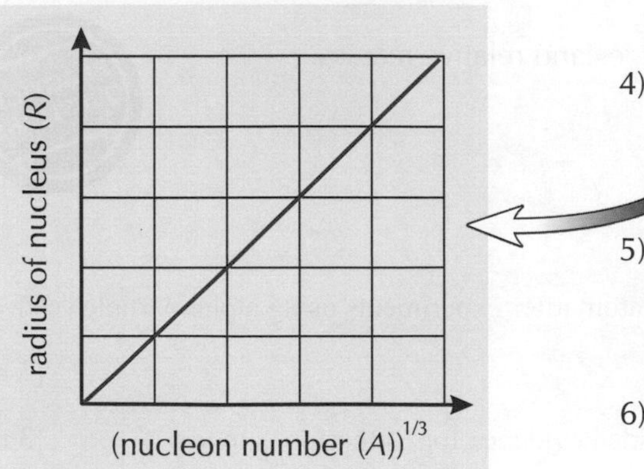

4) In fact, **nuclear radius** increases roughly as the **cube root** of the **nucleon number**. You can see this by plotting **nuclear radius** against the cube root of the **nucleon number**.
5) The fact that this graph is a **straight** line through the origin shows that nuclear radius is **directly proportional** to the cube root of the nucleon number. This relationship can be written as: $R \propto A^{1/3}$.
6) By introducing a constant, r_0, we can make this into an equation:

$$R = r_0 A^{1/3}$$

Where r_0 is about 1.4 fm or 1.4×10^{-15} m.

The Nucleus

Nuclear Density is Much Higher than Atomic Density

1) To calculate the **mean density** of a **nucleus** you need to know the **mass** and **volume** of the nucleus — and the equation for density:

$$\rho = \frac{m}{V}$$

The symbol for density, ρ, is the Greek letter 'rho'. Its unit is kg m^{-3}.

2) If you're asked to **estimate mean nuclear density**, you might have to **work out** the **volume** of the nucleus from its **radius**. So, just assume the nucleus is a **sphere** and bung the value into the equation:

$$V = \frac{4}{3}\pi r^3$$

3) Nuclear density is **pretty much the same**, regardless of the element — roughly 10^{17} kg m^{-3}.
4) Nuclear density is **much higher** than atomic density. This suggests that:

- Most of an atom's mass is in its **nucleus**.
- The nucleus is **small** compared to the atom.
- An atom must contain a lot of **empty space**.

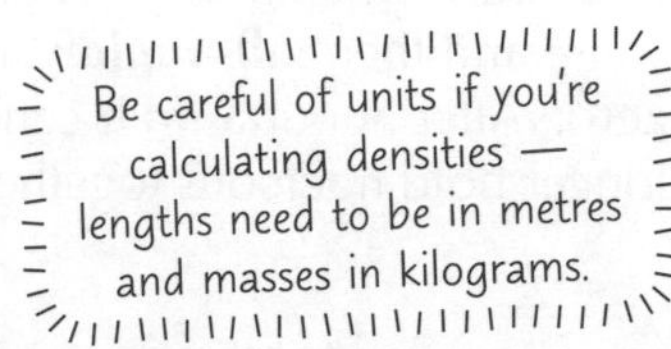

Example: A carbon atom has a mass of 2.00×10^{-26} kg, an atomic radius of 7.0×10^{-11} m, and a nuclear radius of 3.2×10^{-15} m.
a) Calculate its mean atomic density. b) Calculate its mean nuclear density.

a) $V_{\text{atom}} = \frac{4}{3}\pi r^3 = 1.436... \times 10^{-30}\ \text{m}^3$ $\qquad \rho_{\text{atom}} = \frac{m}{V}$ so $\rho = \frac{2.00 \times 10^{-26}}{1.436... \times 10^{-30}} = \mathbf{1.4 \times 10^4\ kg\,m^{-3}\ (to\ 2\ s.f.)}$

b) $V_{\text{nucleus}} = \frac{4}{3}\pi r^3 = 1.372... \times 10^{-43}\ \text{m}^3$ $\qquad \rho_{\text{nucleus}} = \frac{m}{V}$ so $\rho = \frac{2.00 \times 10^{-26}}{1.372... \times 10^{-43}} = \mathbf{1.5 \times 10^{17}\ kg\,m^{-3}\ (to\ 2\ s.f.)}$

So the nucleus is about 10^{13} times as dense as the atom as a whole.

The Strong Nuclear Force Binds Nucleons Together

The **strong nuclear force** is quite **complicated**, but here are the **main points**:

1) To **hold the nucleus together**, the strong nuclear force must be an **attractive force** that **overcomes** the **electrostatic force** (the repulsive force between the positive charges of the protons, p.146).
2) Experiments have shown that the strong nuclear force between nucleons has a **short range**. It can only hold nucleons together when they are separated by up to **a few femtometres** — the size of a **nucleus**.
3) The **strength** of the strong nuclear force between nucleons **quickly falls** beyond this distance.
4) Experiments also show that the strong nuclear force **works equally between all nucleons**. This means that the size of the force is the same whether proton-proton, neutron-neutron or proton-neutron.
5) At **very small separations**, the strong nuclear force must be **repulsive** — otherwise there would be nothing to stop it **crushing** the nucleus to a **point**.

Green, yellow, blue, orange and red — repulsive at short separations.

The Nucleus

You Can Compare the **Strong Nuclear** and **Electrostatic Forces**

The **strong nuclear force** can be plotted on a **graph** to show how it changes with the **distance of separation** between **nucleons**. If the **electrostatic force** is also plotted, you can see the **relationship** between these **two forces**.

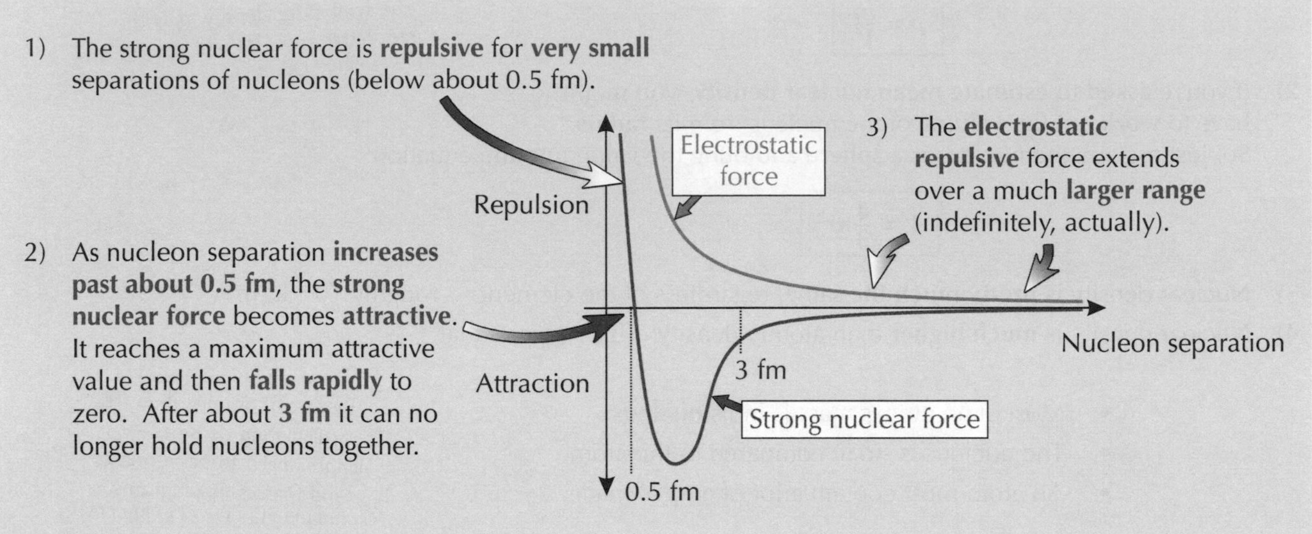

Warm-Up Questions

Q1 What is the approximate diameter of an atom? What is the approximate diameter of the smallest nucleus?

Q2 Explain why the density of atomic matter is much less than that of nuclear matter.

Q3 What causes an electrostatic force inside the nucleus?

Q4 Is the strong nuclear force attractive or repulsive at a nucleon separation of 2 fm?

PRACTICE QUESTIONS

Exam Questions

Q1 a) Given that $r_0 = 1.4$ fm, estimate the radius of the nucleus of an oxygen-16 atom. [1 mark]

b) An atom of iodine has a nucleon number of 127. An atom of nitrogen has a nucleon number of 14. Estimate how many times larger the radius of an iodine nucleus is than the radius of a nitrogen nucleus. [2 marks]

Q2 A radium nucleus has a radius of 8.53×10^{-15} m and a mass of 3.75×10^{-25} kg. Estimate the mean density of the radium nucleus. [2 marks]

Q3 A sample of pure gold has a density of 19 300 kg m^{-3}. If the density of a gold nucleus is 1.47×10^{17} kg m^{-3}, discuss what this implies about the structure of a gold atom. [4 marks]

Q4 The strong nuclear force binds the nucleus together.

a) Explain why the force must be repulsive at very short distances. [1 mark]

b) Explain how the strong nuclear force limits the size of a stable nucleus. [2 marks]

Don't know about you, but this stuff makes me feel pretty dense...

Right then, lots of scary looking stuff on these pages, but the important bits can be condensed into a few points: a) the radius of the nucleus is directly proportional to the cube root of the nucleon number, b) nuclear density is really high compared to the atomic density, c) the strong nuclear force is repulsive for really small separations, but becomes attractive for slightly larger separations, then gets weaker as separation increases. Got that?

Classification of Particles

Time for a quick primer on particles — hope you're as excited as I am...

Hadrons are **Particles** that Feel the **Strong Nuclear Force**

1) **Not all particles** can feel **the strong nuclear force** — the ones that **can** are called **hadrons**.
2) Hadrons **aren't fundamental** particles. They're made up of **smaller particles** called **quarks** (see pages 168-169).
3) **Protons** and **neutrons** are **hadrons**. This is why they can make atomic nuclei — the nucleus of an atom is made up from protons and neutrons held together by the **strong nuclear force** (p.163).
4) As well as **protons** and **neutrons**, there are **other hadrons** that you don't get in normal matter, like **sigmas** (Σ) and **mesons** — luckily you **don't** need to know about them (woohoo!).

The **Proton** is the **Only Stable Hadron**

1) Most **hadrons** will eventually **decay** into **other particles**. The exception is protons — most physicists think that protons don't **decay**.
2) The **neutron** is an **unstable particle** that **decays** into a **proton**. (But it's much more stable when it's part of a nucleus.) It's really just an **example** of β^- **decay** (see p.172), which is caused by the **weak nuclear force**.

3) Free neutrons (i.e. ones not held in a nucleus) have a half-life of about 15 minutes.

Some theories predict that protons should decay with a very long half-life of about 10^{32} years — but there's no experimental evidence for it at the moment.

Leptons Don't Feel the **Strong Nuclear Force**

1) **Leptons** are **fundamental particles** and they **don't** feel the **strong nuclear force**. They **interact** with other particles via the **weak nuclear force** and **gravity** (and the electromagnetic force if they're charged).
2) There are two types of lepton you need to know about — **electrons (e^-)** which should be familiar, and **neutrinos (ν)**.
3) Neutrinos have **zero** (or almost zero) **mass** and **zero electric charge** — so they don't do much. **Neutrinos** only take part in **weak interactions** (see p.169). In fact, a neutrino can **pass right through the Earth** without **anything** happening to it.

Name	Symbol	Charge (relative to e)
electron	e^-	–1
neutrino	ν	0

ν is the Greek letter "nu".

Warm-Up Questions

Q1 What are hadrons made up of?
Q2 Give two differences between a hadron and a lepton.
Q3 Which is the only stable hadron? Name another hadron that will decay into it.
Q4 Name two types of lepton.

Exam Questions

Q1 State the decay products of the neutron. Explain why this decay cannot be due to the strong nuclear force. [3 marks]

Q2 A particle is detected that has no charge and that does not feel the strong nuclear force. Suggest what the particle might be. [1 mark]

Go back to the top of the page — do not pass GO, do not collect £200...

There's a frankly silly number of physics words on this page, but it looks worse than it is. Honestly. Give it another read, and don't move on until you're sure you know it all, otherwise the next few pages will sound like nonsense...

Antiparticles

Antiparticles seem to laugh in the face of common sense — but actually, they help to explain a lot in particle physics...

Antiparticles were Predicted Before they were Discovered

When **Paul Dirac** wrote down an equation obeyed by **electrons**, he found a kind of **mirror image** solution.

1) It predicted the existence of a particle like the **electron** but with **opposite electric charge** — the **positron**.
2) The **positron** turned up later in a cosmic ray experiment. Positrons have **identical mass** to electrons but they carry a **positive** charge.

Every Particle has an Antiparticle

Each particle type has a **corresponding antiparticle** with the **same mass** but with **opposite charge**. For instance, an **antiproton** is a **negatively charged** particle with the same mass as the **proton**.

Even the shadowy **neutrino** has an antiparticle version called the **antineutrino** — it doesn't do much either.

Particle	Symbol	Relative charge	Rest mass (kg)	Antiparticle	Symbol	Relative charge	Rest mass (kg)
proton	p	+1	1.673×10^{-27}	antiproton	$\bar{p}$	–1	1.673×10^{-27}
neutron	n	0	1.675×10^{-27}	antineutron	$\bar{n}$	0	1.675×10^{-27}
electron	e^-	–1	9.11×10^{-31}	positron	e^+	+1	9.11×10^{-31}
neutrino	ν	0	0	antineutrino	$\bar{\nu}$	0	0

1) In the exam, you'll be **given** the masses of protons, neutrons and electrons. Just remember that the mass of an **antiparticle** is the **same** as the mass of its corresponding particle.
2) The masses in the table are all **rest masses** — the mass of the particle when it's **not moving**. This is because the masses of objects change when they're moving at very high speeds, but you don't need to know about that.
3) You need to **learn** the **relative charges** on each type of particle (these are all relative to $e = 1.60 \times 10^{-19}$ C).
4) Neutrinos are **incredibly tiny** — you can assume they have zero mass and zero charge.

You can Create Matter and Antimatter from Energy

You've probably heard about the **equivalence** of energy and mass. It all comes out of Einstein's special theory of relativity. **Energy** can turn into **mass** and **mass** can turn into **energy** if you know how — all you need is one fantastic and rather famous formula:

$$\Delta E = \Delta mc^2$$

As you've probably guessed, there's a bit **more to it** than that:

When **energy** is converted into **mass** you get **equal amounts** of **matter** and **antimatter**.

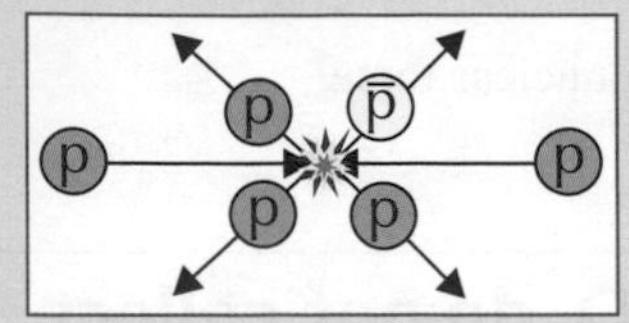

Fire **two protons** at each other at high speed and you'll end up with a lot of **energy** at the point of impact. This energy might be converted into **more particles**.

If an extra **proton** is formed then there will always be an **antiproton** to go with it. It's called **pair production**.

Antiparticles

Each **Particle-Antiparticle Pair** is Produced from a **Single Photon**

Pair production only happens if **one photon** has enough energy to produce that much mass. It also tends to happen near a **nucleus**, which helps conserve momentum.

You usually get **electron-positron** pairs produced (rather than any other pair) — because they have a relatively **low mass**.

The **minimum** amount of energy the **photon** must have is the **combined energy** of the **two** particles **at rest** (i.e. assuming that the particles have **negligible** kinetic energy).

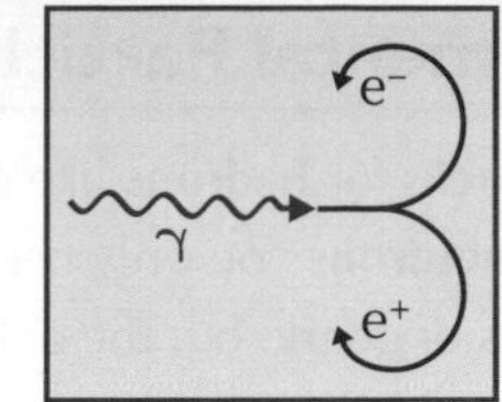

The particle tracks are curved because there's usually a magnetic field present in particle physics experiments. They curve in opposite directions because of the opposite charges on the electron and positron.

You can calculate the **minimum** energy, E_γ, using $\Delta E = \Delta mc^2$:

1) The **minimum energy** a photon must have to undergo pair production (E_γ) must be **equal** to the energy (at rest) of the **particles produced**.
2) A particle and its antiparticle have the **same rest mass** (m), which means that: ⟹ $E_\gamma = 2mc^2$
3) You can go further and find the **maximum wavelength** or **minimum frequency** of the photon using the equation for the **energy of a photon**: ⟹ $E_\gamma = \frac{hc}{\lambda} = hf$
4) Just put these two equations for E_γ together and **rearrange** to find λ or f.

The **Opposite** of **Pair Production** is **Annihilation**

When a **particle** meets its **antiparticle** the result is **annihilation**.
All the **mass** of the particle and antiparticle gets converted to **energy**, in the form of a pair of photons. In ordinary matter antiparticles can only exist for a fraction of a second before this happens, so you won't see many of them.

Just like with pair production, you can calculate the **minimum energy** of each photon produced (i.e. assuming that the particles have **negligible** kinetic energy).

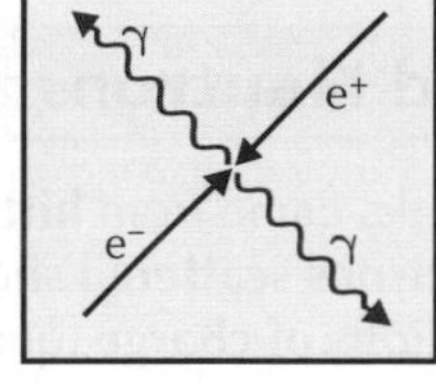

The electron and positron annihilate and their mass is converted into the energy of a pair of identical gamma ray photons.

The combined energy of the photons will be equal to the combined energy of the particles, so $\mathbf{2E_\gamma = 2mc^2}$ and so $\mathbf{E_\gamma = mc^2}$

You can calculate the minimum frequency and maximum wavelength as before.

Warm-Up Questions

Q1 Which antiparticle has zero charge and a rest mass of 1.675×10^{-27} kg?

Q2 What is the symbol for an antineutrino?

Q3 Describe the properties of an antineutrino.

Q4 Write down the charge of a positron, given that the charge on an electron is -1.60×10^{-19} C.

Q5 Give one similarity and one difference between a proton and an antiproton.

Exam Questions

Q1 Explain why the reaction $p + p \rightarrow p + p + n$ is not possible. [1 mark]

Q2 Write down an equation for the reaction between a positron and an electron and state the name of this type of reaction. [2 marks]

Q3 Assuming both particles have negligible kinetic energy, calculate the frequency of the photons produced when a proton and an antiproton annihilate.
($m_p = 1.673 \times 10^{-27}$ kg, $h = 6.63 \times 10^{-34}$ Js, $c = 3.00 \times 10^8$ ms^{-1}) [3 marks]

Pair production — never seems to happen with my socks...

The idea of every particle having an antiparticle might seem a bit strange, but just make sure you know the main points — a) if energy is converted into a particle, you also get an antiparticle, b) an antiparticle won't last long before it bumps into the right particle and annihilates it, c) this releases the energy it took to make them to start with...

Quarks

Quarks are the fundamental particles that make up protons and neutrons. If you haven't yet, it's probably best to read pages 165–167 before you start — then this will all make a bit more sense...

Quarks are Fundamental Particles

Quarks are the **building blocks** for **hadrons** like **protons** and **neutrons**.

1) To make **protons** and **neutrons** you only need two types of quark — the **up** quark (**u**) and the **down** quark (**d**).
2) There a few more types of quark, but the only other one you need to know about is the **strange** quark (**s**).

The **antiparticles** of hadrons (like antiprotons and antineutrons) are made from **anti-quarks.**

Quarks and Anti-quarks have Opposite Charges

The **anti-quarks** have **opposite charges** to the quarks — as you'd expect.

Quarks:

name	symbol	relative charge
up	u	$+{}^{2}/_{3}$
down	d	$-{}^{1}/_{3}$
strange	s	$-{}^{1}/_{3}$

Anti-quarks:

name	symbol	relative charge
anti-up	$\bar{u}$	$-{}^{2}/_{3}$
anti-down	$\bar{d}$	$+{}^{1}/_{3}$
anti-strange	$\bar{s}$	$+{}^{1}/_{3}$

As on p.165 and p.166, these charges are relative to the elementary charge, *e*.

Protons and Neutrons are Made from Three Quarks

Evidence for quarks came from **hitting protons** with **high energy electrons.** The way the **electrons scattered** showed that there were **three concentrations of charge** (quarks) **inside** the proton.

The quarks that a particle is made up from is called its 'quark composition'.

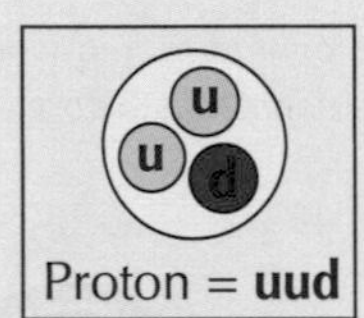

Total relative charge $= \frac{2}{3} + \frac{2}{3} - \frac{1}{3} = 1$

Proton = **uud**

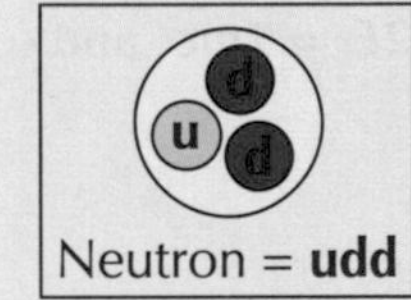

Total relative charge $= \frac{2}{3} - \frac{1}{3} - \frac{1}{3} = 0$

Neutron = **udd**

Antiprotons are $\bar{u}\bar{u}\bar{d}$ and antineutrons are $\bar{u}\bar{d}\bar{d}$ — so no surprises there then.

Not all hadrons have **three quarks** though. Protons and neutrons are a type of hadron called **baryons**, which are made up of **three quarks**. There are also hadrons made up of a **quark** and an **anti-quark**, called **mesons** — but you don't really need to know about them.

There's no Such Thing as a Free Quark

What if you **blasted** a **proton** with **enough energy** — could you **separate out** the quarks? Nope. The energy just gets changed into more **quarks and antiquarks** — it's **pair production** again (see p.166) and it makes **mesons**.

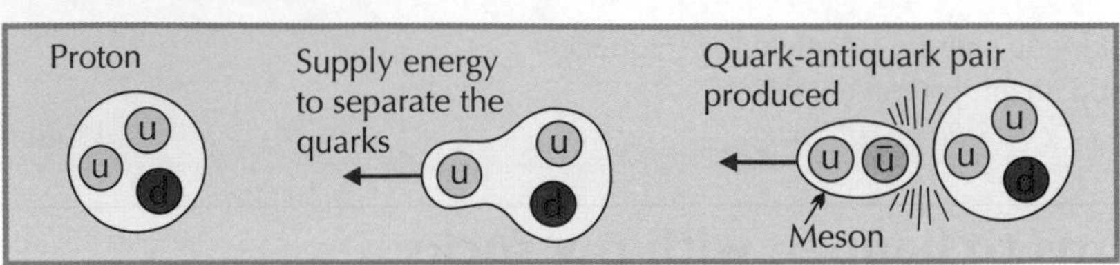

This is called **quark confinement**.

Quarks

The Weak Nuclear Force is Something that Changes the Quark Type

Hadrons can **decay** into other particles via the **weak nuclear force** (p.165).
This is the **only thing** that can change one type of quark into another.

In **beta-minus** (β^-) decay a **neutron** is changed into a **proton** — in other words **udd** changes into **uud**. It means turning a **d** quark into a **u** quark.

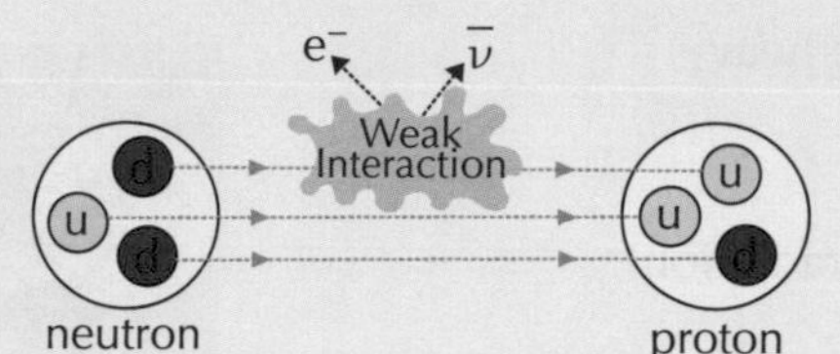

in terms of **quarks**: $d \rightarrow u + e^- + \bar{\nu}$

in terms of **charge**: $(-\frac{1}{3}) \rightarrow (+\frac{2}{3}) + (-1) + 0$

You might also see electrons and positrons written as $^{0}_{-1}e$ and $^{0}_{+1}e$

Some unstable isotopes like **carbon-11** decay by **beta-plus** (β^+) emission. In this case a **proton** changes to a **neutron**, so a **u** quark changes to a **d** quark.

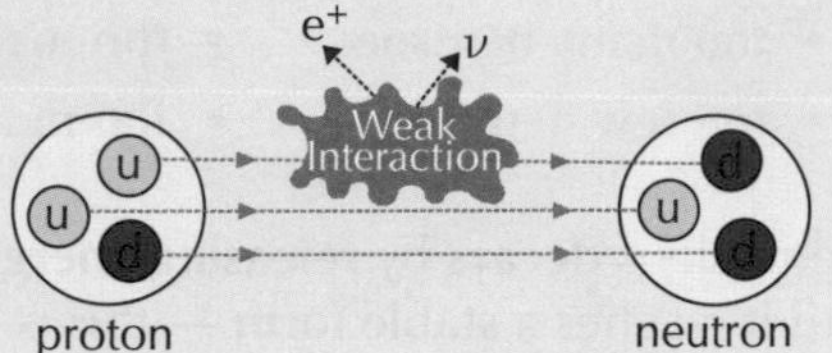

in terms of **quarks**: $u \rightarrow d + e^+ + \nu$

in terms of **charge**: $(+\frac{2}{3}) \rightarrow (-\frac{1}{3}) + (+1) + 0$

In any other kind of interaction, the number of quarks of **any type** must be the same before the interaction as after it.
In **all** interactions, **charge must be conserved**.

Charge is Always Conserved in Particle Reactions

In **any** particle reaction, the **total charge** after the reaction must equal the total charge before the reaction.

Example: A Σ^+ particle can decay to produce a π^+ particle and another particle A. By considering the charge on each quark, identify the missing quark (labelled '?') in this reaction, and hence state the name of particle A.

$$\Sigma^+ \rightarrow A + \pi^+$$
$$uus \rightarrow ?dd + u\bar{d}$$

Write down the charge on each quark and then find the total charge on each particle.

$$u \quad u \quad s \quad \rightarrow \quad ? \quad d \quad d \quad + \quad u \quad \bar{d}$$
$$+\tfrac{2}{3} \quad +\tfrac{2}{3} \quad -\tfrac{1}{3} \quad \rightarrow \quad ? \quad -\tfrac{1}{3} \quad -\tfrac{1}{3} \quad + \quad +\tfrac{2}{3} \quad +\tfrac{1}{3}$$

For charge to be conserved, the missing quark must have a charge of $+\frac{2}{3}$. This means it must be an **up quark**.

$$+1 \quad \rightarrow \quad (? - \tfrac{2}{3}) \quad + \quad +1$$

This means particle A is made up of the quarks udd, so it is a **neutron**.

Warm-Up Questions

Q1 What is a quark? Write down the quark composition of protons and neutrons.

Q2 State the relative charge of: a) a strange quark, b) an anti-strange quark.

Q3 Explain why quarks are never observed on their own.

Q4 Write down the equation for β^+ decay in terms of quarks.

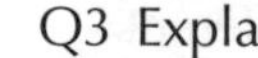

Exam Questions

Q1 Particle interactions involving hadrons can take place via the strong nuclear force and the weak nuclear force. In which of these types of interaction is charge conserved?

A: Strong only B: Weak only C: Strong and weak D: None [1 mark]

Q2 a) State the equation for beta-minus decay:

i) in terms of hadrons and leptons. [2 marks]

ii) in terms of quarks and leptons. [1 mark]

b) Explain, in terms of the charges on quarks and leptons, how this reaction conserves charge. [3 marks]

A quark — not the noise a posh duck makes...

Don't know about you, but I'm getting a wee bit sick of tables of particles to learn. Sadly you need to learn all this stuff, but none of it's too tricky, so make yourself a cuppa and give it all another read...

Radioactive Decay

Despite its best intentions, the strong force can't always hold nuclei together — instead you get radioactive emissions.

Unstable Nuclei are **Radioactive**

1) The nucleus is under the **influence** of the **strong nuclear force holding** it **together** and the **electrostatic force pushing** the **protons apart**. It's a very **delicate balance**, and it's easy for a nucleus to become **unstable**.
2) If a nucleus is **unstable**, it will **break down** to **become** more stable. Its **instability** could be caused by:
   - **too many neutrons**
   - **too few neutrons**
   - **too many nucleons** in total (it's **too heavy**)
   - **too much energy** in the nucleus
3) The nucleus **decays** by **releasing energy** and/or **particles** (nuclear radiation), until it reaches a **stable form** — this is called **radioactive decay**.
4) An individual radioactive decay is **spontaneous** and **random** — it can't be predicted.
5) Although you can't predict the decay of an **individual nucleus**, if you take a **very large number of nuclei**, their **overall behaviour** shows a **pattern**.
6) Any sample of a particular **isotope** (p.161) has the **same rate of decay**, i.e. the same **proportion** of nuclei will **decay** in a **given time** (p.173).

This radio was pretty active...

There are **Four Types** of **Nuclear Radiation**

You need to know all about the **four** different types of **nuclear radiation** — here's a handy **table** to get you started.

Radiation	Symbol	Constituent	Relative Charge	Mass (u)
Alpha	α	A helium nucleus — 2 protons & 2 neutrons	+2	4
Beta-minus (Beta)	β or β^-	Electron	−1	(negligible)
Beta-plus	β^+	Positron	+1	(negligible)
Gamma	γ	Short-wavelength, high-frequency electromagnetic wave.	0	0

u stands for atomic mass unit — see p.161.

See p.166 for more on positrons.

The **Different Types** of Radiation have **Different Properties**

When radiation **hits** an **atom** it can **knock off electrons**, creating an **ion** — so, **radioactive emissions** are also known as **ionising radiation**. The **different types** of radiation have **different ionising powers** as well as different **speeds** and **penetrating powers**.

Radiation	Symbol	Ionising Power	Speed	Penetrating power	Affected by magnetic field
Alpha	α	Strong	Slow	Absorbed by paper or a few cm of air	Yes
Beta-minus (Beta)	β or β^-	Weak	Fast	Absorbed by ~3 mm of aluminium	Yes
Beta-plus	β^+	Annihilated by electron — so virtually zero range			
Gamma	γ	Very weak	Speed of light	Absorbed by many cm of lead, or several m of concrete	No

The **stronger** the **ionising power** of radiation, the **more energy** it **loses** in a given distance, so the **shorter** the **range** of the radiation.

Radioactive Decay

You can Investigate the Penetration of Different Kinds of Radiation in the Lab

PRACTICAL SKILLS

You can investigate the penetration of different kinds of radiation by using different radioactive sources. These can be dangerous if you don't use them properly:

- Radioactive sources should be kept in a **lead-lined box** when they're not being used.
- They should only be picked up using **long-handled tongs** or **forceps**.
- Take care not to **point** them at anyone, and always keep a **safe distance** from them.

Lead will absorb all types of ionising radiation if it's thick enough.

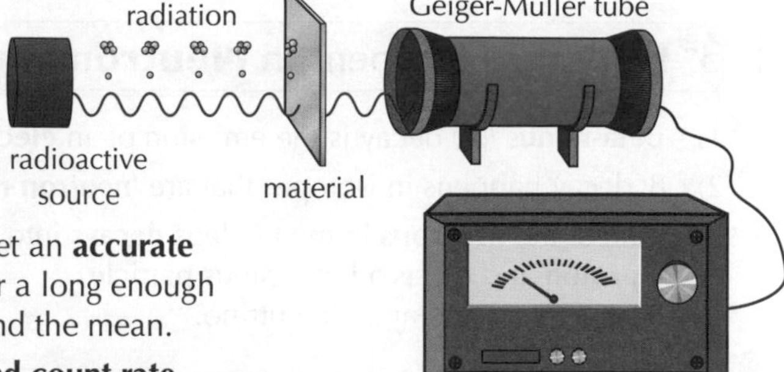

1) Set up the equipment as shown on the right, so that when nothing is placed between the source and tube, the counter records a **high count rate**. You could instead attach the Geiger-Müller tube to a **data-logger** and a **computer** to reduce **human error**.

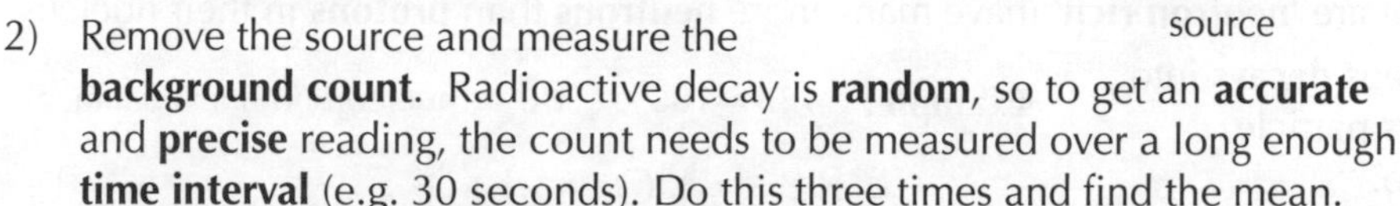

2) Remove the source and measure the **background count**. Radioactive decay is **random**, so to get an **accurate** and **precise** reading, the count needs to be measured over a long enough **time interval** (e.g. 30 seconds). Do this three times and find the mean.

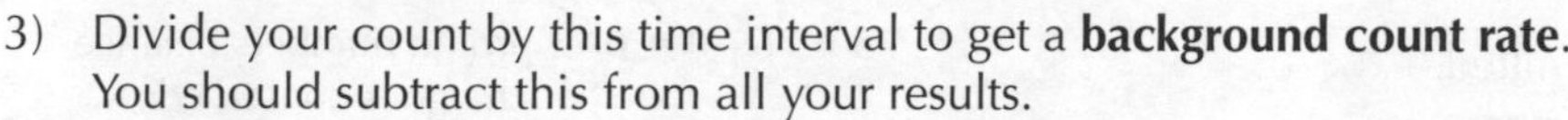

3) Divide your count by this time interval to get a **background count rate**. You should subtract this from all your results.

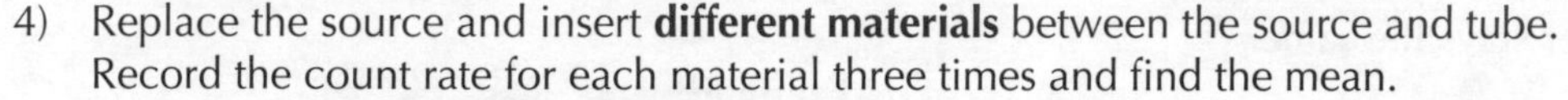

4) Replace the source and insert **different materials** between the source and tube. Record the count rate for each material three times and find the mean.

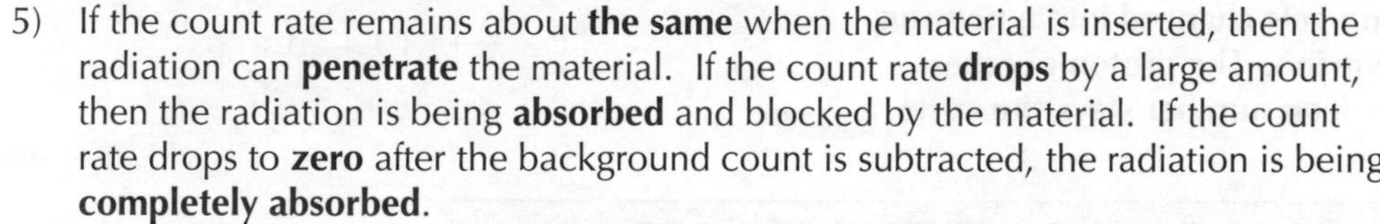

5) If the count rate remains about **the same** when the material is inserted, then the radiation can **penetrate** the material. If the count rate **drops** by a large amount, then the radiation is being **absorbed** and blocked by the material. If the count rate drops to **zero** after the background count is subtracted, the radiation is being **completely absorbed**.

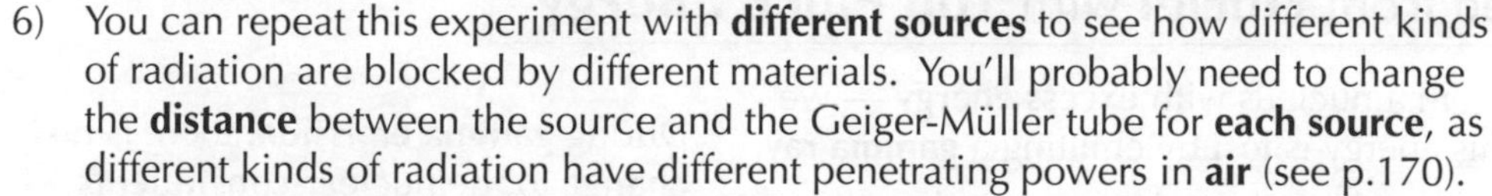

6) You can repeat this experiment with **different sources** to see how different kinds of radiation are blocked by different materials. You'll probably need to change the **distance** between the source and the Geiger-Müller tube for **each source**, as different kinds of radiation have different penetrating powers in **air** (see p.170).
7) You could also adjust this experiment to investigate how the count rate for a particular source is affected by the thickness of a particular material — e.g. by using **sheets** of aluminium for beta radiation or different thicknesses of lead for gamma radiation. Or you could investigate how the count rate changes with distance between the source and the Geiger-Müller tube, and plot a **graph** of your results.

Take repeated measurements of the count rate and calculate averages to make your results more precise.

If you're comparing penetration across different materials, they're unlikely to all have the same thickness. Bear this in mind when you draw your conclusions.

You Can Represent Nuclear Decay Using Equations

1) You usually write the particles in **standard notation** (see page 161) so you can see exactly what happens to the **protons** and **neutrons**.
2) For example, the decay of americium-241 to neptunium-237 looks like this:

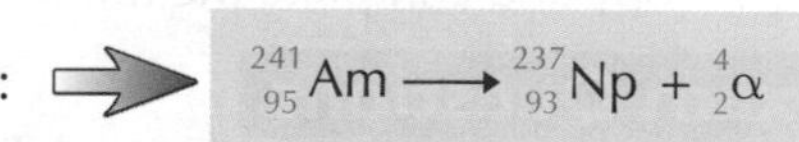

$$^{241}_{95}\text{Am} \longrightarrow ^{237}_{93}\text{Np} + ^{4}_{2}\alpha$$

3) Decay equations need to be **balanced** — in every nuclear reaction, including fission and fusion (p.178-179), **charge** and **nucleon number** must be **conserved**.
4) In this example, there are 241 nucleons **before** the decay (in the americium-241 atom), and 241 nucleons **after** the decay (237 in the neptunium-237 atom and 4 in the alpha particle), so **nucleon number** is conserved.
5) You can see that **charge** is conserved by looking at the **proton number** (the blue numbers in the example above) — there are 95 protons before the decay and 95 after it.
6) Some particles have a **negative** charge. E.g. beta-minus particles are written with a **negative proton number** ($^{0}_{-1}\beta$).
7) **Energy** and **momentum** are also conserved in **all** nuclear reactions. Mass, however, **doesn't** have to be **conserved** — the **mass** of an alpha particle is **less** than the **individual masses** of **two protons** and **two neutrons**. The difference in mass is called the **mass defect** (p.176), and the **energy released** when the nucleons **bond together** to form the alpha particle accounts for the missing mass. More on that later.

Radioactive Decay

α Emission Happens in Heavy Nuclei

1) **Alpha emission** only happens from the nuclei of **very heavy** atoms like **uranium** and **radium**.
2) The **nuclei** of these atoms are **too massive** to be stable.

When an alpha particle is emitted, the **proton number decreases** by **two**, and the **nucleon number decreases** by **four**.

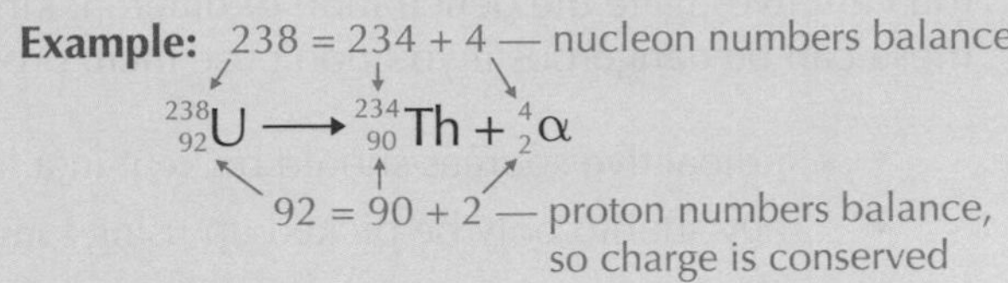

β⁻ Emission Happens in Neutron-Rich Nuclei

1) **Beta-minus** (β^-) decay is the emission of an **electron** from the **nucleus** along with an **antineutrino** (p.166).
2) β^- decay happens in isotopes that are **'neutron rich'** (have many more **neutrons** than **protons** in their nucleus).
3) One of the **neutrons** in the nucleus **decays** into a **proton** and ejects a beta-minus particle (an electron) and an antineutrino.

When a beta-minus particle is emitted, the **proton number increases** by **one**, and the **nucleon number stays the same**.

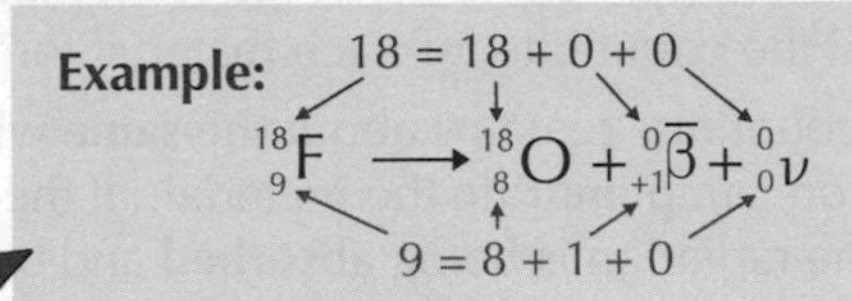

In **beta-plus emission**, a **proton** gets **changed** into a **neutron**, releasing a **positron** and a **neutrino**. The **proton number decreases** by **one**, and the **nucleon number stays the same.**

Example: 18 = 18 + 0 + 0

$$^{18}_{9}F \longrightarrow {}^{18}_{8}O + {}^{0}_{+1}\overline{\beta} + {}^{0}_{0}\nu$$

9 = 8 + 1 + 0

γ Radiation is Emitted from Nuclei with Too Much Energy

Gamma rays can be emitted from a nucleus with **excess energy** — we say the nucleus is **excited**. This energy is **lost** by emitting a **gamma ray**. This often happens after an **alpha** or **beta** decay has occurred.

During **gamma emission**, there is **no change** to the nuclear **constituents** — the nucleus just **loses excess energy**.

Warm-Up Questions

PRACTICE QUESTIONS

Q1 What could make a nucleus unstable?

Q2 What is meant by the statement 'radioactive decay is random'?

Q3 What are the four types of nuclear radiation? What does each one consist of?

Q4 Which type of radiation is the most penetrating? Which is the most ionising?

Q5 Describe the changes that happen in the nucleus during alpha, beta-minus, beta-plus and gamma decay.

Q6 Copy and complete the following equation for beta-plus decay: $^{10}_{6}C \rightarrow {}^{10}_{5}B + {}^{\square}_{\square}\square + {}^{\square}_{\square}\square$

Exam Questions

Q1* A source is known to emit a single type of radiation (alpha, beta-minus or gamma). Describe an experiment to identify the type of radiation that the source emits. [6 marks]

Q2 a) Radium-226 (Ra, proton number 88) decays to radon (Rn) by emitting an alpha particle. Write a balanced nuclear equation for this reaction. [3 marks]

b) Potassium-40 (K, proton number 19) decays to calcium (Ca) by emitting an electron. Write a balanced nuclear equation for this reaction. [3 marks]

*The quality of your extended response will be assessed in this question.

Radioactive emissions — as easy as α, β, γ...

You need to learn the different types of nuclear radiation and their properties, and how to write equations for all the different types of decay. Just remember that charge and nucleon number are conserved, and you won't go far wrong...

Exponential Law of Decay

Different radioactive isotopes emit radiation at different rates. Enter the decay constant and his sidekick half-life...

The Rate of Radioactive Decay is Measured by the Decay Constant

Radioactive decay is random (p.170), but for any radioactive sample, you can **predict** how many nuclei will decay in a given amount of time. The **activity** — the **number** of nuclei that **decay each second** — is **proportional** to the **size of the sample**. For a **given isotope**, **twice** the **number** of nuclei will decay per second in a sample **twice** as **large**.

The **decay constant** (λ) measures how **quickly** an isotope will **decay** — the **bigger** the value of λ, the faster the rate of decay. Its unit is s^{-1}.

Don't get λ confused with wavelength.

activity = decay constant × number of undecayed nuclei In symbols: $A = \lambda N$

Activity is measured in **becquerels** (Bq). An activity of 1 Bq means that 1 nucleus decays per second (s^{-1}).

Because the activity, A, is the number of nuclei that decay each second, you can write it as the **change** in the number of undecayed nuclei, ΔN, during a **given time** (in seconds), Δt: $A = -\frac{\Delta N}{\Delta t}$

There's a minus sign in this equation because ΔN is always a **decrease**.

Combining these two equations for the activity then gives the **rate of change** of the number of undecayed nuclei:

$$-\frac{\Delta N}{\Delta t} = \lambda N$$

$\frac{\Delta N}{\Delta t}$ = rate of change of number of undecayed nuclei, N = number of undecayed nuclei in sample, λ = decay constant

Example: A sample of a radioactive isotope contains 3.0×10^{19} nuclei. Its activity is measured to be 2.4×10^{12} Bq. Calculate the isotope's decay constant.

Rearrange $A = \lambda N$ to give: $\lambda = A/N = (2.4 \times 10^{12}) \div (3.0 \times 10^{19}) = \mathbf{8.0 \times 10^{-8}\ s^{-1}}$

Sometimes you might be given N in mols (p.107). Remember that 1 mol contains 6.02×10^{23} nuclei.

You can Model Radioactive Decay using a Spreadsheet

Radioactive decay is an **iterative** process (the number of nuclei that decay in one time period controls the number that are available to decay in the next). This means that you can use a **spreadsheet** to model how a sample of an isotope will decay if you know the **decay constant**, λ, and the **number of undecayed nuclei** in the initial sample, N_0:

1) Set up a spreadsheet with column headings for **total time (t)**, ΔN and N, and a data input cell for each of Δt and λ.
2) Decide on a Δt that you want to use — this is the **time interval** between the values of N that the spreadsheet will calculate. The most sensible time interval will depend on your decay constant.
3) You can then enter formulas into the spreadsheet to calculate the number of undecayed nuclei left in the sample after each time interval. You'll need to use $\Delta N = -\lambda \times N \times \Delta t$ (rearranged from the purple box above).

If you write the formulas properly, the spreadsheet can automatically fill them in for as many rows (iterations) as you want.

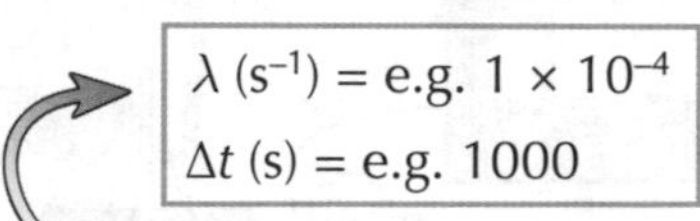

Be careful when you refer to these in your formulas – make sure the cell references don't change when you autofill in new rows (iterations).

t in s	ΔN (from equation above)	N
$t_0 = 0$		N_0 = initial number of nuclei in sample
$t_1 = t_0 + \Delta t$	$(\Delta N)_1 = -\lambda \times N_0 \times \Delta t$	$N_1 = N_0 + (\Delta N)_1$
$t_2 = t_1 + \Delta t$	$(\Delta N)_2 = -\lambda \times N_1 \times \Delta t$	$N_2 = N_1 + (\Delta N)_2$
$t_3 = ...$	$(\Delta N)_3 = ...$	$N_3 = ...$

4) If you plot a graph of the number of undecayed nuclei against time, it should look like this: (You may have to fiddle with your value for Δt to get a graph with a nice shape.) This is an **exponential** graph, and there's more about it coming up on the next few pages. (See p.190-191 for more on exponential functions.)

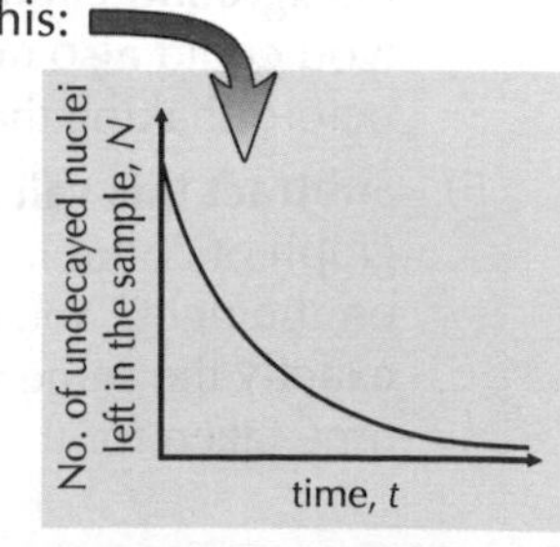

5) You can also simulate radioactive decay using **dice**. The dice represent undecayed nuclei and if they land on a particular number, say 6, they have 'decayed'. Record how many dice you start with (you'll need quite a few) and throw them all, removing any that 'decay', then throw the rest again. Your results of the number of dice remaining against time should show the same pattern.

Exponential Law of Decay

You Need to Learn the Definition of Half-Life

The **half-life** ($t_{1/2}$) of an **isotope** is the **average time** it takes for the **number of undecayed nuclei** to **halve.**

Measuring the **number of undecayed nuclei** isn't the easiest job in the world. **In practice**, half-life isn't measured by counting nuclei, but by measuring the **time it takes** the **activity** or **count rate** to **halve**.

The count rate is the number of decays detected per second (it's lower than the activity).

The **longer** the **half-life** of an isotope, the **longer** it stays **radioactive**.

The Number of Undecayed Nuclei Decreases Exponentially

You **can't** tell when any **one nucleus** is going to **decay**, but you can **predict** how many nuclei will decay in a given time period by generating a **graph** like the one on the previous page, shown again below.

You can use this **graph** to find the **half-life** of an isotope:

1) Read off the number of undecayed nuclei when $t = 0$.
2) Go to half the original value of N.
3) Draw a horizontal line to the curve, then a vertical line down to the x-axis.
4) The half-life is where this line meets the x-axis.
5) It's always a good idea to check your answer. Repeat steps 1-3 for a quarter of the original value of N, and divide the time where the line meets the x-axis by two. That will also give you the half-life. You can do the same for an eighth of the original value (divide the time by 3), and a sixteenth of the original value. Check that you get the same answer each way.

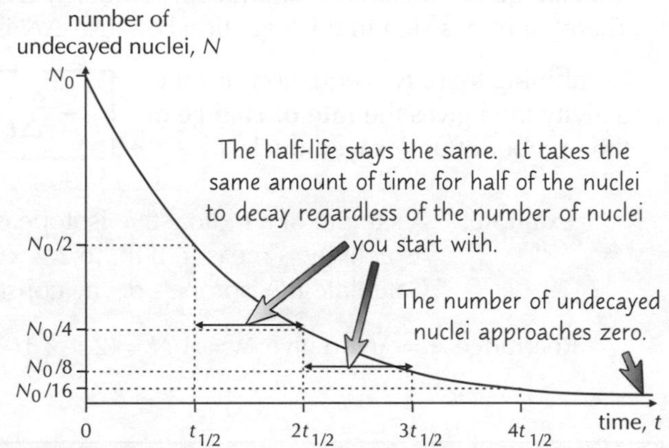

You can Generate a Count-Rate Decay Graph Experimentally

PRACTICAL SKILLS

You're most likely to do this using the isotope **protactinium-234**. Protactinium-234 is formed when **uranium** decays (via another isotope). You can measure protactinium-234's decay rate using a **protactinium generator** — a bottle containing a uranium salt, the decay products of uranium (including protactinium-234) and two solvents, which separate out into layers, like this:

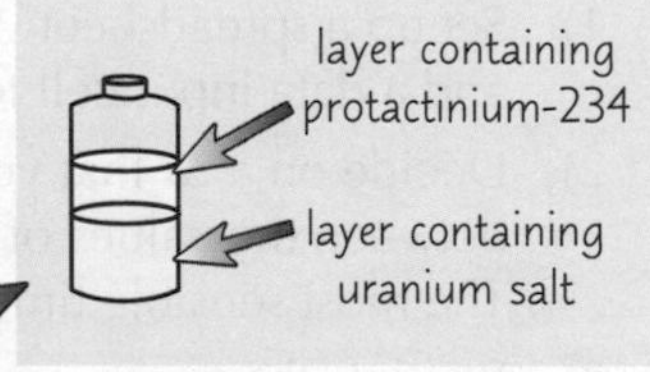

1) **Shake the bottle** to mix the solvents together, then add it to the equipment shown on the right.
2) Wait for the liquids to **separate**. The protactinium-234 will be in solution in the top layer, and the uranium salt will stay in the bottom layer. Then you can point the Geiger-Müller tube at the top layer to measure the activity of the protactinium-234.
3) As soon as the liquids separate, record the count rate (e.g. how many counts you get in 10 seconds). Re-measure the count rate at sensible intervals (e.g. every 30 seconds).
4) Once you've collected your data, leave the bottle to stand for at least ten minutes, then take the count rate again. This is the **background count rate** corresponding to background radiation (you could also do this at the beginning of the experiment, before shaking the bottle).
5) **Subtract this value** from your measured count rates, then plot a graph of count rate against time. It should look like the graph on the right. You can use this graph to find the **half-life** in exactly the same way as above. In this case the half-life is the time taken for the count rate (or activity) to halve.

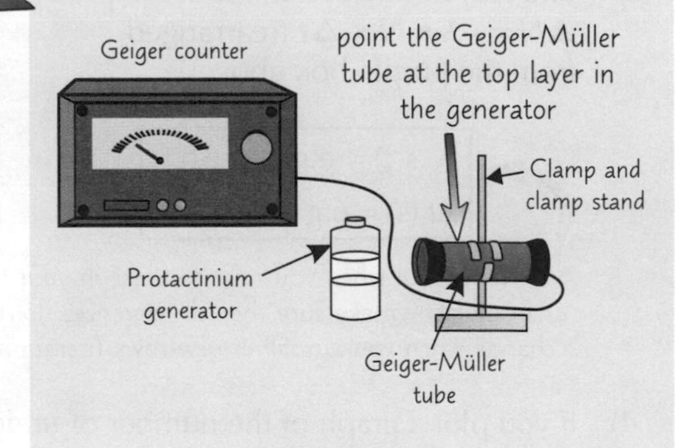

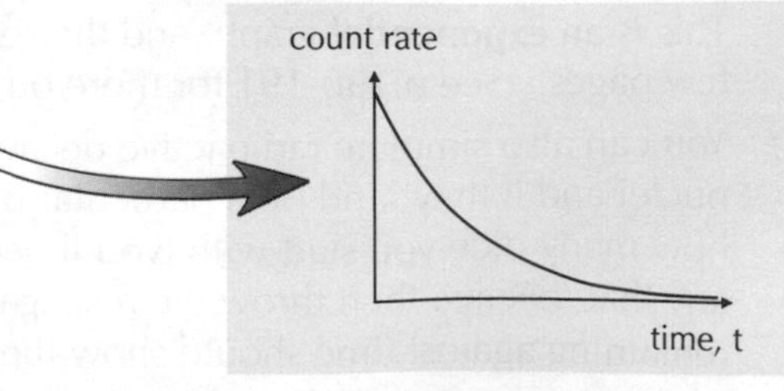

Exponential Law of Decay

You Need to Know the **Equations** for **Half-Life** and **Decay**

1) It won't surprise you to know that you can also calculate an isotope's **half-life** mathematically. The equation for calculating half-life is:

$$\lambda t_{1/2} = \ln 2$$

Where ln is the natural log (p.190), λ is the decay constant in s^{-1}, and $t_{1/2}$ is the half-life in seconds.

2) As you know, the **number of undecayed nuclei remaining**, N, depends on the **number originally present**, N_0, the **decay constant**, λ, and how much **time** has passed, t. There's an equation for this, too:

Here t = time, measured in seconds.

$$N = N_0 e^{-\lambda t}$$

This is the equation of the line generated from the spreadsheet on page 173.

3) Finally, there's an equation for how a sample's **activity** goes down as it decays:

$$A = A_0 e^{-\lambda t}$$

A is the activity at time t, and A_0 is the initial activity (at t = 0 s). Both are measured in Bq.

Radioactive Isotopes can be used to **Date Objects**

The radioactive isotope **carbon-14** is used in **radioactive dating**:

1) Living plants take in carbon dioxide from the atmosphere as part of **photosynthesis**, including the **radioactive isotope carbon-14**. Animals then take this carbon-14 in when they eat the plants. All living things contain the **same percentage** of carbon-14.
2) When they die, the **activity** of carbon-14 in the plant starts to **fall**, with a **half-life** of around **5730 years**.
3) Archaeological finds made from once-living material (like wood) can be tested to find the **current amount** of carbon-14 in them. This can be used to calculate how long the material has been dead for — i.e. how old it is.

According to the latest scientific techniques, Ron's moustache dated back to the early 1980s.

Warm-Up Questions

Q1 Define radioactive activity. Write down an equation relating activity and the number of undecayed nuclei.

Q2 Describe how you could model radioactive decay using a spreadsheet (and if you have a computer handy, have a go at doing it for a sample of 200 000 nuclei with a decay constant of 0.002 s^{-1}).

Q3 Describe how dice could be used to simulate radioactive decay.

Q4 Sketch a general radioactive decay graph showing the activity against time and write an equation for the relationship.

Q5 Define the term 'half life'. Describe an experiment to measure the half-life of protactinium-234.

Q6 Explain how radioactive dating works.

PRACTICE QUESTIONS

Exam Question

Q1 A scientist takes a reading of 750 Bq from a pure radioactive source. The radioactive source initially contains 50 000 undecayed nuclei, and background activity in the lab is measured as 50 Bq.

a) Calculate the decay constant for the sample. [2 marks]

b) Calculate the half-life of the sample. [1 mark]

c) Calculate how many undecayed nuclei of the radioactive source will be left after 300 seconds. [1 mark]

Radioactivity is a random process — just like revision shouldn't be...

Remember the shape of that graph — whether it's count rate, activity or number of nuclei plotted against time, the shape's always the same. The maths is a bit of a pain, but I think the experiment's pretty good. Protactinium generator, sounds like something out of a film that's on at 2 o'clock in the morning...

Binding Energy

Turn off the radio and close the door, 'cos you're going to need to concentrate hard on this stuff about binding energy...

The **Mass Defect** is **Equivalent** to the **Binding Energy**

1) The **mass** of a **nucleus** is **less than** the mass of its **constituent parts** — the difference is called the **mass defect**. Mass and energy are **equivalent**, according to Einstein's equation: $\Delta E = \Delta mc^2$

ΔE is the energy released in J
Δm is the mass defect in kg
c is the speed of light in a vacuum

2) As nucleons join together, the total mass **decreases** — this **'lost'** mass is **converted** into energy and **released**. You can calculate this energy using the equation above.
3) The amount of **energy released** is **equivalent** to the **mass defect**.
4) If you **pulled** the nucleus completely **apart**, the **energy** you'd have to use to do it would be the **same** as the energy **released** when the nucleus formed.

The energy needed to **separate** all of the nucleons in a nucleus is called the **binding energy** (measured in **MeV**), and it is **equivalent** to the **mass defect**.

Atomic mass is usually given in atomic mass units (u), where $1\text{ u} = 1.661 \times 10^{-27}$ kg.

Example: Calculate the binding energy of the nucleus of a lithium atom, ${}^{6}_{3}\text{Li}$, given that its mass defect is 0.0343 u.

1) Convert the mass defect into kg: Mass defect $= 0.0343 \times (1.661 \times 10^{-27}) = 5.69723 \times 10^{-29}$ kg
2) Use $\Delta E = \Delta mc^2$ to calculate the binding energy: $\Delta E = (5.69723 \times 10^{-29}) \times (3.00 \times 10^8)^2 = 5.127507 \times 10^{-12}$ J
3) Convert your answer into electron volts: $5.127507 \times 10^{-12} \div 1.60 \times 10^{-19} = 32046918.75$ eV
$= \mathbf{32.0\ MeV\ (to\ 3\ s.f.)}$

$1\text{ eV} = 1.60 \times 10^{-19}$ J (p.94)

5) The **binding energy per unit of mass defect** can also be calculated. Using the example above:
$$\frac{\textbf{binding energy}}{\textbf{mass defect}} = \frac{32\text{ MeV}}{0.0343\text{ u}} \approx \mathbf{930\ MeV\,u^{-1}}\ \textbf{(to 2 s.f.)}$$
6) This means that a mass defect of **1 u** is equivalent to about **930 MeV** (to 2 s.f.) of binding energy.

The **Binding Energy Per Nucleon** is at a **Maximum** around $A = 50$

A useful way of **comparing** the binding energies of different nuclei is to look at the **binding energy per nucleon**.

$$\textbf{Binding energy per nucleon (in MeV)} = \frac{\textbf{Binding energy } (B)}{\textbf{Nucleon number } (A)}$$

So, the binding energy per nucleon for ${}^{6}_{3}\text{Li}$ (in the example above) is $32 \div 6 = 5.3$ MeV.

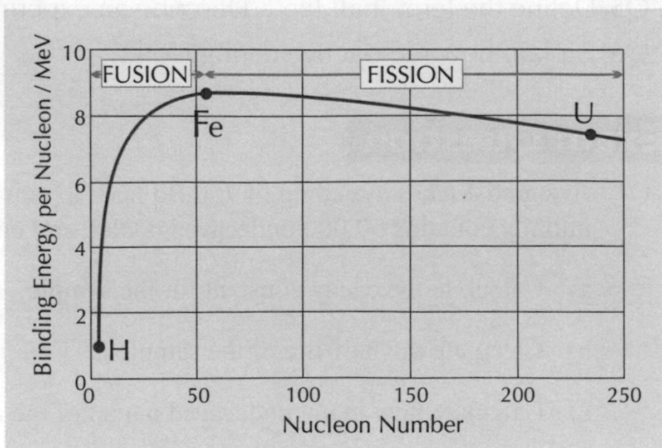

1) If you plot a **graph** of **binding energy per nucleon** against **nucleon number**, for all elements, the line of best fit shows a **curve**. A **high** binding energy per nucleon means that **more energy** is needed to **remove** nucleons from the nucleus.
2) In other words the **most stable** nuclei occur around the **maximum point** on the graph — which is at **nucleon number 56** (i.e. **iron**, Fe).
3) **Combining small nuclei** is called nuclear **fusion** (p.179) — this **increases** the **binding energy per nucleon** dramatically, which means a lot of **energy is released** during nuclear fusion.
4) **Fission** is when **large nuclei** are **split in two** (see p.178) — the **nucleon numbers** of the two **new nuclei** are **smaller** than the original nucleus, which means there is an **increase** in the binding energy per nucleon. So, energy is also **released** during nuclear fission (but not as much energy per nucleon as in nuclear fusion).

Binding Energy

The Change in Binding Energy Gives the Energy Released

The **binding energy per nucleon graph** can be used to **estimate** the **energy released** from nuclear reactions.

Energy released in **nuclear fusion**

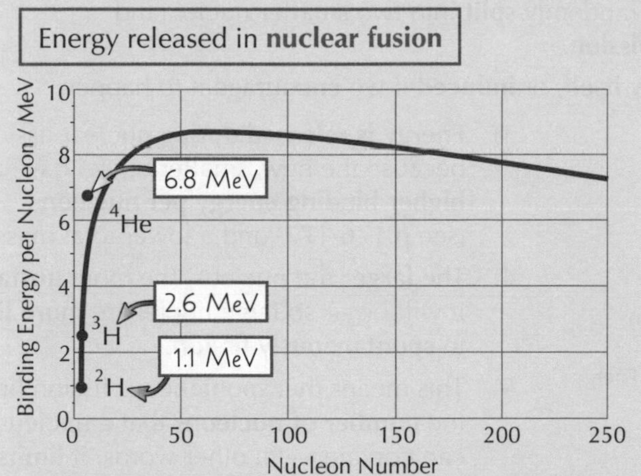

If ^{2}**H** and ^{3}**H** nuclei **fuse** together to form ^{4}**He** (and a neutron):

1) The binding energy before the fusion is:
binding energy ^{2}**H** + binding energy ^{3}**H**
= (2 × 1.1) + (3 × 2.6) = **10.0 MeV**
2) The binding energy after the fusion is:
binding energy ^{4}**He** = 4 × 6.8 = **27.2 MeV**
3) So the **energy released** is:
27.2 – 10.0 = 17.2 = **17 MeV (to 2 s.f.)**

Energy released in **nuclear fission**

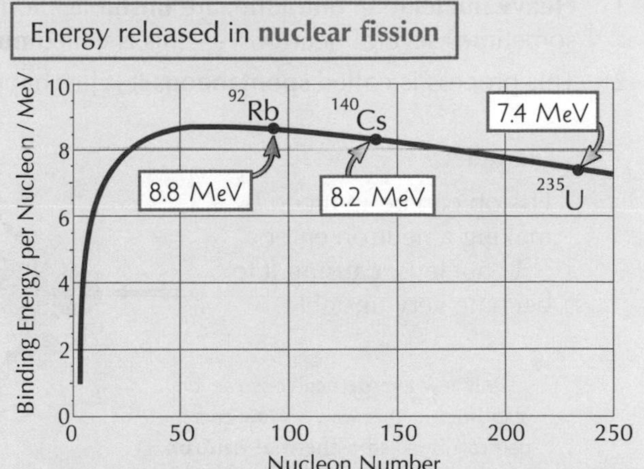

If a ^{235}U nucleus **splits** into ^{92}**Rb** and ^{140}**Cs** (plus a few neutrons) during nuclear **fission**:

1) The binding energy **before** the fission is:
binding energy ^{235}**U** = 235 × 7.4 = **1739 MeV**
2) The binding energy **after** the fission is:
binding energy ^{92}**Rb** + binding energy ^{140}**Cs**
= (92 × 8.8) + (140 × 8.2) = **1957.6 MeV**
3) So the **energy released** is:
1957.6 – 1739 = 218.6
= **220 MeV (to 2 s.f.)**

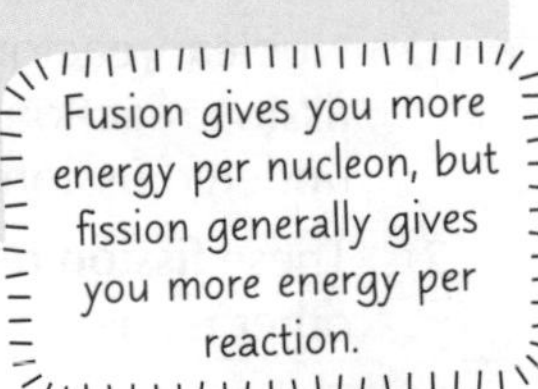

Warm-Up Questions

Q1 What is the binding energy of a nucleus?
Q2 How can you calculate the binding energy for a particular nucleus?
Q3 Sketch a graph of binding energy per nucleon against nucleon number, labelling the regions where fusion and fission occur and the element with the highest binding energy per nucleon.
Q4 Do nuclear fusion or fission reactions release more energy per nucleon?

Exam Questions

Q1 The mass of a $^{14}_{6}$C nucleus is 13.999948 u.
The mass of a proton is 1.007276 u, and the mass of a neutron is 1.008665 u.

a) Calculate the mass defect of a $^{14}_{6}$C nucleus. Give your answer in atomic mass units. [2 marks]

b) Calculate the binding energy of the nucleus in MeV. [3 marks]

Q2 The following equation shows a nuclear reaction between two deuterium ($^{2}_{1}$H) nuclei, to form helium-3 ($^{3}_{2}$He):

$$^{2}_{1}\text{H} + ^{2}_{1}\text{H} \rightarrow ^{3}_{2}\text{He} + ^{1}_{0}\text{n} + \text{energy}$$

a) State what type of nuclear reaction this is. [1 mark]

b) The binding energy per nucleon is 0 MeV for a neutron, approximately 1.11 MeV for a $^{2}_{1}$H nucleus, and approximately 2.58 MeV for a $^{3}_{2}$He nucleus.
Use these values to calculate the energy released by this reaction. [3 marks]

Don't tie yourself up in knots...

This stuff is a bit of a headache — the idea of a particle having a smaller mass than the particles inside it confuses me no end — but you need to know it. You know the drill by now, back to the top of page 176, and read it all again...

Nuclear Fission and Fusion

What did the nuclear scientist have for his tea? Fission chips... hohoho.

Fission Means **Splitting Up** into **Smaller Parts**

1) **Heavy nuclei** (e.g. uranium), are **unstable**. Some can randomly **split** into two **smaller** nuclei (and sometimes several neutrons) — this is called **nuclear fission**.
2) This process is called **spontaneous** if it just happens **by itself**, or **induced** if we **encourage** it to happen.

Example:

Fission can be induced by making a neutron enter a ^{235}U nucleus, causing it to become very unstable.

$^{1}_{0}n$ → $^{235}_{92}U$ → fission → $^{92}_{36}Kr$ + $^{141}_{56}Ba$ + $^{1}_{0}n$ + $^{1}_{0}n$ + $^{1}_{0}n$ + Energy

Only low energy neutrons can be captured in this way. A low energy neutron is called a **thermal neutron**.

3) **Energy is released** during nuclear fission because the new, smaller nuclei have a **higher binding energy per nucleon** (see p.176-177) and a lower total mass.
4) The **larger** the nucleus, the more **unstable** it will be — so large nuclei are **more likely** to **spontaneously fission**.
5) This means that spontaneous fission **limits** the **number of nucleons** that a nucleus can contain — in other words, it **limits** the number of **possible elements**.

Controlled **Nuclear Reactors** Produce Useful **Power**

We can **harness** the **energy** released during nuclear **fission reactions** in a **nuclear reactor**, but it's important that these reactions are very **carefully controlled**.

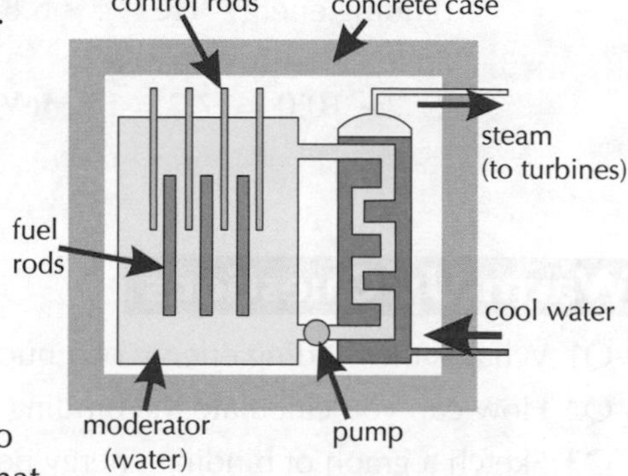

1) Nuclear reactors use **rods of uranium** that are rich in ^{235}**U** as '**fuel**' for fission reactions. (The rods also contain a lot of ^{238}**U**, but that doesn't undergo fission.)
2) These **fission** reactions produce more **neutrons** which then **induce** other nuclei to fission — this is called a **chain reaction**.
3) The **neutrons** will only cause a chain reaction if they are **slowed down**, which allows them to be **captured** by the uranium nuclei — these slowed down neutrons are called **thermal neutrons**.
4) ^{235}U **fuel rods** need to be placed in a **moderator** (for example, **water**) to **slow down** and/or absorb **neutrons**. You need to choose a moderator that will slow down some neutrons enough so they can cause **further fission**, keeping the reaction going at a steady rate.
5) You want the chain reaction to continue on its own at a **steady rate**, where **one** fission follows another. The amount of 'fuel' you need to do this is called the **critical mass** — any less than the critical mass (**sub-critical mass**) and the reaction will just peter out. Nuclear reactors use a **supercritical** mass of fuel (where several new fissions normally follow each fission) and **control the rate of fission** using **control rods**.
6) Control rods control the **chain reaction** by **limiting** the number of **neutrons** in the reactor. They **absorb neutrons** so that the **rate of fission** is controlled. **Control rods** are made up of a material that **absorbs neutrons** (e.g. boron), and they can be inserted by varying amounts to control the reaction rate.
In an **emergency**, the reactor will be **shut down** automatically by the **release of the control rods** into the reactor, which will stop the reaction as quickly as possible.
7) **Coolant** is sent around the reactor to **remove heat** produced in the fission — often the coolant is the **same water** that is being used in the reactor as a **moderator**. The **heat** from the reactor can then be used to make **steam** for powering **electricity-generating turbines**.

If the chain reaction in a nuclear reactor is **left to continue unchecked**, large amounts of **energy** are **released** in a very **short time**.
Many new fissions will follow each fission, causing a **runaway reaction** which could lead to an **explosion**. This is what happens in a **fission (atomic) bomb**.

Nuclear Fission and Fusion

There are **Costs** and **Benefits** to **Nuclear Fission Power Plants**

1) Deciding whether or not to build a **nuclear power station** (and if so, **where** to build it) is a tricky business.
2) Nuclear fission doesn't produce carbon dioxide, unlike burning **fossil fuels**, so it doesn't contribute to **global warming** (p.69). It also provides a **continuous energy supply**, unlike many renewable sources (e.g. wind/solar).
3) However, some of the **waste products** of **nuclear fission** are **highly radioactive** and difficult to handle and store.
4) When material is removed from the reactor, it is initially **very hot**, so it is placed in **cooling ponds** until the **temperature falls** to a safe level. The radioactive waste is then **stored** in **sealed containers** in specialist facilities until its **activity has fallen** sufficiently. This can take **many years**, and there's a risk that material could escape from these containers. A leak of radioactive material could be **harmful** to the environment and local human populations both now and in the future, particularly if the material contaminated **water supplies**.
5) **Accidents** or **natural disasters** pose a risk to nuclear reactors. In 2011 an earthquake and subsequent tsunami in Japan caused a meltdown at the Fukushima nuclear power plant. Over **100 000 people** were evacuated from the area, and many tonnes of contaminated water leaked into the sea. The **perceived risk** of this kind of disaster leads many people to oppose the construction of nuclear power plants near their homes.
6) Because of all of the necessary safety precautions, **building** and **decommissioning** nuclear power plants is very **time-consuming** and **expensive**.

Fusion Means **Joining Nuclei** Together

1) **Two light nuclei** can **combine** to create a larger nucleus. This is called **nuclear fusion.**
2) Nuclei can **only fuse** if they have enough energy to overcome the **electrostatic** (Coulomb) **repulsion** between them (p.146), and get close enough for the **strong interaction** to bind them.
3) This means fusion reactions require **much higher temperatures** than fission, as well as high pressures (or high densities). Under such conditions, generally only found inside stars, matter turns into a state called a **plasma**.
4) A lot of **energy** is released during nuclear fusion because the new, heavier nucleus has a **much higher binding energy per nucleon** (and so a lower total mass, see p.176). The energy released helps to **maintain the high temperatures** needed for further fusion reactions.
5) Although the energy released per reaction is generally **lower** in nuclear fusion than fission (see p.177), the nuclei used in fusion have a **lower mass**, so a mole of the reactants in a fusion reaction weighs less than a mole of the reactants in a fission reaction (p.107). Gram for gram, fusion can release **more energy** than fission.
6) Scientists are trying to develop fusion reactors so that we can generate nuclear **electricity** without the waste you get from fission reactors, but they haven't yet succeeded in creating one that makes more electricity than it uses.

Example: In the Sun, **hydrogen nuclei** fuse to form **helium**:

$$^2_1H + ^1_1H \rightarrow ^3_2He + energy$$

Nuclear fission and fusion equations need to be balanced, see p.171.

Warm-Up Questions

Q1 What is meant by the term 'induced fission'?

Q2 Explain what is meant by the expressions 'chain reaction', 'fuel rods' and 'moderator' in terms of nuclear fission.

Q3 What are the similarities and differences between nuclear fusion and fission?

Exam Questions

PRACTICE QUESTIONS

Q1 Nuclear reactors use carefully controlled chain reactions to produce energy.

a) Describe and explain one feature of a nuclear reactor whose role is to control the rate of fission. Include an example of a suitable material for the feature you have chosen. [3 marks]

b) Explain what happens in a nuclear reactor during an emergency shut-down. [2 marks]

Q2 Discuss two advantages and two disadvantages of using nuclear fission to produce electricity. [4 marks]

If anyone asks, I've gone fission... that joke never gets old...

So, controlled nuclear fission reactions can provide a shedload of energy to generate electricity without producing pesky carbon dioxide, but nuclear energy has costs and risks too... Nothing's ever simple, is it?

X-Ray Imaging

X-ray imaging is one kind of non-invasive diagnostic technique — these techniques let doctors see what's going on (or going wrong) inside your body, without having to open you up and have a look.

X-rays are Produced by Bombarding Tungsten with High Energy Electrons

X-ray tubes are an electrical circuit, with a **cathode** (where electrons are emitted) and an **anode** (the target metal).

1) At the **cathode**, electrons are **emitted** (boiled off) by the **hot filament**.
2) This filament is **heated** by passing a **current** through it. This current is **not** the same as the current going through the **entire X-ray tube**.
3) The cathode is usually in a **cup shape**, to **focus** the **beam** of electrons onto the **target metal**.
4) The **target metal** (tungsten) acts as the **anode** of the circuit, and the **high potential difference** across the tube (**tube voltage**) causes the electrons to **accelerate** towards it.

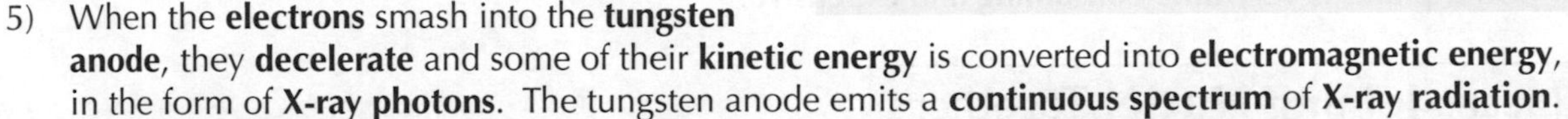

5) When the **electrons** smash into the **tungsten anode**, they **decelerate** and some of their **kinetic energy** is converted into **electromagnetic energy**, in the form of **X-ray photons**. The tungsten anode emits a **continuous spectrum** of **X-ray radiation**.
6) The **maximum energy** of the X-ray photons is equal to the **potential difference** of the X-ray tube multiplied by the **charge** of an electron. So, if a potential difference of 50 kV is used in the tube, the maximum X-ray energy will be 50 keV.
7) Only about **1%** of the electrons' **kinetic energy** is converted into **X-rays**. The rest is converted into **heat**, so, to avoid overheating, the tungsten anode is **rotated** at about 3000 rpm. It's also **mounted** on **copper** — this **conducts** the heat away effectively.

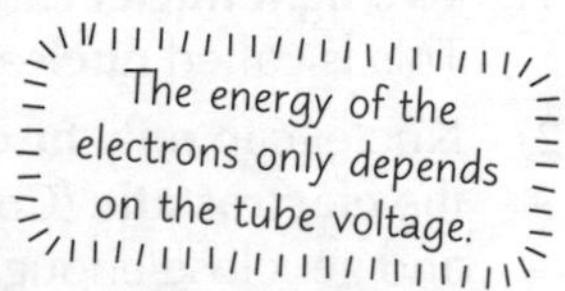

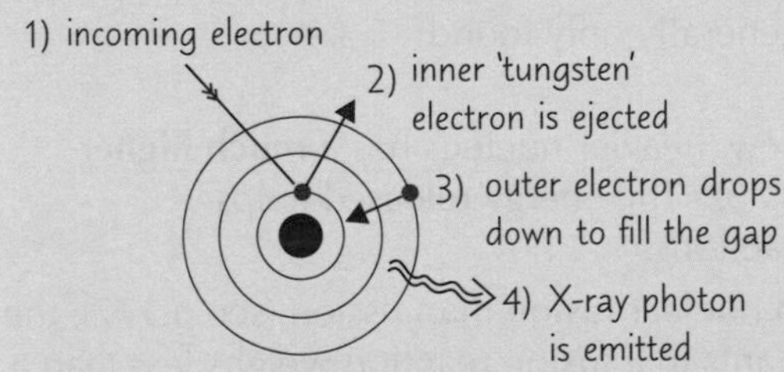

- X-rays are also produced when beam electrons **knock out** other electrons from the **inner shells** of the **tungsten atoms.**
- Electrons in the atoms' **outer shells** move into the **vacancies** in the **lower energy levels**, and **release energy** in the form of **X-ray photons.**

Example: An electron hitting an anode in an X-ray tube produces maximum energy X-rays with a wavelength of 5.0×10^{-11} m. The tube voltage is halved but all other factors are kept the same. Calculate the new wavelength of the maximum energy X-rays.

The maximum energy of the electrons is $E = e \times V$, so halving the voltage would halve the maximum energy of the electrons and hence halve the maximum energy of the X-ray photons.

Since the energy of a photon = $E = \frac{hc}{\lambda}$, halving the energy would double the minimum wavelength.

So the new wavelength is $2 \times 5.0 \times 10^{-11} = \mathbf{1.0 \times 10^{-10}}$ **m.**

There's more about photon energies on p.94.

Beam Intensity is Power per Unit Area

The **intensity** of the X-ray beam is the **power** (energy per second) **per unit area** passing through a surface (at right angles). There are two ways to increase the **intensity** of the X-ray beam:

1) Increase the **tube voltage**. This gives the electrons **more kinetic energy**. Higher energy electrons can **knock out** electrons from shells **deeper** within the tungsten atoms.
2) Increase the **current** supplied to the filament. As the current increases, the **filament temperature** rises. This liberates **more electrons per second** (with the **same final energy per electron** as before), which then produce **more X-ray photons per second**.

Charlotte thought landing on her head would get top marks for beam intensity.

X-Ray Imaging

X-rays are Attenuated when they Pass Through Matter

When X-rays pass through matter (e.g. a patient's body), they are **absorbed** and **scattered**. The intensity (***I***) of the X-ray beam **decreases** (attenuates) **exponentially** with **distance from** the **surface** (*x*), according to the material's attenuation (absorption) coefficient (μ), as the equation on the right shows.

$$I = I_0 e^{-\mu x}$$

Where I_0 is the initial intensity (usually measured in Wm^{-2}), μ has units cm^{-1}, and x is measured in cm.

X-rays are Absorbed More by Bone than Soft Tissue

X-rays are **attenuated** by **absorption** and **scattering**. **Three causes** of this are:

1) The **photoelectric effect** — a **photon** with around **30 keV** of energy is absorbed by an **electron**, which is **ejected** from its atom. The gap in the **electron shell** is filled by another **electron**, which emits a **photon**.
2) **Compton scattering** — a **photon** with around **0.5-5 MeV** of energy knocks an **electron** out of an **atom**, which causes the **photon** to **lose energy** and be **scattered**.
3) **Pair production** — a **high** (> 1.1 MeV) **energy** photon **decays** into an **electron** and a **positron**.

How much **energy is absorbed** by a **material** depends on its **atomic number** — so tissues containing atoms with **different atomic numbers** (e.g. **soft tissue** and **bone**) will **contrast** in the X-ray image.

If the tissues in the region of interest have similar attenuation coefficients then artificial **contrast media** can be used — e.g. **barium meal** or **iodine**. These have **high atomic numbers**, so they show up clearly in X-ray images and can be followed as they move through a patient's body.

CAT Scans use X-rays

1) **Computerised axial tomography** (CT or CAT) scans produce an image of a **two-dimensional slice** through the body.
2) The patient lies on a table, which slides in and out of a **ring**. This ring is made up of **detectors** and a rotating **X-ray beam**.
3) The **X-ray beam fans out** and **rotates** around the body. It is picked up by the **detectors**. A computer works out how much **attenuation** has been caused by each part of the body and produces a **high quality** image.
4) CAT scans produce **more detailed** images than regular X-rays, especially for **soft tissue**. The data can also be manipulated to generate a **3D image**.

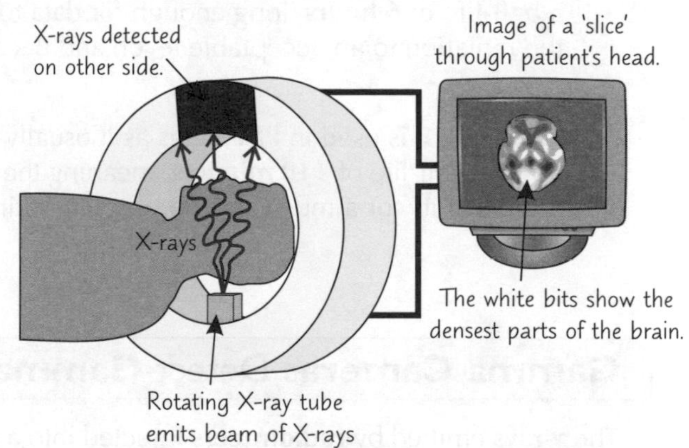

Warm-Up Questions

PRACTICE QUESTIONS

Q1 Draw a diagram of an X-ray tube and describe the function of the cathode, filament and target metal.

Q2 State two ways to increase the beam intensity of the electron beam in an X-ray tube.

Q3 State three mechanisms which cause X-ray attenuation.

Q4 State the reasons for using an artificial contrast medium when taking an X-ray image of a patient's digestive tract.

Q5 Draw a diagram of a CAT scanner and describe how it works. Give an advantage over using X-ray scans.

Exam Questions

Q1 X-rays hit a lead block with an intensity of 200 Wm^{-2}. Lead has a linear attenuation coefficient of 27 cm^{-1}. Calculate the intensity of the X-rays 15 mm into the lead block. [1 mark]

Q2 An X-ray tube has a tube voltage of 40 kV. The tube voltage is then changed so the wavelength of the maximum energy X-ray photons emitted by the tube is a third of its original value. Calculate the new tube voltage. [2 marks]

There's more than just the bare bones of X-ray imaging here...

X-ray images are just shadow pictures — bones absorb X-rays, stop them reaching the film and create a white 'shadow'.

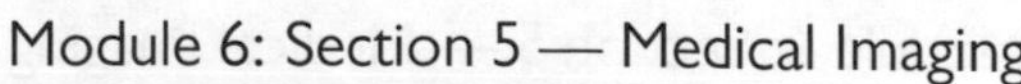

Medical Uses of Nuclear Radiation

Radiation can be incredibly useful in medicine, but any use of radiation carries some risk.

Medical Tracers are Used to **Diagnose** the **Function of Organs**

1) **Medical tracers** are **radioactive substances** that are used to show tissue or **organ function**. Other types of imaging, **e.g. X-rays**, only show the **structure** of organs — medical tracers show **structure and function.**
2) **Medical tracers** usually consist of a **radioactive isotope** — e.g. **technetium-99m** or **fluorine-18** — bound to a **substance** that is **used** by the **body** — e.g. **glucose** or **water**.
3) The tracer is **injected** into or **swallowed** by the patient and then **moves** through the **body** to the region of interest. **Where** the tracer goes depends on the **substance** the isotope is bound to — i.e. it goes anywhere that the substance would **normally go**, and is used how that substance is **normally used.**
4) The **radiation emitted** is **recorded** (e.g. by a **gamma camera** or **PET scanner** — see below and next page) and an **image** of inside the patient produced.

- Tracers can show areas of **damaged tissue** in the heart by detecting areas of **decreased blood flow**. This can reveal **coronary artery disease** and damaged or dead heart muscle caused by **heart attacks.**
- They can identify **active cancer tumours** by showing **metabolic activity** in tissue. **Cancer cells** have a **much higher metabolism** than healthy cells because they're growing fast, so take up more tracer.
- Tracers can show **blood flow and activity** in the **brain**. This helps **research** and **treat** neurological conditions like Parkinson's, Alzheimer's, epilepsy, depression, etc.

Technetium-99m is widely used in medical tracers because it emits **γ-radiation**, has a **half-life of 6 hours** (long enough for data to be recorded, but short enough to limit the radiation to an acceptable level) and **decays** to a **much more stable isotope**.

Fluorine-18 is used in **PET scans** as it usually undergoes **beta plus** decay. It has a half-life of **110 minutes**, meaning the patient is exposed to radioactivity for a much **shorter** amount of time than with **technetium-99m.**

Gamma Cameras Detect **Gamma Radiation**

The **γ-rays** emitted by **radiotracers** injected into a patient's body are detected using a **gamma camera**. **Gamma cameras** (like the one shown **below**) consist of **five** main parts:

1) **Lead shield** — **stops radiation** from **other sources** entering the camera.
2) **Lead collimator** — a **piece of lead** with thousands of **vertical holes** in it — only γ-rays **parallel** to the holes can **pass through**.
3) **Sodium iodide crystal** — emits a **flash of light** (**scintillates**) whenever a **γ-ray** hits it.
4) **Photomultiplier tubes** — **detect** the flashes of **light** from the crystal and turn them into **pulses of electricity**.
5) **Electronic circuit** — **collects** the **signals** from the photomultiplier tubes and sends them to a **computer** for processing into an **image** which is used to help the doctor **diagnose** the patient.

Gamma cameras are useful in helping to **diagnose** patients without the need for **surgery**.
They are **cheaper** than a PET scanner but are still fairly **expensive**.
They also use **ionising radiation** which is bad for you — see the next page.

Medical Uses of Nuclear Radiation

PET Scanning Involves Positron/Electron **Annihilation**

1) In a PET (**positron emission tomography**) scan, the patient is injected with a substance used by the body, e.g. glucose, containing a **positron-emitting** radiotracer with a **short half-life**, e.g. ^{13}N, ^{15}O, ^{18}F.
2) The patient is left for a time to allow the radiotracer to **move through the body** to the organs.
3) **Positrons** emitted by the radioisotope collide with **electrons** in the organs, causing them to **annihilate**, emitting **high-energy gamma rays** in the process.
4) **Detectors** around the body record these **gamma rays**, and a computer builds up a **map of the radioactivity** in the body.
5) The **distribution of radioactivity** matches up with **metabolic activity**. This is because **more** of the radioactive glucose (or whatever) injected into the patient is taken up and **used** by cells that are **doing more work** (cells with an **increased metabolism**, in other words).
6) By looking at which **cells** are doing more **work**, doctors can help **diagnose** illnesses in patients — like detecting the **higher activity** of cancer cells, p.182. PET scanners allow patients to be diagnosed without having to have **surgery** and the **radiotracers** used have a **short half-life** so the patient is **exposed** to radiation for only a **short time**.
7) However, this short time period means there is only a **limited** time when a patient can be scanned — unlike with gamma cameras, where the tracer takes much longer to decay.
PET scanners are also incredibly **expensive**, meaning not many hospitals own one. This means some doctors may have to make **difficult decisions** about whether a patient should be sent for a PET scan.

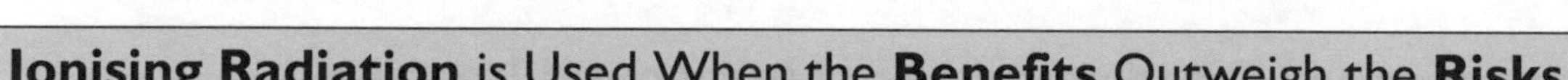

Ionising Radiation is Used When the **Benefits** Outweigh the **Risks**

X-rays, **γ-rays**, and α and β **particles** are all classed as **ionising radiation**. When they **interact** with matter they **ionise atoms** or **molecules** to form **ions** — usually by **removing an electron** — and this can **damage** cells. Cell damage is bad news — it can cause:

1) **Cell mutations** and **cancerous tumours** by altering or damaging the cell's DNA.
2) **Cell sterility** by stopping the cell from reproducing.
3) **Cell death** — the cell is destroyed completely.

The **macroscopic effects** of ionising radiation (i.e. the large-scale effects) include **tumours**, **skin burns**, **sterility**, **radiation sickness**, **hair loss** and **death** — nice. The result is that radiation is only used when the **benefits** to the patient **outweigh** the **risks** — i.e. **radiation** doses are **limited** and only used when it's **absolutely necessary**.

Warm-Up Questions

Q1 Why are medical tracers useful?
Q2 What are the five main parts of a gamma camera?
Q3 Describe how an image is formed in PET scanning.
Q4 What are the drawbacks of using medical tracers?

Exam Question

Q1 A doctor suspects that his patient has a cancerous tumour.
Describe a non-invasive technique that could be used to confirm the doctor's diagnosis, giving one advantage and one disadvantage of this method. [4 marks]

The biological effects of a page on radiation — a sore head...
The radiation emitted by medical tracers is used to help diagnose patients without sending them for exploratory surgery.

Ultrasound Imaging

Ultrasound is a 'sound' with higher frequencies than we can hear.

Ultrasound has a **Higher Frequency** than **Humans** can **Hear**

1) Ultrasound waves are **longitudinal** waves with **higher frequencies** than humans can hear (>20 000 Hz).
2) For **medical** purposes, frequencies are usually from **1** to **15 MHz**.
3) When an ultrasound wave meets a **boundary** between two **different materials**, some of it is **reflected** and some of it passes through (undergoing **refraction** if the **angle of incidence** is **not 90°**).
4) The **reflected waves** are detected by the **ultrasound scanner** and are used to **generate an image**.

The Amount of **Reflection** depends on the Change in **Acoustic Impedance**

1) The **acoustic impedance**, Z, of a medium is defined as: $Z = \rho c$ where ρ is the density of the material and c is the speed of sound in that material
Z has units of kgm^{-2}s^{-1}.
2) Say an ultrasound wave travels through a material with an impedance Z_1. It hits the boundary between this material and another with an impedance Z_2. The incident wave has an intensity of I_0.
3) If the two materials have a **large difference** in **impedance**, then **most** of the energy is **reflected** (the intensity of the reflected wave I_r will be high). If the impedance of the two materials is the **same** then there is **no reflection**.
4) The **fraction** of wave **intensity** that is reflected is given by: $$\frac{I_r}{I_0} = \frac{(Z_2 - Z_1)^2}{(Z_2 + Z_1)^2}$$

You don't need to learn this equation. Just practise using it.

There are **Advantages** and **Disadvantages** to **Ultrasound Imaging**

ADVANTAGES:
1) There are **no** known **hazards** — in particular, **no** exposure to **ionising radiation.**
2) It's good for imaging **soft tissues**, since you can obtain **real-time** images.
3) Ultrasound devices are relatively **cheap** and **portable.**
4) The scan is a **quick procedure** (10-15 minutes) and the patient **can move** during the scan.

DISADVANTAGES:
1) Ultrasound **doesn't penetrate bone** — so it **can't** be used to **detect fractures** or examine the **brain.**
2) Ultrasound **cannot** pass through **air spaces** in the body (due to the **mismatch** in **impedance**) — so it can't produce images from behind the lungs.
3) It **can't** give detail on **solid masses.**
4) Ultrasound **can't** give information about any **solid masses found.**

Ultrasound Images are **Produced** Using the **Piezoelectric Effect**

1) **Piezoelectric crystals** produce a **potential difference** when they are **deformed** (squashed or stretched) — the rearrangement in structure displaces the **centres of symmetry** of their electric **charges.**
2) When you **apply a p.d.** across a piezoelectric crystal, the crystal **deforms**. If the p.d. is **alternating**, then the crystal **vibrates** at the **same frequency**.
3) A piezoelectric crystal can act as a **receiver** of **ultrasound**, converting **sound waves** into **alternating voltages**, and also as a **transmitter**, converting **alternating voltages** into **sound waves.**
4) Ultrasound transducers use **lead zirconate titanate** (**PZT**) crystals. The **thickness** of the crystal is **half the wavelength** of the ultrasound that it produces. Ultrasound of this frequency will make the crystal **resonate** (see p.118) and produce a large signal.
5) The PZT crystal is **heavily damped**, to produce **short pulses** and **increase** the **resolution** of the device.

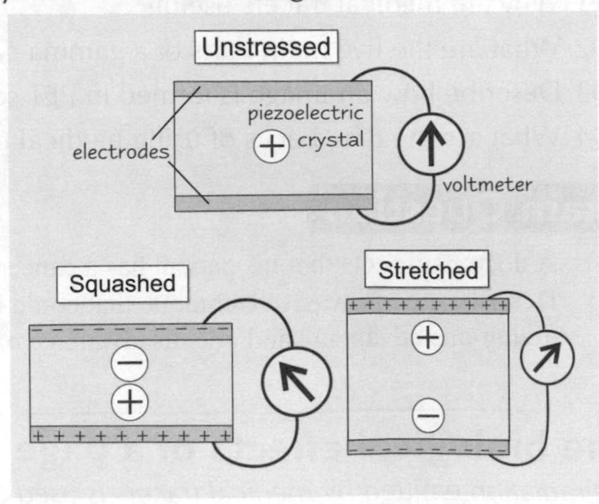

Ultrasound Imaging

You need a Coupling Medium between the Transducer and the Body

1) **Soft tissue** has a very different **acoustic impedance** from **air**, so almost all the ultrasound **energy** is **reflected** from the surface of the body if there is air between the **transducer** and the **body**.
2) To avoid this, you need a **coupling medium** (usually a **gel**) between the transducer and the body — this **displaces** the **air** and has an impedance much closer to that of body tissue.
The use of **coupling media** is an example of **impedance matching**.

The A-Scan is a Range Measuring System

1) The **amplitude scan** (**A-Scan**) sends a short **pulse** of ultrasound into the body simultaneously with an **electron beam** sweeping across a cathode ray oscilloscope (**CRO**) screen.
2) The scanner receives **reflected** ultrasound pulses that appear as **vertical deflections** on the CRO screen. **Weaker** pulses (that have travelled further in the body and **arrive later**) are **amplified** more to avoid the loss of valuable data — this process is called **time-gain compensation** (**TGC**).
3) The **horizontal positions** of the reflected pulses indicate the **time** the 'echo' took to return, and are used to work out **distances** between structures in the body (e.g. the **diameter** of a **baby's head** in the uterus).
4) A **stream** of pulses can produce a **steady image** on the screen, although modern CROs can store a digital image after just one exposure.

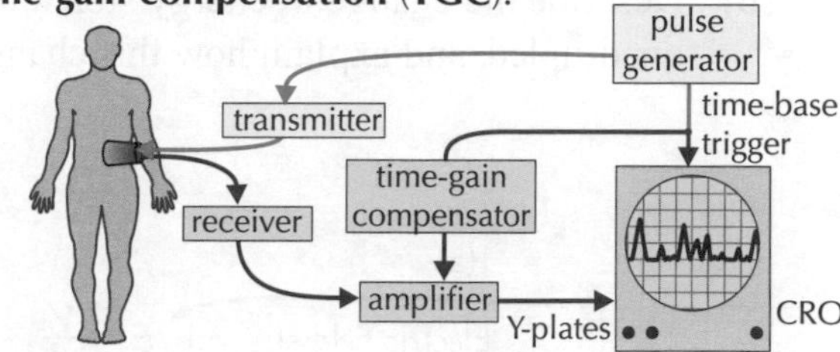

In a B-Scan, the Brightness Varies

1) In a **brightness scan** (**B-Scan**), the electron beam sweeps **down** the screen rather than across.
2) The amplitude of the reflected pulses is displayed as the **brightness** of the spot.
3) You can use a **linear array** of transducers to produce a **two-dimensional** image.

Ultrasound Waves are Affected by the Doppler Effect

1) Ultrasound waves reflected at an angle to **moving** cells undergo a change of **frequency** (or wavelength). This is caused by the **Doppler effect** (p.134).
2) This change of frequency (beat frequency) can allow doctors to find the **speed** at which those cells are moving (for example, blood cells in an artery).

$$\frac{\Delta f}{f} = \frac{2v\cos\theta}{c} \text{ or } v = \frac{c\Delta f}{2f\cos\theta}$$

where f is initial frequency, Δf is change in frequency,
v is the velocity of the moving cell,
c is the speed of sound in that medium and
θ is the angle between the ultrasound receiver and the direction in which the cell is moving.

Warm-Up Questions

Q1 What is ultrasound? How are ultrasound waves produced and received in an ultrasound transducer?

Q2 What are the two types of ultrasound scan? Give one use of ultrasound scans.

Q3 Explain how ultrasound imaging can be used to detect the speed of blood in an artery.

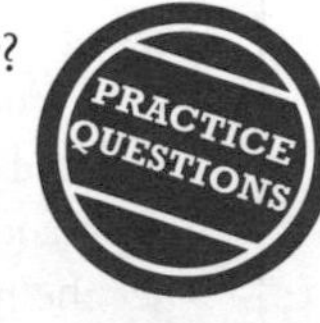

Exam Questions

Q1 The acoustic impedance of a certain soft tissue is 1.63×10^6 kgm^{-2}s^{-1} and its density is 1.09×10^3 kgm^{-3}. Calculate the velocity at which the ultrasound waves travel in this medium. [2 marks]

Q2 Calculate the ratio between the intensity of the ultrasound that enters the body when a coupling gel is used and when none is used (and there is an air gap). Give your answer to the nearest power of ten.
($Z_{gel} = 1500 \times 10^3$ kgm^{-2}s^{-1}, $Z_{air} = 0.430 \times 10^3$ kgm^{-2}s^{-1}, $Z_{tissue} = 1630 \times 10^3$ kgm^{-2}s^{-1}) [5 marks]

Ultrasound — Mancunian for 'très bien'

You can use ultrasound to make images in cases where X-rays would do too much damage — like to check up on the development of a baby in the womb. You have to know what you're looking for though, or it just looks like a blob.

Extra Exam Practice

Module 6 over and out. But to keep you on your toes, here are some practice exam questions which will have you applying your knowledge from all over the module. You're *so* welcome.

- Have a look at this example of how to answer a tricky exam question.
- Then check how much you've understood from Module 6 by having a go at the questions that follow.

There's a load of synoptic questions covering the entire course on pages 192-201. Take a look at these when you're confident with all the modules separately.

1 A teacher is demonstrating a parallel plate capacitor. The capacitor consists of two metal plates of a fixed area, separated by air. The teacher is able to change the distance between the plates without any charge being added to or removed from the capacitor.

(a) The plates are initially at a distance of x from each other. Explain what happens to the electric field strength between the plates if the teacher increases the separation of the plates to $4x$.

(2 marks)

(b) Describe the change in energy stored by the capacitor as the separation of plates is quadrupled, and explain how this change in energy takes place.

(2 marks)

Because the electric field is between two parallel plates, it is a uniform field, see p.147.

In the equation $E = \frac{V}{d}$, there are two variables that E is dependant on. You need to find an equation for E in which d is the only variable, so you can see exactly how E varies with d.

1(a)

Electric field strength, $E = \frac{V}{d}$

Combining $C = \frac{Q}{V}$ and $C = \frac{\varepsilon A}{d}$ gives:

$V = \frac{Qd}{\varepsilon A}$

Substitute this into $E = \frac{V}{d}$: $E = \frac{V}{d} = \frac{Qd}{d\varepsilon A} = \frac{Q}{\varepsilon A}$

Q and A remain constant as the distance is increased, so E is independent of d and **the electric field strength remains the same if the distance is quadrupled**.

Make sure you include a conclusion so that you've answered the question fully.

You'd get 1 mark for stating that the electric field strength doesn't change, and 1 mark for a correct explanation.

1(b)

$W = \frac{1}{2}QV$ and from part 1(a), $V = \frac{Qd}{\varepsilon A}$. If the distance quadruples, the voltage **quadruples**, therefore the energy stored by the capacitor **quadruples**.

When comparing quantities you need to say by what factor one is bigger than the other. Just saying that the energy stored has increased might not be enough to get the marks.

The teacher does work to separate the plates. The teacher applies a force over a distance to overcome the force of attraction between the plates. This work done transfers energy to the capacitor.

You'd get 1 mark for showing that the energy quadruples and 1 mark for saying that the energy transfer is due to the work done as the teacher applies a force to overcome the attraction between the plates.

There are two parts to this question — explaining the change in energy, and how this energy is transferred. Be sure to answer both parts.

2 **Figure 1** shows an electron and a proton whose centres are separated by a distance of 1.00×10^{-10} m. Point P is at the midpoint between the centres of the two particles.

Figure 1

electron P proton

not to scale

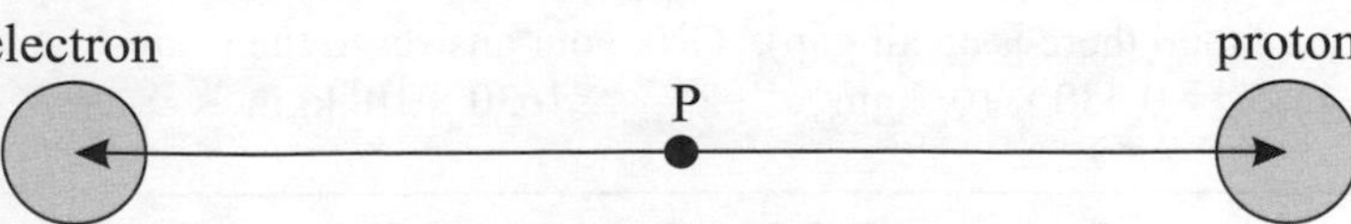

(a) Explain why the electric potential is 0 V at point P.

(2 marks)

Extra Exam Practice

(b) Calculate the magnitude and direction of the electric field strength at point P.
($e = 1.60 \times 10^{-19}$ C, $\varepsilon_0 = 8.85 \times 10^{-12}$ $C^2N^{-1}m^{-2}$)

(3 marks)

3 Nuclear fission and fusion can be used to produce large amounts of energy.

(a)* Use the concept of mass defect to explain how fission and fusion release energy. Your answer should include a graph sketch and a discussion of the conditions under which energy can and cannot be released by fusion and fission.

(6 marks)

(b) A fast neutron reactor is a nuclear fission reactor in which neutrons do not have to be slowed down in order to be absorbed by the fuel. Explain how the design of a fast neutron reactor would differ from a thermal neutron reactor.

(1 mark)

(c) Iodine-131 is a product of nuclear fission that was once the main medical tracer used for imaging of the thyroid. Technetium-99m is now the preferred isotope used for this purpose. **Table 1** shows the properties of the two isotopes.

Table 1

	Half-life	**Radiation emitted**
Technetium-99m	6 hours	Gamma
Iodine-131	8 days	Beta and gamma

The medical tracer isotope is taken into the body and an external gamma camera is used to track the isotope. The procedure can take up to a few hours. Exposure to radiation can damage the human body, so doctors attempt to minimise exposure as much as possible.
Suggest **two** reasons why technetium-99m is preferred to iodine-131 for use as a medical tracer.

(2 marks)

4 **Figure 2** shows a wire being moved downwards between two pairs of magnets. Each magnet has a square face with dimensions 5.5 cm × 5.5 cm and there is a uniform magnetic flux density of 155 mT between each pair. The wire is connected in a closed circuit with no battery. A voltmeter is connected in parallel across points A and B. The wire is moved downwards at a constant velocity of 1.2 ms^{-1}, which causes a charge to build up at point B and the voltmeter to display a reading.

Figure 2

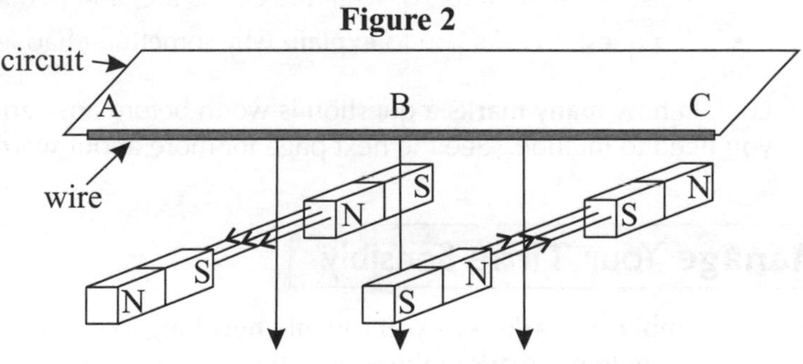

(a) State and explain whether the build up of charge at point B is positive or negative.

(3 marks)

(b) Calculate the magnitude of the maximum reading on the voltmeter. You can assume that the magnetic flux density outside of the area between the magnets is negligible, and that there are no energy losses.

(3 marks)

(c) A battery is connected in the circuit so a current flows from points A to C. The wire is moved back to the position shown in **Figure 2** and then dropped between the magnets. Suggest and explain what happens to the motion of the wire when it is dropped through the magnets. You may ignore the effects of any induced e.m.f. in the wire.

(2 marks)

* You will be assessed on the quality of your written response in this question.

Exam Structure and Technique

Good exam technique can make a big difference to your mark, so make sure you read this stuff carefully.

Get Familiar With the **Exam Structure**

You'll also do a Practical Endorsement as part of your A-level. It'll involve doing practicals throughout the course, and will be reported separately from your exam results.

For A-level Physics, you'll be sitting **three papers**. Find out your **exam timetable** and use the info below to **plan** your revision carefully.

Paper 1 — Modelling Physics **2 hours 15 minutes** **37%** of your A-level **100** marks: **15** for **Section A** (**multiple choice** questions) **85** for **Section B** (**short answer** and **extended response** questions)	Covers material from **modules 1, 2, 3 and 5** of this book.
Paper 2 — Exploring Physics **2 hours 15 minutes** **37%** of your A-level **100** marks: **15** for **Section A** (**multiple choice** questions) **85** for **Section B** (**short answer** and **extended response** questions)	Covers material from **modules 1, 2, 4 and 6** of this book.
Paper 3 — Unified Physics **1 hour 30 minutes** **26%** of your A-level **70 marks**: all **short answer** and **extended response** questions.	Covers material from **all modules** **(1-6)** of this book.

If you're taking AS Physics, you'll do different exams altogether, so this information isn't relevant to you.

Make Sure You **Read the Question**

1) It sounds obvious, but it's really important you read each question **carefully**, and give an answer that matches what you've been asked.
2) Look for **command words** in the question — they'll give you an idea of the **kind of answer** you should write. Commonly used command words for written questions are **state**, **describe**, **discuss** and **explain**:
   - If a question asks you to **state** something, you just need to give a **definition**, **example** or **fact**.
   - If you're asked to **describe** what happens in a particular situation, don't waste time explaining why it happens — that's not what the question is after.
   - For **discuss** questions, you'll need to include more **detail** — depending on the question you might need to cover what happens, what the effects are, and perhaps include a brief explanation of why it happens.
   - If a question asks you to **explain** why something happens you must give **reasons**, not just a description.
3) Look at **how many marks** a question is worth before answering. It'll tell you roughly **how much information** you need to include. See the next page for more about **wordy questions**.

Manage Your **Time** Sensibly

1) The **number of marks** tells you roughly **how long** to spend on a question — you've got just over a minute per mark in the exam. If you get stuck on a question for too long, it may be best to **move on** so you don't run out of time for the others.
2) The **multiple choice questions** are only worth **one mark each**, so it's not worth stressing over one for ages if you get stuck — **move on** and come back to it later.
3) You don't have to work through the paper **in order** — you could leave questions on topics you find harder until last.

Don't be **Put Off** if a Question Seems **Strange**

1) You may get some weird questions that seem to have nothing to do with anything you've learnt. **DON'T PANIC.** Every question will be something you can answer **using physics you know**, it just may be in a new **context**.
2) Answering these **trickier questions** will get you **top marks**, but make sure you get the **easier marks** in the bag first.
3) All of the A-level exams could **pull together** ideas from different parts of physics, so check the question for any **keywords** that you recognise. For example, if a question talks about acceleration, think about the rules and equations you know, and whether any of them apply to the situation in the question.

Exam Structure and Technique

Watch out for **Practical Questions...**

1) Each paper could test anything in module 1 (on practical skills) or on pages 12-13 on **uncertainty** in module 2. You may have to **describe an experiment** to investigate something, or **answer questions** on an experiment you've been given.
2) These could be experiments you've **met before**, or they could be **entirely new** to you. All the questions will be based on physics that you've **covered**, but may include bits from different topics put together in ways you haven't seen before. Don't let this put you off, just **think carefully** about what's going on.
3) Make sure you know the difference between **precision**, **accuracy** and **validity** (p.8). Learn what **uncertainty**, **random errors** and **systematic errors** are (p.12) and make sure you can give some examples of where each might come from.
4) You need to be able to **calculate errors** and **plot** and **interpret graphs** too.

...and **Wordy Ones**

For some questions, you'll need to write a slightly longer answer, where the '**quality** of your **extended response**' will be taken into account. You'll need to make sure you can develop a **clear** and **logical**, **well-structured line of reasoning**, backed up with **relevant information**.
You can avoid losing marks in these questions by making sure you do the following things:

1) Think about your answer before you write it. Your answer needs to be **logically structured** to get the top marks.
2) Make sure your answer is **relevant** to the question being asked and that you **explain** your ideas or argument **clearly**. It's dead easy to go off on a tangent.
3) Back up your points with **evidence** or **explanation**. You'll lose marks if you just make statements without supporting them.
4) Write in **whole sentences** and keep an eye on your **spelling**, **grammar** and **punctuation**. It'll help make sure your answer is clear and easy to read.

Questions like this will be marked in some way in the exam — e.g. with an asterisk (*). Check the instructions on the front of your paper to find out.

Example: A large group of people walk across a footbridge. When the frequency of the group's footsteps is 1 Hz, the bridge noticeably oscillates.
Describe the phenomenon causing the bridge to oscillate, and suggest what engineers could do to solve this problem. *[6 marks]*

Good Answer

The pedestrians provide a driving force on the bridge, causing it to oscillate. At around 1 Hz, the driving frequency from the pedestrians is roughly equal to the natural frequency of the bridge, causing it to resonate. The amplitude of the bridge's oscillations when resonating at 1 Hz will be greater than at any other driving frequency. The oscillations at this frequency are large enough to be noticed by pedestrians. Engineers could fix this problem by critically damping the bridge to stop any oscillations as quickly as possible. They could also adjust the natural frequency of the bridge so that it was not so close to a known walking frequency of large groups of people.

Bad Answer

resonance
driving frequency = natural frequency
damping

There's nothing fundamentally wrong with the physics in the bad answer, but you'd miss out on some nice easy marks just for not bothering to link the physics with the context given and not putting your answer into proper sentences.

The penultimate joke in the book better be good... here goes... Oh, I've run out of space...
Making sure you're prepared for what the exams will be like, reading questions carefully and managing your time all sounds like pretty basic advice, but you'd be surprised how many people don't follow it. Make sure you do...

Maths Skills

At least 40% of the marks up for grabs in A-level Physics will require maths skills, so make sure you know your stuff. As well as being given some tricky calculations, you could be asked to work with exponentials and logarithms and work out values from log graphs. And it's easy when you know how...

Be **Careful** With **Calculations**

1) In calculation questions you should always **show your working** — you may get some marks for your **method** even if you get the answer wrong.
2) Don't **round** your answer until the **very end**. A lot of calculations in A-level Physics are quite **long**, and if you round too early you could introduce errors to your final answer.
3) Be careful with **units**. Lots of formulas require quantities to be in specific units (e.g. time in seconds), so it's best to **convert** any numbers you're given into these before you start. And obviously, if the question **tells** you which units to give your **answer** in, don't throw away marks by giving it in different ones.
4) You should give your final answer to the same number of **significant figures** as the data that you use from the question with the **least number** of significant figures (or one more). If you can, write out the **unrounded answer**, then your **rounded** answer with the number of significant figures you've given it to — it shows you know your stuff.

There's more on quantities and their units on p.10-11.

Many Relationships in Physics are **Exponential**

A fair few of the relationships you need to know about in A-level Physics are **exponential** — where the **rate of change** of a quantity is **proportional** to the **amount** of the quantity left. Here are a few that crop up in the A-level course (if they don't ring a bell, go have a quick read about them)...

Charge on a capacitor — the decay of charge on a discharging capacitor is proportional to the amount of charge left on the capacitor: $Q = Q_0 e^{\frac{-t}{CR}}$ (see p.144)

There are also exponential relationships for *I* and *V* and for charging capacitors.

Radioactive decay — the rate of decay of a radioactive sample is proportional to the **number of undecayed nuclei** in the sample: $N = N_0 e^{-\lambda t}$ (see p.175)

The activity of a radioactive sample behaves in the same way.

X-ray attenuation — the reduction of **intensity** of X-rays over distance is proportional to their **initial intensity**: $I = I_0 e^{-\mu x}$ (see p.181)

You can **Plot** Exponential Relations Using the **Natural Log, ln**

1) Say you've got two variables, *x* and *y*, which are related to each other by the formula $y = ke^{-ax}$ (where *k* and *a* are constants).
2) The **natural logarithm** of *x*, **ln *x***, is the power to which e (the base) must be raised to to give *x*.
3) So, by definition, $e^{\ln x} = x$ and $\ln(e^x) = x$. So far so good... now you need some **log rules**:

$\ln(AB) = \ln A + \ln B$ $\quad$ $\ln\left(\frac{A}{B}\right) = \ln A - \ln B$ $\quad$ $\ln x^n = n \ln x$

A logarithm can be to any base you want. Another common one is 'base 10' which is usually written as '$\log_{10}$' or just 'log'.

These log rules work for all logs (including the natural logarithm) and you're given them on your formula sheet.

4) So, for $y = ke^{-ax}$, if you take the natural log of both sides of the equation you get:

$\ln y = \ln(ke^{-ax}) = \ln k + \ln(e^{-ax})$ ⟶ $\ln y = \ln k - ax$

5) Then all you need to do is plot (ln *y*) against *x*, and Eric's your aunty: ⟶

ln *y*
ln *k*
gradient = –*a*
x

You get a **straight-line** graph with (**ln *k***) as the **vertical intercept**, and –*a* as the **gradient**.

Maths Skills

You Might be Asked to find the **Gradient** of a Log Graph

This log business isn't too bad when you get your head around which bit of the log graph means what.

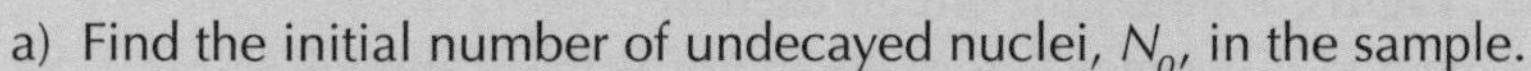

Example: The graph shows the radioactive decay of isotope X.

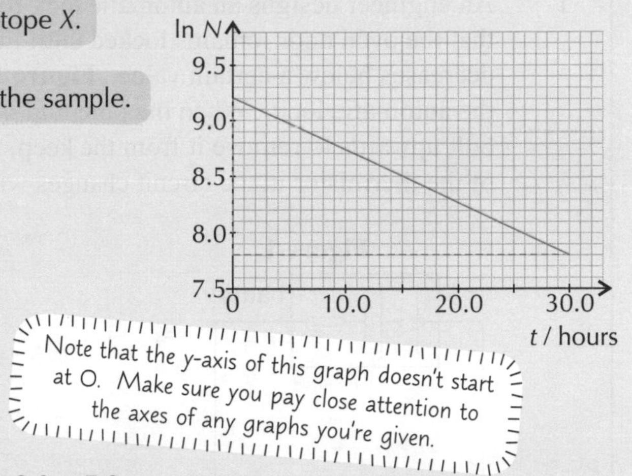

a) Find the initial number of undecayed nuclei, N_0, in the sample.

You know that the number of undecayed nuclei in a sample, N, is related to the initial number of undecayed nuclei, N_0, by the equation $\boldsymbol{N = N_0 e^{-\lambda t}}$.

So: $\ln N = \ln N_0 - \lambda t$

The y-intercept of the graph is $\ln N_0 = 9.2$

$N_0 = e^{9.2} = 9897.129... =$ **9900 nuclei (to 2 s.f.)**

Note that the y-axis of this graph doesn't start at O. Make sure you pay close attention to the axes of any graphs you're given.

b) Find the decay constant λ of isotope X.

$-\lambda$ is the gradient of the graph, so: $\lambda = \frac{\Delta \ln N}{\Delta t} = \frac{9.2 - 7.8}{30.0 \times 60 \times 60} = \mathbf{1.3 \times 10^{-5}\ s^{-1}}$ **(to 2 s.f.)**

You can Plot **Any Power Law** as a **Log-Log Graph**

You can use logs to plot a straight-line graph of **any power law** — it doesn't have to be an exponential.

Say the relationship between two variables x and y is:

$$y = kx^n$$

Take the **log** (base 10) of both sides to get:

$$\log y = \log k + n \log x$$

When it came to logs, Geoff always took time to smell the flowers...

So **log k** will be the **y-intercept** and **n** will be the **gradient** of the graph.

Example:

The graph shows how the intensity of radiation from the Sun, I, varies with distance from the Sun, d. I is related to d by the power law $I = kd^n$.
Find n.

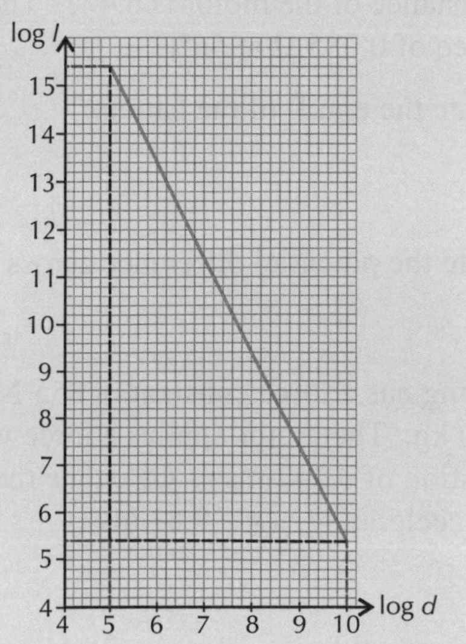

$$\log I = \log(kd^n) = \log k + \log d^n = \log k + n \log d$$

So n is the gradient of the graph.
Reading from the graph:

$$n = \frac{\Delta \log I}{\Delta \log d} = \frac{5.4 - 15.4}{10 - 5} = \mathbf{-2}$$

Lumberjacks are great musicians — they have a natural logarhythm...

I'm guessing that all this talk of maths skills and extended responses has got you itching to sit the heck out of these exams. Well, if possible, refrain from pitching your tent outside the exam hall just yet. Instead, get your teeth into the generous helping of synoptic questions we've lined up for you in the next two sections. They're great.

AS/Year 1 Synoptic Practice

Time to shake things up a bit. In the exam, questions might link different parts of the course in single questions, and it's not always that easy to spot which module a question part is testing. I recommend practising with a big bunch of mixed questions on the content from the AS course/Year 1 of A-level.

There's also a section of synoptic questions on the rest of the full A-level course on pages 196-201.

1 An engineer designs an automatic lock for a pottery oven to ensure that the oven door remains locked until the oven temperature decreases below a certain value. **Figure 1** shows the circuit used in the automatic lock. When the potential difference across the motor is large enough, it pulls the bolt upwards to remove it from the keep, unlocking the door. **Figure 2** shows how the resistance of the thermistor in the circuit changes with temperature. The resistance of the wires is negligible.

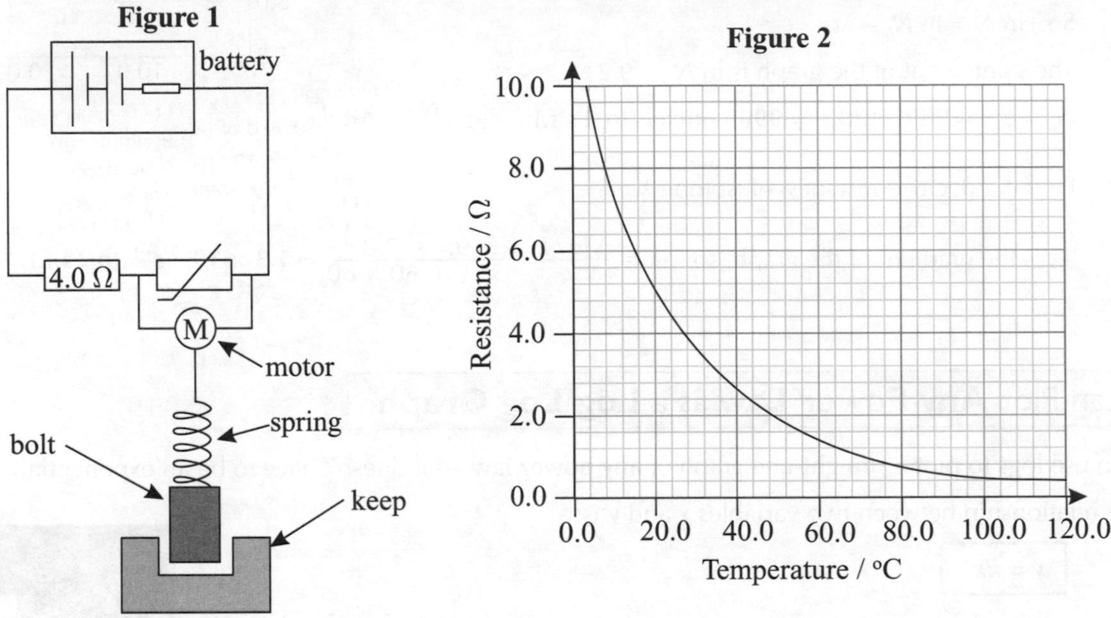

(a) Explain how the system unlocks the pottery oven as it cools. **(2 marks)**

When the temperature of the oven is 56 °C, the total current through the circuit is 4.6 A. The resistance of the motor is 6.4 Ω. The circuit is powered by a battery which has an internal resistance of 0.085 Ω at 56°C.

(b) Calculate the e.m.f. of the battery. **(3 marks)**

(c) Calculate the potential difference across the motor at 56 °C. **(2 marks)**

(d) The spring has a force constant of 855 Nm^{-1}. The bolt hung on the end of the spring has a mass of 0.540 kg. The motor applies a force which extends the spring and then lifts the mass with an acceleration of 0.142 ms^{-2}. Calculate the total elastic potential energy stored in the spring as the bolt is accelerating. ($g = 9.81$ ms^{-2}) **(4 marks)**

(e) The engineer redesigns the circuit using wires in which the resistance is no longer negligible. The length of the electrical wire from the battery to the resistor is 1.8 cm. The current through the circuit is 1.6 A and the potential difference across this length of wire is 1.04 mV. The wire is made of a material with a resistivity of 2.65×10^{-8} Ωm. Calculate the diameter of the wire. **(4 marks)**

AS/Year 1 Synoptic Practice

2 A 'solar sail' is a method of propulsion for spacecraft. A solar sail consists of a large sheet of metal foil which uses the pressure of incident photons to accelerate the spacecraft. When a photon is incident on the solar sail it is either absorbed or reflected. The pressure exerted on a solar sail can be calculated by the following equation:

$$p = (1 + R)\frac{I}{c}$$

Where I is the intensity of incident photons, c is the speed of light and R is the fraction of photons reflected by the sail, which ranges from 0 to 1.

Information about two solar sails is given in **Table 1**. Each sail has the same area.

Table 1

	Sail A	Sail B
Percentage of incident photons absorbed	2%	12%
Percentage of incident photons reflected	98%	88%

(a) The two sails in **Table 1** are attached to two different spacecraft. Explain how the acceleration of the spacecraft with sail A compares to the acceleration of the spacecraft with sail B. Assume both spacecraft have the same mass, the intensity of incident photons is the same at each sail, and that the incident photons strike the sail perpendicular to the surfaces of the sails.

(4 marks)

(b) A scientist estimates that incident photons have an average momentum of 1.33×10^{-27} kgms^{-1}, and that each absorbed photon is absorbed over a time period of approximately 1.00 ms. During this time period, 1.60×10^{24} photons are incident on the surface of each sail. Estimate the total force exerted on sail B in 1.00 ms by absorbed photons.

(3 marks)

Figure 3 shows the angle to the normal of the sail, θ, at which photons strike a third sail, sail C. Sail C has a surface area of 1700 m^2, and is attached to a spacecraft. Initially, the incident photons hit the sail at $\theta = 0°$.

Figure 3

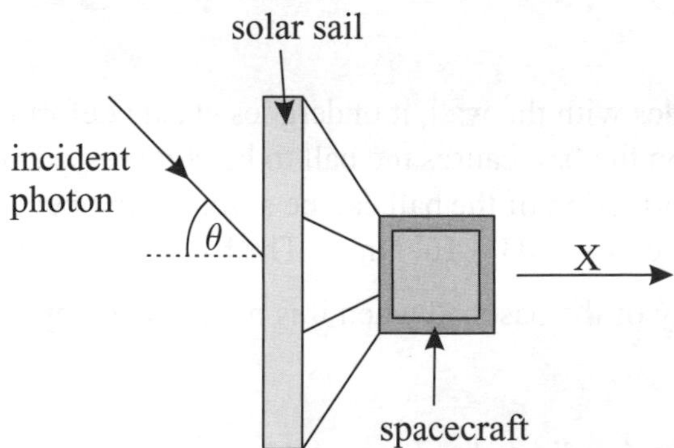

(c) The intensity of light on sail C is equal to 1362 Wm^{-2}. The energy transferred to sail C in 60.0 s is 1.28×10^8 J. Calculate the efficiency of sail C.

(3 marks)

(d) When $\theta = 0°$, the force on the spacecraft in the direction of X due to incident photons is $2a$ N. The spacecraft begins to change direction causing the angle θ to increase.
Calculate the angle θ at which the component of the force in the direction of X equals a N.

(1 mark)

AS/Year 1 Synoptic Practice

During use, solar sails can become positively charged, which can cause damage to the sail. The larger the positive charge, the more likely the sail is to become damaged.

(e) The intensity of light from the Sun decreases with distance from the Sun. Explain why a solar sail is less likely to suffer damage if it is further from the Sun.

(2 marks)

3 A baseball pitching machine is being used to bounce a baseball against the wall of a house, as shown in **Figure 4**. The baseball has a mass of 145 g.

Figure 4

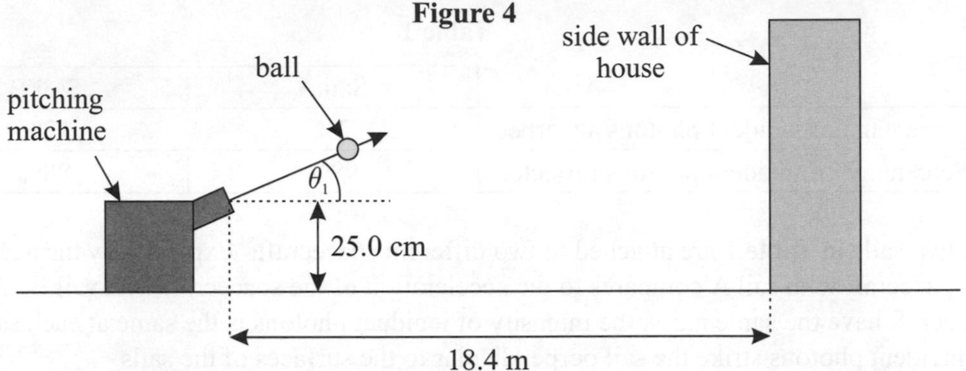

(a) The ball is launched at an initial speed of 30.0 ms^{-1} at an angle of $\theta_1 = 5.00°$. Calculate the speed of the ball when it reaches the wall. You can assume that the air resistance is negligible. ($g = 9.81$ ms^{-2})

(4 marks)

The pitching machine is adjusted so that the ball hits the wall at an angle of $\theta_2 = 35.0°$ to the normal, and bounces off the wall at an angle of $\theta_3 = 48.2°$, as shown in **Figure 5**. The ball hits the wall at 28.6 ms^{-1}, and the wall exerts an impulse on the ball with a horizontal component of 5.08 Ns.

Figure 5

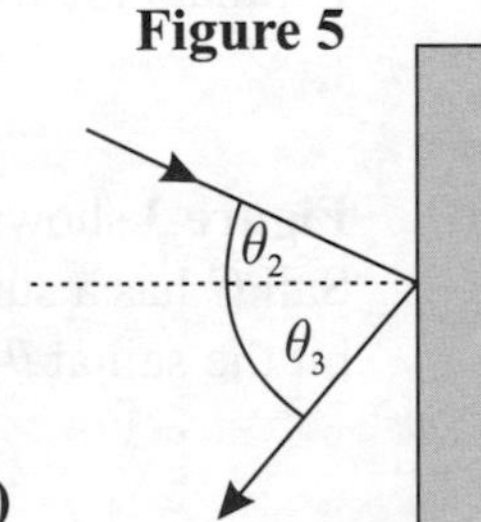

(b) Calculate the speed of the ball immediately after it has bounced off the wall.

(4 marks)

When the ball collides with the wall, it undergoes elastic deformation. The horizontal component of the force acting on the ball causes the ball to be compressed horizontally to 65% of its diameter. This horizontal deformation of the ball can be assumed to obey Hooke's law, where the baseball has a force constant of $k = 1.03 \times 10^5$ Nm^{-1}. The ball is in contact with the wall for 1.8 ms.

(c) Calculate the density of the baseball when it is not being compressed.

(4 marks)

(d) The pitching machine is adjusted again, and this time the baseball lands on the roof of the house and rolls down the roof, as shown in **Figure 6**. $h_1 = 6.50$ m and $h_2 = 5.40$ m. At its highest point on the roof, the ball is stationary. The ball leaves the roof at an angle of $\theta_4 = 32.5°$ and hits the floor 0.812 s after leaving the roof. Calculate the horizontal distance travelled by the ball between leaving the roof and reaching the floor.

(4 marks)

Figure 6

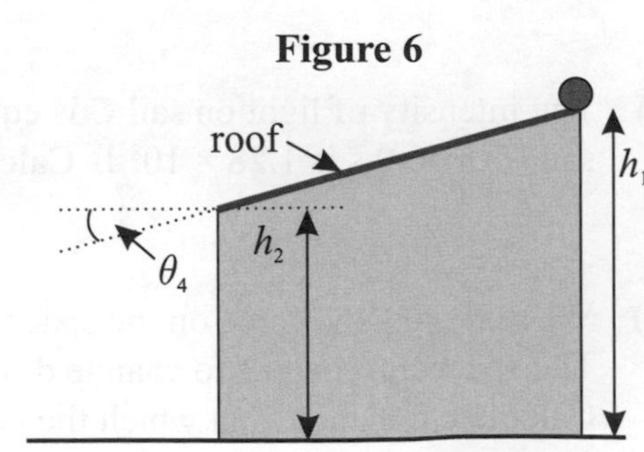

AS/Year 1 Synoptic Practice

4 A scientist carries out an experiment to investigate the properties of a prototype photocell. The circuit she uses in her experiment is shown in **Figure 7**. A photocell consists of a negatively charged photocathode and a positively charged anode separated by a small gap. When photons are incident on the photocathode, electrons can be emitted by the photoelectric effect. A potential difference between the photocathode and the anode causes the electrons to be accelerated across the gap towards the anode, creating a current flow.

Figure 7

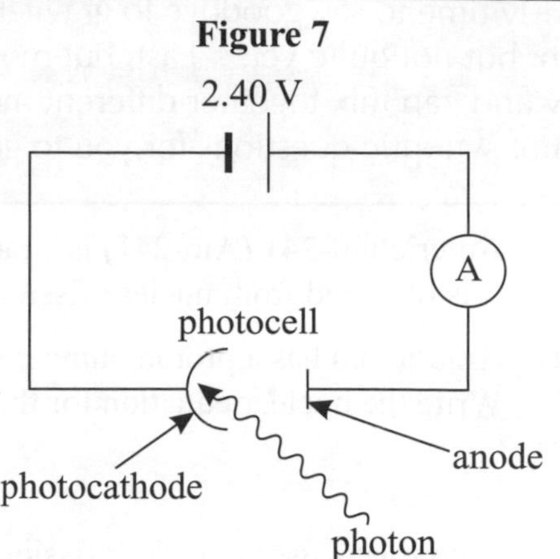

In her experiment, the scientist shines lasers of increasing wavelengths onto the photocell and records the current read by the ammeter. Her results are shown in **Figure 8**. Each laser has the same intensity.

Figure 8

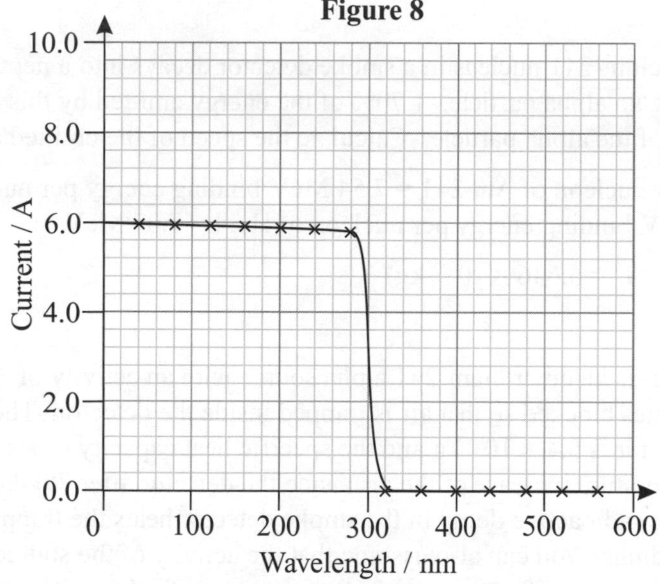

(a) Radiation with a wavelength of 255 nm is shone onto the photocathode. The scientist calculates the maximum initial velocity of photoelectrons emitted from the photocathode to be 5.90×10^5 ms^{-1}. Use the results in **Figure 8** to verify the scientist's answer. ($h = 6.63 \times 10^{-34}$ Js, $m_e = 9.11 \times 10^{-31}$ kg, $c = 3.00 \times 10^8$ ms^{-1})

(4 marks)

(b) Comment on the accuracy of the scientist's result for the maximum initial velocity of the photoelectrons, and suggest how the scientist could improve the accuracy of her result.

(2 marks)

(c) Sketch a second curve on the graph to show what the curve would look like if the intensity of the lasers used in the experiment were all increased by the same amount. Label your curve 'A'.

(2 marks)

(d) The scientist uses one of the lasers to investigate how light behaves as a wave. She directs the laser through various double-slit arrangements and observes the diffraction pattern produced on a screen at a fixed distance from the double-slit. When the scientist uses a double-slit with a slit spacing of 2×10^{-6} m, the fringe spacing is 5 cm. Calculate the fringe spacing when she uses a double-slit with a slit spacing of 1.25×10^{-6} m.

(2 marks)

A-Level Synoptic Practice

It's nearly time to say goodbye to gravitational fields, adios to atomic structures, and ciao to circular motion, but not quite yet... Last, but most definitely not least, it's A-level synoptic time. The exams are sneaky and can mix together different modules, but don't worry — I've got you covered with a huge bunch of synoptic questions for you to get stuck into. What's that you say? You're right, I am the best...

1 Americium-241 (Am-241) is a radioactive isotope commonly used in smoke detectors. It is obtained from nuclear fission reactors from the decay of plutonium-241 (Pu-241).

(a) Americium has a proton number of 95, and plutonium has a proton number of 94. Write the nuclear equation for the decay of plutonium-241 into americium-241.

(2 marks)

(b) A company uses a nuclear fission reactor to produce the americium-241 needed to manufacture their smoke detectors. The reactor produces 2.65×10^{-9} moles of Am-241 per second. Calculate the number of moles of Pu-241 needed to produce Am-241 at this rate. The half-life of Pu-241 is 4.42×10^{8} s. ($N_A = 6.02 \times 10^{23}$)

(4 marks)

(c) A stationary americium-241 nucleus in a smoke detector decays into a neptunium-237 (Np-237) nucleus by emitting an alpha particle. 1.70% of the energy emitted by this decay is transferred to the kinetic energy of the alpha particle. Calculate the speed of the emitted alpha particle.

Binding energy per nucleon of Am-241 = 7.54 MeV, binding energy per nucleon of Np-237 = 7.58 MeV, binding energy per nucleon of He-4 = 7.07 MeV.

($e = 1.60 \times 10^{-19}$ C, $m_\alpha = 6.646 \times 10^{-27}$ kg)

(4 marks)

(d) A smoke detector uses an americium-241 alpha source with an activity of 38 kBq. The detector becomes blocked so that air is trapped inside the detector. The mass of the air trapped in the detector is 3.4×10^{-3} kg and the specific heat capacity of air is 720 $\text{Jkg}^{-1}\text{K}^{-1}$. Calculate the temperature increase of the air inside the detector after 7.0 days. Assume that all the energy from the radioactive decay in the smoke detector heats the trapped air and no heat is lost to the surroundings. You can also assume that the activity of the source remains constant, and that the decay products of americium-241 do not decay further within the 7.0 days.

(3 marks)

2 A ball game uses a tennis ball attached to the top of a vertical pole with a piece of string as shown in **Figure 1**. The string has a length l. When the ball is hit, it moves around the pole in a horizontal circle with radius r. l and r are the distances to the centre of mass of the ball.

Figure 1

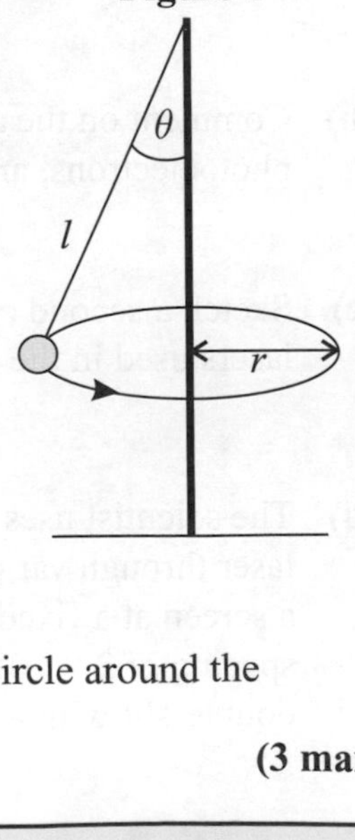

For question 2 you may assume that air resistance is negligible, and that the angle, θ, is small. For small angles, $\sin\theta \approx \tan\theta$.

(a) Show that the resultant force acting on the ball is equal to $F = \frac{mgr}{l}$ where g is the gravitational field strength and m is the mass of the ball.

(3 marks)

(b) Derive an expression for the time taken for the ball to complete one full circle around the pole, T, in terms of g and l.

(3 marks)

A-Level Synoptic Practice

(c) In one particular game, the length of the string is set to 1.45 m and the ball moves in a circle with a radius of 0.205 m and speed v. Whilst the ball is in flight, a child hits the ball with a racket. The force applied by the racket has an average magnitude of 98.4 N and acts in the opposite direction to the motion of the ball. The racket is in contact with the ball for 6.5 ms. After the ball has been hit, the ball has the same speed v as its original motion, but is now moving in the opposite direction. Calculate the mass of the ball. ($g = 9.81\ \text{ms}^{-2}$)

(3 marks)

3 A pulmonary embolism is a blood clot in the blood vessels of the lungs. Different procedures can be used to diagnose it.

In one procedure, an iodine-based contrast medium is injected into the patient's blood. This enables an X-ray image of the blood flow in the lungs to be produced. **Figure 2** shows the relationship between the mass attenuation coefficient, μ_m, and the potential difference supplied to the X-ray tube for iodine and lung tissue.

Figure 2

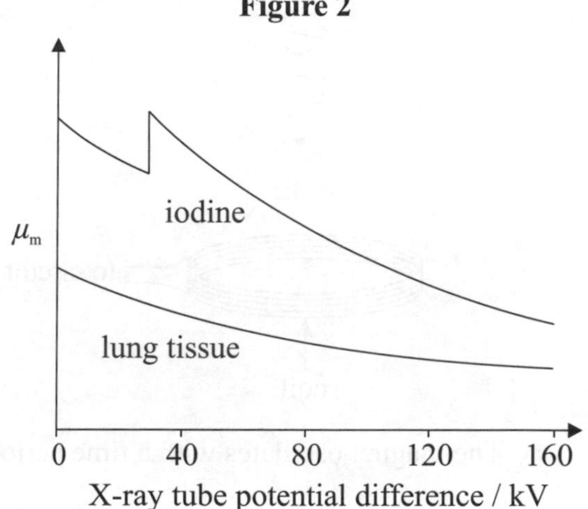

(a) Suggest and explain the X-ray tube potential difference that would produce the best image of blood flow in the lungs.

(3 marks)

A CAT scan can also be used to help diagnose a pulmonary embolism using xenon-133 as a contrast medium. During the procedure the patient is asked to take one deep breath of a gas containing the radioactive isotope xenon-133 (Xe-133). 32% of the molecules in the gas are Xe-133 molecules. **Table 1** shows data about the lungs and the radioactive isotope Xe-133.

Table 1

Volume inhaled per breath	$0.0035\ \text{m}^3$
Pressure of air in lungs	1.01×10^5 Pa
Temperature of air in lungs	37 °C
Half-life of Xe-133	5.2 days

(b) Use the data in **Table 1** to calculate the activity of Xe-133 in the lungs after one inhalation of the gas. Xenon exists as single atoms. You can assume that the gas in the lungs is an ideal gas. ($k = 1.38 \times 10^{-23}\ \text{JK}^{-1}$)

(3 marks)

The lungs are made up of thousands of tubes filled with air and millions of tiny air sacs. Each air sac is surrounded by tissue that contains blood vessels supplying the air sacs with blood. The acoustic impedance of air is 400 kgms^{-2}.
The acoustic impedance of lung tissue is $1.8 \times 10^5\ \text{kgms}^{-2}$.

(c) Suggest why the structure of the lungs may make it difficult to image the lungs using an ultrasound scan. Justify your answer with a calculation.

(3 marks)

A-Level Synoptic Practice

4 A student is investigating the motion of a magnet on a spring. He uses a magnet with a mass of 20.0 g attached to a spring made from a non-magnetic material, as shown in **Figure 3**. When the magnet is attached to the spring, the spring extends by 7.848 mm. The magnet is suspended above a coil. The coil has exactly 300 turns and is connected to a complete circuit. The student pulls the magnet downwards and releases it so that it oscillates vertically above the coil. Air resistance and any magnetic forces from induced e.m.f. can be considered to be negligible. **Figure 4** shows how the magnetic flux through the coil changes with time.

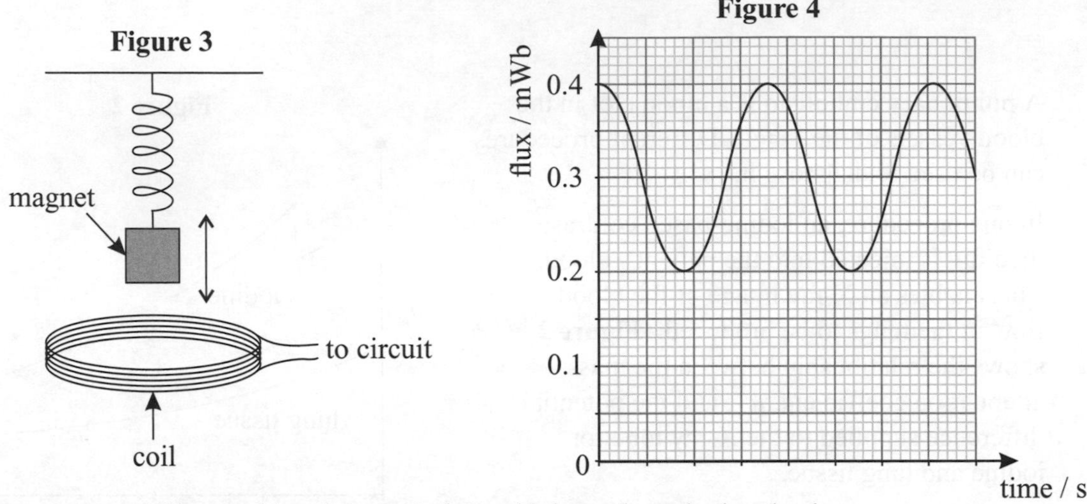

The magnet oscillates with a time period, T, which can be calculated using:

$$T = 2\pi\sqrt{\frac{m}{k}}$$

where m is the mass of the magnet in kg, and k is the force constant of the spring in Nm^{-1}.

(a) Determine the scale of the x-axis in **Figure 4**. ($g = 9.81\ \text{ms}^{-2}$)

(3 marks)

(b) Calculate the maximum induced e.m.f. in the coil.

(2 marks)

(c) Sketch a graph showing how the induced e.m.f. varies with time. Include a correct scale on each axis.

(3 marks)

(d) The number of turns on the coil is increased so that any magnetic forces from induced e.m.f. can no longer be treated as negligible. Describe and explain what effect this has on the motion of the magnet as it oscillates.

(3 marks)

5 An astronomer is investigating a distant star.

The astronomer observes the hydrogen spectral lines from an absorption spectrum of the star. **Figure 5** shows the energy levels for hydrogen. The astronomer observes an absorption line at a wavelength of 494 nm, corresponding to an electron being excited from the energy level $n = 2$ to $n = 4$.

Figure 5

Level	Energy
n = 5	−0.54 eV
n = 4	−0.85 eV
n = 3	−1.5 eV
n = 2	−3.4 eV
n = 1	−13.6 eV

(a) Calculate the speed of the star relative to the Earth.
($c = 3.00 \times 10^{8}\ \text{ms}^{-1}$, $h = 6.63 \times 10^{-34}$ Js, $e = 1.60 \times 10^{-19}$ C)

(3 marks)

A-Level Synoptic Practice

(b) The astronomer can also compare emission spectra from the lab to the absorption spectra of stars to calculate their speed. He observes the light from emission spectra by passing them through a diffraction grating. An emission line with an unknown wavelength produces a first order maxima at $\theta = 15.8°$. Calculate the angle of the second order diffraction maxima.

(2 marks)

(c) The peak wavelength of a star, λ_{max}, is related to the star's surface temperature, T, by the equation:

$$\lambda_{max} = \frac{2.9 \times 10^{-3}}{T}$$

where λ_{max} is in m and T is in K. The star has a radius of 8.98×10^8 m and a peak wavelength of 439 nm. Calculate the energy emitted from the surface of the star in 4.5 hours. ($\sigma = 5.67 \times 10^{-8}$ Wm^{-2}K^{-4})

(3 marks)

6 A plasma ball consists of an inner solid metal sphere and an outer spherical casing made from glass. Gases are contained in the gap between the inner sphere and the outer casing, as shown in **Figure 6**. When the plasma ball is switched on, the inner metal sphere is charged with a high alternating potential difference.

The radius of the inner sphere, r_a, is equal to 3.50 cm and the radius of the outer sphere, r_b, is equal to 12.0 cm. **Table 2** shows information about the composition of the gases within the plasma ball. Both neon and argon exist as single atoms.

Figure 6

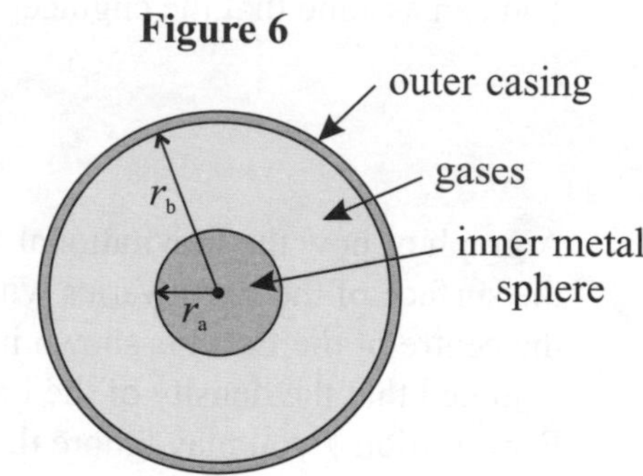

Table 2

Element	Percentage abundance	Molecular mass
Neon	99%	20.1797 u
Argon	1%	39.9481 u

When the ball is switched off, the pressure of the gas is 1.01×10^5 Pa and the temperature is 298 K. The gas inside the plasma ball is assumed to be an ideal gas.

(a) Calculate the mass of argon inside the plasma ball. (u = 1.661×10^{-27} kg, $k = 1.38 \times 10^{-23}$ JK^{-1})

(3 marks)

(b) When the plasma ball is switched on, the temperature of the gas inside the ball begins to rise. The pressure increases to 1.03×10^5 Pa. Calculate the root mean square speed of the neon gas particles inside the plasma ball at this pressure.

(3 marks)

An engineer is investigating how the absolute electric potential varies with the distance from the surface of a plasma ball's inner metal sphere. She removes the inner sphere from a plasma ball with unknown dimensions and places it on an insulating stand. She then charges the sphere with a constant potential difference and uses an electric potential probe to measure how the absolute electric potential, V, varies with distance, d, as shown in **Figure 7**.

Figure 7

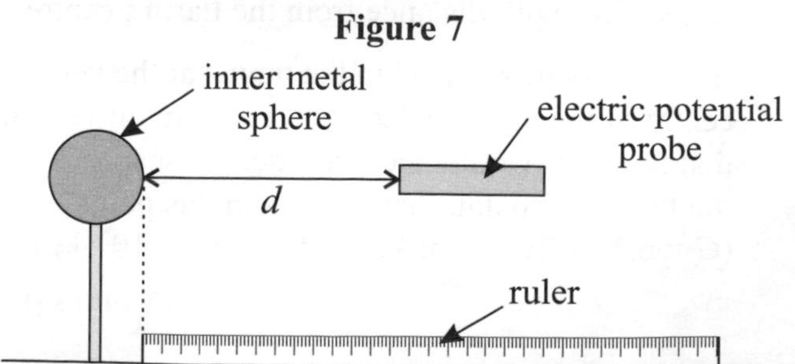

A-Level Synoptic Practice

The probe measures the absolute electric potential with a percentage uncertainty of ± 5.0%. The distance is measured with a ruler with an uncertainty of ± 0.001 m. The engineer uses the following formula to analyse the data:

$$V = \frac{Q}{4\pi\varepsilon_0(d + A)}$$

Where V is the absolute electric potential at a distance d from the surface of the sphere, Q is the charge on the sphere and A is a constant. After collecting results for a range of distances, the engineer plots a graph of d on the y-axis against $\frac{1}{V}$ on the x-axis.

(c) State what physical quantity is represented by A in the formula above.

(1 mark)

(d)* Explain how the engineer could use her graph in order to calculate the values of Q and A. In your answer you should include an explanation of how the engineer could plot error bars on her graph and use them to calculate the absolute uncertainties in the calculated values of Q and A. You can assume that the engineer knows the value of ε_0 with negligible uncertainty.

(6 marks)

7 A graph of how the gravitational field strength below the surface of the Earth varies with the distance from the centre of the Earth is shown in **Figure 8**. It can be assumed that the density of the Earth is constant. For question 7 you may ignore the effect of air resistance.

Figure 8

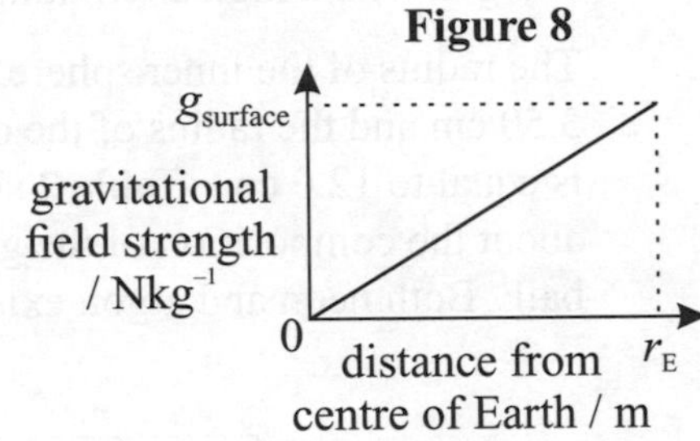

(a) Suggest why the gravitational field strength at the centre of the Earth is 0 Nkg^{-1}.

(1 mark)

(b) Hypothetically, if a vertical tunnel was to be constructed through the centre of the Earth from the North Pole to the South Pole, calculate the weight of a 1.50 kg object if it was 4.75×10^6 m from the centre of the Earth. ($g_{surface} = 9.81$ ms^{-2}, $r_E = 6.37 \times 10^6$ m)

(2 marks)

(c) If an object was released from rest in the tunnel at a distance from the Earth's centre, the object would oscillate vertically through the tunnel with simple harmonic motion. Calculate the time it would take for the object in **(b)** to perform one complete oscillation if released from rest at 4.75×10^6 m from the centre of the Earth.

(2 marks)

(d) **Figure 9** shows how the gravitational force acting on a different mass, with $m = 2.55$ kg, in the tunnel would vary with distance from the Earth's centre.

If this mass was placed in the tunnel at the very centre of the Earth, calculate the minimum velocity that the mass would need in order to escape the Earth's gravitational field from this point. ($G = 6.67 \times 10^{-11}$ Nm^{2}kg^{-2}, $M_E = 5.97 \times 10^{24}$ kg)

(5 marks)

Figure 9

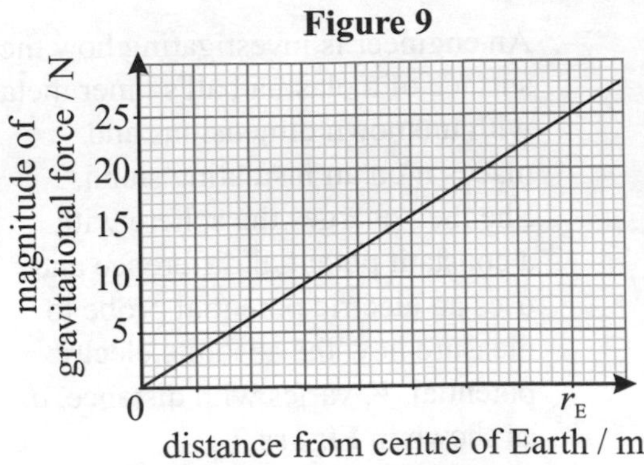

* You will be assessed on the quality of your written response in this question.

A-Level Synoptic Practice

8 Two oppositely charged metal plates are wrapped around each other to form two cylinders, as shown in **Figure 10**.

Figure 10

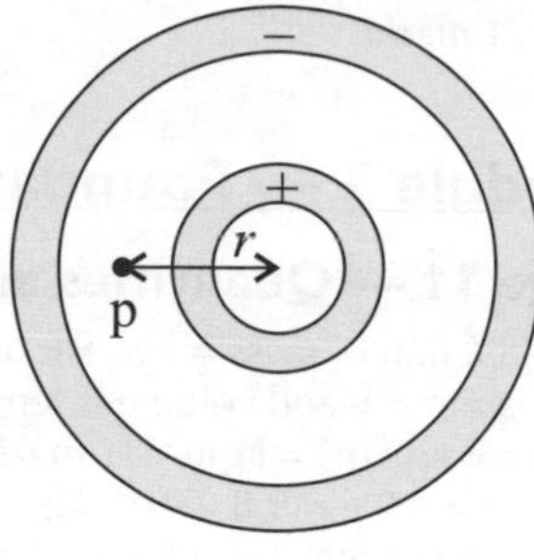

top view

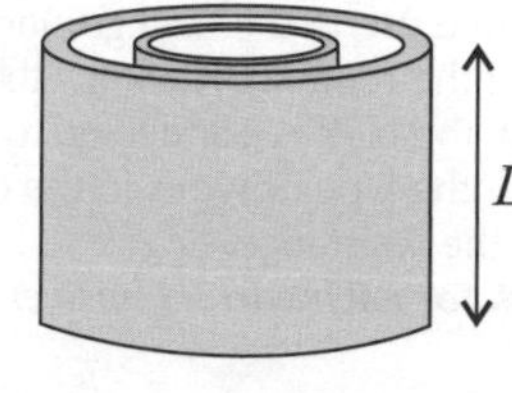

side view

(a) In the top view in **Figure 10**, draw the electric field lines in the space between the two cylinders. Describe how your diagram shows that the electric field is not uniform between the cylinders.

(2 marks)

The electric field strength at any point, p, between the plates is given by:

$$E = \frac{Q_{\text{cylinder}}}{2\pi\varepsilon_0 rL}$$

Where Q_{cylinder} is the charge of the inner cylinder, r is the distance of the point from the centre of the cylinders and L is the length of the cylinders as shown in **Figure 10**.

(b) An electron is injected into the space between the cylinders so that it moves in a circle with a radius r. The charge of the inner cylinder is 5.66 nC and the length of the cylinder is 25.3 cm. Calculate the speed of the electron.
($\varepsilon_0 = 8.85 \times 10^{-12}$ Fm^{-1}, $m_e = 9.11 \times 10^{-31}$ kg, $e = 1.60 \times 10^{-19}$ C)

(3 marks)

(c) A proton is injected into the space between the cylinders. Explain whether it is possible for the proton to move in a circle between the two cylinders.

(2 marks)

(d) The gap between the cylinders is filled with a dielectric material with relative permittivity of 2.25. The cylinders now act like a capacitor with a capacitance:

$$C = \frac{2\pi\varepsilon_0\varepsilon_r}{\ln\left(\frac{b}{a}\right)}$$

where ε_r is the relative permittivity of the dielectric material, a is the radius of the inner cylinder and b is the radius of the outer cylinder, as shown in **Figure 11**. The outer cylinder has double the radius of the inner cylinder.

Figure 11

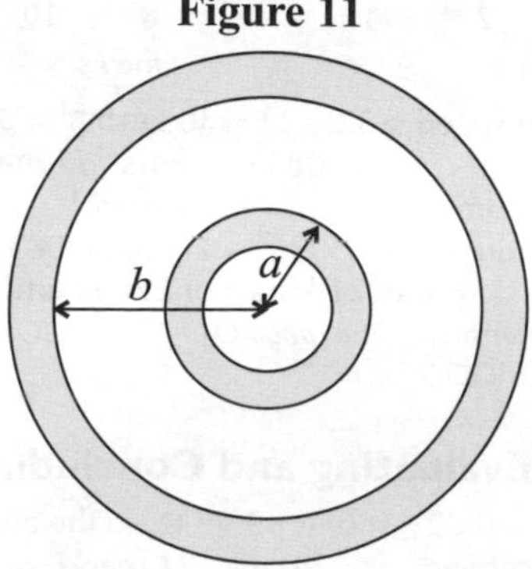

The capacitor is charged so that there is a potential difference of V_0 between the outer cylinder and the inner cylinder. The capacitor is then connected to a circuit with an electrical resistance of 1.85 kΩ, and discharged through the circuit. Calculate the time taken for the potential difference to fall to half of its original value.

(3 marks)

Answers

Module 1 — Development of Practical Skills in Physics

Page 5 — Planning and Implementing

1 a) Independent variable: light level / distance from the light source, dependent variable: resistance of the LDR ***[1 mark]***.

b) Any two of: e.g. the light source used / the background lighting in the room / the temperature of the room/LDR/wires / the potential difference / the power supply the LDR is connected to / the length of wires in the circuit / the type of wires in the circuit / the multimeter used to measure the resistance.
[2 marks available — 1 mark for each correct answer.]

Page 7 — Analysing Results

1 a)

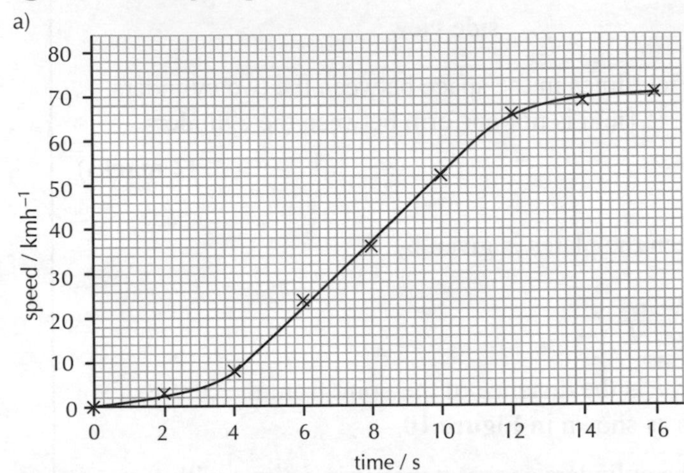

[1 mark for both axes drawn to a sensible scale and 1 mark for labelling both axes correctly, 1 mark for all the points drawn correctly, and 1 mark for a sensible line of best fit.]

b) The graph is linear between 4 and 10 seconds ***[1 mark]***.
Accept 11 seconds as the upper limit if the graph in part a) agrees.

c) The maximum acceleration is the value of the steepest gradient, which is the linear portion of the graph ***[1 mark]***:

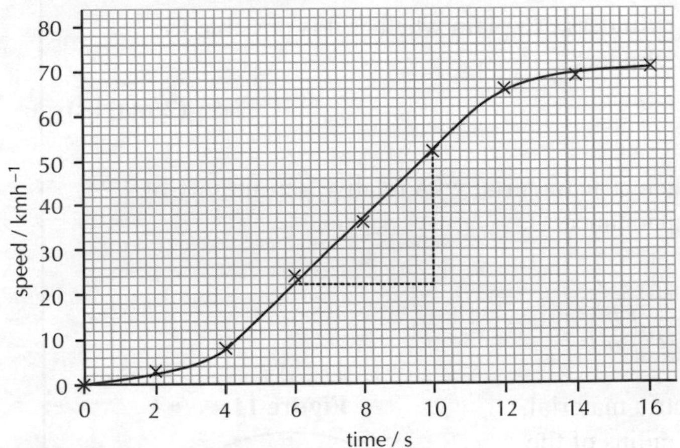

change in speed = 52 – 22 = 30 km hr^{-1} = 30 ÷ (60 × 60) = 0.008333... km s^{-1} ***[1 mark]***
change in time = 10 – 6 = 4 s ***[1 mark]***
acceleration = 0.008333... ÷ 4 = 0.002083... km s^{-2}
= **0.0021 km s^{-2}** or **27000 km hr^{-2} (to 2 s.f.)** ***[1 mark]***
Accept an answer in the range 0.0020-0.0022 km s^{-2} or 26000-28000 km hr^{-2}.

Page 9 — Evaluating and Concluding

1 50 – (50 × 0.02 / 100) = 49.99 Ω, so the answer is **B**. ***[1 mark]***

2 a) t = 0.32 seconds, v = 2.0 ms^{-1} ***[1 mark]***

b) E.g. The results do not support this conclusion ***[1 mark]***, because the student has only collected data for a small range of times so he cannot draw conclusions about times longer than those he measured ***[1 mark]*** / because the student has only investigated one object so he cannot draw conclusions about other objects ***[1 mark]***.

Module 2 — Foundations of Physics

Page 11 — Quantities and Units

1 a) S.I. unit of mass = kg. S.I. unit of volume = m^3.
$\rho = m / V$ and volume is length cubed, so in S.I. base units
ρ = kg / m^3 = **kg m^{-3}** ***[1 mark]***

b) m = 9.8 g = 9.8 × 10^{-3} kg
V = (11 mm)^3 = (11 × 10^{-3} m)^3 = 1.331 × 10^{-6} m^3 ***[1 mark]***
$\rho = m / V$ = (9.8 × 10^{-3}) ÷ (1.331 × 10^{-6})
= 7362.88... = **7400 kg m^{-3} (to 2 s.f.)** ***[1 mark]***
You could also have worked this out in g mm^{-3} then converted your answer, but this way is much easier.

Page 13 — Measurements and Uncertainties

1 a) (0.02 ÷ 0.52) × 100 = 3.846... = **3.8 % (to 2 s.f.)** ***[1 mark]***

b) (0.02 ÷ 0.94) × 100 = 2.127... = **2.1% (to 2 s.f.)** ***[1 mark]***

c) acceleration = change in velocity / time = (0.94 – 0.52) ÷ 2.5 = 0.168 ms^{-2} ***[1 mark]***
Absolute error in change of velocity = 0.02 + 0.02 = 0.04 ms^{-1}
Percentage error in change of velocity: (0.04 ÷ (0.94 – 0.52)) × 100 = 9.523...%
[1 mark]
Percentage error in time taken = (0.5 ÷ 2.5) × 100 = 20%
Percentage error in acceleration = 9.523...% + 20% = 29.523...% ***[1 mark]***
Absolute error in acceleration = 0.168 × (29.523... ÷ 100) = 0.0496 ms^{-2}
So the acceleration = **0.17 ± 0.05 ms^{-2} (to 2 s.f.)** ***[1 mark]***

Page 15 — Scalars and Vectors

Weight 75 N
Resultant force, F
θ
Wind 20 N

1 $F^2 = 20^2 + 75^2 = 6025$
So F = 78 N (to 2 s.f.)
$\tan\theta$ = 20 / 75 = 0.266...
So $\theta = \tan^{-1}$ 0.266... = 15° (to 2 s.f.)
The resultant force on the rock is **78 N (to 2 s.f.)** ***[1 mark]*** at an angle of **15° (to 2 s.f.)** ***[1 mark]*** to the vertical.
Make sure you know which angle you're finding — and label it on your diagram.

2

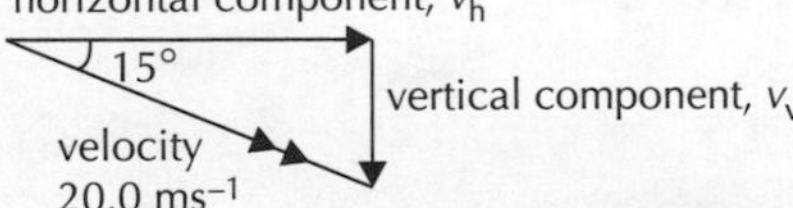

horizontal component v_h = 20.0 × cos 15.0°
= **19.3 ms^{-1} (to 3 s.f.)** ***[1 mark]***
vertical component v_v = 20 × sin 15.0°
= **5.18 ms^{-1} (to 3 s.f.)** ***[1 mark]***

3 E.g.
current, v_{river} = 0.20 ms^{-1} v_h
120° 60°
driving velocity, v_{boat} = 1.54 ms^{-1}
R
v_v

horizontal component v_{river} = 0.20 ms^{-1}
vertical component v_{river} = 0 ms^{-1}
horizontal component v_{boat} = 1.54 × cos 60 = 0.77 ms^{-1}
vertical component v_{boat} = 1.54 × sin 60 = 1.333... ms^{-1}

Answers

So, horizontal $v_{resultant} = 0.20 + 0.77 = 0.97 \text{ ms}^{-1}$ ***[1 mark]***
vertical $v_{resultant} = 0 + 1.333... = 1.333... \text{ ms}^{-1}$ ***[1 mark]***
Combine the vertical and horizontal components of R.

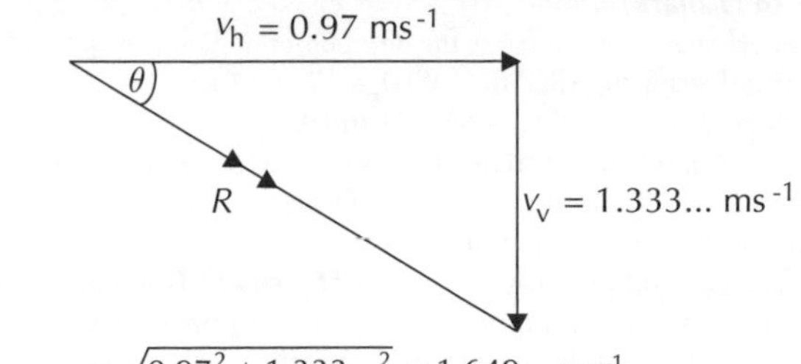

$v_{resultant} = \sqrt{0.97^2 + 1.333...^2} = 1.649... \text{ ms}^{-1}$

$= \mathbf{1.6 \text{ ms}^{-1}}$ **(to 2 s.f)** ***[1 mark]***

$\tan\theta = 1.333... \div 0.97 = \tan^{-1} 1.374...$ so $\theta =$ **54° (to 2 s.f.)**

So the resultant velocity of the boat is 1.6 ms^{-1} at an angle of 54° to the current ***[1 mark]***.

Module 3: Section 1 — Motion

Page 17 — Motion with Constant Acceleration

1 a) $a = -9.81 \text{ ms}^{-2}$, $t = 5$ s, $u = 0 \text{ ms}^{-1}$, $v = ?$
use : $v = u + at$
$v = 0 + 5 \times -9.81$ ***[1 mark]***
$v = -49.05 =$ **-49 ms^{-1} (to 2 s.f.)** ***[1 mark]***.
NB: It's negative because she's falling downwards and we took upwards as the positive direction.

b) Use: $s = \left(\frac{u+v}{2}\right)t$ or $s = ut + \frac{1}{2} at^2$
$s = \frac{-49.05}{2} \times 5$ $s = 0 + \frac{1}{2} \times -9.81 \times 5^2$ ***[1 mark]***
$s = -122.625$ m $s = -122.625$ m
So she falls **120 m (to 2 s.f.)** ***[1 mark]***

2 a) $v = 0 \text{ ms}^{-1}$, $t = 3.2$ s, $s = 40$ m, $u = ?$
use: $s = \left(\frac{u+v}{2}\right)t$
$40 = 3.2u \div 2$ ***[1 mark]***
$u = 80 \div 3.2 =$ **25 ms^{-1}** ***[1 mark]***

b) Use: $v^2 = u^2 + 2as$
$0 = 25^2 + 80a$ ***[1 mark]***
$-80a = 625$
$a = -7.81... =$ **-7.8 ms^{-2} (to 2 s.f.)** ***[1 mark]***
You could also have solved this using $v = u + at$.

3 a) Take upstream as negative: $v = 5 \text{ ms}^{-1}$, $a = 6 \text{ ms}^{-2}$, $s = 1.2$ m, $u = ?$, so use: $v^2 = u^2 + 2as$
$5^2 = u^2 + 2 \times 6 \times 1.2$ ***[1 mark]***
$u^2 = 25 - 14.4 = 10.6$
$u = -3.255... =$ **-3.3 ms^{-1} (to 2 s.f.)** ***[1 mark]***
The negative root is taken because the boat is pushed upstream at the start, which we've taken to be the negative direction.

b) From furthest point: $u = 0 \text{ ms}^{-1}$, $a = 6 \text{ ms}^{-2}$, $v = 5 \text{ ms}^{-1}$, $s = ?$
use: $v^2 = u^2 + 2as$ ***[1 mark]***
$5^2 = 0 + 2 \times 6 \times s$
$s = 25 \div 12 =$ **2.1 m (to 2 s.f.)** ***[1 mark]***

4 a) Use $v = u + at$
In the first second, $u = 3$, $v = 3 + a$
In the second second, $u = 3 + a$, $v = (3 + a) + a = 3 + 2a$
In the third second, $u = 3 + 2a$, $v = (3 + 2a) + a = 3 + 3a$
[1 mark]
For the third second, use: $s = \left(\frac{u+v}{2}\right)t$

$$6 = \left(\frac{3 + 2a + 3 + 3a}{2}\right) \times 1 = \left(\frac{6 + 5a}{2}\right)$$

$12 = 6 + 5a$

$6 = 5a$ so $a =$ **1.2 ms^{-1}** ***[1 mark]***

There's another way to work out acceleration — the cyclist travelled 6 m in the third second, so at $t = 2.5$ seconds his speed must have been exactly 6 ms^{-1}. You can use acceleration = change in speed ÷ time taken and get $a = 3 \div 2.5 = 1.2 \text{ ms}^{-2}$.

b) In the fourth second, $u = 3 + 3a$, $v = (3 + 3a) + a = 3 + 4a$
Use $s = \left(\frac{u+v}{2}\right)t$ for the fourth second:
$s = \frac{1}{2}(3 + 3a + 3 + 4a) \times 1 = \frac{1}{2}(6 + 7 \times 1.2) \times 1$
$= 3 + 4.2 =$ **7.2 m** ***[1 mark]***

Page 19 — Free Fall

1 a) The student needs the computer to record:
The time for the first strip of card to pass through the beam ***[1 mark]***
The time for the second strip of card to pass through the beam ***[1 mark]***
The time between these events ***[1 mark]***

b) Average speed of first strip while it breaks the light beam = width of strip ÷ time to pass through beam ***[1 mark]***
Average speed of second strip while it breaks the light beam = width of strip ÷ time to pass through beam ***[1 mark]***
Acceleration = (second speed – first speed) ÷ time between light beam being broken ***[1 mark]***

c) E.g. the device will accelerate while the beam is broken by the strips ***[1 mark]***.

2 a) You know $s = 5$ m, $a = -g$, $v = 0$
You need to find u, so use $v^2 = u^2 + 2as$
$0 = u^2 - 2 \times 9.81 \times 5$ ***[1 mark]***
$u^2 = 98.1$, so $u = 9.90... =$ **9.9 ms^{-1} (to 2 s.f.)** ***[1 mark]***

b) You know $a = -g$, $v = 0$ at highest point, $u = 9.90... \text{ ms}^{-1}$
You need to find t, so use $v = u + at$
$0 = 9.90... - 9.81t$ ***[1 mark]***
$t = 9.90.../9.81 =$ **1.0 s (to 2 s.f.)** ***[1 mark]***

c) Her velocity as she lands back on the trampoline will be **-9.9 ms^{-1} (to 2 s.f.)** (same magnitude, opposite direction) ***[1 mark]***

Page 21 — Projectile Motion

1 a) You only need to worry about the vertical motion of the stone.
$u = 0 \text{ ms}^{-1}$, $s = -560$ m, $a = -g = -9.81 \text{ ms}^{-2}$, $t = ?$
You need to find t, so use: $s = ut + \frac{1}{2} at^2$
$-560 = 0 + \frac{1}{2} \times -9.81 \times t^2$
$t = \sqrt{\frac{2 \times (-560)}{-9.81}}$ ***[1 mark]***
$t = 10.68... =$ **11 s (to 2 s.f.)** ***[1 mark]***

b) You know that in the horizontal direction:
$v = 20$ m/s, $t = 10.68...$ s, $a = 0$, $s = ?$
$s = v \times t = 20 \times 10.68...$ ***[1 mark]***
$s = 213.69... =$ **210 m (to 2 s.f.)** ***[1 mark]***

2 C ***[1 mark]***
Use $v^2 = u^2 + 2as$ to find the vertical displacement when $v = 0$. The arrow was fired from 1 m above the ground so don't forget to include the extra metre in your calculations.

Page 23 — Displacement-Time Graphs

1 Split graph into four sections:

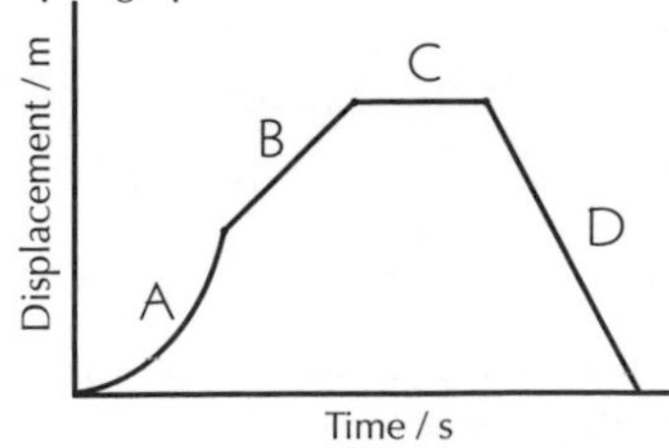

A: acceleration ***[1 mark]***
B: constant velocity ***[1 mark]***
C: stationary ***[1 mark]***
D: constant velocity in opposite direction to A and B ***[1 mark]***

Answers

2 a)

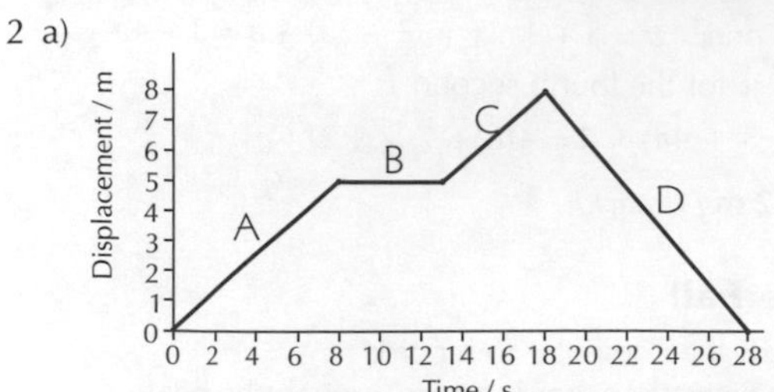

[4 marks — 1 mark for each section correctly drawn]

b) At A: $v = s \div t = 5 \div 8 = 0.625$ = **0.63 ms⁻¹ (to 2 s.f.)**
At B: v = **0 ms⁻¹**
At C: $v = 3 \div 5$ = **0.6 ms⁻¹**
At D: $v = -8 \div 10$ = **–0.8 ms⁻¹**
[2 marks for all correct or just 1 mark for 2 or 3 correct]

Page 25 — Velocity-Time Graphs

1 a)

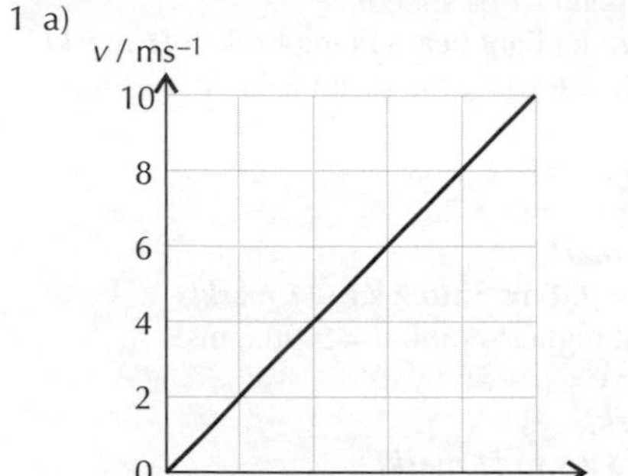

[1 mark for correct axes, 1 mark for correct line]

b) Use $s = ut + \frac{1}{2}at^2$
$t = 1$, s = **1 m**
$t = 2$, s = **4 m**
$t = 3$, s = **9 m**
$t = 4$, s = **16 m**
$t = 5$, s = **25 m**
[2 marks for all correct or 1 mark for at least 3 pairs of values right]

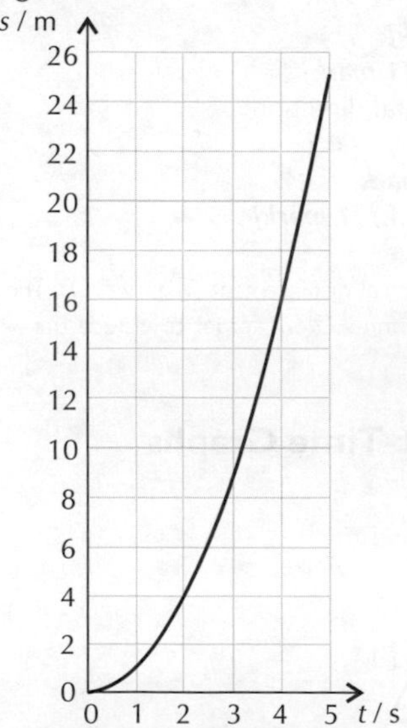

[1 mark for correctly labelled axes, 1 mark for correct curve]

c) E.g. another way to calculate displacement is to find the area under the velocity-time graph *[1 mark]*.
E.g. total displacement = ½ × 5 ×10 = **25 m** *[1 mark]*

Page 27 — Motion Experiments and Stopping Distances

1 a) Reaction time is 0.5 s, speed is 20 ms⁻¹
$s = vt = 20 \times 0.5$ *[1 mark]* = **10 m** *[1 mark]*

b) Use $F = ma$ to get a: $a = -10\,000/850 = -11.76...$ *[1 mark]*
Use $v^2 = u^2 + 2as$, and rearrange
$s = (0^2 - 20^2) \div (2 \times -11.76...)$ *[1 mark]*
= **17 m** *[1 mark]*
Remember that a force against the direction of motion is negative.

c) No. Total stopping distance = 10 + 17 = 27 m
She stops 3 m before the cow. *[1 mark]*

2 a) Using a rougher ramp material would create more friction *[1 mark]*, which would cause more drag on the toy car and decrease its velocity *[1 mark]*.

b) E.g. The starting position of the car *[1 mark]*. The higher the car started up the ramp, the more time it would have to accelerate, so the greater its velocity would be *[1 mark]*. /
Using similar sized but different shaped cars *[1 mark]*. The cars which were more streamlined would achieve a higher velocity as they are less affected by air resistance *[1 mark]*.

Module 3: Section 2 — Forces in Action

Page 29 — Forces and Acceleration

1 a) b)

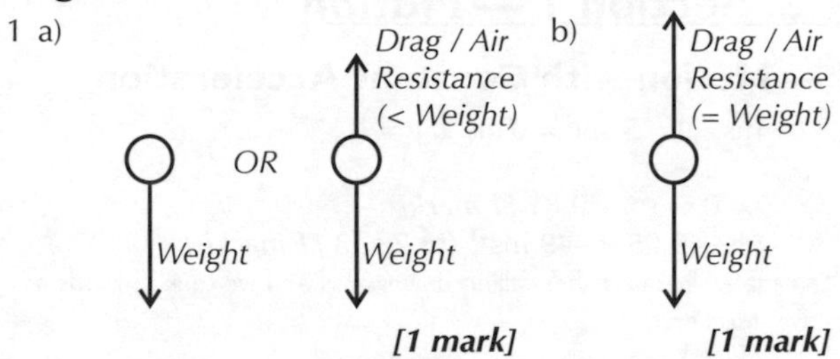

The relative sizes of the arrows in a force diagram tell you the relative magnitude of the forces.

2 a) Net force = 500 – 100 – 300 = **100 N** *[1 mark]*

b) $a = F \div m$ (from $F = ma$)
= 100 ÷ 250 = **0.4 ms⁻²** *[1 mark]*

Page 31 — Forces and Equilibrium

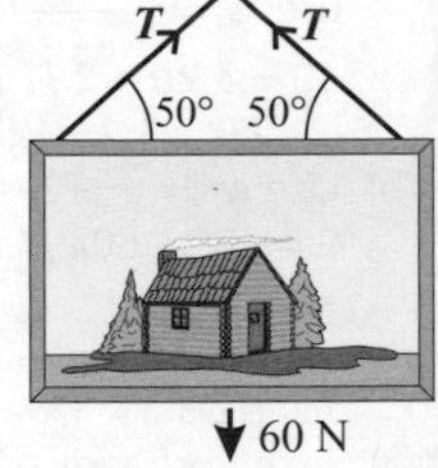

1 Weight = vertical component of tension × 2
$60 = 2T \sin 50°$ *[1 mark]*
$60 = 2T \times 0.766...$
$78.3... = 2T$
$T = 39.1...$ = **39 N (to 2 s.f.)** *[1 mark]*

2

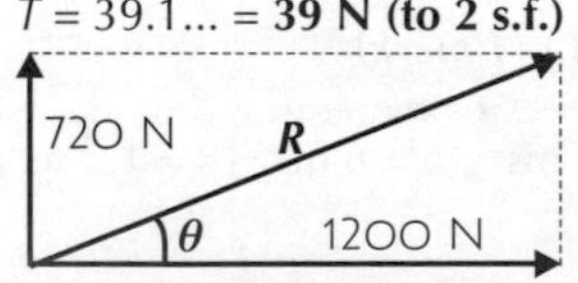

By Pythagoras:
$R = \sqrt{1200^2 + 720^2} = 1399.42...$ = **1400 N (to 3 s.f.)** *[1 mark]*
$\tan\theta = \frac{720}{1200}$, so $\theta = \tan^{-1} 0.6 = 30.96... = 31.0°$ (to 3 s.f.)
So the direction of the resultant force is **31.0° (to 3 s.f.) from the horizontal** *[1 mark]*

Page 33 — Mass, Weight and Centre of Mass

1 B *[1 mark]*
On Earth, W = mg, so m = W/g = X/g.

2 a) Hang the object freely from a point so that it hangs vertically. Hang a plumb bob from the same point, and use it to draw a vertical line down the object *[1 mark]*. Repeat for a different point and find the point of intersection *[1 mark]*.
The centre of gravity is halfway through the thickness of the object (by symmetry) at the point of intersection *[1 mark]*.

b) E.g. Source: the object and/or plumb line might move slightly while you're drawing the vertical line *[1 mark]*.
Reduced by: hang the object from a third point to confirm the position of the point of intersection *[1 mark]*.

Answers

Page 36 — Drag and Terminal Velocity

1 a) The velocity increases at a steady rate, which means the acceleration is constant ***[1 mark]***.
Constant acceleration means there must be no atmospheric resistance (atmospheric resistance would increase with velocity, leading to a decrease in acceleration). So there must be no atmosphere ***[1 mark]***.

b)

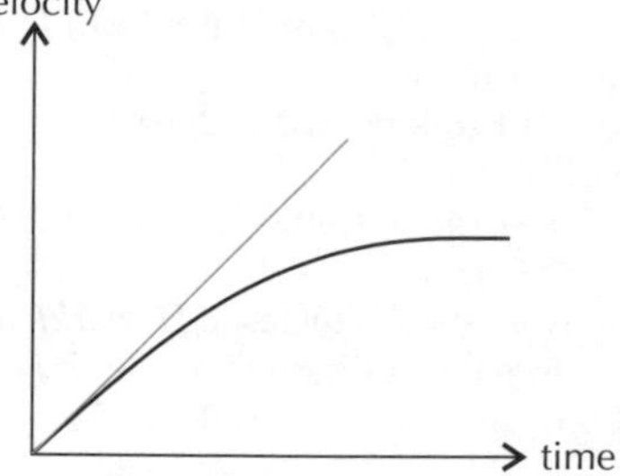

[1 mark for a smooth curve that levels out, 1 mark for correct position relative to existing line]
Your graph must be a smooth curve which levels out. It must NOT go down at the end.

c) (The graph becomes less steep)
because the acceleration is decreasing ***[1 mark]***
because air resistance increases with speed ***[1 mark]***
(The graph levels out)
because air resistance has become equal to weight ***[1 mark]***
If the question says 'explain', you won't get marks for just describing what the graph shows — you have to say why it is that shape.

2 a) The 15 cm cone will have the lowest terminal velocity ***[1 mark]*** because it has the largest surface area and therefore the largest drag ***[1 mark]***.

b)

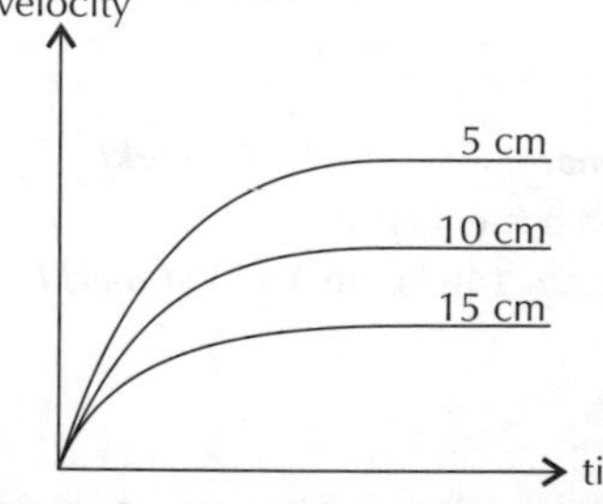

[3 marks, 1 mark for each correct line.]

c) E.g. The shape/slant/height of the cone because it would affect the amount of air resistance ***[1 mark]***.

d) The curve for the largest cone would reach a higher terminal velocity ***[1 mark]*** because the shape is more streamlined ***[1 mark]*** so the air resistance would be lower at a given speed ***[1 mark]***.

Page 37 — Density, Pressure and Upthrust

1 a) $\rho = \frac{m}{V}$
V of cylinder $= \pi r^2 h = \pi \times 4^2 \times 6 = 301.59...\ \text{cm}^{-3}$ ***[1 mark]***
$\rho = 820 \div 301.59... = 2.71... =$ **2.7 g cm^{-3} (to 2 s.f.)** ***[1 mark]***

b) $V = 5 \times 5 \times 5 = 125\ \text{cm}^3$
$m = \rho \times V = 2.71... \times 125 = 339.86... =$ **340 g (to 2 s.f.)** ***[1 mark]***

2 $A = 1.72 \times 1.72 = 2.9584\ \text{m}^2$ ***[1 mark]***
$p = \frac{F}{A} = \frac{17}{2.9584} = 5.746... =$ **5.75 Pa (to 3 s.f.)** ***[1 mark]***

3 $p = h\rho g = 2.4 \times 1024 \times 9.81 = 24109.056$
= 24000 Pa (to 2 s.f.) ***[1 mark]***

4 Upthrust = weight of fluid displaced.
Volume of water displaced $= \frac{4}{3}\pi r^3 = \frac{4}{3}\pi \times (0.052)^3$
$= 5.889... \times 10^{-4}$ m ***[1 mark]***
$\rho = \frac{m}{V}$, so mass of water displaced $= \rho V$
$= 1050 \times 5.889... \times 10^{-4}$
$= 0.6184...$ kg ***[1 mark]***
$W = mg = 0.6184... \times 9.81 = 6.066...$
= **6.07 N (to 3 s.f.)** ***[1 mark]***

Page 39 — Moments and Torques

1 torque = force × distance
$60 = 0.4F$, so $F =$ **150 N** ***[1 mark]***

2
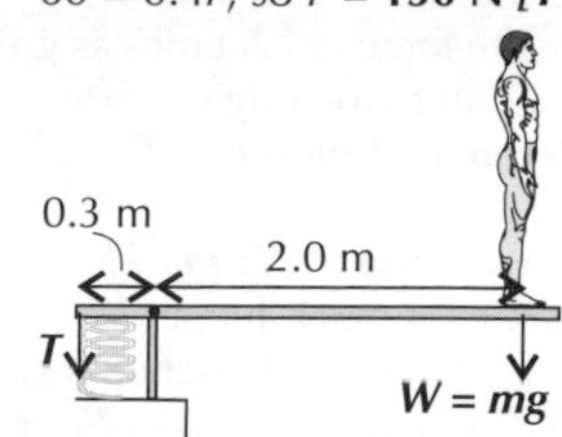

clockwise moment = anticlockwise moment
$W \times 2.0 = T \times 0.3$
$60 \times 9.81 \times 2.0 = T \times 0.3$ ***[1 mark]***
$T =$ **3900 N (to 2 s.f.)** ***[1 mark]***
The tension in the spring is equal and opposite to the force exerted by the diver on the spring.

Module 3: Section 3 — Work, Energy and Power

Page 41 — Work and Power

1 a)
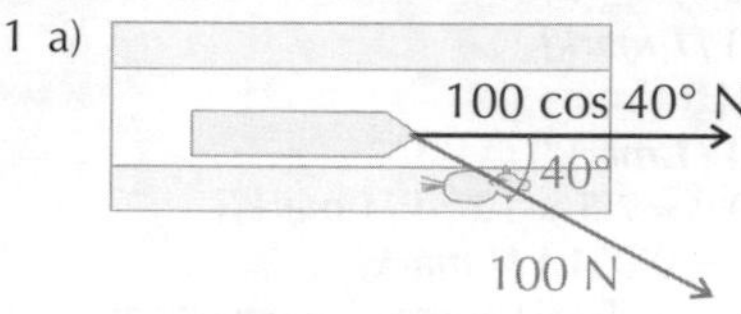

Force in direction of travel = 100 cos40° = 76.6... N ***[1 mark]***
$W = Fx = 76.6... \times 1500 = 114906...$
= **110 000 J (to 2 s.f.)** ***[1 mark]***

b) Use $P = Fv$
= 100 cos40° × 0.8 ***[1 mark]*** = 61.2... = **61 W (to 2 s.f.)** ***[1 mark]***

2 a) Use $W = Fx$
$= 20 \times 9.81 \times 3$ ***[1 mark]*** $= 588.6 =$ **590 J (to 2 s.f.)** ***[1 mark]***
Remember that 20 kg is not the force — it's the mass. So you need to multiply it by 9.81 Nkg^{-1} to get the weight.

b) Use $P = Fv$
$= 20 \times 9.81 \times 0.25$ ***[1 mark]*** $= 49.05 =$ **49 W (to 2 s.f.)** ***[1 mark]***

Page 43 — Conservation of Energy and Efficiency

1 a) Use $E_k = ½mv^2$ and $E_p = mgh$ ***[1 mark]***
$½mv^2 = mgh$
$½v^2 = gh$
$v^2 = 2gh = 2 \times 9.81 \times 2 = 39.24$ ***[1 mark]***
$v = \sqrt{39.24} =$ **6.3 ms^{-1} (to 2 s.f.)** ***[1 mark]***
'No friction' allows you to say that the changes in kinetic and potential energy will be the same.

b) 2 m — no friction means the kinetic energy will all change back into potential energy, so he will rise back up to the same height as he started ***[1 mark]***.

c) Put in some more energy by actively 'skating' / 'pumping the board' ***[1 mark]***.

2 a) If there's no air resistance, $E_k = E_p = mgh$ ***[1 mark]***
$E_k = 0.02 \times 9.81 \times 8 = 1.5696 =$ **1.6 J (to 2 s.f.)** ***[1 mark]***

b) If the ball rebounds to 6.5 m, it has gravitational potential energy:
$E_p = mgh = 0.02 \times 9.81 \times 6.5 = 1.2753$ ***[1 mark]***
So $1.5696 - 1.2753 = 0.2943 =$ **0.29 J (to 2 s.f.)** is converted to other forms ***[1 mark]***.
You could also work out the loss of E_p from the difference in height — $E_p = 0.02 \times 9.81 \times (8 - 6.5) = 0.29$ J (to 2 s.f.).

3 Use efficiency $= \frac{\text{useful output energy}}{\text{total input energy}} \times 100\ \%$
$= (140 - 65) \div 140 \times 100 = 53.5... =$ **54% (to 2 s.f.)** ***[1 mark]***

Answers

Module 3: Section 4 — Materials

Page 45 — Hooke's Law

1 a) Force is proportional to extension. The force is 1.5 times as great, so the new extension will also be 1.5 times the original extension. new extension = 1.5 × 4.0 mm = **6.0 mm** ***[1 mark]***

b) $F = kx$ and so $k = F/x$
$k = 10 \div 4.0 \times 10^{-3}$ = **2500 Nm^{-1}** or **2.5 Nmm^{-1}** ***[1 mark]***

c) Any one from e.g. the string now stretches much further for small increases in force ***[1 mark]***. / When the string is loosened it is longer than at the start ***[1 mark]***.

2 The rubber band does not obey Hooke's law ***[1 mark]*** because when the force is doubled from 2.5 N to 5.0 N, the extension increases by a factor of 2.3. ***[1 mark]***.
Or you could show that k is different for 2.5 N and 5.0 N.

Page 47 — Stress, Strain and Elastic Potential Energy

1 a) $\varepsilon = x/l = 4.0 \times 10^{-3}/2.00$ = **2.0×10^{-3} (to 2 s.f.)** ***[1 mark]***

b) $\sigma = F/A$
$A = \pi r^2$ or $\pi(d^2/4) = \pi \times ((1.0 \times 10^{-3})^2 \div 4)$
$= 7.8539... \times 10^{-7}$ m^2 ***[1 mark]***
$\sigma = F/A = 300/(7.8539... \times 10^{-7})$
= **3.8×10^8 Nm^{-2} (to 2 s.f.)** ***[1 mark]***

2 a) $F = kx$ so $k = F/x = 50/(3.0 \times 10^{-3})$
= **1.7×10^4 Nm^{-1} (to 2 s.f.)** ***[1 mark]***

b) $E = ½Fx = ½ \times 50 \times 3.0 \times 10^{-3}$ = **7.5×10^{-2} J** ***[1 mark]***

3 $E = ½kx^2 = ½ \times 40.8 \times 0.05^2 = 0.051$ J ***[1 mark]***
To find maximum speed, assume all this energy is converted to kinetic energy in the ball. $E_{kinetic} = E$
$E = ½mv^2$, so $v^2 = 2E/m$ ***[1 mark]***
$v^2 = (2 \times 0.051)/0.012 = 8.5$, so v = **2.92 ms^{-1} (to 3 s.f.)** ***[1 mark]***

Page 49 — The Young Modulus

1 a) Cross-sectional area = πr^2 or $\pi(d^2/4)$.
So the cross-sectional area = $\pi \times ((0.6 \times 10^{-3})^2 \div 4)$
$= 2.827.... \times 10^{-7}$ = **2.8×10^{-7} m^2 (to 2 s.f.)** ***[1 mark]***

b) $\sigma = F/A = 80/(2.827... \times 10^{-7}) = 2.829... \times 10^8$
= **2.8×10^8 Nm^{-2} (to 2 s.f.)** ***[1 mark]***

c) $\varepsilon = x/l = 3.6 \times 10^{-3}/2.50$ = **1.44×10^{-3}** ***[1 mark]***

d) $E = \sigma/\varepsilon = 2.829... \times 10^8 /(1.44 \times 10^{-3})$ ***[1 mark]*** $= 1.964... \times 10^{11}$
= **2.0×10^{11} Nm^{-2} (to 2 s.f.)** ***[1 mark]***

2 a) $E = \sigma/\varepsilon$ so $\varepsilon = \sigma/E = 2.6 \times 10^8/1.3 \times 10^{11}$ ***[1 mark]***
= **2.0×10^{-3}** ***[1 mark]***

b) $\sigma = F/A$ so $A = F/\sigma = 100/(2.6 \times 10^8)$ = **3.8×10^{-7} m^2 (to 2 s.f.)** ***[1 mark]***

c) Elastic potential energy per unit volume = $½ \times \sigma \times \varepsilon$
$= ½ \times 2.6 \times 10^8 \times 2.0 \times 10^{-3}$ = **2.6×10^5 Jm^{-3}** ***[1 mark]***

Page 51 — Interpreting Stress-Strain Graphs

1 a) E.g.

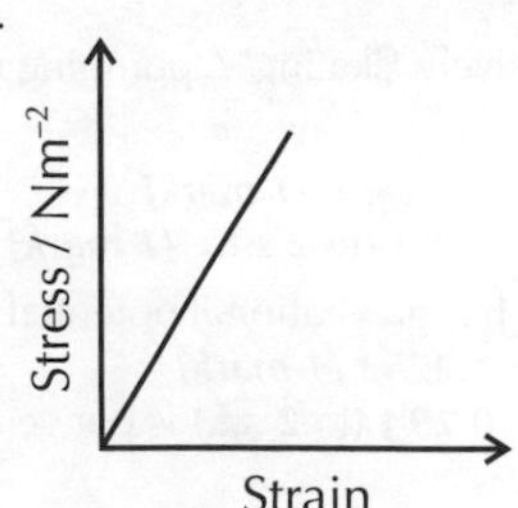

[1 mark for straight line through the origin.]

b) E.g. Both materials will initially obey Hooke's law. After a certain point, the hardened steel will snap ***[1 mark]***, whereas the stress-strain graph for copper will begin to curve / copper will start to show large deformations for small increases in load / copper will begin to deform plastically ***[1 mark]***.

2 a) A ***[1 mark]***

b) B ***[1 mark]***

Module 3: Section 5 — Newton's Laws of Motion and Momentum

Page 53 — Momentum and Impulse

1 a) total momentum before collision = total momentum after
$(0.145 \times 1.94) + 0 = (0.145 \times -0.005) + 0.148v$ ***[1 mark]***
$0.2813 + 0.000725 = 0.148v$, so $v = 1.90557...$
= **1.9 ms^{-1} (to 2 s.f.)** ***[1 mark]***

b) Kinetic energy before the collision =
$(½ \times 0.145 \times 1.94^2) + (½ \times 0.148 \times 0^2) = 0.272861$ J
Kinetic energy after the collision =
$(½ \times 0.145 \times 0.005^2) + (½ \times 0.148 \times 1.90557...^2) = 0.26871...$ J ***[1 mark]***
The collision is not perfectly elastic / is inelastic ***[1 mark]***, as the kinetic energy is greater before the collision than after it ***[1 mark]***.

c) $F\Delta t = \Delta p = (0.145 \times 0.005) - (0.145 \times 0) = 0.000725$
so $F = \Delta p \div \Delta t$
$= 0.000725 \div 0.15$ ***[1 mark]***
$= 0.00483...$ = **4.8×10^{-3} N (to 2 s.f.)** ***[1 mark]***

Page 55 — Newton's Laws of Motion

1 a) When the parachutist first jumps out of the plane, the only vertical force acting on her is due to gravity, so there is a net downward force ***[1 mark]***. Newton's 2nd law states that, for a body of constant mass, the acceleration is proportional to the net force, so she will accelerate downwards ***[1 mark]***.

b) $F = ma = mg = 78 \times 9.81$ = **765 N (to 3 s.f.)** ***[1 mark]***

c) Newton's 1st law states that a net force is needed to change the velocity of an object — the parachutist's velocity is not changing, so the net force acting on her must be zero ***[1 mark]***.

2 $F = \Delta p / \Delta t$, where $F = 2143 - 213 = 1930$, $\Delta t = 15$
and $\Delta p = m\Delta v = m \times (26.3 - 5.5) = 20.8m$
So $1930 = 20.8m \div 15$
$m = (1930 \times 15) \div 20.8$ ***[1 mark]*** $= 1391.82...$ ***[1 mark]***
So the combined mass of the passengers is
$1391.82... - 1244 = 147.82...$ = **148 kg (to 3 s.f.)** ***[1 mark]***

Page 57 — Car Safety

1 ***5-6 marks:***
The answer clearly explains more than one way that air bags protect passengers, with reference to Newton's second law of motion to explain the forces involved where appropriate. The answer clearly explains the risks associated with air bags when used incorrectly, and suggests how to reduce the risks.
The answer is structured in a logical way, with relevant information supporting it throughout.

3-4 marks:
The answer describes ways in which air bags protect passengers, and explains them with reference to forces involved. The explanation is partly incomplete. The answer gives the risks associated with air bags when used incorrectly, and includes some explanation of these risks or ways to reduce the risks.
The answer has some logical structure, with mostly relevant information supporting it.

1-2 marks:
The answer includes some description of how air bags protect passengers, but no relevant explanation involving forces. The answer has some limited description of the risks associated with air bags when used incorrectly.
The answer is basic, poorly structured and unsupported by relevant information.

0 marks:
No relevant information is given.

Here are some points your answer may include:

- Air bags protect passengers by stopping them from hitting the dashboard/steering wheel/hard surfaces inside the car in a crash.

Answers

- Air bags increase the time taken for passengers to come to a complete stop.
- Newton's 2nd Law, $F = \Delta p \div \Delta t$, so by increasing the time that passengers take to come to a stop, air bags reduce the forces acting on passengers in a crash (for a given momentum change).
- Air bags can be dangerous if a passenger isn't properly restrained / isn't wearing a seat belt.
- This is because passengers who aren't properly restrained keep moving forwards in a crash and hit the air bag whilst it is still inflating / with a lot of force.
- This risk can be reduced by wearing a seat belt at all times.
- Air bags are also dangerous if used with rear-facing child seats.
- This is because the air bag inflates behind the child seat, so can throw the child into the car seat with a lot of force.
- This risk can be reduced by not placing rear-facing child seats in seats where an air bag is fitted.

Extra Exam Practice for Module 3

Pages 58-59

2 a) Some of the elastic potential energy (E) stored in the spring is converted to the kinetic energy of the pellet. Find the elastic potential energy when the spring is fully compressed:

$x = 4.0 \text{ cm} = 0.040 \text{ m}$,

$E = \frac{1}{2}kx^2 = \frac{1}{2} \times 275 \times 0.040^2 = 0.22 \text{ J}$ ***[1 mark]***

92% of the elastic potential energy is transferred to kinetic energy (the useful output energy).

$\text{efficiency} = \frac{\text{useful output energy}}{\text{total input energy}} \times 100$

$\text{useful output energy} = \frac{\text{efficiency}}{100} \times \text{total input energy}$

$= \frac{92}{100} \times 0.22 = 0.2024 \text{ J}$ ***[1 mark]***

Rearrange $E_k = \frac{1}{2}mv^2$ to make v the subject: $v = \sqrt{\frac{2E_k}{m}}$

$m = 1.2 \text{ g} = 1.2 \times 10^{-3} \text{ kg}$

$v = \sqrt{\frac{2 \times 0.2024}{1.2 \times 10^{-3}}}$ ***[1 mark]***

$= 18.366... \text{ ms}^{-1} =$ **18 ms^{-1} (to 2 s.f.)** ***[1 mark]***

b) $F = \frac{\Delta p}{\Delta t}$ and $p = mv$

The gun and pellet are still to begin with ($v = 0$), so the total momentum before the pellet was fired = 0.

Momentum is always conserved, so the total momentum after the pellet was fired = 0. This means that the magnitude of the change in momentum of the pellet, Δp_{pellet}, must equal the magnitude of the change in momentum of the gun as it recoils.

$\Delta p_{pellet} = ((1.2 \times 10^{-3}) \times 18.366...) - 0$

$= 0.02203... \text{ kg ms}^{-1} = \Delta p_{gun}$ ***[1 mark]***

Resultant force acting on the gun, $F = 4.1 \text{ N}$

$\Delta t = \frac{\Delta p}{F} = \frac{0.02203...}{4.1} = 5.3756... \times 10^{-3} \text{ s}$

$= 5.4 \times 10^{-3}$ s (to 2 s.f.) ***[1 mark]***

You'd still get the marks if you used 18 ms^{-1} for the initial speed of the pellet.

c) No forces act horizontally, so the pellet maintains a constant horizontal velocity throughout its flight:

$v_h = v\cos\theta = (18.366...\cos 20.0°) \text{ ms}^{-1} = 17.258... \text{ ms}^{-1}$.

Resolve vertically, taking upwards as positive to calculate the vertical component of the velocity as the pellet hits the lawn:

$u = (18.366...\sin 20.0°) \text{ ms}^{-1}$, $v = ?$, $a = -9.81 \text{ ms}^{-2}$, $t = 1.7 \text{ s}$

$v = u + at = 18.366...\sin 20.0° + (-9.81 \times 1.7)$

$= -10.395... \text{ ms}^{-1}$ ***[1 mark]***

So as the pellet hits the lawn:

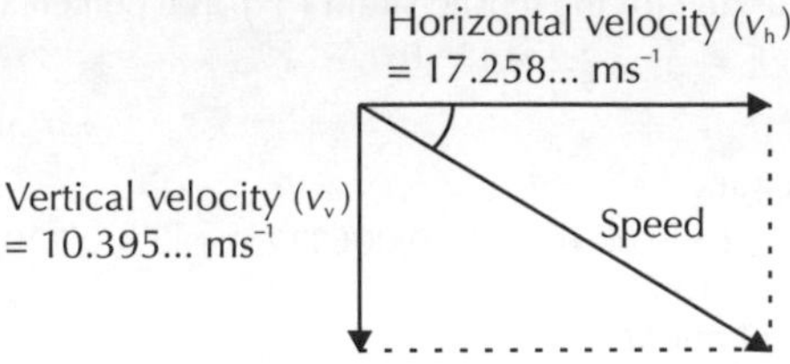

Calculate the speed of the pellet using Pythagoras' theorem:

$\text{speed} = \sqrt{v_h^2 + v_v^2} = \sqrt{17.258...^2 + 10.395...^2}$

$= 20.147... \text{ ms}^{-1} =$ **20 ms^{-1} (to 2 s.f.)** ***[1 mark]***

Calculate θ using trigonometry:

$\tan\theta = \frac{\text{opposite}}{\text{adjacent}}$

$\theta = \tan^{-1}\left(\frac{10.395...}{17.258...}\right) = 31.060...° =$ **31° (to 2 s.f.)** ***[1 mark]***

You'd still get the marks if you used 18 ms^{-1} for the initial speed of the pellet.

3 a) $W = mg$ and $\rho = \frac{m}{V}$

Circumference $= 2\pi r = 9.2 \text{ cm} = 0.092 \text{ m}$

$r = \frac{0.092}{2\pi} = 0.01464... \text{ m}$

$V_{sphere} = \frac{4}{3}\pi r^3 = \frac{4}{3}\pi \times 0.01464...^3 = 1.3149... \times 10^{-5} \text{ m}^3$ ***[1 mark]***

$m_{sphere} = \rho V = (0.55 \times 10^3) \times (1.3149... \times 10^{-5})$

$= 7.2322... \times 10^{-3} \text{ kg}$ ***[1 mark]***

$W = mg = (7.2322... \times 10^{-3}) \times 9.81$

$= 0.07094... \text{ N} =$ **0.071 N (to 2 s.f.)** ***[1 mark]***

b) The mobile is in equilibrium. The principle of moments states that the sum of the clockwise moments will be balanced by the sum of the anticlockwise moments about the pivot.

The pivot is the point where the string is attached to the mobile.

Take moments about the point of suspension:

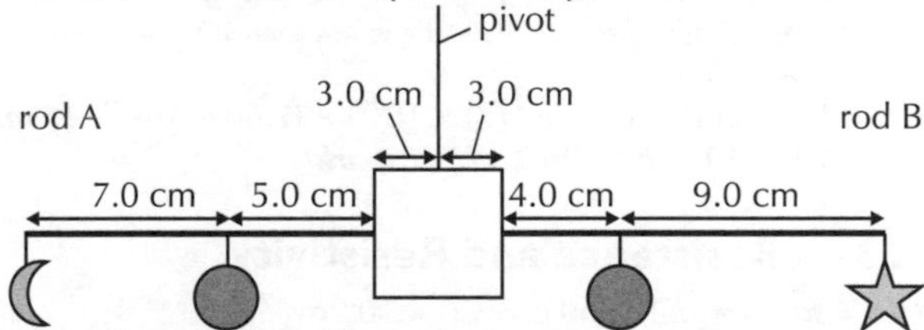

To calculate the moment of each component, use $M = F \times d$, where F = weight of a component and d = distance between the pivot and the component.

Anticlockwise moments:

$M_{moon} = 0.025 \times 0.15 = 0.00375 \text{ Nm}$

$M_{sphere} = 0.071 \times 0.08 = 0.00568 \text{ Nm}$

The centre of mass of an object is the point at which its whole weight can be considered to act. For uniform regular solids, the centre of mass is at the centre of the object, so the centre of mass of the cylindrical rod will occur halfway along its length.

$M_{rod\ A} = 0.120 \times 0.09 = 0.0108 \text{ Nm}$ ***[1 mark]***

The centre of the cube lies directly below the pivot, so it does not exert a moment.

Clockwise moments:

$M_{sphere} = 0.071 \times 0.07 = 0.00497 \text{ Nm}$

$M_{star} = 0.16\ W_{star}$

$M_{rod\ B} = 0.150 \times 0.095 = 0.01425 \text{ Nm}$ ***[1 mark]***

Equating clockwise and anticlockwise moments:

$0.00497 + 0.16\ W_{star} + 0.01425 = 0.00375 + 0.00568 + 0.0108$ ***[1 mark]***

$0.16\ W_{star} + 0.01922 = 0.02023$

$0.16\ W_{star} = 0.00101$

$W_{star} = 0.00101 \div 0.16 = 0.0063125 \text{ N}$

$= 0.0063$ N (to 2 s.f.) ***[1 mark]***

You still get full marks if you used the unrounded value of the weight of the sphere in your calculation.

Answers

c) The question is asking for the tensile strain $\left(\frac{x}{L}\right)$ as a percentage.
Young modulus, $E = \frac{\sigma}{\varepsilon} = 2.2 \times 10^9$ Pa
$\sigma = \frac{F}{A}$
F = weight of mobile
$= (4 \times 0.071) + (2 \times 0.025) + (2 \times 0.0063125) + (2 \times 0.120) + (2 \times 0.150) + 1.165$
$= 2.051625$ N ***[1 mark]***
radius of string is 1.0 mm $= 1 \times 10^{-3}$ m
$A = \pi r^2 = \pi \times (1 \times 10^{-3})^2 = 3.1415... \times 10^{-6}$ m²
$\sigma = \frac{F}{A} = \frac{2.051625}{3.1415... \times 10^{-6}} = 6.5305... \times 10^5$ Pa ***[1 mark]***
$\varepsilon = \frac{\sigma}{E} = \frac{6.5305... \times 10^5}{2.2 \times 10^9}$
$= 2.9684... \times 10^{-4}$ ***[1 mark]***
As a percentage:
$(2.9684... \times 10^{-4}) \times 100 = 0.029684...\%$
= 0.030% (to 2 s.f.) ***[1 mark]***
You also still get full marks for using the unrounded value of the weight of the sphere in your calculation.

Module 4: Section 1 — Electricity

Page 61 — Charge, Current and Potential Difference

1 Time in seconds = 10 × 60 = 600 s
$I = \Delta Q / \Delta t = 4500 / 600 =$ **7.5 A** ***[1 mark]***

2 Energy transferred to water = 0.88 × electrical energy input so the energy input will be 308 / 0.88 = 350 J ***[1 mark]***
$W = VQ$ so $Q = W / V$
$Q = 350 / 230 =$ **1.5 C (to 2 s.f.)** ***[1 mark]***
The heat energy that the kettle transfers to the water is less than the electrical energy input because the kettle is less than 100% efficient.

3 $I = Anev$ so $v = I / Ane$
so $v = 13 \div ((5.0 \times 10^{-6}) \times (1.0 \times 10^{29}) \times (1.60 \times 10^{-19}))$ ***[1 mark]***
= 1.6×10^{-4} ms⁻¹ (to 2 s.f.) ***[1 mark]***

Page 63 — Resistance and Resistivity

1 Area $= \pi r^2 = \pi(d/2)^2$ and $d = 1.0 \times 10^{-3}$ m
so area $= \pi \times (0.5 \times 10^{-3})^2 = 7.853... \times 10^{-7}$ m² ***[1 mark]***
$R = \rho L / A = (2.8 \times 10^{-8} \times 4) \div 7.853... \times 10^{-7}$ ***[1 mark]***
= 0.14 Ω (to 2 s.f.) ***[1 mark]***

2 a) $R = V / I = 7.00 \div (9.33 \times 10^{-3}) = 750.267...$
= 750 Ω (to 3 s.f.) ***[1 mark]***

b) For $V = 3.00$ V, $R = 3.00 \div (4.00 \times 10^{-3}) = 750$ Ω
for $V = 11.00$ V, $R = 11.00 \div (14.67 \times 10^{-3}) = 749.82...$ Ω ***[1 mark]***
The component is an ohmic conductor (for the range considered) ***[1 mark]***, because there is no significant change in resistance for different potential differences ***[1 mark]***.

Page 65 — I-V Characteristics

1 a)

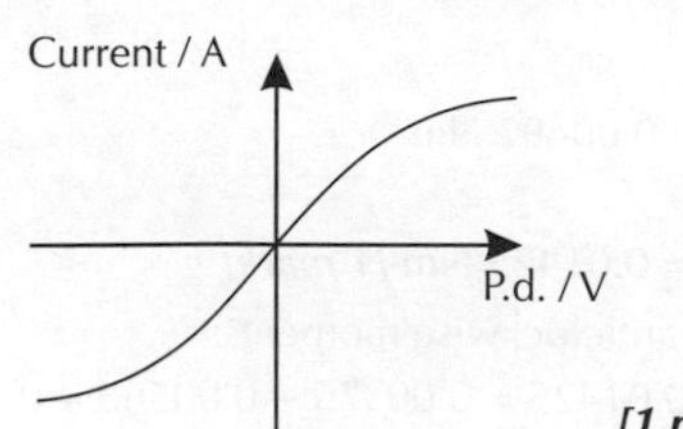

[1 mark]

b) E.g. The gradient of the *I-V* curve for a filament bulb gets shallower as the potential difference increases, whereas the gradient of the *I-V* curve for a thermistor gets steeper as the potential difference increases ***[1 mark]***. For both a filament bulb and a thermistor, increasing the voltage and therefore the current increases the temperature of the circuit component ***[1 mark]***. For a filament bulb, increasing the temperature increases the resistance, as it causes the metal ions in the wire filament to vibrate more, causing the charge carrying electrons to collide with them more frequently and impeding their flow ***[1 mark]***. For a thermistor, increasing the temperature decreases the resistance as it releases more charge carriers ***[1 mark]***.

Page 67 — Electrical Energy and Power

1 a) $I = P / V = 920 / 230 =$ **4.00 A (to 3 s.f.)** ***[1 mark]***

b) $I = V / R = 230 / 190 = 1.210... =$ **1.21 A (to 3 s.f.)** ***[1 mark]***

c) $P_{motor} = VI = 230 \times 1.210... = 278.421...$ W ***[1 mark]***
Total power = motor power + heater power
= 278.421... + 920 = **1.20 kW (to 3 s.f.)** ***[1 mark]***
You could also answer this question by calculating using $P_{total} = V_{total}I_{total}$ where $V_{total} = 230$ V (the source p.d.) and $I_{total} = 4.00 + 1.210...$ A.

2 a) Energy transferred $= W = VIt = 12 \times 48 \times 2.0$
= 1150 J (to 3 s.f.) ***[1 mark]***

b) Energy wasted in wires $= W = I^2Rt = 48^2 \times 0.01 \times 2.0$
= 46 J (to 2 s.f.) ***[1 mark]***

Page 69 — Domestic Energy and Energy Saving

1 a) $W = Pt$
i) $W = 1550 \times (15 \times 60) =$ **1 400 000 J (to 3 s.f.)** ***[1 mark]***
ii) $W = 1.55 \times (15 \div 60)$
$= 0.3875 =$ **0.388 kWh (to 3 s.f.)** ***[1 mark]***

b) Cost = number of units × price per unit
= 0.3875 × 15.9 = **6.16p (to 3 s.f.)** ***[1 mark]***

2 $P = VI = 230 \times (6.5 \times 10^{-3}) = 1.495$ W $= 0.001495$ kW ***[1 mark]***
$W = Pt = 0.001495 \times 10 = 0.01495$ kWh ***[1 mark]***
Cost = 0.01495 × 16.2 = 0.24219 = **0.24p (to 2 s.f.)** ***[1 mark]***

3 a) $W = Pt$
Model A: $W = 0.47 \times (135 \div 60)$
$= 1.0575 =$ **1.06 kWh (to 3 s.f.)** ***[1 mark]***
Model B: $W = 0.41 \times (125 \div 60)$
$= 0.85416... =$ **0.854 kWh (to 3 s.f.)** ***[1 mark]***

b) Weeks in a year = 52, so the customer will do 52 × 2 = 104 loads.
Model A:
Energy used per year = 1.0575 × 104 = 109.98 kWh ***[1 mark]***
Cost per year = 109.98 × 16.2 = **1780p (to 3 s.f.)** (or £17.80) ***[1 mark]***
Model B:
Energy used per year = 0.854... × 104 = 88.833... kWh ***[1 mark]***
Cost per year = 88.833... × 16.2 = **1440p (to 3 s.f.)** (or £14.40) ***[1 mark]***

Page 71 — E.m.f and Internal Resistance

1 a) $\varepsilon = I(R + r)$ so $I = \varepsilon / (R + r)$
$= 24 / (4.0 + 0.8) =$ **5.0 A** ***[1 mark]***

b) $V = IR = 5.0 \times 4.0 =$ **20 V** ***[1 mark]***
You could also have used $\varepsilon = V + Ir$.

2 C ***[1 mark]***
$\varepsilon = I(R + r)$, but since there are two cells in series replace r with $2r$, and ε with 2ε, then rearrange to find I.

Page 73 — Conservation of Charge & Energy in Circuits

1 a) Resistance of parallel resistors:
$1/R_{parallel} = 1/6.0 + 1/3.0 = 1/2$
$R_{parallel} = 2.0$ Ω ***[1 mark]***
Total resistance:
$R_{total} = 4.0 + R_{parallel} = 4.0 + 2.0 =$ **6.0 Ω** ***[1 mark]***

Answers

b) $V = I_3 R_{total}$ so rearranging $I_3 = V / R_{total} = 12 / 6.0$
$= \mathbf{2.0\ A}$ ***[1 mark]***

c) $V = IR = 2.0 \times 4.0 = \mathbf{8.0\ V}$ ***[1 mark]***

d) E.m.f. = sum of p.d.s in circuit, so $12 = 8.0 + V_{parallel}$
$V_{parallel} = 12 - 8.0 = \mathbf{4.0\ V}$ ***[1 mark]***

e) $I = V/R$, so
$I_1 = 4.0 / 3.0 =$ **1.3 A (to 2 s.f.)** ***[1 mark]***
$I_2 = 4.0 / 6.0 =$ **0.67 A (to 2 s.f.)** ***[1 mark]***
You can check your answers by making sure that $I_3 = I_2 + I_1$.

Page 75 — The Potential Divider

1 a) $V_A / V_B = R_A / R_B$ so $V_A = V_B \times (R_A / R_B)$
$= 6.75 \times (35 \div 45) = \mathbf{5.25\ V}$ ***[1 mark]***

b) Input p.d. $= V_A + V_B = 5.25 + 6.75 = \mathbf{12\ V}$ ***[1 mark]***

c) $V_B = \frac{R_B}{R_A + R_B} V_{in} = \frac{45}{75 + 45} \times 12 = \mathbf{4.5\ V}$ ***[1 mark]***

2 a) $V_{AB} = \frac{R_2}{R_1 + R_2} V_{in} = (50 / (30 + 50)) \times 12 = 7.5\ V$ ***[1 mark]***
Ignore the 10 Ω — no current flows that way.

b) Total resistance R_T of the parallel circuit:
$1/R_T = 1 / 50 + 1 / (10 + 40) = 1 / 25$
$R_T = 25\ \Omega$ ***[1 mark]***
Use $V_{out} = (R_2 / (R_1 + R_2)\ V_{in}$ to find the p.d. over the whole parallel arrangement: $(25 / (30 + 25)) \times 12 = 5.454...\ V$ ***[1 mark]***
Use $V_{out} = (R_2 / R_1 + R_2)\ V_{in}$ again to find the p.d. across AB:
$V_{AB} = 40 / (40 + 10) \times 5.454... = 4.363...$
$=$ **4.4 V (to 2 s.f.)** ***[1 mark]***
current through 40 Ω resistor $= V/R$
$= 4.363... / 40 =$ **0.11 A (to 2 s.f.)** ***[1 mark]***
This question might look tricky, but it's basically just one potential divider on top of another.

Module 4: Section 2 — Waves

Page 77 — Wave Basics

1 a) The gain is set to 2.0 volts/div and the trace has a maximum amplitude of 2 divisions.
So, the maximum voltage $= 2 \times 2.0 = \mathbf{4.0\ V}$ ***[1 mark]***

b) One wavelength spans 3 divisions, so
$T = 3 \times 3.0\ ms = 9.0\ ms = 9.0 \times 10^{-3}\ s$ ***[1 mark]***
$f = 1/T = 1 / 9.0 \times 10^{-3}$ ***[1 mark]***
$f = 111.1... =$ **110 Hz (to 2 s.f.)** ***[1 mark]***

c) $v = f\lambda$ so $\lambda = v / f$
$\lambda = 280/111.1...$ ***[1 mark]***
$\lambda = 2.52\ m =$ **2.5 m (to 2 s.f.)** ***[1 mark]***

Page 79 — Types of Wave

1 a) $I = P \div A = 10.0 \div 0.002 = \mathbf{5000\ Wm^{-2}}$ ***[1 mark]***

b) D ***[1 mark]***

Page 81 — Polarisation of Waves

1 a) They are at right angles to one another (90°, 270° etc.) ***[1 mark]***.

b) It would be half of the intensity of the original light ***[1 mark]***.
This is because at 45° the vertical and horizontal contributions are equal, so the intensity is halved between them.

c) Any of: Polaroid sunglasses or 3D film glasses ***[1 mark]***.

Page 83 — Diffraction and Reflection

1 When a wavefront meets an obstacle, the waves will diffract round the corners of the obstacle. When the obstacle is much bigger than the wavelength, little diffraction occurs. In this case, the mountain is much bigger than the wavelength of short-wave radio. So the "shadow" where you cannot pick up short wave is very long ***[1 mark]***.

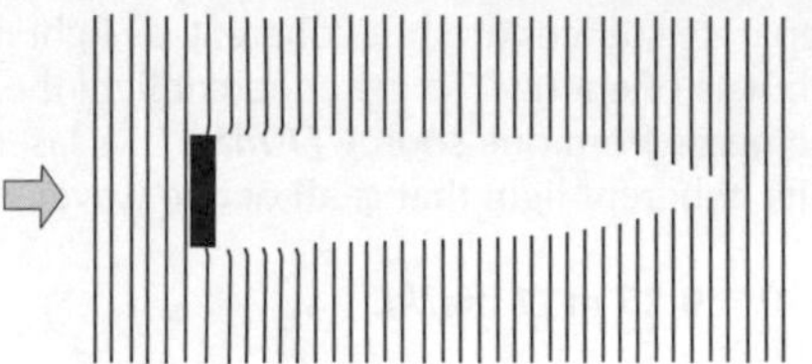

[1 mark]

When the obstacle is comparable in size to the wavelength, as it is for the long-wave radio waves, more diffraction occurs. The wavefront re-forms after a shorter distance, leaving a shorter "shadow" ***[1 mark]***.

2 E.g. Set up a ripple tank, using an oscillating paddle to create straight, parallel waves. Place two objects into the water, creating a barrier with a gap in the middle ***[1 mark]***. Vary the sizes of the objects to increase and decrease the gap width. Observe the amount of diffraction of the water waves as the gap width varies ***[1 mark]***. The most diffraction will be seen when the gap is roughly the same size as the wavelength of the water waves ***[1 mark]***.

Page 85 — Refraction and Refractive Index

1 a) $n_{diamond} = c / v = (3.00 \times 10^8) / (1.24 \times 10^8) = 2.419...$
$=$ **2.42 (to 3 s.f.)** ***[1 mark]***

b) $n_{air} \sin\theta_i = n_{diamond} \sin\theta_r$, $n_{air} = 1$
So, $n_{diamond} = \sin\theta_i / \sin\theta_r$ ***[1 mark]***
$\sin\theta_r = \sin 50 / 2.419... = 0.316...$
$\theta_r = \sin^{-1}(0.316...) = 18.459... =$ **18° (to 2 s.f.)** ***[1 mark]***
You can assume the refractive index of air is 1, and don't forget to write the degree sign in your answer.

2 a) When the light is pointing steeply upwards some of it is refracted and some reflected — the beam emerging from the surface is the refracted part ***[1 mark]***.
However when the beam hits the surface at more than the critical angle (to the normal to the boundary) refraction does not occur. All the beam is totally internally reflected to light the tank, hence its brightness ***[1 mark]***.

b) The critical angle is 90° – 41.25° = 48.75° ***[1 mark]***.
$n_{water} = 1 / \sin C$
$= 1 / \sin 48.75°$
$= 1 / 0.7518... = 1.3300... =$ **1.330 (to 4 s.f.)** ***[1 mark]***
The question talks about the angle between the light beam and the floor of the aquarium. This angle is 90° minus the incident angle — measured from a normal to the surface of the water.

Page 87 — Superposition and Coherence

1 a) The frequencies and wavelengths of the two sources must be equal ***[1 mark]*** and the phase difference must be constant ***[1 mark]***.

b) Interference will only be noticeable if the amplitudes of the two waves are approximately equal ***[1 mark]***.

2 B ***[1 mark]***

Page 89 — Two-Source Interference

1 a)

S_1
S_2
Constructive
Destructive
Constructive
Destructive
Constructive

[1 mark for correct placement of constructive interference patterns, 1 mark for correct placement of destructive interference patterns]

Answers

b) Light waves from separate sources are not coherent, as light is emitted in random bursts of energy. To get coherent light the two sets of waves must emerge from one source ***[1 mark]***. A laser is used because it emits coherent light that is all of one wavelength ***[1 mark]***.

2 a) $\lambda = v / f = 330 / 1320 =$ **0.25 m *[1 mark]***.

b) Separation $= x = \lambda D / a$
$= 0.25\text{ m} \times 7\text{ m} / 1.5\text{ m}$ ***[1 mark]*** **= 1.2 m (to 2 s.f.) *[1 mark]***.

Page 91 — Diffraction Gratings

1 a) Use $\sin\theta = n\lambda / d$
For the first order, $n = 1$
So, $\sin\theta = \lambda / d$ ***[1 mark]***
No need to actually work out d. The number of lines per metre is $1 / d$. So you can simply multiply the wavelength by that.
$\sin\theta = 6.00 \times 10^{-7} \times 4.0 \times 10^5 = 0.24$
$\theta = \sin^{-1}(0.24) = 13.8865... =$ **14° (to 2 s.f.) *[1 mark]***
For the second order, $n = 2$ and $\sin\theta = 2\lambda / d$. ***[1 mark]***
You already have a value for λ / d. Just double it to get $\sin\theta$ for the second order.
$\sin\theta = 0.48$
$\theta = \sin^{-1}(0.48) = 28.685... =$ **29° (to 2 s.f.) *[1 mark]***

b) No. Putting $n = 5$ into the equation gives a value of $\sin\theta$ of 1.2, which is impossible ***[1 mark]***.

2 $\sin\theta = n\lambda / d$, so for the 1st order maximum, $\sin\theta = \lambda / d$
$\sin 14.2° = \lambda \times 3.70 \times 10^5$ ***[1 mark]***
$\lambda = 663$ nm (or 6.63×10^{-7} m) (to 3 s.f.) *[1 mark]*.

Page 93 — Stationary (Standing) Waves

1 a)

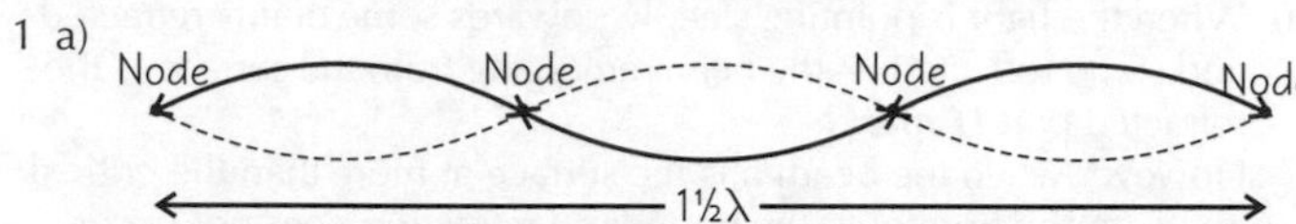

[1 mark for the correct shape, 1 mark for labelling the length]

b) For a string vibrating at three times the first harmonic, length $= 3\lambda / 2$
$1.2\text{ m} = 3\lambda / 2$
$\lambda =$ **0.8 m** ***[1 mark]***

c) When the string forms a standing wave, its amplitude varies from a maximum at the antinodes to zero at the nodes ***[1 mark]***. In a progressive wave all the points have the same amplitude ***[1 mark]***

2 Distance between nodes $= \lambda/2$ ***[1 mark]***
$\lambda = 2 \times 15.0\text{ cm} = 30.0\text{ cm} = 0.30\text{ m}$ ***[1 mark]***
$v = f\lambda$ so $v = 1.00 \times 10^9 \times 0.30$ ***[1 mark]***
$v = 3.0 \times 10^8$ ms⁻¹ ***[1 mark]***

Module 4: Section 3 — Quantum Physics

Page 95 — Light — Wave or Particle

1 a) At threshold voltage:
$E_{kinetic}$ of an electron $= E_{photon}$ emitted ***[1 mark]***
So $E_{photon} = e \times V = 1.60 \times 10^{-19} \times 1.70 =$ **2.72×10^{-19} J** ***[1 mark]***

b) $E = \frac{hc}{\lambda}$ so $h = \frac{E\lambda}{c}$
$\lambda = 7.00 \times 10^{-7}$, $c = 3.00 \times 10^8$
So, $h = \frac{2.72 \times 10^{-19} \times 7.00 \times 10^{-7}}{3.00 \times 10^8}$ ***[1 mark]***
$= 6.346.... \times 10^{-34} =$ **6.35×10^{-34} Js (to 3 s.f.)** ***[1 mark]***

Page 97 — The Photoelectric Effect

1 $\phi = 2.9\text{ eV} = 2.9 \times (1.60 \times 10^{-19})\text{ J} = 4.64 \times 10^{-19}\text{ J}$ ***[1 mark]***
$f = \frac{\phi}{h} = \frac{4.64 \times 10^{-19}}{6.63 \times 10^{-34}} = 6.99... \times 10^{14}$
$=$ **7.0×10^{14} Hz (to 2 s.f.)** ***[1 mark]***

2 a) $E = hf$
$= (6.63 \times 10^{-34}) \times (2.0 \times 10^{15}) = 1.326 \times 10^{-18}\text{ J}$ ***[1 mark]***
$1.326 \times 10^{-18}\text{ J} = \frac{1.326 \times 10^{-18}}{1.60 \times 10^{-19}}\text{ eV}$
$= 8.2875 =$ **8.3 eV (to 2 s.f.) *[1 mark]***

b) $E_{photon} = E_{max\ kinetic} + \phi$
$E_{max\ kinetic} = E_{photon} - \phi$
$= 8.2875 - 4.7 = 3.5875$ ***[1 mark]***
= 3.6 eV (to 2 s.f.) (or 5.7×10^{-19} J) ***[1 mark]***

3 An electron needs to gain a certain amount of energy (the work function energy) before it can leave the surface of the metal ***[1 mark]***.
If the energy carried by each photon is less than this work function energy, no electrons will be emitted ***[1 mark]***.

Page 99 — Wave-Particle Duality

1 a) Electromagnetic radiation can show characteristics of both particles and waves ***[1 mark]***.

b) $\lambda = \frac{h}{p}$
so $p = \frac{h}{\lambda}$ ***[1 mark]***
$= \frac{6.63 \times 10^{-34}}{590 \times 10^{-9}} = 1.123... \times 10^{-27}$
$= 1.1 \times 10^{-27}$ kgms⁻¹ (to 2 s.f.) ***[1 mark]***

2 a) $\lambda = \frac{h}{p} = \frac{h}{mv}$
$\lambda = \frac{6.63 \times 10^{-34}}{9.11 \times 10^{-31} \times 3.50 \times 10^6}$ ***[1 mark]***
$= 2.079... \times 10^{-10}$
$= 2.08 \times 10^{-10}$ m (to 3 s.f.) ***[1 mark]***

b) Either $\lambda = \frac{h}{p} = \frac{h}{mv}$
So $v = \frac{h}{m\lambda} = \frac{6.63 \times 10^{-34}}{1.673 \times 10^{-27} \times 2.079... \times 10^{-10}}$ ***[1 mark]***
$= 1905.85... =$ **1910 ms⁻¹ (to 3 s.f.)** ***[1 mark]***
Or momentum of protons = momentum of electrons
so $m_p \times v_p = m_e \times v_e$
$v_p = v_e \times \frac{m_e}{m_p} = 3.50 \times 10^6 \times \frac{9.11 \times 10^{-31}}{1.673 \times 10^{-27}}$ ***[1 mark]***
$= 1905.85... =$ **1910 ms⁻¹ (to 3 s.f.)** ***[1 mark]***

c) The proton has a larger mass, so it will have a smaller speed, since the two have the same kinetic energy ***[1 mark]***. Kinetic energy is proportional to the square of the speed, while momentum is proportional to the speed, so they will have different momenta ***[1 mark]***. Wavelength depends on the momentum, so the wavelengths are different ***[1 mark]***.
This is a really hard question. If you didn't get it right, make sure you understand the answer fully. Do the algebra if it helps.

3 B ***[1 mark]***

Extra Exam Practice for Module 4

Pages 100-101

2 a) E.g. the terminal potential difference supplied by the battery is equal to the e.m.f generated by the battery minus the lost volts ($V = \varepsilon - v$). The lost volts are equal to the current through the battery multiplied by the internal resistance ($V = \varepsilon - Ir$) ***[1 mark]***. Because the current supplied is very large, the internal resistance must be very small to avoid a large value for the lost volts/to provide a large enough terminal potential difference for the starter motor to start the engine ***[1 mark]***.

Answers

b) ***5-6 marks:***
The answer describes the full experimental procedure including correct suggestions of how to ensure the results are valid and accurate, and includes explanations of why the validity/accuracy is improved. The answer may include a diagram, but this is not essential. The answer has a clear and logical structure. The information given is relevant and detailed.
3-4 marks:
The answer describes most of the experimental procedure with a correct suggestion of how to improve the accuracy or validity of the results, and how this improves the accuracy / validity. The answer may include a diagram, but this is not essential. The answer has some structure. Most of the information given is relevant and there is some detail involved.
1-2 marks:
A few simple steps for the experiment are described. The answer may not include ways to ensure the results are accurate or valid, or may give one or two simple suggestions without detail or explanation. The answer has no clear structure. The information given is basic and lacking in detail. It may not all be relevant.
0 marks:
No relevant information is given.
Here are some points your answer may include:
The student should connect the battery to a variable resistor, with a voltmeter connected in parallel with the battery and an ammeter in series with the battery.
E.g.

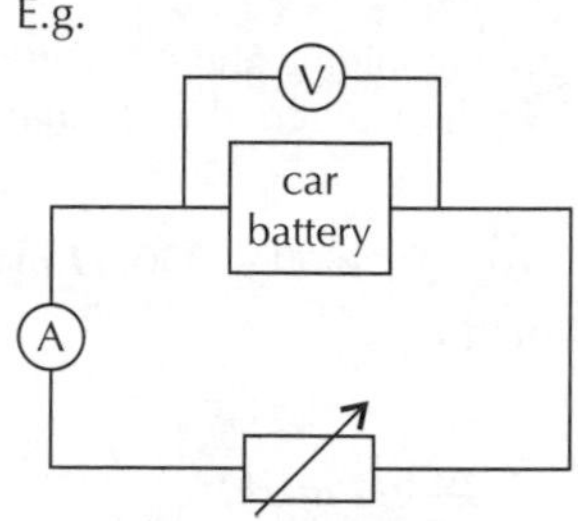

The variable resistor should be adjusted to vary the current through the circuit.
For each value of current, measure the current and the potential difference across the battery.
A graph of p.d. (V) against current (I) should be plotted.
$\varepsilon = V + Ir$ so rearrange this to look like $y = mx + c$. V is on the y-axis and I is on the x-axis so $V = -rI + \varepsilon$, so the gradient of the graph is equal to $-r$.
To achieve valid results, make sure only the relationship between current and p.d. is being tested / make sure that the current and the p.d. are the only variables that change / make sure all other variables are controlled.
In order for the resistance of the circuit to remain constant, the temperature of the circuit must remain constant.
Keep the temperature of the room constant.
Turn off the circuit between readings to reduce the heating of the circuit.
Use low currents to minimise heating.
Valid results must be precise. To ensure the results are precise, use a voltmeter and ammeter that have small intervals on their scales. This reduces the uncertainty in readings and makes them more precise.
Take multiple readings of the p.d. and calculate the mean to reduce the effect of random errors to improve the precision.
To achieve accurate results, calibrate equipment to avoid systematic errors.

c) $R = \frac{\rho L}{A}$

$A = \pi r^2$ and $r = d \div 2$

$R = \frac{\rho L}{\pi(d \div 2)^2}$ ***[1 mark]*** $= \frac{3.86 \times 10^{-8} \times 1.25}{\pi(0.102 \times 10^{-3} \div 2)^2}$

$= 5.904...\ \Omega$ ***[1 mark]***

The potential difference across each wire is equal to the potential difference across the thermistor, because they are in parallel. The potential difference across the thermistor and wires is $V_{out} = \frac{R_2}{R_1 + R_2}V_{in}$ where R_2 is the combined resistance of the thermistor and the wires.
$R_{thermistor}$ is 38.0 Ω at 1.0 °C.

$\frac{1}{R_2} = \frac{1}{R_{thermistor}} + \left(5 \times \frac{1}{R_{wire}}\right) = \frac{1}{38.0} + \frac{5}{5.904...} = 0.873...$

$R_2 = 1 \div 0.873... = 1.145...\ \Omega$ ***[1 mark]***

$V_{out} = \frac{R_2}{R_1 + R_2}V_{in} = \frac{1.145...}{2.50 + 1.145...} \times 12$

$= 3.770...\ \text{V} = \mathbf{3.8\ V}$ **(to 2 s.f.)** ***[1 mark]***

d) $R = \frac{V}{I}$, so the current in one wire, $I_{wire} = \frac{V}{R_{wire}} = \frac{3.8}{5.904...}$

$= 0.643...\ \text{A}$ ***[1 mark]***

Current is split between branches in parallel:

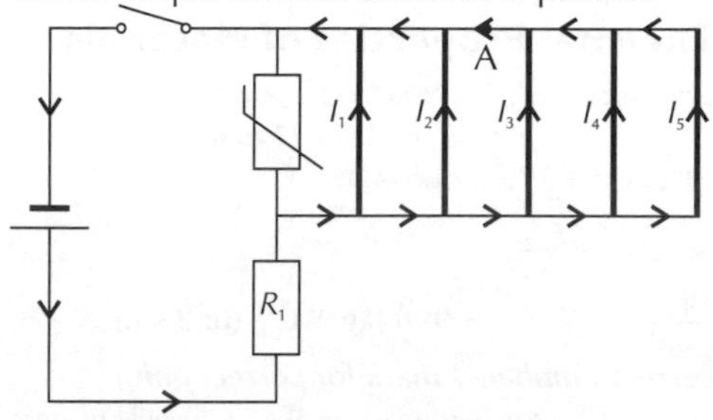

Kirchhoff's first law says that the total current entering a junction equals the total current leaving it.
So, the current at point A is:

$I_3 + I_4 + I_5 = 3 \times I_{wire} = 3 \times 0.643...$

$= 1.930... = \mathbf{1.9\ A}$ **(to 2 s.f.)** ***[1 mark]***

If you correctly used your unrounded answer from c) you still get full marks.

3 a) The maximum speed of the photoelectrons reaching the anode can be used to find their maximum kinetic energy when they reach the anode.

$KE_{anode} = \frac{1}{2}mv^2 = \frac{1}{2} \times (9.11 \times 10^{-31}) \times (1.5 \times 10^6)^2$

$= 1.024... \times 10^{-18}$ J ***[1 mark]***

The maximum kinetic energy of the photoelectrons at the anode (KE_{anode}) is the sum of the maximum kinetic energy of photoelectrons emitted from the photocathode (KE_{max}), and the work done by the accelerating potential difference (W):

$KE_{anode} = KE_{max} + W$, so $KE_{max} = KE_{anode} - W$

$W = QV = eV = 1.60 \times 10^{-19} \times 3.8 = 6.08 \times 10^{-19}$ J ***[1 mark]***

So $KE_{max} = KE_{anode} - W = (1.024... \times 10^{-18}) - (6.08 \times 10^{-19})$

$= 4.16... \times 10^{-19}$

$= \mathbf{4.2 \times 10^{-19}\ J}$ **(to 2 s.f.)** ***[1 mark]***

b) $hf = \phi + KE_{max}$

Convert ϕ to joules: $4.1 \times 1.60 \times 10^{-19} = 6.56 \times 10^{-19}$ J

$hf = \phi + KE_{max}$ so $f = \frac{\phi + KE_{max}}{h}$

$= \frac{(6.56 \times 10^{-19}) + (4.16... \times 10^{-19})}{6.63 \times 10^{-34}}$

$= 1.618... \times 10^{15}$ Hz ***[1 mark]***

$v = f\lambda$, so $\lambda = \frac{v}{f} = \frac{3.00 \times 10^8}{1.618... \times 10^{15}} = 1.85... \times 10^{-7}$ m ***[1 mark]***

$\lambda = \frac{h}{p}$, so $p = \frac{h}{\lambda} = \frac{6.63 \times 10^{-34}}{1.85... \times 10^{-7}}$

$= 3.57... \times 10^{-27}$

$= \mathbf{3.6 \times 10^{-27}\ kgms^{-1}}$ **(to 2 s.f.)** ***[1 mark]***

c) The current in the circuit would increase. A higher intensity means more photons are hitting the photocathode per second, which leads to more photoelectrons being emitted per second ***[1 mark]***. More photoelectrons will flow from the photocathode to the anode, and as current is the rate of flow of charge, more photoelectrons flowing means a higher current ***[1 mark]***.

Answers

Module 5: Section 1 — Thermal Physics

Page 103 — Phases of Matter and Temperature

1 In a solid the particles are very close together in a lattice structure and vibrate a little ***[1 mark]***. In a liquid the particles are still quite close together but are free to move past each other ***[1 mark]***. In a gas the particles are far apart, are randomly distributed and free to move around ***[1 mark]***.

2 a) For example, put some smoke into a glass cell and shine a beam of light onto it ***[1 mark]***. Use a microscope to view the smoke particles ***[1 mark]***.

b) In Brownian motion, particles continually change direction so must be acted on by an external force ***[1 mark]***. The nature of this force is uneven and random, which is consistent with a force caused by collisions between randomly moving particles ***[1 mark]***.

Page 105 — Thermal Properties of Materials

1 Electrical energy supplied: $E = 90.0 \times 3.0 \times 60$
$= 16\,200$ J ***[1 mark]***

The temperature rise is 12.7 – 4.5 = 8.2 °C

$E = mc\Delta\theta$, so $c = \frac{E}{m\Delta\theta}$

so $c = \frac{16\,200}{2.0 \times 8.2} = 987.8... =$ **990 Jkg^{-1}°C^{-1} (to 2 s.f.)**

[1 mark for correct number, 1 mark for correct unit.]

You need the right unit for the third mark — Jkg^{-1}K^{-1} would be right too.

2 The heat transferred to the water is equal to the heat leaving the block so: $m_w c_w(T_s - T_w) = m_b c_b(T_b - T_s)$.

Rearranging for c_b gives: $c_b = \frac{m_w c_w(T_s - T_w)}{m_b(T_b - T_s)}$

$c_b = \frac{2.0 \times 4180 \times (26 - 19)}{4.0(100 - 26)}$ ***[1 mark]***

$= 197.7... =$ **200 J kg^{-1} K^{-1} (to 2 s.f.)** ***[1 mark]***

3 Total amount of energy needed to boil all the water:
$E = mL = 0.500 \times 2.26 \times 10^6 = 1.13 \times 10^6$ J ***[1 mark]***
3.00 kW means you get 3000 J in a second, so
time in seconds $= 1.13 \times 10^6 \div 3000$ ***[1 mark]***
$= 376.6... =$ **377 s (to 3 s.f.)** ***[1 mark]***

Page 107 — Ideal Gases

1 $\frac{p}{T}$ = constant, so $\frac{p_1}{T_1} = \frac{1.04 \times 10^6}{10.0 + 273} = 3674.91...$ ***[1 mark]***

$\frac{p_2}{T_2} = 3674.91...$ so $p_2 = 3674.91... \times (62.3 + 273)$
$= 1.232... \times 10^6$
= **1.23×10^6 Pa (to 3 s.f.)** ***[1 mark]***

2 a) i) Number of moles $= \frac{\text{mass of gass}}{\text{molar mass}}$
$= \frac{0.0140}{0.0280} =$ **0.500 moles** ***[1 mark]***

ii) Number of molecules = number of moles × Avogadro's constant $= 0.500 \times 6.02 \times 10^{23} =$ **3.01×10^{23}** ***[1 mark]***

b) $pV = nRT$, so $p = \frac{nRT}{V}$

$p = \frac{0.5 \times 8.31 \times (27.0 + 273)}{0.0100}$ ***[1 mark]***

$= 124\,650 =$ **125 000 Pa (to 3 s.f.)** ***[1 mark]***

c) The pressure would also halve ***[1 mark]*** (because it is proportional to the number of molecules — $pV = NkT$).

3 $\frac{pV}{T}$ = constant

At ground level, $\frac{pV}{T} = \frac{1.00 \times 10^5 \times 10.0}{293}$
$= 3412.9...$ JK^{-1} ***[1 mark]***

Higher up, $\frac{pV}{T}$ will equal this same constant.

So higher up, $p = \frac{\text{constant} \times T}{V} = \frac{3412.9... \times 261}{25.0}$ ***[1 mark]***
$= 35\,631.39... =$ **35 600 Pa (to 3 s.f.)** ***[1 mark]***

Page 109 — The Pressure of an Ideal Gas

1 Pressure is affected by the volume of the container — increasing the volume lowers the frequency of collisions between particles and the container walls, so pressure decreases ***[1 mark]***.
The number of particles also affects pressure — more particles means the frequency of collisions between particles and the container will increase, increasing the total force exerted by all the collisions ***[1 mark]***. Because force is proportional to mass ($F = ma$), heavier particles will also increase the total force exerted on the container by collisions, increasing the pressure ***[1 mark]***.
The speed of particles also affects the change in momentum when particles collide with the container, changing the force exerted on the container and therefore the pressure ***[1 mark]***.

2 a) $pV = \frac{1}{3}Nm\overline{c^2}$ Rearrange the equation: $\overline{c^2} = \frac{3pV}{Nm}$

$\overline{c^2} = \frac{3 \times (1.03 \times 10^5) \times (7.00 \times 10^{-5})}{(2.17 \times 10^{22}) \times (6.65 \times 10^{-27})}$ ***[1 mark]***
$= 149\,890.8... =$ **150 000 m^{2}s^{-2} (to 3 s.f.)** ***[1 mark]***

b) *r.m.s. speed* $= \sqrt{\overline{c^2}} = \sqrt{149\,890.8...} = 387.15...$
= **387 ms^{-1} (to 3.s.f)** ***[1 mark]***

Page 111 — Internal Energy of an Ideal Gas

1 a) 6.02×10^{23} molecules ***[1 mark]***

b) $E = \frac{3}{2}kT = \frac{3}{2} \times (1.38 \times 10^{-23}) \times 300$ ***[1 mark]***
= **6.21×10^{-21} J** ***[1 mark]***

c) The nitrogen molecules are constantly colliding and transferring energy between themselves, so have different energies ***[1 mark]***.

2 a) $U = \frac{3}{2}NkT$ so $\Delta U = \frac{3}{2}Nk\Delta T$

$\Delta U = \frac{3}{2} \times 3.00 \times 10^{23} \times 1.38 \times 10^{-23} \times (500 - 300)$ ***[1 mark]***
$= 1242 =$ **1240 J (to 3 s.f.)** ***[1 mark]***

b) $pV = NkT$ so $V = \frac{NkT}{p}$

$V = \frac{3.00 \times 10^{23} \times 1.38 \times 10^{-23} \times 500}{1.66 \times 10^4}$ ***[1 mark]***
$= 0.1246... =$ **0.125 m^3 (to 3 s.f.)** ***[1 mark]***

Module 5: Section 2 — Circular Motion and Oscillations

Page 113 — Circular Motion

1 a) $\omega = \theta/t = 2\pi / 3.2 \times 10^7 = 1.963... \times 10^{-7}$
= **2.0×10^{-7} rad s^{-1} (to 2 s.f.)** ***[1 mark]***
$v = r\omega = 1.5 \times 10^{11} \times 1.963... \times 10^{-7} = 29452.43...$ms^{-1}
= **30 kms^{-1} (to 2 s.f.)** ***[1 mark]***

b) $F = m\omega^2 r = 6.0 \times 10^{24} \times (1.963... \times 10^{-7})^2 \times 1.5 \times 10^{11}$
$= 3.469... \times 10^{22} =$ **3.5×10^{22} N (to 2 s.f.)** ***[1 mark]***
This force is the gravitational force between the Sun and the Earth ***[1 mark]***.

2 a) To stop the water from falling out of the bucket at the top of its swing, the acceleration due to gravity must be equal to or less than the acceleration due to the bucket's circular motion, so $\omega^2 r \geq g$ ***[1 mark]***.
f is at a minimum when ω is at a minimum, so find the smallest value of ω for which $\omega^2 r \geq g$:
$\omega^2 r = g$
$r = 1$ m, $g = 9.81$ ms^{-2}, so $\omega^2 = 9.81$
$\omega = 3.132...$ rads^{-1} ***[1 mark]***
$\omega = 2\pi f$ so $f = \omega/2\pi = 3.132... \div 2\pi = 0.498...$
= **0.5 Hz (to 1 s.f.)** ***[1 mark]***

b) $F = m\omega^2 r = 10 \times 5^2 \times 1 = 250$ N ***[1 mark]***
This force is provided by both the tension in the rope, T, and gravity:
$T + (10 \times 9.81) = 250$. So $T = 250 - (10 \times 9.81) = 151.9$
= **150 N (to 2 s.f.)** ***[1 mark]***

Answers

Page 115 — Simple Harmonic Motion

1 a) Simple harmonic motion is an oscillation in which the acceleration of an object is directly proportional to its displacement from the midpoint ***[1 mark]***, and is directed towards the midpoint ***[1 mark]***.

b) The acceleration of a falling bouncy ball is constant, so the motion is not SHM. ***[1 mark]***.

2 a) Maximum velocity = $\omega A = (2\pi f)A = 2\pi \times 1.5 \times 0.05 = 0.4712...$
$= \mathbf{0.47\ ms^{-1}}$ **(to 2 s.f.)** ***[1 mark]***

b) $x = A\cos(\omega t) = A\cos(2\pi ft) = 0.05 \times \cos(2\pi \times 1.5 \times 0.1)$
$= 0.0294... = \mathbf{0.029\ m}$ **(to 2 s.f.)** ***[1 mark]***

c) $x = A\cos(\omega t) = A\cos(2\pi ft)$ so $0.01 = 0.05 \times \cos(2\pi \times 1.5t)$
$0.01 \div 0.05 = \cos(2\pi \times 1.5t)$
$0.2 = \cos(3\pi t)$ so $\cos^{-1}(0.2) = 3\pi t$ ***[1 mark]***
$3\pi t = 1.369...$ so $t = 0.145... = \mathbf{0.15\ s}$ **(to 2 s.f.)** ***[1 mark]***

Don't forget to put your calculator in radian mode when you're solving questions on circular motion — it's an easy mistake to make.

3 $\omega_X = 2\omega_Y$
maximum acceleration = $\omega^2 A$
$a_{max,X} = \omega_X^2 A = (2\omega_Y)^2 A = 4\omega_Y^2 A$
$a_{max,Y} = \omega_Y^2 A$
So $a_{max,X} = 4a_{max,Y}$
D ***[1 mark]***

Page 117 — Investigating Simple Harmonic Motion

1 a) E.g. hang a mass from the spring. Suspend the spring (from a length of string) above a position sensor attached to a data logger ***[1 mark]*** then lift the mass slightly and let it go to start the mass oscillating ***[1 mark]***. Measure the time period of the oscillation from the displacement-time graph generated by the computer ***[1 mark]***. Repeat the experiment for different masses, then plot time period against mass ***[1 mark]***.

b) The time period increases with increasing mass ***[1 mark]*** and the relationship is not linear ***[1 mark]***.

Page 119 — Free and Forced Vibrations

1 a) When a system is forced to vibrate at a frequency that's close to, or the same as, its natural frequency ***[1 mark]*** and oscillates with a much larger than usual amplitude ***[1 mark]***.

b) E.g.

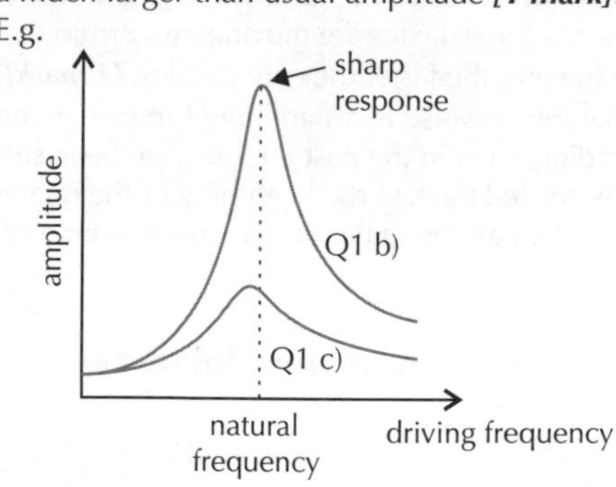

[1 mark for showing a peak at the natural frequency, 1 mark for a sharp peak.]

c) ***[See graph in part b). 1 mark for a smaller peak at the natural frequency.]***

The peak will actually be slightly to the left of the natural frequency due to the damping, but you'll get the mark if the peak is at the same frequency in the diagram.

2 A system is critically damped if it returns to rest in the shortest time possible when it's displaced from equilibrium and released ***[1 mark]***. It is used in e.g. the suspension in a car ***[1 mark]***.

Module 5: Section 3 — Gravitational Fields

Page 121 — Gravitational Fields

1 $g = -\frac{GM}{r^2}$ so $M = -\frac{gr^2}{G}$

$M = -\frac{-9.81 \times (6400 \times 10^3)^2}{6.67 \times 10^{-11}}$ ***[1 mark]***

$= 6.024... \times 10^{24} = \mathbf{6.0 \times 10^{24}\ kg}$ **(to 2 s.f.)** ***[1 mark]***

2 a) $g = -\frac{GM}{r^2} = -\frac{6.67 \times 10^{-11} \times 7.35 \times 10^{22}}{(1740 \times 10^3)^2}$

$= -1.619... = \mathbf{-1.6\ Nkg^{-1}}$ **(to 2 s.f.)** ***[1 mark]***

b) $F = -\frac{GMm}{r^2} = -\frac{6.67 \times 10^{-11} \times 7.35 \times 10^{22} \times 25}{((1740 \times 10^3) + 10)^2}$ ***[1 mark]***

$= -40.4... = \mathbf{-40\ N}$ **(to 2 s.f.)** ***[1 mark]***

3 $\frac{-GM}{r_1^2} = 4$ and $\frac{-GM}{r_2^2} = 2$ so $4r_1^2 = 2r_2^2$
so $r_2 = \sqrt{2}\,r_1$
If g decreases until it's at half of its original value, r will increase by a factor of $\sqrt{2} \approx 1.4$.
So the answer is **B** ***[1 mark]***

Page 123 — Gravitational Potential and Energy

1 a) At the surface:
$V_g = \frac{-GM}{r}$ so $r = \frac{-GM}{V_g}$

$r = \frac{-6.67 \times 10^{-11} \times 2.67 \times 10^{19}}{-1.52 \times 10^4}$ ***[1 mark]***

$= 117163.8... = \mathbf{117\ 000\ m}$ **(to 3 s.f.)** ***[1 mark]***

b) $v = \sqrt{\frac{2GM}{r}} = \sqrt{\frac{2 \times 6.67 \times 10^{-11} \times 2.67 \times 10^{19}}{117\,163.8...}}$

$v = 174.3...... = \mathbf{174\ ms^{-1}}$ **(to 3 s.f.)** ***[1 mark]***

c) V_g at 2000 m above the surface $= \frac{-GM}{r}$
$= \frac{-6.67 \times 10^{-11} \times 2.67 \times 10^{19}}{(117\,163.8... + 2000)}$
$= -1.49448... \times 10^4$ ***[1 mark]***

$\Delta W = m\Delta V_g$
so $\Delta W = 300 \times (-1.49448... \times 10^4 - (-1.52 \times 10^4))$ ***[1 mark]***
$= 7.653... \times 10^4 = \mathbf{7.65 \times 10^4\ J}$ **(to 3 s.f.)** ***[1 mark]***

Page 125 — Motion of Masses in Gravitational Fields

1 a) $T = \sqrt{\frac{4\pi^2 r^3}{GM}} = \sqrt{\frac{4\pi^2((6400 + 200.0) \times 10^3)^3}{6.67 \times 10^{-11} \times 5.98 \times 10^{24}}}$ ***[1 mark]***

= 5334.3... seconds
= **5300 seconds or 1.5 hours (to 2 s.f.)** ***[1 mark]***

b) $v = \sqrt{\frac{GM}{r}} = \sqrt{\frac{6.67 \times 10^{-11} \times 5.98 \times 10^{24}}{(6400 + 200.0) \times 10^3}}$

$= 7773.9...\ ms^{-1} = \mathbf{7800\ ms^{-1}}$ **(to 2 s.f.)** ***[1 mark]***

2 Period = 24 hours = 24 × 60 × 60 = 86 400 s ***[1 mark]***
Rearrange $T^2 = \frac{4\pi^2 r^3}{GM}$ for r

$r = \sqrt[3]{\frac{T^2 GM}{4\pi^2}} = \sqrt[3]{\frac{86400^2 \times 6.67 \times 10^{-11} \times 5.98 \times 10^{24}}{4\pi^2}}$

$r = 4.22... \times 10^7$ m ***[1 mark]***
Height above Earth = $4.22... \times 10^7 - 6.4 \times 10^6$ = 35 850 500 m
= **36 000 000 m or 3.6 × 10⁴ km (to 2 s.f.)** ***[1 mark]***

3 50 000 years is 50 000 × 365 × 24 × 3600 = $1.57... \times 10^{12}$ s
This means the sun will have lost:
$1.57... \times 10^{12} \times 6 \times 10^9 = 9.46... \times 10^{21}$ kg of mass ***[1 mark]***.
This is less than 5×10^{-7}% of the Sun's mass, so will not have caused any significant change in the Earth's orbit ***[1 mark]***.

Answers

Module 5: Section 4 — Astrophysics & Cosmology

Page 127 — The Solar System & Astronomical Distances

1 Planets have almost circular orbits whereas comets have highly elliptical orbits *[1 mark]*. Comets can take millions of years to orbit the Sun; planets have much shorter periods *[1 mark]*.

2 a) A light-year is the distance travelled by a photon of light / a light wave through a vacuum in one year *[1 mark]*.

b) Light travels at a finite speed, so it takes time for light from objects to reach us *[1 mark]*. Therefore, when we look at distant objects, we are seeing them as they were in the past, when the light left them, rather than as they are now *[1 mark]*.

3 a) $(5 \times 10^{-5})° \times 3600 = 0.18$ arcseconds *[1 mark]*
$d = 1 \div 0.18 = 5.555555.....$ = **5.6 parsecs (to 2 s.f.)** *[1 mark]*

b) $5.55555... \times 3.1 \times 10^{16} = 1.722... \times 10^{17}$ m *[1 mark]*
$1.722... \times 10^{17} \div 9.5 \times 10^{15} = 18.128...$
= **18 ly (to 2 s.f.)** *[1 mark]*

Page 130 — Stellar Evolution

1 a) The Chandrasekhar limit is the maximum mass at which the electron degeneracy pressure is sufficient to counteract the force of gravity once a star has run out of fuel *[1 mark]*.

b) ***5-6 marks:***
The answer clearly describes both the similarities and differences between the life cycles of high and low mass stars, and explains some of these with reference to gravity and electron degeneracy pressure. The answer has a clear, logical structure.
3-4 marks:
The answer describes the similarities and differences between the life cycles of high and low mass stars. The answer includes some explanation of why high and low mass stars evolve differently, but the answer is incomplete.
The answer has some logical structure.
1-2 marks:
The answer includes a limited description of the similarities and differences between high and low mass stars, but is lacking explanation.
The answer is basic and poorly structured.
0 marks:
No relevant information is given.
Here are some points your answer may include:

- Both low and high mass stars exist as main sequence stars for most of their lives.
- High mass stars spend less time as main sequence stars than low mass stars, as they use up their fuel more quickly.
- During the main sequence, both low and high mass stars fuse hydrogen in their core.
- When both low mass and high mass stars run out of hydrogen in their cores, the core contracts and the outer layers expand. The star continues to fuse hydrogen in its shells, then begins to burn helium when it becomes hot and dense enough.
- Low mass stars become red giants when they start burning hydrogen in their shells. High mass stars are able to fuse heavier nuclei than helium in their shells (up to iron) to become super red giants (rather than red giants).
- Once high and low mass stars have run out of fuel, they both start to contract.
- A low mass star contracts until its electron degeneracy pressure is enough to counteract the gravitational force, preventing the star from collapsing any further, and the star becomes stable. However, for a high mass star, the electron degeneracy pressure is not enough to counteract the contraction caused by gravity, and so the star continues to contract.
- High mass stars explode in a supernova, and leave behind either a neutron star or a black hole, depending on their size, whilst low mass stars become white dwarfs which gradually cool and fade away, and leave behind a planetary nebula.

2 A *[1 mark]*

Page 133 — Spectra from Stars

1 a) $d \sin\theta = n\lambda$ so $\lambda = d \sin\theta / n$
$= (8.3 \times 10^{-7}) \sin 30.0 / 1$
$=$ **4.15 × 10⁻⁷ m (to 3 s.f.)** *[1 mark]*

b) The gases around the Sun absorb photons to move their electrons to higher energy levels *[1 mark]*. They can only absorb photons with the same energy as the energy needed for transitions between electron energy levels, hence only photons with certain wavelengths are absorbed *[1 mark]*.

c) $\Delta E = hc / \lambda = (6.63 \times 10^{-34} \times 3.00 \times 10^{8}) / 4.15 \times 10^{-7}$
$= 4.792... \times 10^{-19} =$ **4.79×10^{-19} J (to 3 s.f.)** *[1 mark]*

You could have also have given your answer in electronvolts — its 3.00 eV, to 3 s.f.

d) $\lambda_{max} \propto \frac{1}{T}$, so $T\lambda_{max}$ = constant.

This means $T_{(Sun)}\lambda_{max\,(Sun)} = T_{(Rigel)}\lambda_{max\,(Rigel)}$

so $T_{(Sun)} = \frac{T_{(Rigel)}\lambda_{max\,(Rigel)}}{\lambda_{max\,(Sun)}}$ *[1 mark]*

$= \frac{12\,000 \times 240 \times 10^{-9}}{490 \times 10^{-9}}$

$= 5877.55... =$ **5900 K (to 2 s.f.)** *[1 mark]*

e) $L = 4\pi r^2 \sigma T^4$
$= 4\pi \times (1.4 \times 10^{9} \div 2)^2 \times 5.67 \times 10^{-8} \times 5877.55...^4$
$=$ **4.2×10^{26} W (to 2 s.f.)** *[1 mark]*

Page 135 — The Big Bang Theory

1 a) $\frac{\Delta\lambda}{\lambda} \approx \frac{v}{c}$ so $v \approx c\frac{\Delta\lambda}{\lambda} \approx 3.00 \times 10^{8} \times \frac{890 \times 10^{-9} - 650 \times 10^{-9}}{650 \times 10^{-9}}$
$= 1.107... \times 10^{8} =$ **1.1×10^{8} ms⁻¹ (to 2 s.f.)** *[1 mark]*
away from us *[1 mark]*

You can tell the galaxy is moving away from us as the wavelength of the spectral line has increased (it has been red shifted).

b) $v = H_0 d$ so $d = v / H_0 = 1.107... \times 10^{8} / 2.4 \times 10^{-18}$
$= 4.615... \times 10^{25}$ m *[1 mark]*
$4.615... \times 10^{25} / 9.5 \times 10^{15} =$ **4.9×10^{9} ly (to 2 s.f.)** *[1 mark]*

2 The light from other galaxies, apart from those closest to us, is red shifted, and the further away the galaxy, the greater the red shift. This shows that the galaxies are moving away from us, and the further away the are, the faster they are moving *[1 mark]*, which implies that the universe is expanding *[1 mark]*. If the universe is expanding, then in the past it must have been smaller, and if this logic is carried back to the beginning of the universe ($t = 0$) this suggests that all the matter in the universe existed in a single point *[1 mark]*.

Page 137 — The Evolution of the Universe

1 a) $H_0 = v / d = 50$ kms⁻¹ / 1 Mpc⁻¹.
50 kms⁻¹ = 50×10^{3} ms⁻¹ and 1 Mpc = 3.1×10^{22} m
So, $H_0 = 50 \times 10^{3}$ ms⁻¹ $\div 3.1 \times 10^{22}$ m $= 1.61... \times 10^{-18}$ s⁻¹
$= 1.6 \times 10^{-18}$ s⁻¹ to (2 s.f.) ***[1 mark for the correct value, 1 mark for the correct unit]***

b) $t = H_0^{-1}$ so $t = 1 / 1.61... \times 10^{-18} = 6.2 \times 10^{17}$ s *[1 mark]*
$6.2 \times 10^{17} \div (3.16 \times 10^{7}) = 1.962... \times 10^{10}$
= **20 billion years (to 2 s.f.)** *[1 mark]*

So the observable universe has a radius of **20 billion light-years**. *[1 mark]*

2 E.g. the mass of clusters of galaxies as calculated from their velocities is greater than their mass as calculated from their luminosity *[1 mark]*, and stars at the edges of galaxies move faster than they should given the measurable mass and distribution of the stars within them *[1 mark]*. Both of these observations imply that there are extra sources of mass in the universe that we can't see *[1 mark]*. It is thought that this dark matter cannot all be made up of ordinary matter, as this would require more protons and neutrons to exist in the universe than is compatible with our current understanding of the Big Bang *[1 mark]*.

Answers

Extra Exam Practice for Module 5

Pages 138-139

2 a) $a = -\omega^2 x$

$\omega = 2\pi f = 2\pi \times 28 = 56\pi$ rad s^{-1} ***[1 mark]***

At $t = 0$, the cone is at the midpoint of the oscillation ($x = 0$), so $x = A\sin(\omega t)$.

$A = 4.2$ mm $= 4.2 \times 10^{-3}$ m

At $t = 0.21$ s, $x = (4.2 \times 10^{-3}) \times \sin(56\pi \times 0.21)$
$= -2.875... \times 10^{-3}$ m ***[1 mark]***

$a = -\omega^2 x = -(56\pi)^2 \times -2.875... \times 10^{-3}$
$= 88.98...$ ms^{-2} = **89 ms^{-2} (to 2 s.f.)** ***[1 mark]***

b) How to grade your answer:

5-6 marks:
A detailed explanation is given of the effects of resonance and damping on the output of loudspeakers, as well as the advantage of using different-sized cones. The answer successfully links these points to improvements in sound quality in a clear and logical way.

3-4 marks:
An explanation is given of the effects of resonance and damping on the output of loudspeakers, and an attempt has been made to explain the advantage of using different-sized cones. The answer tries to link these points to improvements in sound quality, but it lacks some clarity. There is some structure to the answer, and the information is mostly relevant to the question.

1-2 marks:
A brief explanation is given of the effects of resonance and damping on the output of loudspeakers, but no attempt has been made to correctly explain the advantage of using different-sized cones. The answer doesn't link points to improvements in sound quality, lacks detail, and the information given may not be relevant to the question.

0 marks:
No relevant information is given.

Here are some points your answer may include:
An ideal loudspeaker unit will produce a sound with an amplitude that only depends on the amplitude of the electrical (a.c.) signal driving it.
The amplitude of the sound produced should not be dependent on the frequency of sound being produced (otherwise different pitches would have different volumes).
However, due to the effects of resonance, a cone forced to vibrate at its natural frequency will oscillate with a much larger amplitude than at other frequencies.
This means that the loudspeaker cone will produce a louder sound at its natural frequency compared to at other frequencies, so the relative amplitudes of the sounds produced won't match the input signal.
Damping a loudspeaker cone reduces the effects of resonance — this means the amplitude of the sound produced will be more similar as its frequency varies.
Critically damping the system will make the response as similar as possible at different frequencies whilst still allowing it to oscillate, so this improves the sound quality of a loudspeaker cone.
The graph shows that the amplitude of the sound produced is very small for frequencies that are far away from the natural frequency. This can be improved by using different-sized cones with different natural frequencies, as frequencies that are far from the natural frequency of one cone will be closer to the natural frequency of the second cone.
Filtering the signals by frequency and using different cones to produce them as sounds means sound can be produced at comparable amplitudes over a much wider range of frequencies.

3 a) $g = -\frac{GM}{r^2}$, so rearrange this equation to get $-G = \frac{gr^2}{M}$.

As G is constant:

$\frac{g_1 r_1^2}{M_1} = \frac{g_2 r_2^2}{M_2}$ ***[1 mark]***

(where 1 and 2 denote the planet, and r in this case is the radius of the relevant planet)

so $M_1 = \frac{g_1 r_1^2 M_2}{g_2 r_2^2} = \frac{2g \times (5r)^2 \times M}{g \times r^2}$ ***[1 mark]***

$= \frac{50gr^2 M}{gr^2}$ = **$50M$** ***[1 mark]***

b) $V_g = -\frac{GM}{r}$ so:

$V_{g(total)} = \left(-\frac{GM_1}{r_1}\right) - \left(-\frac{GM_2}{r_2}\right) = -\frac{GM}{6.65 \times 10^8}$ ***[1 mark]***

(where r in this case is the distance from the centre of each planet)

$-\frac{G \times 50M}{3.10 \times 10^{10}} + \frac{G \times M}{r_2} = -\frac{GM}{6.65 \times 10^8}$

$-\frac{50}{3.10 \times 10^{10}} + \frac{1}{r_2} = -\frac{1}{6.65 \times 10^8}$

$\frac{1}{r_2} = -\frac{1}{6.65 \times 10^8} + \frac{50}{3.10 \times 10^{10}}$

$= 1.0914... \times 10^{-10}$ ***[1 mark]***

So $r_2 = \frac{1}{1.0914... \times 10^{-10}} = 9.1622... \times 10^9$ m ***[1 mark]***

Distance between centres of planets:

$r_1 + r_2 = (3.10 \times 10^{10}) + (9.162... \times 10^9)$
$= 4.0162... \times 10^{10}$
= **4.02×10^{10} m (to 3 s.f.)** ***[1 mark]***

If you got the answer to 3(a) wrong, but carried out the calculations in 3(b) correctly, then you'd still get full marks.

c) The value of peak wavelength that the scientist measures at Earth is red-shifted. So use $\frac{\Delta\lambda}{\lambda} \approx \frac{v}{c}$, where $\Delta\lambda = \lambda_{observed} - \lambda_{emitted}$ and $\lambda_{observed} = 645$ nm.

$\lambda_{emitted}$ can be found from the actual surface temperature of the star (T_1), using Wien's displacement law and the value that the scientist calculated for the temperature of the star (T_2) from $\lambda_{observed}$:

$\lambda_{max} \propto \frac{1}{T}$, so $\lambda_{max} T$ = constant so $\lambda_{emitted} T_1 = \lambda_{observed} T_2$.

So $\lambda_{emitted} = \frac{\lambda_{observed} T_2}{T_1} = \frac{645 \times 10^{-9} \times 4487}{4553}$

$= 6.3565... \times 10^{-7}$ m $= 635.65...$ nm ***[1 mark]***

$\frac{\Delta\lambda}{\lambda} \approx \frac{v}{c}$

so $v \approx \frac{c\Delta\lambda}{\lambda}$

$= \frac{3.00 \times 10^8 \times ((645 \times 10^{-9}) - (635.65... \times 10^{-9}))}{635.65... \times 10^{-9}}$ ***[1 mark]***

$= 4.412... \times 10^6$
= **4.41×10^6 ms^{-1} (to 3 s.f.)** ***[1 mark]***

d) To find the angle of parallax, you'll need to calculate the distance to the star using $v \approx H_0 d$:

Age of the universe in seconds, $t \approx H_0^{-1}$

$H_0 = 1 \div t = 1 \div 4.4 \times 10^{17} = 2.272... \times 10^{-18}$ s^{-1} ***[1 mark]***

$v \approx H_0 d$, so $d \approx \frac{v}{H_0} = \frac{4.412... \times 10^6}{2.272... \times 10^{-18}}$

$= 1.941... \times 10^{24}$ m ***[1 mark]***

$p = \frac{1}{d}$ where d is the distance in parsecs (pc) and p is the angle of parallax in seconds of arc.

Convert to pc: $(1.941... \times 10^{24}) \div (3.1 \times 10^{16}) = 6.263... \times 10^7$ pc

so $p = \frac{1}{6.263... \times 10^7} = 1.596... \times 10^{-8}$ seconds of arc ***[1 mark]***

In degrees: $1.596... \times 10^{-8} \div 3600 = 4.435... \times 10^{-12}$ °.

The angle of parallax of the distant star is incredibly small, and therefore would be impossible to measure ***[1 mark]***.

Answers

Module 6: Section 1 — Capacitors

Page 141 — Capacitors

1 Capacitance is the gradient of the Q-V graph.
$C = \frac{Q}{V} = \frac{660 \times 10^{-6}}{3}$ **[1 mark]** $= 220\ \mu$**F [1 mark]**
Charge stored is the area under the I-t graph.
$\Delta Q = I\Delta t = 15 \times 10^{-3} \times 66$ **[1 mark]** = **990 mC [1 mark]**

2 a) In series:
$\frac{1}{C_{total}} = \frac{1}{C_1} + \frac{1}{C_2} = \frac{1}{12 \times 10^{-12}} + \frac{1}{7 \times 10^{-12}} = 2.26... \times 10^{11}$
$C_{total} = \frac{1}{2.26... \times 10^{11}} = 4.42... \times 10^{-12}$ **[1 mark]**
$Q = CV = 4.42... \times 10^{-12} \times 12 = 5.305... \times 10^{-11}$
$=$ **5.3×10^{-11} C (to 2 s.f.) [1 mark]**

b) In parallel, $C_{total} = C_1 + C_2 = 12\text{ pF} + 7.0\text{ pF} = 19\text{ pF}$ **[1 mark]**
$Q = CV = 19 \times 10^{-12} \times 12 = 2.28 \times 10^{-10}$
$=$ **2.3×10^{-10} C (to 2 s.f.) [1 mark]**

Page 142 — Energy Stored by Capacitors

1 $W = \frac{1}{2}QV = \frac{1}{2} \times (0.6 \times 10^{-9}) \times 12 =$ **3.6×10^{-9} J [1 mark]**

2 $W = \frac{1}{2}CV^2$ so $C = \frac{2W}{V^2} = \frac{2 \times (2.5 \times 10^{-10})}{5^2} =$ **2×10^{-11} F**
[1 mark]

Page 145 — Charging and Discharging

1 a) The charge falls to 37% after CR seconds **[1 mark]**
so $t = 1000 \times 250 \times 10^{-6} =$ **0.25 s [1 mark]**

b) $Q = Q_0 e^{\frac{-t}{CR}}$, so after 0.7 seconds: $Q = Q_0 e^{\frac{-0.7}{0.25}}$
$= Q_0 \times 0.06$ (to 1 s.f.) **[1 mark]**
So there is **6%** of the initial charge left on the capacitor after 0.7 seconds **[1 mark]**.

c) i) The total charge stored will double (as $Q = CV$) **[1 mark]**.
ii) None (the capacitance is fixed — the charge increases as the voltage increases, so $C = Q/V$ is constant) **[1 mark]**.
iii) None (only capacitance and resistance can affect charging time) **[1 mark]**.

Module 6: Section 2 — Electric Fields

Page 147 — Electric Fields

1
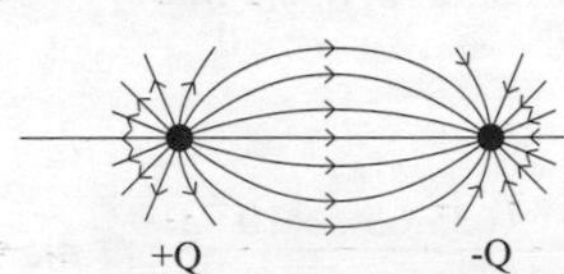

Recognisable pattern around the charges (not just in between) **[1 mark]**, lines equally spaced around the charges and joined to the charges, and general symmetry of the diagram **[1 mark]**, arrows along field lines between the charges with arrows pointing away from the positive and towards the negative charge **[1 mark]**.

2 $E = \frac{Q}{4\pi\varepsilon_0 r^2}$
$E = \frac{-1.60 \times 10^{-19}}{4\pi \times 8.85 \times 10^{-12} \times (1.75 \times 10^{-10})^2}$ **[1 mark]**
$= -4.697... \times 10^{10} =$ **-4.70×10^{10} NC^{-1} (to 3 s.f.) [1 mark]**

3 $E = V/d = 1500/(4.5 \times 10^{-3}) = 3.33... \times 10^5$ Vm^{-1}
$=$ **3.3×10^5 Vm^{-1} (to 2 s.f.) [1 mark]**
The field is perpendicular to the plates. **[1 mark]**

4 $A = 5.0 \times 10^{-3} \times 5.0 \times 10^{-3} = 2.5 \times 10^{-5}$ m^2 **[1 mark]**
$\varepsilon = \varepsilon_r\varepsilon_0 = 4.1 \times 8.85 \times 10^{-12} = 3.6285 \times 10^{-11}$ **[1 mark]**
$C = \frac{\varepsilon A}{d} = \frac{3.6285 \times 10^{-11} \times 2.5 \times 10^{-5}}{2 \times 10^{-3}}$
$C = 4.535... \times 10^{-13} =$ **4.5×10^{-13} F (to 2 s.f.) [1 mark]**

Page 149 — Electric Potential

1 a) $V = \frac{Q}{4\pi\varepsilon_0 r} = \frac{-1.60 \times 10^{-19}}{4\pi \times 8.85 \times 10^{-12} \times 0.00100}$ **[1 mark]**
$= -1.438... \times 10^{-6} =$ **-1.44×10^{-6} V (to 3 s.f.) [1 mark]**

b) electric potential energy $= Vq = -1.438... \times 10^{-6} \times 1.60 \times 10^{-19}$
$= -2.301... \times 10^{-25}$
$=$ **-2.30×10^{-25} J (to 3 s.f.) [1 mark]**

c) $V = \frac{Q}{4\pi\varepsilon_0 r}$ so $r = \frac{Q}{4\pi\varepsilon_0 V}$
$r = \frac{-1.60 \times 10^{-19}}{4\pi \times 8.85 \times 10^{-12} \times -1.0 \times 10^{-6}}$ **[1 mark]**
$r = 1.4386... \times 10^{-3}$ m = **1.4×10^{-3} m (to 2 s.f.) [1 mark]**

2 diameter $= 2r$ so $r = 5.00$ cm
$C = 4\pi\varepsilon_0 r = 4 \times \pi \times 8.85 \times 10^{-12} \times 0.0500 = 5.560... \times 10^{-12}$
$=$ **5.56×10^{-12} F (to 3 s.f.) [1 mark]**

3 Similarities — Any two from: gravitational field strength, g, is force per unit mass and electric field strength, E, is force per unit positive charge. Gravitational potential, V, is potential energy per unit mass and electric potential, V, is potential energy per unit charge. Both are zero at infinity. The force between two point masses is an inverse square law, and so is the force between two point charges. The field lines for a point mass and the field lines for a negative point charge are the same.
Differences — Any one from: gravitational forces are always attractive, whereas electric forces can be attractive or repulsive. The size of an electric force depends on the medium between the charges, e.g. plastic or air. For gravitational forces, this makes no difference. Objects can be shielded from electric fields, but not from gravitational fields. **[1 mark for each correct statement]**

Module 6: Section 3 — Electromagnetism

Page 151 — Magnetic Fields

1 a) $F = BIl = 2.00 \times 10^{-5} \times 3.00 \times 0.0400 =$ **2.40×10^{-6} N [1 mark]**
b) $F = BIl\sin\theta = 2.40 \times 10^{-6} \times \sin(30.0) =$ **1.20×10^{-6} [1 mark]**

Page 153 — Charged Particles in Magnetic Fields

1 a) $F = BQv = 0.770 \times 1.60 \times 10^{-19} \times 5.00 \times 10^6$ **[1 mark]**
$=$ **6.16×10^{-13} N [1 mark]**

b) The force acting on the electron is always at right angles to its velocity and the speed of the electron is constant. This is the condition for circular motion. **[1 mark]**

2 Electromagnetic force = centripetal force **[1 mark]**
$BQv = \frac{mv^2}{r}$, so $r = \frac{mv}{BQ}$ **[1 mark]**
$= \frac{(9.11 \times 10^{-31}) \times (2.30 \times 10^7)}{(0.600 \times 10^{-3}) \times (1.60 \times 10^{-19})}$
$= 0.21826... =$ **0.218 m (to 3 s.f.) [1 mark]**

3 $r = \frac{mv}{BQ}$, which rearranges to give $B = \frac{mv}{rQ}$ **[1 mark]**
For the Cl-35 ions and the Cl-37 ions, v, r and Q are all constant, so $\frac{B}{m}$ = constant.
Find the constant when $B = 0.200$ T, $m = 35$ u
$0.200 \div 35 = 5.714... \times 10^{-3}$ **[1 mark]**
Now use this value to find B when $m = 37$ u
$B = 37 \times 5.714... \times 10^{-3} = 0.2114... =$ **0.21 T (to 2 s.f.) [1 mark]**
The units of the atomic masses in this question don't matter — you're just interested in the ratio of B to m to get the constant.

Page 155 — Electromagnetic Induction

1 a) $\phi = BA = (2.00 \times 10^{-3}) \times 0.230 =$ **4.60×10^{-4} Wb [1 mark]**
b) Flux linkage $= BAN = (2.00 \times 10^{-3}) \times 0.230 \times 151 = 0.06946$
$=$ **0.0695 Wb (to 3 s.f.) [1 mark]**
c) $\varepsilon = -\frac{\Delta(N\phi)}{\Delta t} = -\frac{\Delta(NBA)}{\Delta t} = -\frac{NA\Delta B}{\Delta t}$ **[1 mark]**
$= -\frac{151 \times 0.230 \times (1.50 \times 10^{-3} - 2.00 \times 10^{-3})}{2.5}$ **[1 mark]**
$= 6.946 \times 10^{-3} =$ **6.95×10^{-3} V (to 3 s.f.) [1 mark]**

Answers

2 a) Flux linkage = $BAN = 0.92 \times 0.010 \times 550 =$ **5.06 Wb** ***[1 mark]***

b) Flux linkage after movement
$= BAN \cos\theta$
$= 550 \times 0.92 \times 0.010 \times \cos 90° = 0$ Wb ***[1 mark]***
$\varepsilon = -\frac{\Delta(N\phi)}{\Delta t} = -\frac{0 - 5.06}{0.5} = 10.12 =$ **10 V (to 2 s.f.)** ***[1 mark]***

3

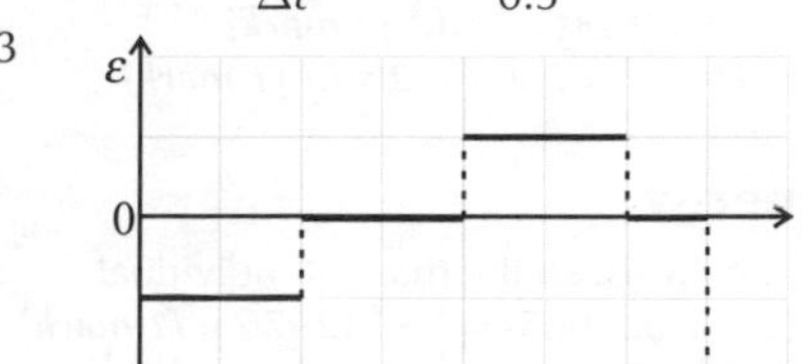

Step graph ***[1 mark]*** with the first and fifth steps negative and third step positive ***[1 mark]*** and the last step twice as negative as the others ***[1 mark]***.

Page 157 — Electromagnetic Induction

1 a) Distance travelled by plane, $s = v\Delta t$.
Wingspan = length l, so area of flux cut $A = lv\Delta t$.
So total magnetic flux cut $\phi = BA = Blv\Delta t$. ***[1 mark]***
E.m.f. $\varepsilon = -\frac{\Delta(N\phi)}{\Delta t} = -\frac{\Delta\phi}{\Delta t}$ (since $N = 1$), so
$\varepsilon = -\frac{Blv\Delta t}{\Delta t} = -Blv$ ***[1 mark]***
$= -6.00 \times 10^{-5} \times 33.9 \times 148 = 0.301032$
$=$ **– 0.301 V (to 3 s.f.)** ***[1 mark]***

b)

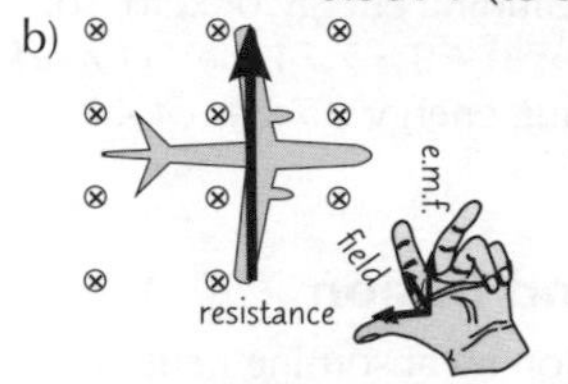

[1 mark]

Although there's no induced current, the direction that the current would be induced in if the plane were part of a complete circuit tells you the direction of the e.m.f..

2 a) $\varepsilon = -\frac{\Delta(N\phi)}{\Delta t} = -\frac{\Delta(BAN)}{\Delta t} = -\frac{AN\Delta B}{\Delta t}$ ***[1 mark]***
$= -\frac{0.030 \times 75 \times ((150 \times 10^{-3}) - 0)}{7.5}$
$=$ **– 0.045 V** ***[1 mark]***

b) When viewed from the south pole (on the right), the current will be clockwise ***[1 mark]***. Lenz's law says that the e.m.f. induced in a coil will always be in such a direction as to oppose the change that caused it. The magnetic field due to the current induced in the coil must act from right to left to create a field that opposes the strengthening field, so by the right hand rule the current will be clockwise ***[1 mark]***.

Page 159 — Uses of Electromagnetic Induction

1 a) i) $\frac{n_s}{n_p} = \frac{V_s}{V_p}$ so, $n_s = \frac{V_s \times n_p}{V_p} = \frac{45.0 \times 158}{9.30}$
$= 764.51... =$ **765 turns** ***[1 mark]***

ii) $\frac{n_s}{n_p} = \frac{V_s}{V_p}$, so $V_s = V_p \times \frac{n_s}{n_p} = 9.30 \times \frac{90}{158}$
$= 5.297... =$ **5.30 V (to 3 s.f.)** ***[1 mark]***

b) $\frac{I_s}{I_p} = \frac{V_p}{V_s}$ so, $I_s = I_p \times \frac{V_p}{V_s} = \frac{9.30 \times 1.50}{5.297...} = 2.6333...$
$=$ **2.63 A (to 3 s.f.)** ***[1 mark]***

2 a) power transmitted = power received + power wasted ***[1 mark]***
power transmitted = $943\,000 + I^2 \times R$
$= 943\,000 + 15.6^2 \times 132 = 975\,123.52$
$=$ **975 kW (to 3 s.f.)** ***[1 mark]***

b) Transformers are used to reduce the current (and increase the voltage) of electricity generated by power stations prior to transmitting it over the national grid ***[1 mark]***. Transmitting electricity using a low current significantly reduces power lost during transmission because power lost is proportional to the current squared ($P = I^2R$) ***[1 mark]***.

Module 6: Section 4 — Nuclear and Particle Physics

Page 161 — Atomic Structure

1 a) The nuclear model states that an atom consists of a positive nucleus containing protons and neutrons ***[1 mark]***, surrounded by orbiting negative electrons ***[1 mark]***. The nucleus makes up a tiny proportion of the volume of an atom, but most of its mass ***[1 mark]***.

b) E.g. Most alpha particles passed straight through the foil, so there must be a lot of empty space in an atom ***[1 mark]***. Some alpha particles were deflected through large angles, so the centre of the atom must have a large positive charge to repel them — the nucleus ***[1 mark]***. Very few particles were deflected by more than 90 degrees, so the nucleus must be tiny ***[1 mark]***.

2 Proton number = 57, so there are **57 protons** and **57 electrons**.
Nucleon number = no. of protons + no. of neutrons = 139
so no. of neutrons = 139 – 57 = **82 neutrons**
[2 marks for all correct, 1 mark for two correct]

Page 164 — The Nucleus

1 a) $R = r_0A^{1/3} = 1.4 \times 10^{-15} \times 16^{1/3}$
$=$ **3.5×10^{-15} m (to 2 s.f.)** ***[1 mark]***

b) Nuclear radius is proportional to the cube root of A, so
$R \propto A^{1/3}$, so $\frac{R_{\text{iodine}}}{R_{\text{nitrogen}}} = \frac{(A_{\text{iodine}})^{1/3}}{(A_{\text{nitrogen}})^{1/3}} = \left(\frac{127}{14}\right)^{1/3}$ ***[1 mark]***
$= 2.08...$
So the radius of the iodine nucleus is approximately **2 times** the radius of the nitrogen nucleus ***[1 mark]***.

2 $V = \frac{4}{3}\pi r^3 = \frac{4}{3}\pi(8.53 \times 10^{-15})^3 = 2.599... \times 10^{-42}$ m^3 ***[1 mark]***
$\rho = \frac{m}{V} = (3.75 \times 10^{-25}) \div (2.599... \times 10^{-42})$
$=$ **1.44×10^{17} kg m^{-3} (to 3 s.f.)** ***[1 mark]***

3 The density of a gold nucleus is much larger than the density of a gold atom ***[1 mark]***. This implies that the majority of a gold atom's mass is contained in the nucleus ***[1 mark]***.
As the nucleus is small compared to the size of the atom ***[1 mark]*** there must be a lot of empty space inside each atom ***[1 mark]***.

4 a) The strong nuclear force must be repulsive at very small nucleon separations to prevent the nucleus being crushed to a point ***[1 mark]***.

b) Beyond a few fm, the strong nuclear force is smaller than the electrostatic force ***[1 mark]***. This means the protons in the nucleus would be forced apart. So a nucleus bigger than this would be unstable ***[1 mark]***.

Page 165 — Classification of Particles

1 A proton, an electron and an antineutrino ***[1 mark]***.
The electron and the antineutrino are leptons ***[1 mark]***. Leptons are not affected by the strong nuclear force, so the decay can't be due to the strong nuclear force ***[1 mark]***.

2 A neutrino / an antineutrino ***[1 mark]***

Page 167 — Antiparticles

1 The creation of a particle of matter requires the creation of its antiparticle. In this case no antineutron has been produced ***[1 mark]***.

2 $e^+ + e^- \rightarrow \gamma + \gamma$ ***[1 mark]***.
This is called annihilation ***[1 mark]***.

3 The energy of each particle is equal to $\Delta E = mc^2$ (assuming kinetic energy is negligeable)
When the proton and the antiproton annihilate, two photons are produced. So $2E_\gamma = 2mc^2$ or $E_\gamma = mc^2$.
$E_\gamma = hf$ and equating, $mc^2 = hf$,
so $f = \frac{mc^2}{h}$ ***[1 mark]*** $= \frac{(1.673 \times 10^{-27})(3.00 \times 10^8)^2}{(6.63 \times 10^{-34})}$ ***[1 mark]***
$=$ **2.27×10^{23} Hz (to 3 s.f.)** ***[1 mark]***

Answers

Page 169 — Quarks

1 **C** ***[1 mark]***

2 a) i) $n \rightarrow p + e^- + \bar{\nu}$ ***[2 marks — 1 mark for n → p and 1 mark for the electron and antineutrino]***

ii) $d \rightarrow u + e^- + \bar{\nu}$ ***[1 mark]***

b) A down quark has a charge of –1/3, so the total charge on the left hand side of the equation is –1/3 ***[1 mark]***. An up quark has a charge of +2/3, an electron has a charge of –1 and an antineutrino has no charge, so the total charge on the right-hand side of the equation is –1/3 ***[1 mark]***. The charge is the same on both sides of the equation, so charge is conserved ***[1 mark]***.

Page 172 — Radioactive Decay

1 ***5-6 marks:***
The answer gives a full description of an experiment to identify the type of radiation emitted by a source, including the results expected for alpha, beta and gamma emitters. The answer includes a discussion of correcting for background radiation, and the safety measures that should be taken when working with radioactive sources. The answer has a clear and logical structure.
3-4 marks:
The answer describes an experiment to identify the type of radiation emitted by a source, including the results expected for alpha, beta and gamma emitters, but may omit some details. There is a limited discussion of the safety measures that should be taken when working with radioactive sources. The answer has some structure.
1-2 marks:
There is some description of an experiment to identify the type of radiation emitted by a source, but the answer lacks detail. The answer has no clear structure.
0 marks:
No relevant information is given.
Here are some points your answer may include:

- Measure the background count for a fixed amount of time (e.g. at least 30 seconds) and divide by the time to get the count rate.
- Take at least three measurements and calculate an average background count rate.
- The background count rate should be subtracted from all of the results.
- Place the source in front of a Geiger-Müller tube attached to a Geiger-Müller counter, so that the counter records a high count rate.
- Insert different materials between the source and the tube, and record the count rate by measuring the count over fixed time interval e.g. 30 seconds.
- If the count rate drops significantly, then some of the radiation is being absorbed by the material. If it drops to zero after the background count rate has been subtracted, then all of the radiation is being absorbed.
- If the radiation is blocked by a piece of paper, the source is emitting alpha radiation.
- If the radiation is blocked by a thin (3 mm) sheet of aluminium, the source is a beta emitter.
- If a thick sheet of lead is needed to block the radiation, then the source is a gamma emitter.
- The radioactive source should only be handled using long-handled tongs and should not be pointed at anyone.
- The radioactive source should be kept in a lead-lined box when not in use.
- Repeat the experiment to confirm the results.

2 a) ${}^{226}_{88}\text{Ra} \rightarrow {}^{222}_{86}\text{Rn} + {}^{4}_{2}\alpha$ ***[3 marks available — 1 mark for alpha particle, 1 mark each for proton and nucleon number of radon]***

b) ${}^{40}_{19}\text{K} \rightarrow {}^{40}_{20}\text{Ca} + {}^{0}_{-1}\beta + {}^{0}_{0}\bar{\nu}$ ***[3 marks available — 1 mark for beta particle and antineutrino, 1 mark each for proton and nucleon number of calcium]***

Page 175 — Exponential Law of Decay

1 a) Activity, A = measured activity – background activity
= 750 – 50 = 700 Bq ***[1 mark]***
$A = \lambda N$, so $\lambda = A/N = 700 \div 50\,000 =$ **0.014 s^{-1}** ***[1 mark]***

b) $\lambda t_{1/2} = \ln 2$, so $t_{1/2} = (\ln 2)/\lambda = (\ln 2) \div 0.014$
= **50 s (to 2 s.f.)** ***[1 mark]***

c) $N = N_0 e^{-\lambda t} = 50\,000 \times e^{-0.014 \times 300} =$ **750 (to 2 s.f.)** ***[1 mark]***

Page 177 — Binding Energy

1 a) There are 6 protons and 8 neutrons, so the mass of individual parts = (6 × 1.007276) + (8 × 1.008665) = 14.112976 u ***[1 mark]***
Mass of ${}^{14}_{6}\text{C}$ nucleus = 13.999948 u
Mass defect = 14.112976 – 13.999948 = **0.113028 u** ***[1 mark]***

b) $0.113028 \times 1.661 \times 10^{-27} = 1.87739... \times 10^{-28}$ kg ***[1 mark]***
$\Delta E = \Delta mc^2 = (1.87739... \times 10^{-28}) \times (3.00 \times 10^8)^2$
$= 1.68965... \times 10^{-11}$ J ***[1 mark]***
1 eV = 1.60×10^{-19} J, so energy = $1.68965... \times 10^{-11} / 1.60 \times 10^{-19}$
$= 1.056... \times 10^8$ eV
= **106 MeV (to 3 s.f.)** ***[1 mark]***

2 a) Fusion ***[1 mark]***

b) There are two deuterium atoms before the reaction, each containing two nucleons, so:
binding energy before reaction = 2 × 2 × 1.11 = 4.44 MeV ***[1 mark]***
There is one helium atom after the reaction, containing three nucleons, and a free neutron with a binding energy of zero, so:
binding energy after reaction = (2.58 × 3) + 0 = 7.74 MeV ***[1 mark]***
Energy released = difference in binding energy = 7.74 – 4.44
= **3.30 MeV** ***[1 mark]***

Page 179 — Nuclear Fission and Fusion

1 a) E.g. control rods limit the rate of fission by absorbing neutrons ***[1 mark]***. The number of neutrons absorbed by the rods is controlled by varying the amount they are inserted into the reactor ***[1 mark]***. A suitable material for the control rods is boron ***[1 mark]***.

b) In an emergency shut-down, the control rods are released into the reactor ***[1 mark]***. The control rods absorb the neutrons, and stop the reaction as quickly as possible ***[1 mark]***.

2 Advantages: e.g., the reaction in a nuclear reactor doesn't produce carbon dioxide ***[1 mark]***, it can produce a continuous supply of electricity, unlike some renewable sources ***[1 mark]***.
[1 mark for each advantage, maximum 2 marks]
Disadvantages — any two of: e.g. it could be dangerous if the reactor gets out of control, as a runaway reaction could cause an explosion ***[1 mark]*** / nuclear fission produces radioactive waste which is dangerous if it escapes into the environment ***[1 mark]*** / nuclear power-plants are expensive to build and decommission ***[1 mark]*** / nuclear waste has a long half-life, so has to be managed for a long time ***[1 mark]***.
[1 mark for each disadvantage, maximum 2 marks]

Module 6: Section 5 — Medical Imaging

Page 181 — X-Ray Imaging

1 $I = I_0 e^{-\mu x} = 200 \times e^{-(27 \times 1.5)}$
$= 5.15... \times 10^{-16} =$ **5.2 × 10^{-16} Wm^{-2} (to 2 s.f.)** ***[1 mark]***

2 Equate the two equations for the energy of the photon
$eV = \frac{hc}{\lambda}$ so $V \propto \frac{1}{\lambda}$
If $\lambda \rightarrow \frac{\lambda}{3}$, then $V \propto \frac{3}{\lambda}$, so V increases by a factor of 3 ***[1 mark]***.
V = 3 × 40 kV = **120 kV** ***[1 mark]***

Answers

Page 183 — Medical Uses of Nuclear Radiation

1 E.g. the patient is injected with a medical tracer consisting of a gamma source/positron-emitter bound to a substance used by the body *[1 mark]*. After a period of time, the radiation emitted from different points in the patient's body is recorded using a gamma camera/PET scanner *[1 mark]*. A computer uses this information to form an image, which might show a tumour as an area of high metabolic activity *[1 mark]*. One advantage of this method is that a diagnosis can be made without the patient having to undergo surgery.
A disadvantage is the use of ionising radiation, which can damage and even kill cells in a patient's body *[1 mark]*.

Page 185 — Ultrasound Imaging

1 $Z = \rho c$, $c = (1.63 \times 10^6)/(1.09 \times 10^3)$ *[1 mark]*
$= 1495\ \text{ms}^{-1}$ = **1.50 kms^{-1} (to 3 s.f.)** *[1 mark]*

2 When no gel is used:
$$\frac{(Z_{tissue} - Z_{air})^2}{(Z_{tissue} + Z_{air})^2} = \frac{(1630 \times 10^3 - 0.430 \times 10^3)^2}{(1630 \times 10^3 + 0.430 \times 10^3)^2}$$
= 0.9989... *[1 mark]*
So when no gel is used, 99.89...% is reflected, and so only 0.105...% enters the body *[1 mark]*.
$$\frac{(Z_{tissue} - Z_{gel})^2}{(Z_{tissue} + Z_{gel})^2} = \frac{(1630 \times 10^3 - 1500 \times 10^3)^2}{(1630 \times 10^3 + 1500 \times 10^3)^2}$$
= 0.00172... *[1 mark]*
So when gel is used, 0.172...% is reflected, and so 99.82...% of the ultrasound enters the body *[1 mark]*.
So the ratio is 99.82...% ÷ 0.105...%
= **1000 : 1 (to the nearest power of 10)** *[1 mark]*.

Extra Exam Practice for Module 6

Pages 186-187

2 a) E.g. $V = \frac{Q}{4\pi\varepsilon_0 r}$
A proton and an electron have charges of equal magnitude but of different signs and are the same distance from P. This means that at point P the electric potential from the proton is equal to minus the electric potential from the electron *[1 mark]*. The sum of the electric potentials at P due to the electron and the proton is therefore equal to zero *[1 mark]*.

b) An electric field points in the direction that a positive charge would move. Therefore both electric fields point towards the electron, and so the field strength at point P is equal to their magnitudes at point P added together *[1 mark]*.
The distance from the electron/proton to point P:
$r = (1.00 \times 10^{-10}) \div 2 = 5.00 \times 10^{-11}$ m
Magnitude of a proton's electric field strength:
$$E = \frac{Q}{4\pi\varepsilon_0 r^2} = \frac{e}{4\pi\varepsilon_0 r^2}$$
Similarly the magnitude of an electron's electric field strength:
$$E = \frac{Q}{4\pi\varepsilon_0 r^2} = \frac{e}{4\pi\varepsilon_0 r^2}$$
Total electric field strength at point P:
$$\frac{e}{4\pi\varepsilon_0 r^2} + \frac{e}{4\pi\varepsilon_0 r^2} = \frac{2e}{4\pi\varepsilon_0 r^2}$$ *[1 mark]*
$$= \frac{2 \times 1.60 \times 10^{-19}}{4\pi \times 8.85 \times 10^{-12} \times (5.00 \times 10^{-11})^2}$$
$= 1.150... \times 10^{12}$
= **1.15 × 10^{12} NC^{-1} (to 3 s.f.)** *[1 mark]*
pointing from the proton to the electron

3 a) ***5-6 marks:***
The answer includes the correct graph with suitable axis labels and the graph shows a clear peak. The answer includes an explanation of how mass defect links to binding energy and how the graph shows the energy absorbed / emitted during fission and fusion. The answer has a clear and logical structure. The information given is relevant and detailed.
3-4 marks:
The answer includes the correct graph with suitable axis labels and with a clear peak. The answer describes mass defect and binding energy with some link to the energy absorbed / emitted during fission and fusion. The answer has some structure. Most of the information given is relevant and there is some detail involved.
1-2 marks:
There is no correct graph, or the graph is of the correct shape, but may have no labels. The answer describes fission and fusion but does not explain mass defect and binding energy and how they relate to energy absorbed / released. The answer has no clear structure. The information given is basic and lacking in detail. It may not all be relevant.
0 marks:
No relevant information is given.
Here are some points your answer may include:
The mass of a nucleus is less than the total mass of the nucleons that make up the nucleus.
The difference in mass is called the mass defect.
The mass defect is caused by mass being converted to energy which is released when nucleons join.
This energy is known as the binding energy.
The change in binding energy per nucleon during a reaction tells you if energy is released or absorbed. An increase in binding energy per nucleon means energy is released.
The graph of binding energy per nucleon against nucleon number looks like:

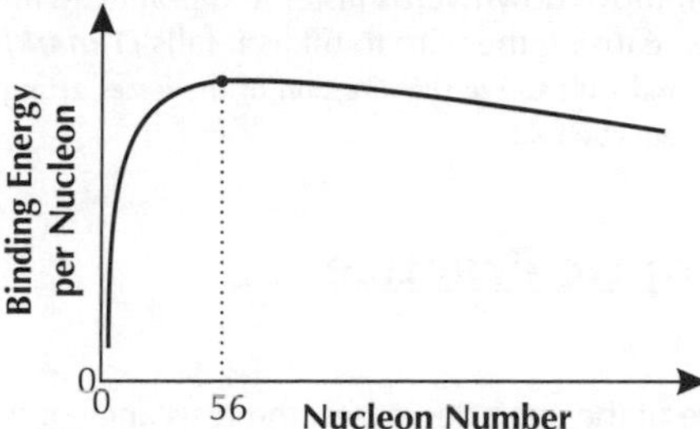

Nuclei combining is known as fusion and nuclei splitting into smaller nuclei is known as fission.
Fusion results in nucleon number increasing.
This leads to an increase in binding energy per nucleon for nucleon numbers below the peak.
This means that fusion releases energy as long as the product has a nucleon number less than or equal to the peak.
For nucleon numbers above the peak, the binding energy per nucleon decreases as nucleon number increases, so energy would be absorbed during fusion.
Fission results in nucleon number decreasing.
This leads to an increase in binding energy per nucleon for nucleon numbers above the peak.
This means that fission releases energy as long as the products have nucleon numbers greater than or equal to the peak.
For nucleon numbers below the peak, the binding energy per nucleon decreases as nucleon number decreases, so energy would be absorbed during fission.

b) The neutrons do not need to be slowed down to thermal neutrons so there is no need for a moderator in the nuclear reactor *[1 mark]*.

c) E.g. technetium-99m has a shorter half-life than iodine-131 (but still long enough for the procedure to finish). This means that the patient will be exposed to radiation for a shorter time/exposure is minimised *[1 mark]*.
As well as gamma radiation, iodine-131 emits beta radiation, which isn't used for the procedure/isn't detected by the gamma camera/has a low penetration and so won't reach outside the body easily, so the patient is exposed to radiation that isn't needed for the scan/not all of the radiation can be detected *[1 mark]*.

Answers

4 a) As the wire is moved downwards through the magnetic field, Lenz's law states that the induced e.m.f. in the wire will act to oppose the motion of the wire ***[1 mark]***. This means that as the wire is moved downwards, electrons between A and B will flow from A to B and the electrons between B and C will flow from C to B ***[1 mark]***. As electrons flow towards point B from both sides of point B, a negative charge builds up at B ***[1 mark]***.

Use Fleming's Left-Hand Rule to work out the direction of movement of the electrons — the force is in the opposite direction to the motion of the wire (Lenz's law), and your second finger shows the direction of motion of a positive charge, so an electron will move in the opposite direction.

b) $\varepsilon = -\frac{\Delta(N\Phi)}{\Delta t}$ and $\Phi = BA$ so calculate the area cut by the wire.
The area cut is the area of the square face of the magnet.
$A = (5.5 \times 10^{-2})^2 = 3.025 \times 10^{-3}\ \text{m}^2$
$\Phi = BA = 155 \times 10^{-3} \times 3.025 \times 10^{-3}$
$= 4.68875 \times 10^{-4}$ Wb ***[1 mark]***
The time taken for the wire to fall through the magnetic field:
$s = v\Delta t$ so $\Delta t = \frac{s}{v} = \frac{5.5\times10^{-2}}{1.2} = 0.0458...$ s ***[1 mark]***
$\varepsilon = -\frac{\Delta(N\Phi)}{\Delta t} = -\frac{1\times4.68875\times10^{-4}}{0.0458...} = -0.01023$ V
So the magnitude of the maximum reading on the voltmeter is **0.010 V (to 2 s.f.)** ***[1 mark]***

c) Between A and B, the direction of the force acting on the wire, due to passing through the magnetic field, is downwards. Between B and C the direction of force acting on the wire, due to passing through the magnetic field, is upwards ***[1 mark]***. So overall point A will move downwards faster and point C will move downwards slower, causing the wire to tilt as it falls ***[1 mark]***.

Use Fleming's Left-Hand Rule to see the direction of the forces acting on the wire due to the magnetic fields.

AS/Year 1 Synoptic Practice

Pages 192-195

1 a) As the temperature of the oven decreases, the resistance of the thermistor increases ***[1 mark]***. This means the thermistor gets a larger share of the potential difference and therefore the motor gets a larger share of the potential difference, which will cause the door to unlock when the p.d. across the motor is great enough ***[1 mark]***.

b) From Figure 2, the resistance of the thermistor at 56 °C is 1.6 Ω.
First calculate the total resistance (R_2) of the motor (R_M) and thermistor (R_T) in parallel:
$\frac{1}{R_2} = \frac{1}{R_M} + \frac{1}{R_T} = \frac{1}{6.4} + \frac{1}{1.6} = 0.78125$
$R_2 = 1 \div 0.78125 = 1.28\ \Omega$ ***[1 mark]***
Now calculate the total resistance of the circuit:
The resistor and the combined resistance of the motor and thermistor are in series, so $R_{total} = R_1 + R_2 = 4.0 + 1.28$
$= 5.28\ \Omega$ ***[1 mark]***
$\varepsilon = I(R + r) = 4.6 \times (5.28 + 0.085)$
$= 24.679 =$ **25 V (to 2 s.f.)** ***[1 mark]***

c) At 56 °C, the current through the circuit is 4.6 A.
The voltage supplied by the battery is:
$\varepsilon = V + Ir$ so $V = \varepsilon - Ir = 24.679 - (4.6 \times 0.085)$
$= 24.228$ V ***[1 mark]***
You could have also done this by using $V = IR$ where R is the total resistance of the circuit calculated in part b (5.28 Ω).
The circuit is a potential divider, so the voltage across the motor is $V_{out} = \frac{R_2}{R_1 + R_2}V_{in}$, where R_1 is the resistance of the resistor and R_2 is the combined resistance of the thermistor and motor in parallel at 56 °C, which equals 1.28 Ω (from part b).
$V_{out} = \frac{1.28}{4.0+1.28} \times 24.228 = 5.873...$ V
$=$ **5.9 V (to 2 s.f.)** ***[1 mark]***

d) $E = \frac{1}{2}kx^2$, so calculate the total extension of the spring first:
To calculate the extension of the spring when the bolt is accelerating, consider the forces acting on the bolt:
E.g.
resultant force = ma
$F_{spring} - mg = ma$ and $F_{spring} = kx$, so:
$kx - mg = ma$ ***[1 mark]***
$x = \frac{mg + ma}{k} = \frac{m(g+a)}{k}$
$= \frac{0.540 \times (9.81 + 0.142)}{855}$ ***[1 mark]***
$= 6.285... \times 10^{-3}$ m ***[1 mark]***

$E = \frac{1}{2}kx^2 = \frac{1}{2} \times 855 \times (6.285... \times 10^{-3})^2$
$= 0.01688... =$ **0.0169 J (to 3 s.f.)** ***[1 mark]***

e) $R = \frac{V}{I} = \frac{1.04\times10^{-3}}{1.6} = 6.5 \times 10^{-4}\ \Omega$ ***[1 mark]***
$R = \rho L \div A$ so $A = \rho L \div R$
$= (2.65 \times 10^{-8} \times 1.8 \times 10^{-2}) \div (6.5 \times 10^{-4})$
$= 7.338... \times 10^{-7}\ \text{m}^2$ ***[1 mark]***
$A = \pi r^2$ so $r = \sqrt{\frac{A}{\pi}} = \sqrt{\frac{7.338...\times10^{-7}}{\pi}}$
$= 4.833... \times 10^{-4}$ m ***[1 mark]***
diameter = radius × 2
$= 4.833... \times 10^{-4} \times 2$
$= 9.666... \times 10^{-4} =$ **9.7 × 10⁻⁴ m (to 2 s.f.)** ***[1 mark]***

2 a) E.g. $p = (1 + R)\frac{I}{c}$, and I and c are constant, so the greater the fraction of reflected photons (R), the greater the pressure exerted on the solar sail ***[1 mark]***. $p = \frac{F}{A}$, and A is constant, so the greater the pressure on the sail is, the greater the force on the sail ***[1 mark]***. $F = ma$, and m is constant, so a larger force on the sail gives a larger acceleration of the sail, hence the acceleration of the spacecraft is larger when a greater fraction of photons are reflected ***[1 mark]***. Sail A reflects a larger fraction of photons than sail B, so the spacecraft with sail A will have a larger acceleration than the spacecraft with sail B ***[1 mark]***.

b) The force exerted by a single photon being absorbed by the sail:
$F = \frac{\Delta p}{\Delta t} = \frac{1.33\times10^{-27}}{1.00\times10^{-3}}$
$= 1.33 \times 10^{-24}$ N ***[1 mark]***
The number of photons absorbed by sail B
= number of incident photons × percentage of photons absorbed
$= 1.60 \times 10^{24} \times 0.12 = 1.92 \times 10^{23}$ ***[1 mark]***
Total force = force per photon × number of absorbed photons
$= 1.33 \times 10^{-24} \times 1.92 \times 10^{23}$
$= 0.25536 =$ **0.255 N (to 3 s.f.)** ***[1 mark]***
You'd also get full marks if you worked out the total change in momentum of all the photons and divided it by 1.00 ms.

c) Calculate the total input energy to sail C:
$I = \frac{P}{A}$ so $P = IA = 1362 \times 1700$
$= 2.3154 \times 10^6$ W ***[1 mark]***
$P = \frac{W}{t}$ where W is the work done. Work done is the same as energy transferred, so $P = \frac{E}{t}$.
The input energy in 60 s is $E = Pt = 2.3154 \times 10^6 \times 60.0$
$= 1.38924 \times 10^8$ J ***[1 mark]***
$\text{efficiency} = \frac{\text{useful output energy}}{\text{total input energy}} \times 100$
$= \frac{1.28\times10^8}{1.38924\times10^8} \times 100$
$= 92.136... =$ **92% (to 2 s.f.)** ***[1 mark]***

Answers

d) Resolve the force of the incident photons in the X direction to get the force applied by a photon in the direction of X.

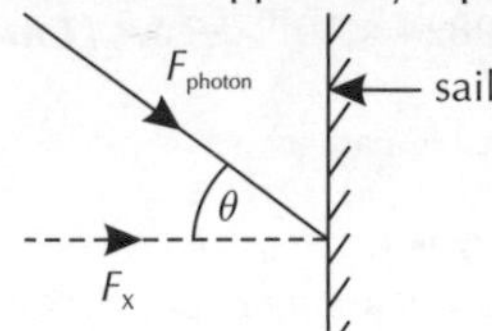

$F_X = F_{photon}\cos\theta$. The force in the direction of X halves when $F_X = \frac{1}{2}F_{photon}$. Substitute to get $\frac{1}{2}F_{photon} = F_{photon}\cos\theta$.

Divide by F_{photon}:

$\frac{1}{2} = \cos\theta$, so $\theta = \cos^{-1}(\frac{1}{2}) = $ **60°** ***[1 mark]***

e) The solar sail is positively charged due to photons releasing electrons from the surface of the sail by the photoelectric effect ***[1 mark]***. The further the solar sail is from the Sun, the lower the intensity of light incident on the sail, so fewer photons hit the sail in a certain amount of time. This means fewer photoelectrons will be released, so the solar sail will have a lower positive charge and is therefore less likely to suffer damage ***[1 mark]***.

3 a) The horizontal component of the velocity will remain constant because there is no air resistance.

$v_h = 30.0\cos(5.00) = 29.885...\ ms^{-1}$ ***[1 mark]***

To calculate v_v use $v_v = u_v + at$, so first calculate t using the horizontal velocity and displacement:

$t = \frac{s_h}{v_h} = \frac{18.4}{29.885...} = 0.6156...\ s$ ***[1 mark]***

$v_v = u_v + at = u_v + -gt$

The acceleration g is negative here because it's acting in the opposite direction to the initial vertical velocity of the ball.

$u_v = 30.0\sin(5.00)$

$v_v = 30.0\sin(5.00) + (-9.81 \times 0.6156...) = -3.425...\ ms^{-1}$ ***[1 mark]***

Use Pythagoras' theorem to find the resultant speed:

$v^2 = v_h^2 + v_v^2$ so $v = \sqrt{v_h^2 + v_v^2} = \sqrt{(29.855...)^2 + (-3.425...)^2}$

$= 30.081... = $ **30.1 ms⁻¹ (to 3 s.f.)** ***[1 mark]***

b) Use the horizontal impulse to find the change in horizontal momentum, and therefore the change in horizontal velocity:

The following calculations take motion to the right as positive and motion to the left as negative.

Momentum is conserved in both the horizontal and vertical directions, so you can just use the horizontal components of the velocity and impulse for these calculations.

You know $F = \frac{\Delta p}{\Delta t}$ and $p = mv$, so $F_h\Delta t = \Delta p = \Delta(mv_h)$ ***[1 mark]***.

The mass of the ball remains constant, so $F_h\Delta t = m\Delta v_h$

$m = 145\ g = 0.145\ kg$

$\Delta v_h = \frac{F_h\Delta t}{m} = \frac{5.08}{0.145} = 35.034...\ ms^{-1}$

Calculate the initial horizontal velocity:

$u_h = u\cos\theta_2 = 28.6\cos(35.0) = 23.427...\ ms^{-1}$

So $v_h = 23.427... - 35.034...$ ***[1 mark]***

$= -11.606...\ ms^{-1}$ ***[1 mark]***

The ball is initially moving to the right, but bounces off the wall and moves to the left. This means that the change in velocity (35.034... ms⁻¹) is negative because the ball has changed direction.

The final horizontal velocity, $v_h = v\cos\theta_3$,

so $v = \frac{v_h}{\cos\theta_3} = \frac{-11.606...}{\cos(48.2)} = -17.413...$

So the final speed = **17.4 ms⁻¹ (to 3 s.f.)** ***[1 mark]***

You can ignore the final minus sign, as this indicates the direction of the velocity, but the question is asking for the speed.

c) First calculate the horizontal component of the force acting on the baseball as it collides with the wall:

Impulse $= F\Delta t$ so $F = \frac{\text{impulse}}{\Delta t} = \frac{5.08}{1.8 \times 10^{-3}}$

$= 2822.22...\ N$ ***[1 mark]***

Then calculate the horizontal compression of the ball:

$F = kx$ so $x = \frac{F}{k} = \frac{2822.22...}{1.03 \times 10^5} = 0.02740...\ m$ ***[1 mark]***

This is 35% of the baseball's diameter, so the diameter of the baseball is:

$0.02740... \times \frac{100}{35} = 0.07828...\ m$

Volume of baseball $= \frac{4}{3}\pi r^3 = \frac{4}{3} \times \pi \times (0.07828... \div 2)^3$

$= 2.5122... \times 10^{-4}\ m^3$ ***[1 mark]***

Then calculate the density:

$\rho = \frac{m}{V} = \frac{0.145}{2.5122... \times 10^{-4}} = 577.18...$

= **580 kgm⁻³ (to 2 s.f.)** ***[1 mark]***

d) When the ball rolls down the roof, the ball's gravitational potential energy (GPE) is transferred to kinetic energy (KE).

Energy is conserved, so the change in GPE between the top and bottom of the roof equals the ball's final KE:

$\frac{1}{2}mv^2 = mgh$, where h is the change in height, Δh.

The mass remains constant so:

$\frac{1}{2}v^2 = g\Delta h$, so $v = \sqrt{2g\Delta h}$ ***[1 mark]***

$= \sqrt{2 \times 9.81 \times (6.50 - 5.40)}$

$= 4.645...\ ms^{-1}$ ***[1 mark]***

Find the horizontal component of the initial velocity when the ball leaves the roof:

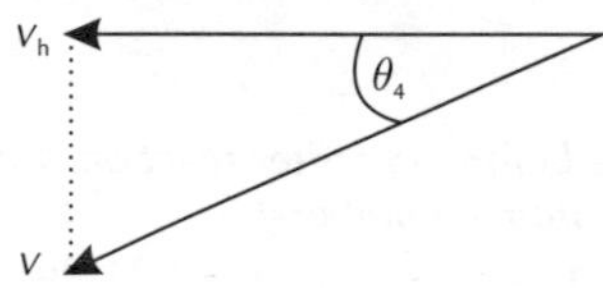

$v_h = v\cos\theta_4 = 4.645... \times \cos(32.5) = 3.918...\ ms^{-1}$ ***[1 mark]***

$s = vt = 3.918... \times 0.812$

$= 3.181... = $ **3.18 m (to 3 s.f.)** ***[1 mark]***

4 a) $hf = \phi + KE_{max}$ so first determine the work function, ϕ.

The work function is the minimum energy needed to release electrons from the photoelectric material. Figure 8 shows that this happens at 320 nm ***[1 mark]***.

$E = \frac{hc}{\lambda}$, so $\phi = \frac{hc}{\lambda} = \frac{6.63 \times 10^{-34} \times 3.00 \times 10^8}{320 \times 10^{-9}}$

$= 6.215... \times 10^{-19}\ J$ ***[1 mark]***

You'd get the marks if you used any value for the wavelength between 280 nm and 320 nm.

Now calculate the kinetic energy of photoelectrons when a laser of 255 nm is shone onto the photocathode:

$hf = \phi + KE_{max}$, so:

$KE_{max} = hf - \phi = \frac{hc}{\lambda} - \phi$

$= \frac{6.63 \times 10^{-34} \times 3.00 \times 10^8}{255 \times 10^{-9}} - 6.215... \times 10^{-19}$

$= 1.584... \times 10^{-19}\ J$ ***[1 mark]***

$KE_{max} = \frac{1}{2}mv_{max}^2$

so $v_{max} = \sqrt{\frac{2 \times KE_{max}}{m}} = \sqrt{\frac{2 \times 1.584... \times 10^{-19}}{9.11 \times 10^{-31}}}$

$= 5.897... \times 10^5$

= **5.90 × 10⁵ ms⁻¹ (to 3 s.f.)** ***[1 mark]***

b) The value at which the current drops to zero lies somewhere between 280 and 320 nm. The wavelength at which the current drops to zero was used to calculate ϕ and v, so the answer to 4a) may not be accurate ***[1 mark]***. The accuracy could be improved by repeating the experiment for smaller intervals between 280 and 320 nm to find a more accurate value for the wavelength when the current drops to zero ***[1 mark]***.

Answers

c) E.g.

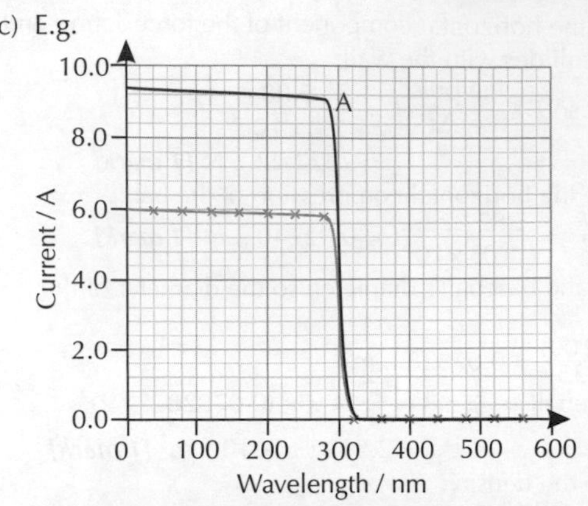

[1 mark for all non-zero values of current being higher than the original graph, 1 mark for the current dropping to zero at the same wavelength as the original graph]

d) $\lambda = \frac{ax}{D}$. The student uses the same laser for both diffraction patterns, so the wavelength is constant, and the distance to the screen is kept constant. λ and D are both constants, so $ax = \lambda D$ = constant.

$a_1x_1 = a_2x_2$

$x_2 = \frac{a_1 x_1}{a_2} = \frac{2\times10^{-6}\times5\times10^{-2}}{1.25\times10^{-6}}$ ***[1 mark]*** = **0.08 m** ***[1 mark]***

A-Level Synoptic Practice

Pages 196-201

1 a) ${}^{241}_{94}\text{Pu} \rightarrow {}^{241}_{95}\text{Am} + {}^{0}_{-1}\beta + \bar{\nu}$

[1 mark for all correct symbols before and after reaction, 1 mark for correct mass numbers and atomic numbers]

You'd still get full marks if you put proton and mass numbers of zero on the neutrino. You also could have represented the beta-minus particle with ${}^{0}_{-1}e$.

b) First calculate the number of Am-241 atoms produced per second:

$N = nN_A = (2.65 \times 10^{-9}) \times (6.02 \times 10^{23})$

$= 1.5953 \times 10^{15}$ atoms ***[1 mark]***

The number of Am-241 atoms produced per second by the Pu-241 is equal to the activity of the Pu-241 source, so $A = 1.5953 \times 10^{15}$ Bq.

$A = \lambda N$ so calculate the decay constant, λ, of Pu-241:

$\lambda t_{1/2} = \ln 2$ so $\lambda = \frac{\ln 2}{t_{1/2}} = \frac{\ln 2}{4.42\times10^{8}}$

$= 1.568... \times 10^{-9}\ \text{s}^{-1}$ ***[1 mark]***

$A = \lambda N$ so $N = \frac{A}{\lambda} = \frac{1.5953\times10^{15}}{1.568...\times10^{-9}}$

$= 1.017... \times 10^{24}$ atoms ***[1 mark]***

Calculate the number of moles:

$N = nN_A$, so $n = \frac{N}{N_A} = \frac{1.017...\times10^{24}}{6.02\times10^{23}}$

$= 1.689...$ = **1.69 moles (to 3 s.f.)** ***[1 mark]***

c) The energy released is the difference in the binding energy (BE) per nucleus before and after the reaction. The binding energy per nucleus is the binding energy per nucleon × mass number:

BE per nucleus: Am-241 = 7.54 × 241 = 1817.14 MeV

Np-237 = 7.58 × 237 = 1796.46 MeV

He-4 = 7.07 × 4 = 28.28 MeV ***[1 mark]***

Energy released = BE after – BE before

= (1796.46 + 28.28) – 1817.14 = 7.6 MeV ***[1 mark]***

1.70% of this energy is transferred to the KE of the alpha particle.

E_k = energy per decay × percentage energy transferred to alpha

$= 7.6 \times 10^6 \times 0.0170 = 129\,200$ eV

Convert E_k into joules: $129\,200 \times 1.60 \times 10^{-19} = 2.0672 \times 10^{-14}$ J

$E_k = \frac{1}{2}mv^2$ and $m_\alpha = 6.646 \times 10^{-27}$ kg

so $v = \sqrt{\frac{2E_k}{4m_p}} = \sqrt{\frac{2\times2.0672\times10^{-14}}{6.646\times10^{-27}}}$ ***[1 mark]***

$= 2.494... \times 10^6$ = $\mathbf{2.49 \times 10^6\ ms^{-1}}$ **(to 3 s.f.)** ***[1 mark]***

d) The activity is the number of decays per second, so the number of decays in 7.0 days is:

$7.0 \times 24 \times 60 \times 60 \times 38 \times 10^3 = 2.29824 \times 10^{10}$ decays ***[1 mark]***

Energy released per decay = 7.6 MeV

The energy released per decay was calculated in part (c).

Convert this energy to joules:

$7.6 \times 10^6 \times 1.60 \times 10^{-19} = 1.216 \times 10^{-12}$ J

Total energy released = number of decays × energy per decay

$= 2.29824 \times 10^{10} \times 1.216 \times 10^{-12}$

= 0.0279... J ***[1 mark]***

$E = mc\Delta\theta$ so $\Delta\theta = \frac{E}{mc} = \frac{0.279...}{3.4\times10^{-3}\times720}$

= 0.0114... = **0.011 K (to 2 s.f.)** ***[1 mark]***

You could also have given your answer in °C. $\Delta\theta$ = 0.011 °C (to 2 s.f.).

2 a) Find sinθ using the length of the string and the radius of the circle.

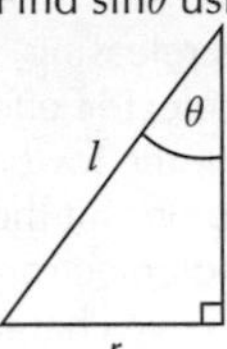

So $\sin\theta = \frac{r}{l}$ ***[1 mark]***

Find tanθ using the forces acting on the ball.

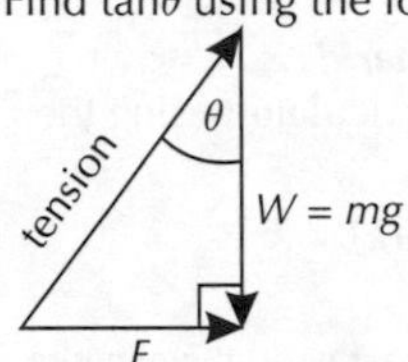

So $\tan\theta = \frac{F}{mg}$ ***[1 mark]***

The small angle approximation states that $\sin\theta \approx \tan\theta$

so $\frac{r}{l} = \frac{F}{mg}$ which rearranges to give $F = \frac{mgr}{l}$ ***[1 mark]***.

b) The centripetal force on the ball is $F = m\omega^2 r$ and $\omega = \frac{2\pi}{T}$,

so $F = m \times \left(\frac{2\pi}{T}\right)^2 \times r$ ***[1 mark]***

The centripetal force is equal to the resultant force:

$F = m \times \left(\frac{2\pi}{T}\right)^2 \times r = \frac{mgr}{l}$ ***[1 mark]***

Rearrange for T:

$\left(\frac{2\pi}{T}\right)^2 = \frac{g}{l}$ so $T = 2\pi\sqrt{\frac{l}{g}}$ ***[1 mark]***

c) If the ball is initially moving from left to right, then the force being applied to the ball will be towards the left. The ball will therefore be moving from right to left after being hit. For this answer, towards the right is being taken as the positive direction, and towards the left is being taken as the negative direction.

When dealing with vectors it's always a good idea to set which direction is positive and which direction is negative before doing any calculations.

$F = \frac{\Delta p}{\Delta t}$ so $F\Delta t = \Delta p$

$p = mv$ so $F\Delta t = \Delta(mv)$

mass of the ball is constant, so $F\Delta t = m\Delta v$

To find the change in velocity of the ball, first calculate its initial velocity:

$v = r\omega$ and $\omega = \frac{2\pi}{T}$, so $v = \frac{2\pi r}{T}$

$T = 2\pi\sqrt{\frac{l}{g}}$ so $v = r\sqrt{\frac{g}{l}} = 0.205 \times \sqrt{\frac{9.81}{1.45}}$

$= 0.5332...\ \text{ms}^{-1}$ ***[1 mark]***

Therefore the final velocity is $-0.5332...\ \text{ms}^{-1}$, as the speed after being hit is equal to the speed before being hit but the ball is travelling in the opposite direction.

Δv = final velocity – initial velocity = (–0.5332...) – (0.5332...)

$= -1.0664...\ \text{ms}^{-1}$ ***[1 mark]***

$F\Delta t = m\Delta v$ so:

$m = \frac{F\Delta t}{\Delta v} = \frac{-98.4\times6.5\times10^{-3}}{-1.0664...} = 0.5997...$

= **0.60 kg (to 2 s.f.)** ***[1 mark]***

Answers

3 a) An X-ray tube potential difference of about 30 kV would produce the best image ***[1 mark]***, because the difference between the mass attenuation coefficient of iodine and lung tissue is largest here ***[1 mark]***. A larger difference in the mass attenuation coefficient means a larger difference in the amount of X-rays absorbed. This means the image with the best contrast between lung tissue and blood vessels containing iodine contrast will be produced when around 30 kV is used ***[1 mark]***.

You can give yourself the mark if you've suggested an X-ray tube potential difference of between 25-35 kV.

b) $A = \lambda N$ so first calculate λ:

$t_{1/2} = 5.2 \text{ days} = 5.2 \times 24 \times 60 \times 60 = 449\ 280 \text{ s}$

$\lambda t_{1/2} = \ln 2$ so $\lambda = \frac{\ln 2}{t_{1/2}} = \frac{\ln 2}{449\ 280} = 1.542... \times 10^{-6} \text{ s}^{-1}$ ***[1 mark]***

$pV = NkT$ and $T = 273 + 37 = 310 \text{ K}$

$N = \frac{pV}{kT} = \frac{1.01 \times 10^5 \times 0.0035}{1.38 \times 10^{-23} \times 310}$

$= 8.263... \times 10^{22}$ molecules ***[1 mark]***

32% of these are Xenon-133 molecules:

$0.32 \times 8.263... \times 10^{22} = 2.644... \times 10^{22}$ molecules

$A = \lambda N = 1.542... \times 10^{-6} \times 2.644... \times 10^{22}$

$= 4.079... \times 10^{16}$

$=$ **4.1 × 10¹⁶ Bq (to 2 s.f.)** ***[1 mark]***

c) $\frac{I_r}{I_0} = \left(\frac{Z_2 - Z_1}{Z_2 + Z_1}\right)^2$

When the ultrasound reaches a tissue-air boundary, the proportion of the ultrasound energy that is reflected is:

$\frac{I_r}{I_0} = \left(\frac{400 - (1.8 \times 10^5)}{400 + (1.8 \times 10^5)}\right)^2 = 0.99115... = 99.115...\%$ ***[1 mark]***

You would end up with the same answer if you calculated the proportion of ultrasound energy reflected as it goes from air to lung tissue (instead of from lung tissue to air).

So almost all of the ultrasound energy will be reflected from the first air-tissue boundary it meets ***[1 mark]***. The lungs contain a lot of air-tissue boundaries, so it is difficult for the ultrasound to reach all parts of the lungs ***[1 mark]***.

4 a) To work out the scale of the x-axis, calculate the period of the oscillations. $T = 2\pi\sqrt{\frac{m}{k}}$, so calculate k first.

$F = kx$ and when the magnet is attached to the spring, the force acting on the spring due to the magnet is equal to $F = mg$,

so $k = \frac{F}{x} = \frac{mg}{x} = \frac{20.0 \times 10^{-3} \times 9.81}{7.848 \times 10^{-3}} = 25 \text{ Nm}^{-1}$ ***[1 mark]***

$T = 2\pi\sqrt{\frac{m}{k}} = 2\pi\sqrt{\frac{20.0 \times 10^{-3}}{25}} = 0.1777... \text{ s}$ ***[1 mark]***

One full oscillation in the graph in Figure 4 takes roughly 3.6 large squares on the x-axis. One large square must be equal to $0.1777... \div 3.6 \approx 0.05$ s, so the scale of the x-axis must be 0.05 s per large square:

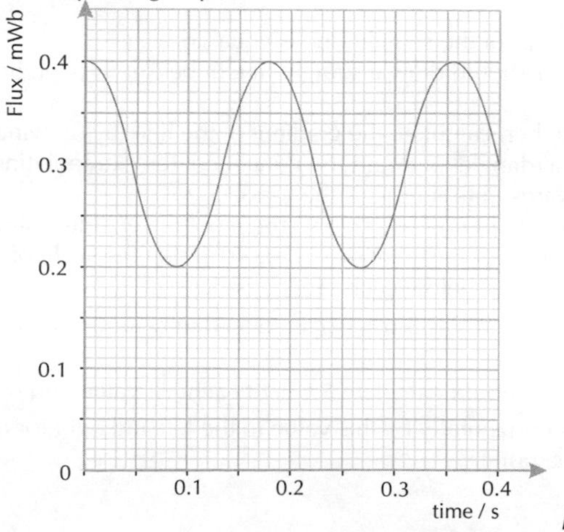

[1 mark]

There are 2.25 oscillations shown on the graph in Figure 4, so to work out the scale you could also have calculated the time taken for the 2.25 oscillations to take place: $0.1777... \times 2.25 = 0.399... \approx 0.4$ s.
So the final scale marking is 0.4 s.

b) $\varepsilon = -\frac{\Delta(N\Phi)}{\Delta t}$

N is the number of turns, which is constant, and so can be taken out of the $\Delta(N\Phi)$ and put in front of the fraction. The question is also only asking for the magnitude of the e.m.f., so the minus sign can be ignored here.

So the magnitude of the e.m.f. is $\varepsilon = N\frac{\Delta\Phi}{\Delta t}$, where $\frac{\Delta\Phi}{\Delta t}$ is the gradient of the graph. So the e.m.f. is a maximum when the graph is steepest. Draw a tangent to one of the steepest parts of the graph and calculate the gradient of the tangent:

E.g.

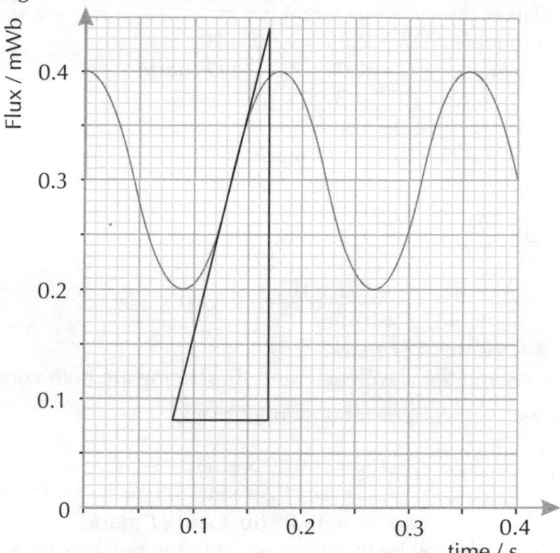

gradient $= \frac{\Delta y}{\Delta x} = \frac{(0.44 \times 10^{-3}) - (0.08 \times 10^{-3})}{0.17 - 0.08}$

$= 4 \times 10^{-3} \text{ Wbs}^{-1}$ ***[1 mark]***

Magnitude of e.m.f., $\varepsilon = N\frac{\Delta\Phi}{\Delta t} = N \times \text{gradient}$

$= 300 \times 4 \times 10^{-3}$

$=$ **1.2 V** ***[1 mark]***

You'd get 1 mark for calculating a gradient between 3.7×10^{-3} Wbs^{-1} and 4.5×10^{-3} Wbs^{-1}, and 1 mark for correctly using your value of the gradient to find the magnitude of the e.m.f., ε.

c) E.g.

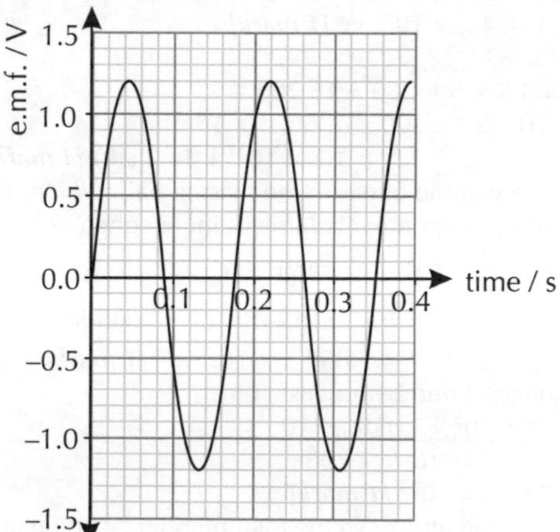

[1 mark for a sine graph (starting at zero and with an initial positive gradient), 1 mark for the maximum and minimum values being equal to ± the value calculated in part b) and 1 mark for a period of 0.1777... s]

The induced e.m.f. can be found using the change in flux in the coil. When the gradient of the flux graph is negative, the value of the induced e.m.f. is positive, and when the gradient is positive, the value of the induced e.m.f. is negative. This also means that the induced e.m.f. will be equal to zero when the gradient of the flux graph is equal to zero.

Answers

d) The moving magnet will induce an e.m.f., which will cause a current to flow in the coil, which will induce a magnetic field around the coil ***[1 mark]***. Lenz's law states that the induced e.m.f. will act to oppose the change that caused it, i.e. the motion of the oscillating magnet ***[1 mark]***. The amplitude of oscillation of the magnet will therefore decrease as the magnetic force from the coil acts to slow it down ***[1 mark]***.

5 a) Calculate the emitted wavelength of light using the energy level diagram:

$\Delta E = \frac{hc}{\lambda}$ and $\Delta E = E_{n=2} - E_{n=4} = -3.4 - -0.85$
$= -2.55$ eV

You can ignore the minus sign here, it just means that energy was absorbed.

Convert to joules: $\Delta E = 2.55 \times 1.60 \times 10^{-19}$
$= 4.08 \times 10^{-19}$ J ***[1 mark]***

$\lambda = \frac{hc}{\Delta E} = \frac{6.63 \times 10^{-34} \times 3.00 \times 10^{8}}{4.08 \times 10^{-19}}$
$= 4.875 \times 10^{-7}$ m ***[1 mark]***

$\frac{\Delta\lambda}{\lambda} \approx \frac{v}{c}$,

so $v \approx \frac{\Delta\lambda}{\lambda} \times c$

$= \frac{(494 \times 10^{-9}) - (4.875 \times 10^{-7})}{487.5 \times 10^{-9}} \times 3.00 \times 10^{8}$

= 4 × 10⁶ ms⁻¹ ***[1 mark]***

b) $d\sin\theta = n\lambda$ and the wavelength and slit spacing are both constant.

Rearrange: $\frac{\lambda}{d} = \frac{\sin\theta}{n}$ = constant ***[1 mark]***

so $\frac{\sin\theta_1}{1} = \frac{\sin\theta_2}{2}$, so $\theta_2 = \sin^{-1}(2 \times \sin\theta_1)$
$= \sin^{-1}(2 \times \sin(15.8)) = 32.994...$
= 33.0° (to 3 s.f.) ***[1 mark]***

c) The energy released by the star is equal to the power × time ($P = \frac{W}{t}$, where W is the work done. Work done is the same as energy transferred, so $P = \frac{E}{t}$). The power of the star is equal to its luminosity (they both have the units W). So first calculate the luminosity.

To calculate the luminosity, first find the surface temperature of the star:

$\lambda_{max} = \frac{2.9 \times 10^{-3}}{T}$ so $T = \frac{2.9 \times 10^{-3}}{\lambda_{max}} = \frac{2.9 \times 10^{-3}}{439 \times 10^{-9}}$
$= 6605.922...$ K ***[1 mark]***

$L = 4\pi r^2 \sigma T^4 = 4\pi \times (8.98 \times 10^{8})^2 \times 5.67 \times 10^{-8} \times (6605.922...)^4$
$= 1.094... \times 10^{27}$ W ***[1 mark]***

$E = P \times t = L \times t$

$t = 4.5$ hours $= 4.5 \times 60 \times 60 = 16\,200$ s

$E = 1.094... \times 10^{27} \times 16\,200 = 1.772... \times 10^{31}$
= 1.8 × 10³¹ J (to 2 s.f.) ***[1 mark]***

6 a) First calculate the volume of gas in the plasma ball. Volume of gas = volume of outer sphere – volume of inner sphere.

$V_{total} = \frac{4}{3}\pi(r_b)^3 - \frac{4}{3}\pi(r_a)^3 = \frac{4}{3}\pi((r_b)^3 - (r_a)^3)$
$= \frac{4}{3}\pi((12.0 \times 10^{-2})^3 - (3.50 \times 10^{-2})^3)$
$= 7.058... \times 10^{-3}$ m³ ***[1 mark]***

$pV = NkT$ so the total number of gas atoms:

$N = \frac{pV}{kT} = \frac{1.01 \times 10^{5} \times 7.058... \times 10^{-3}}{1.38 \times 10^{-23} \times 298}$
$= 1.733... \times 10^{23}$ ***[1 mark]***

1% of these are argon atoms, so the total number of argon atoms:
$1.733... \times 10^{23} \times 0.01 = 1.733... \times 10^{21}$

Total mass = number of argon atoms × mass of 1 argon atom
$= 1.733... \times 10^{21} \times 39.9481 \times$ u
$= 1.733... \times 10^{21} \times 39.9481 \times 1.661 \times 10^{-27}$
$= 1.150... 10^{-4}$ = **1.15 × 10⁻⁴ kg (to 3 s.f.)** ***[1 mark]***

b) $pV = NkT$ so $\frac{p}{T} = \frac{Nk}{V}$ = constant, so $\frac{p_1}{T_1} = \frac{p_2}{T_2}$.

$T_2 = \frac{p_2 T_1}{p_1} = \frac{1.03 \times 10^{5} \times 298}{1.01 \times 10^{5}} = 303.900...$ K ***[1 mark]***

$\frac{1}{2} m\overline{c^2} = \frac{3}{2} kT$

so $c_{rms} = \sqrt{\overline{c^2}} = \sqrt{\frac{3kT}{m}}$

$= \sqrt{\frac{3 \times 1.38 \times 10^{-23} \times 303.900...}{20.1797 \times 1.661 \times 10^{-27}}}$ ***[1 mark]***

$= 612.666...$ = **613 ms⁻¹ (to 3 s.f.)** ***[1 mark]***

c) A is the radius of the inner sphere ***[1 mark]***.

Electric potential is given by $\frac{Q}{4\pi\varepsilon_0 r}$, and comparing this to the given equation shows that $r = d + A$. r is the total distance from the centre of the sphere to the detector, which equals the distance from the surface of the inner sphere to the detector (d), plus the radius of the inner sphere, so A must equal the radius of the inner sphere.

d) ***5-6 marks:***

The formula has been rearranged correctly for d, and this has been used to explain fully how the gradient and the y-intercept can be used to calculate Q and A. A full explanation of how the error bars should be drawn has been given, including how to use them to determine the absolute uncertainties of Q and A. The answer has a clear and logical structure. The information given is relevant and detailed.

3-4 marks:

The formula has been rearranged for d and this has been linked to how Q and A can be calculated. A brief description of how the error bars should be drawn has been included. There is some description of how error bars can be used to calculate the absolute uncertainties. The answer has some structure. Most of the information given is relevant and there is some detail involved.

1-2 marks:

An attempt at rearranging the formula for d has been made. There is some attempt to link the formula to finding Q and A. A description of error bars and uncertainties may not be included, or may be included with little detail. The answer has no clear structure. The information given is basic and lacking in detail. It may not all be relevant.

0 marks:

No relevant information is given.

Here are some points your answer may include:

Rearranging the formula to make d the subject gives:

$d = \frac{Q}{4\pi\varepsilon_0}\frac{1}{V} - A$.

This formula gives a straight line when plotting d on the y-axis against $\frac{1}{V}$ on the x-axis.

Comparing this to $y = mx + c$ shows that the gradient of the line is equal to $\frac{Q}{4\pi\varepsilon_0}$.

The y-intercept of the straight line is equal to $-A$.

The engineer should draw a straight line of best fit through her results.

She should then calculate the gradient of the line (by drawing an appropriate triangle) and find the y-intercept (by extrapolating the line backwards until it crosses the y-axis).

The uncertainty in d is ±0.001 m. Therefore the engineer should draw vertical error bars that extend 0.001 m (on the scale of the y-axis) above and below each plotted data point.

The uncertainty in V is 5.0%, so the uncertainty in $\frac{1}{V}$ is also 5.0%.

The engineer should calculate 5.0% of each $\frac{1}{V}$ value and draw errors bars horizontally by this value to the left and right for each plotted data point.

Answers

The engineer should find the uncertainty in Q by drawing lines with maximum and minimum gradients that still pass within the range of the error bars.
The worst gradient is the gradient of the line furthest from the gradient of the line of best fit.
Use the worst gradient to calculate the worst value of Q, i.e. Q_{worst} = worst gradient × $4\pi\varepsilon_0$.
The absolute uncertainty in Q is the difference between the value of Q calculated using the line of best fit, and the value of Q_{worst}.
To find the uncertainty in A, find the y-intercept from the line that is furthest away from the y-intercept of the line of best fit.
The absolute uncertainty of A equals the difference between their y-intercepts.

7 a) The gravitational force on an object at the centre of the Earth would be of equal magnitude in all directions and so cancel each other out to give zero ***[1 mark]***.

b) The graph in Figure 8 shows that the gravitational field strength, g, is directly proportional to the distance from the centre of the Earth, r. This means that $\frac{g}{r}$ = constant, so $\frac{g_1}{r_1} = \frac{g_2}{r_2}$

$g_2 = \frac{g_1 r_2}{r_1} = \frac{9.81 \times 4.75 \times 10^6}{6.37 \times 10^6} = 7.315...\ \text{Nkg}^{-1}$ ***[1 mark]***

$W = mg = 1.50 \times 7.315... = 10.972...$

$= \mathbf{11.0\ N}$ **(to 3 s.f.)** ***[1 mark]***

c) $\omega = 2\pi \div T$ so first calculate ω:
$a = -\omega^2 x$ and we know that the maximum acceleration (a_{max}) is equal to the acceleration due to gravity calculated in part (b) (g_2).
$x = A\sin\omega t$, so $a = -\omega^2 A\sin\omega t$. a_{max} is when $-\sin\omega t = 1$, so $a_{max} = \omega^2 A$.

$\omega = \sqrt{\frac{a_{max}}{A}} = \sqrt{\frac{7.315...}{4.75 \times 10^6}} = 1.240... \times 10^{-3}\ \text{rads}^{-1}$ ***[1 mark]***

$\omega = 2\pi \div T$ so $T = 2\pi \div \omega = 2\pi \div 1.240... \times 10^{-3}$

$= 5063.083...$

$= \mathbf{5060\ s}$ **(to 3 s.f.)** ***[1 mark]***

d) To escape the Earth's gravitational field, the mass must do work against the gravitational force. The mass will have escaped the Earth's gravitational field when it is at infinity.
Work done by the mass moving from the centre of the Earth to the surface of the Earth is equal to the area under the F-r graph in Figure 9:

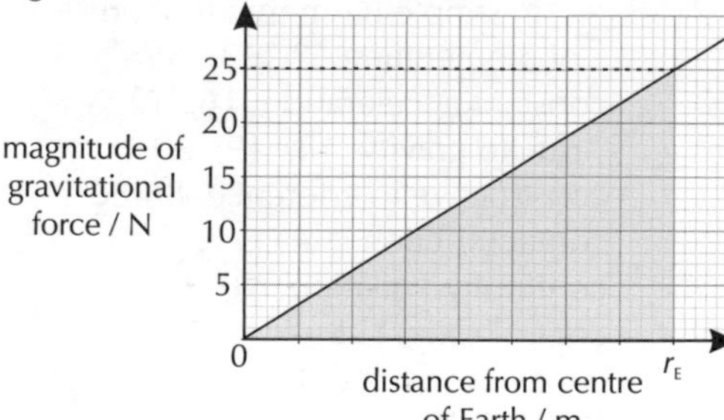

$W = \frac{1}{2} \times 25 \times 6.37 \times 10^6 = 7.9625 \times 10^7\ \text{Nm}^{-1}$ ***[1 mark]***

The work done to move the mass from the surface of the Earth to completely out of the Earth's gravitational field can be found by calculating the gravitational potential energy (GPE) at both points:
Work done = GPE at infinity – GPE at surface of Earth

$= 0 - \left(-\frac{GMm}{r}\right)$

$= \frac{6.67 \times 10^{-11} \times 5.97 \times 10^{24} \times 2.55}{6.37 \times 10^6}$

$= 1.594... \times 10^8$ J ***[1 mark]***

So the total work done in moving the mass
$= (7.9625 \times 10^7) + (1.594... \times 10^8) = 2.390... \times 10^8$ J ***[1 mark]***

Equate the work done and the kinetic energy of the mass:

$W = \frac{1}{2}mv^2$, so $v = \sqrt{\frac{2W}{m}} = \sqrt{\frac{2 \times 2.390... \times 10^8}{2.55}}$ ***[1 mark]***

$= 13\ 692.1...$

$= \mathbf{13\ 700\ ms^{-1}}$ **(to 3 s.f.)** ***[1 mark]***

8 a) E.g.

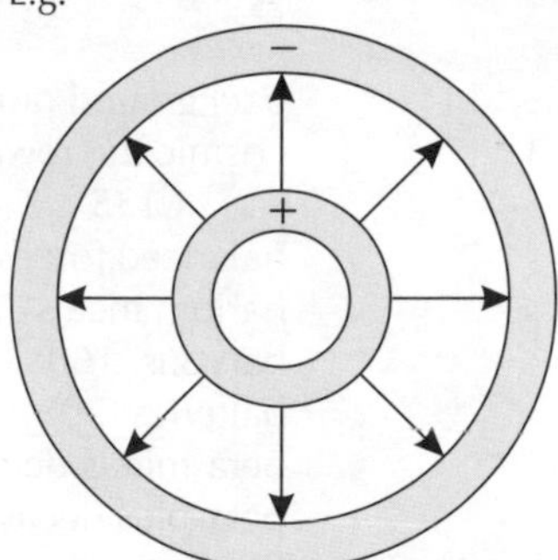

[1 mark for straight lines between the inner and outer cylinders that are perpendicular to the surfaces of the cylinders and pointing from the inner to the outer cylinder]

The strength of a field is indicated by how close together the field lines are, and the distance between the field lines changes depending on the distance from the centre, which shows that the electric field strength is not constant and so the electric field is not uniform ***[1 mark]***.

b) Equate centripetal force and the force on a charge in an electric field:

$E = \frac{F}{Q}$ so $F = EQ$.

$F = \frac{mv^2}{r} = EQ$

$E = \frac{Q_{cylinder}}{2\pi\varepsilon_0 rL}$ and $Q = e$

$\frac{m_e v^2}{r} = \frac{Q_{cylinder}}{2\pi\varepsilon_0 rL} \times e$ ***[1 mark]***

$v = \sqrt{\frac{Q_{cylinder}e}{2\pi\varepsilon_0 L m_e}}$

$= \sqrt{\frac{5.66 \times 10^{-9} \times 1.60 \times 10^{-19}}{2\pi \times 8.85 \times 10^{-12} \times 25.3 \times 10^{-2} \times 9.11 \times 10^{-31}}}$ ***[1 mark]***

$= 8.405... \times 10^6 = \mathbf{8.41 \times 10^6\ ms^{-1}}$ **(to 3 s.f.)** ***[1 mark]***

c) A proton is positively charged, so the electric force on the proton will be towards the outer, negative cylinder ***[1 mark]***. For circular motion to happen, there needs to be a force towards the centre of the circle, so the proton will not move in a circle ***[1 mark]***.

d) $V = V_0 e^{-t/CR}$. When the voltage has halved, $V = \frac{V_0}{2}$:

$\frac{V_0}{2} = V_0 e^{-t/CR}$ so $\frac{1}{2} = e^{-t/CR}$

Take the natural logarithm of both sides of the equation:

$\ln\left(\frac{1}{2}\right) = \frac{-t}{CR}$ ***[1 mark]***

$C = \frac{2\pi\varepsilon_0\varepsilon_r}{\ln\left(\frac{b}{a}\right)}$ and the outer radius (b) is double that of the inner radius (a), so $b = 2a$.

$C = \frac{2\pi\varepsilon_0\varepsilon_r}{\ln\left(\frac{2a}{a}\right)} = \frac{2\pi\varepsilon_0\varepsilon_r}{\ln(2)}$

$t = -CR \times \ln\left(\frac{1}{2}\right)$

$= -\frac{2\pi\varepsilon_0\varepsilon_r}{\ln(2)} \times R \times \ln\left(\frac{1}{2}\right)$

$= -\frac{2\pi \times 8.85 \times 10^{-12} \times 2.25}{\ln(2)} \times 1.85 \times 10^3 \times \ln\left(\frac{1}{2}\right)$ ***[1 mark]***

$= 2.314... \times 10^{-7} = \mathbf{2.31 \times 10^{-7}\ s}$ **(to 3 s.f.)** ***[1 mark]***

Index

Index

Index

Index

Index